THE **RUNNING** AND
MA
MA   **:RY**

Southampton
SOLENT
University

WARSASH LIBRARY
Tel: 0148 955 6269

Please return this book no later than the date stamped.
Loans may usually be renewed - in person, by phone,
or via the web OPAC. Failure to renew or return on time
may result in an accumulation of penalty points.

0 1 NOV 2007	1 1 JUN 2009	
2 5 FEB 2008	1 9 OCT 2009	
0 5 MAR 2008	0 1 FEB 2010	
0 6 JUN 2008	1 0 FEB 2010	
2 5 JUN 2008		
0 8 SEP 2008	2 1 APR 2010	
2 9 OCT 2008	2 1 JUL 2010	
2 3 FEB 2009	0 6 OCT 2010	
	1 9 MAR 2015	

THE **RUNNING** AND **MAINTENANCE** OF **MARINE MACHINERY**

Edited by Dr J Cowley

CBE, BSc, PhD, FREng, HonFIMarEST, FIMechE, HonFNI

published by

IMArEST

publications

Published by IMarEST
The Institute of Marine Engineering, Science and Technology
80 Coleman Street • London • EC2R 5BJ

www.imarest.org

A charity registered in England and Wales
Registered Number 212992

First published in 1933 by The Institute of Marine Engineers
Reprinted 1941, 1943, 1946, 1949, 1955, 1965, 1972, 1974, 1976, 1979, 1982, 1985
Sixth Edition published 1992
Reprinted with corrections 1994
This reprint 2006

All mentions in the text to The Institute of Marine Engineers (IMarE) and/or Marine Management (Holdings) Ltd now refer to The Institute of Marine Engineering, Science and Technology (IMarEST)

A CIP catalogue record for this book is available from the British Library

ISBN 0-907206-42-5

Contents

The authors

R Beams BA, IEng, AMIMarE
After serving as an Engineer Cadet from 1963 to 1967, Rod Beams worked for various shipping companies until 1979, at which time he was serving as Chief Engineer. He then took up a lectureship at the College of Further Education, Plymouth, and in 1985 became Senior Lecturer at Maritime Operations Centre, Warsash, Southampton, responsible for the operation and development of the machinery space simulator. In 1990 he joined Haven Automation Ltd, Swansea, as Simulation Systems Manager, where he is responsible for simulator projects and the development of computer based teaching and training systems, worldwide. He holds a BA(OU) Technology degree in electronics, instrumentation and computer technology.

S G Christensen CEng, FIMarE, Extra First Class Engineer DoT, BSc
Stanley G Christensen, Professor Emeritus in the Department of Engineering at the US Merchant Marine Academy, Kings Point, New York, served at sea as a Chief Engineer in steamships and motor ships. He was the silver medallist of The Institute of Marine Engineers in 1948, and is a William Nevins' prizewinner. He has held senior positions in shipowning organizations in the United Kingdom and the United States of America, as a company board member, technical director, chief superintendent, and senior superintendent engineer, and is now a consulting marine engineer.

J Cowley CBE, BSc, PhD, FEng, HonFIMarE, FIMechE, Extra First Class Engineer DoT
Dr Cowley, Past President of The Institute of Marine Engineers, and now an Honorary Fellow, was Surveyor General in the Department of Transport from August 1981 to May 1988. He has served as a visiting Professor and a member of the Board of Governors of the World Maritime University. He was awarded the Denny Gold Medal in 1982, and the IMO International Maritime Prize in 1988.

P Durham BA, CEng, FIMarE
After serving a mechanical apprenticeship with ICI, Mr P Durham joined The British India Steam Navigation Co. as Junior Engineer, subsequently obtaining a First Class Combined Certificate of Competency. After serving with Sir William Reardon Smith's Steam Navigation Co as Chief Engineer, he was appointed Lecturer in Marine Engineering by the, then, Llandaff College of Technology. He graduated through the Open University in the early 1980s and at the time of writing was Head of the Marine Engineering section of the School of Maritime Studies (Wales).

A W Finney BSc(Eng), CEng, MIMechE
After obtaining a degree in Mechanical Engineering from Imperial College, University of London, Mr Finney served a graduate apprenticeship at the Fraser and Chalmers turbine works of the General Electric Company. Training included analogue computing and experience with early digital computers. Following a period in the drawing office of the Admiralty and Special Projects Division at GEC Mr Finney transferred to the Development Laboratory eventually becoming Deputy Manager. In 1980 Mr Finney moved to Lloyd's Register of Shipping, where he is currently Senior Surveyor in the Control Engineering Department.

A Hodgkin CEng, MIMarE, AIED
After a shipwright apprenticeship at H.M. Dockyard Chatham, Alan Hodgkin joined Babcock and Wilcox as a project draughtsman, becoming marine project engineer and then section leader. He was appointed Chief Marine Project Engineer in 1966, and Chief Design Engineer, Industrial and Marine Division in 1980. He retired in 1987 after 40 years service.

D G Nicholas BSc, FIMarE, MIMechE

After a graduate apprenticeship at the English Electric steam turbine factory at Rugby, and various other appointments, he became Chief Designer for the Industrial Steam Turbine Division in 1964, and Engineering Manager of the Industrial and Marine Steam Turbine Division formed in 1969, when GEC took over English Electric. He was then responsible for a range of main propulsion machinery and turbo-generators supplied for VLCCs, container ships, fast ferries and naval vessels. He continued as Manager of the Naval Department, and then Deputy General Manager of the Medium Turbine Division, before retiring in 1991.

D G Redpath MSc, CEng, FIMarE

After serving a Marine Engineering apprenticeship with Texaco Tankers, Mr Redpath obtained OND in Mechanical Engineering at Stow College, Glasgow, and Second and First Class Certificates of Competency (Steam), and rose to the rank of Second Engineer. He then served as Chief and Second Engineer with British Rail and Burns Laird, and obtained his Motor endorsement. After working as an Engineer with Northern Ireland Electricity Authority, and gaining an HNC in Naval Architecture, he joined Lloyd's Register of Shipping as Ship and Engineer Surveyor. In 1978 he became Senior Lecturer in Marine Engineering at Ulster Polytechnic, and is currently Lecturer in the Department of Engineering, University of Ulster.

A C Stera MSc, MInstR

After graduating from Warsaw Technical University, and specialising in refrigeration, Mr Stera was awarded a Master's Degree in Mechanical Engineering in 1960. He then joined Blue Star Line Ltd as a seagoing engineer, and sailed on 22 reefer vessels, working as Assistant Engineer, through Second Refrigeration Engineer to Chief Engineer in 1964. He joined Lloyd's Register of Shipping in 1970, where his brief centred on the classification of newly built reefers, container ships and containers. He carried out a number of investigations, machinery and insulation performance measurements at sea, the results of which have, to a large extent, been implemented in perfecting the refrigeration installation on new vessels. Following a short sojourn in Kuwait, where he looked after the refrigeration interest of Lloyd's Register in the Middle East, he was appointed to his present position as Principal Surveyor and Manager of the Refrigeration Department at Lloyd's Register headquarters. Mr Stera is the President of the International Institute of Refrigeration Commission D2/3, dealing with refrigerated transport.

F Taylor BSc, PGCE, CEng, MIMarE, AMIEE

Fred Taylor joined Shell Tankers in 1964 as Marine Engineer Cadet, and graduated from Newcastle Polytechnic in 1971 with a degree in Electrical Engineering, sponsored by C A Parsons. On graduation he transferred to Transformer and Generator Instrumentation as an Applications Engineer. In 1972 he was appointed Lecturer at South Tyneside College (then South Shields Marine and Technical College), teaching electrical subjects, and obtained his PGCE from Huddersfield Polytechnic in 1976. He is currently Senior Lecturer, mainly involved with Marine Engineering Certificates of Competency and specialist electrical courses for the marine and offshore industries.

J Templeton ARCST (Hons), MSc, CEng, MIMechE

James Templeton studied Mechanical Engineering at The Royal College of Science and Technology, Glasgow, followed by a year at the School of Thermodynamics, University of Birmingham. In 1961 he took up a post with Torry Research Station, MAFF, working on the development of ship board plant for chilling, freezing and refrigerated storage of fish. He joined Christian Salvesen (Seafoods) Limited in 1970 with responsibilities for the specifications and installation of fish freezing and refrigerated storage plant. From 1981 to 1990 he worked on development projects in a number of developing countries as a management, refrigeration and training consultant. In 1990 he joined Lloyd's Register of Shipping, working in the refrigeration department on the appraisal and classification of marine refrigeration installations for refrigerated cargo vessels, liquefied gas tankers and refrigerated containers.

R F Thomas CEng, FIMarE, Extra First Class Engineer DoT

Robert Thomas joined BP Tanker Co Ltd in 1958 as an Engineer Cadet under the alternative training scheme. On completion of his cadetship he served as an engineer in the fleet before taking up a shore appointment with BP Shipping in 1971. In 1981 he was awarded the Denny Gold Medal for his paper 'Development of Marine Fuel Standards'. After serving in various parts of the BP Group, he joined DNV Petroleum Services as Technical Coordinator in 1992.

Acknowledgments

The editor, authors and publisher gratefully acknowledge the help, information and drawings supplied by the following companies, journals and publishers.

Aalborg Ciserv International A/S
ABB Industry Ltd
Allen Gears
Alfa Laval Engineering Ltd
APV Baker Ltd
Babcock and Wilcox Co
Babcock Power Ltd
British Maritime Technology
Brown Bros and Co Ltd
Brush Electrical Machines Ltd
Butterworth Heinemann
Danfoss A/S
Detroit Stoker Company
Diamond Power Specialty Ltd
EGT Turbochargers Ltd
Electrical Review
GEC ALSTHOM Gears Ltd
GEC ALSTHOM Turbine Generators Ltd
General Electric Company
Hagglunds Denison Ltd
Hamworthy Combustion Systems Ltd
Harland & Wolff plc
Haven Automation Ltd
Hitachi Zosen Corporation
HMSO
Ishikawajima-Harima Heavy Industries Co Ltd
J M Voith GmbH
KaMeWa AB
Kawasaki Heavy Industries (UK) Ltd
Lloyd's Register of Shipping
Macawber Engineering Ltd
MAN B & W Diesel AG
McDermott International, inc

New Sulzer Diesel Ltd
Peter Brotherhood Ltd
Railko Ltd
Redler Ltd
Saacke Ltd
Sabroe Refrigeration A/S
Senior Thermal Engineering Ltd
Siemens plc
Simplex-Turbulo Co Ltd
South Tyneside College
Sprecher + Schuh UK Ltd
Stone Manganese Marine Ltd
Stone Vickers Ltd
Telemechanique
Terasaki (UK) Ltd
Videotel Marine Interational Ltd
Vokes Ltd
Weir Pumps Ltd
Wetherby
Whipp & Bourne Ltd
Woodward Governor Company

Reference is made to the following British Standards, and extracts are reproduced with the permission of BSI Standards. Complete copies of the standards can be obtained by post from BSI Publications.

BS MA100; BS 1170; BS 1427; BS 1523; BS 2690; BS 2917; BS 3939; BS 4099; BS 4941; BS 5345; and BS 5750.

Chapter 1
Marine Boilers

A Hodgkin

INTRODUCTION

Boilers of varied design and working conditions are installed in both steam and motor vessels. The most modern steamships have boiler plant of a sophisticated nature, and even on motorships the steam plant can be quite extensive, providing useful services and enhancing the overall efficiency of the vessel.

The demand for steam propulsion is currently very low, being confined to specialised ships such as liquid natural gas (LNG) carriers. However, a number of steamships may still be found in service having boiler plant resulting from many years of development. Design modifications have been made to eliminate problem areas and to adjust to changing operational constraints in much the same way that the diesel engine has progressed to its present advanced state. Some of the incentives for and results of this development are touched upon in this chapter.

Water tube marine boilers have been dominant, as far as steam propulsion is concerned, since the period between the two world wars. Even the generation of steam for auxiliary purposes aboard ship has come into the province of the water tube boiler, a practice which grew to prominence with increasing demand for large quantities of auxiliary steam and which persists today in ships such as the large motor tanker. Nevertheless in the field of auxiliary steam production many non-water tube boilers can still be found, especially where steam output and pressure are not high.

Water tube boilers can be made for steam duties as low as 1.5 ton/h and as high as 2.5×10^3 ton/h. At the lower end of the range, the water tube boiler is found to be uneconomical and would only be considered for very specialised applications where very high steam pressure was involved. Boilers having duties in the upper end of the output range would be found in central power stations ashore. Steam pressure in water tube boilers can vary between 7 bar and supercritical values such as 225 bar, although natural circulation would only be applicable to pressures below about 175 bar. Steam temperature could range from saturation to 600–650°C, depending upon the fuel and method of firing. With this vast range of duties it is not surprising that the shape and detail of water tube boilers should vary considerably. Although the marine sphere is only a particular section of the whole range, the number of different boiler designs available is large.

As with most engineering endeavour, marine boiler design is a compromise. A balance must be sought between first cost, longevity, running cost and maintenance. First cost can always be reduced at the expense of the other factors by adopting minimum construction standards and high forcing rates. A proper compromise in any particular case depends upon the operating profile of the vessel. For a warship, construction standards are high because of such factors as shock loads which have to be withstood. Forcing rates are also high to enable overall bulk and weight to be kept low. Reasonable longevity and maintenance levels can be expected as time spent at maximum load may not be much more than 5% of the life of the plant. Running cost is not normally an overriding factor. For merchant ships a good compromise is achieved by building to classification requirements and adopting the low forcing rates that experience has shown will enable good levels of the other factors to be obtained. Even so, there are distinctions to be observed, such as between main propulsion and auxiliary boilers. Auxiliary boilers, receiving possibly much less use than main propulsion boilers, may usefully employ higher forcing rates.

WATER TUBE BOILERS

The major designers of marine water tube boilers are Foster Wheeler (USA, UK), Babcock (USA, UK, Germany), Combustion Engineering (USA) and Kawasaki Heavy Industries (Japan).

All of the above have extensive international licensee networks so that boilers to one basic design can be manufactured in many different places. Although marine boilers have been, and can still be, offered with forced or assisted circulation, present day practice is for these designers to offer main propulsion boilers based upon natural circulation. Forced circulation units will, however, be found in many exhaust gas heat recovery boilers used on motorships. Some of these, and many auxiliary boiler designs, are offered by companies other than these four, but for main propulsion, they are dominant.

From an operational point of view it is essential that the boiler be kept clean. This is particularly true on the water sides as overheating, and subsequent failure, is only prevented by a good supply of water boiling within a clean tube. The importance of this is clear when considering the high heat fluxes found in the furnace zone, where a deposit scale 0.6 mm thick can elevate the tube temperature some 215°C above what it would be were the tube clean. This is because the scale has a very high resistance to heat flow, requiring a large temperature difference to pass the heat flow incident upon the tube. Such an increase in tube temperature can bring the tube material into the range where oxidation occurs, leading to eventual tube failure.

In early designs the need for internal cleanliness was recognised and catered for by making provision to simplify cleaning operations with the mechanical means then in vogue. This meant using straight tubes, or tubes with a minimum number of easy bends, to allow passage of tube cleaning brushes, and the provision of access to the ends of each. As a result the boiler pressure parts were perforated with numerous access openings each of which had to have a pressure tight closure when the boiler was operational. The making and keeping tight all of these fittings was to prove the downfall of the straight tube boiler and encouraged the acceptance of a greater degree of welding in boiler pressure parts and the adoption of chemical cleaning.

External cleanliness is important, not only because of the risk of corrosion associated with the presence of fire side deposits, but also due to the risk of differential fouling. In a superheater, for example, if some parts become more fouled than others the products of combustion will be forced to take a preferential path through the less fouled area, locally increasing heat transfer in this zone and elevating tube temperature as a result. This too can lead to eventual tube failure. Further external fouling means that the products of combustion leave the boiler at a higher temperature, reducing efficiency, wasting fuel and imposing a fire risk.

The object of the circulation system is to provide a good supply of water to all of the heated tubes in a water tube boiler. Heat transferred through the tube walls produces steam bubbles in the water within. Tubes in high heat transfer zones will contain more steam than tubes in lower heat zones so the density of steam/water mixture will be lower in the former than in the latter. If these separate zones are connected top and bottom by collecting vessels, such as drums or headers, then circuits are formed in which the different densities will cause flow to occur— upwards in the low density tubes, downwards in the others. The greater the difference in density, the brisker the flow will tend to be. This is the essence of a natural or gravity circulating system (Fig 1) and in practical designs the principle is enhanced by specific design features such as drum internals aimed at preventing steam inclusion into downflowing tubes

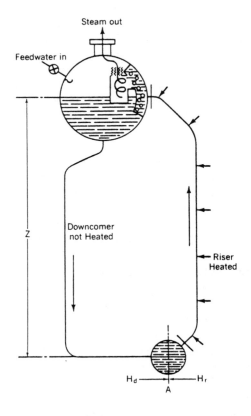

Figure 1   Simple natural circulation circuit (diagrammatic) including primary steam separator in drum.

(to obtain maximum density) or by arranging all downflow tubes to be unheated (for the same reason).

A boiler will be divided into many such circuits with varying heat absorption rates. The flow in each is established at the heat absorption corresponding to maximum load when a total balance flow condition exists. It is normally sufficient to make such calculations at maximum load but further analysis may be required if the boiler is to operate at more than one pressure level and, in the case of a warship, investigation may be needed for extended operation in a heeled damage condition when the circulating head is reduced due to the inclination. The work involved in analysing the many circuits which make up a modern marine boiler is tedious and time consuming and is best achieved with the aid of a computer.

BOILER TYPES

The three main classes or types of water tube boiler in use at sea today are bi-drum convection bank boilers, bi-drum radiant boilers and single drum radiant boilers.

Bi-drum convection bank boilers are developments from the integral furnace boilers introduced in the USA during 1939–45, which were characterised by partially water cooled and highly rated furnace zones followed by a convection superheater receiving some radiant heat from the furnace through a screen of generating tubes and completed by a further substantial bank of smaller bore generating tubes. These units were designed to fit into the small spaces available in the ships of the period, having limited headroom. Steam conditions were modest at around 30 bar, 400°C at the superheater outlet. At these pressure levels a large amount of latent heat has to be provided when generating steam. With the advent of larger ships, particularly VLCCs, and advancing steam conditions up to around 60 bar, 510°C at the superheater outlet, it was possible to consider an alternative design basis characterised by a large, moderately rated furnace, fully water cooled, and followed by a convection superheater receiving no direct furnace radiation. At these higher steam conditions the amount of latent heat added is much reduced and, in combination with the large water cooled furnace, a steaming economiser behind the superheater provides adequate generating surface. Figure 2 shows how the distribution of heat has changed, allowing elimination of the generating bank. A steaming economiser is defined as one where the water temperature rise within is more than 60% of the

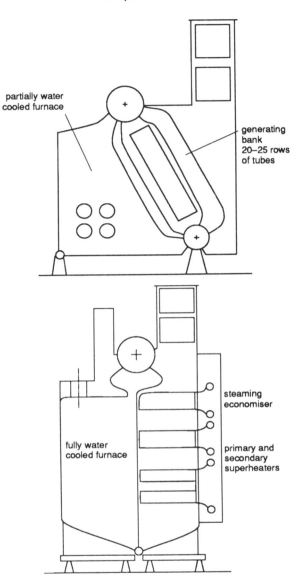

Figure 2 Heat distribution related to steam conditions: a) bi-drum D type, 31 bar 400°C; b) radiant, 63 bar 513°C.

Proportion of total heat added	bi-drum type	radiant type
to feedwater	20.3%	23.8%
to generation	64.3%	52.9%
to superheat	15.4%	23.3%

difference between saturation temperature and that of the inlet water, and it may or may not generate a small amount of steam in service.

The early versions of the bi-drum boiler were an important advance in their time but changes in refining methods on crude from various sources produced residual type fuel oils which began to reveal their shortcomings. The furnaces, being small and employing large amounts of refractory, operated at very high temperature. Flame impingement was not unknown and conditions generally for the refractories were severe and resulted in high maintenance. Refractories broke down requiring replacement. They were frequently covered in glass-like deposits, and on the furnace floor especially thick vitreous accumulations often required the use of road drills for removal.

In the superheater zone the products of combustion were still at high temperature and deposits from impurities in the fuel condensed out on the tubes, reducing heat transfer and steam temperature. Eventually, gas passages between the tubes would become so badly blocked that the forced draught fans would be unable to supply sufficient air to the burners, combustion became impaired and the fouling conditions accelerated. Sodium and vanadium compounds present in the deposits proved very corrosive to superheater tubes causing frequent repeated failure. Due to the fouled conditions there was a loss of efficiency and expensive time consuming cleaning routines were required.

There were many palliative steps introduced between that time and the early 1960s when the first marine radiant boiler was designed. Varying degrees of success were achieved by increasing the proportion of furnace wall cooling using stud tubes or tangent tubes (Fig 3) and by artifices such as wider superheater tube spacing or by removing the whole superheater to a more protected zone at lower temperature. It was, however, the impetus provided by the bulk transportation of crude oil that concentrated minds sufficiently to attack all of the problem areas of the past and to introduce features such as all welded gas tight membrane tube or monowall furnace enclosures (Fig 3) leading to boiler types which have generally proved successful in achieving high efficiency with much reduced levels of maintenance, namely the radiant boiler described in its various guises in the following pages.

Foster Wheeler

D type boiler

This is an early bi-drum design in which the two drums are connected by a multi-row bank of small bore generating tubes, and three rows of larger bore screen tubes in front of a U-loop superheater (Fig 4). The furnace side wall tubes extend upwards from a header at floor level, turn over to form the furnace roof and are connected to the steam drum. The furnace rear wall is water cooled and the lower headers of this and the side wall are fed with water from the lower drum. The two drums are connected by un-

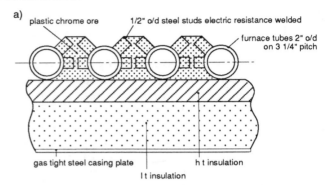

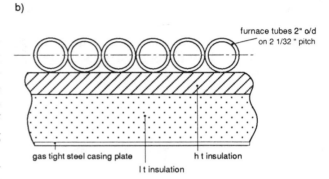

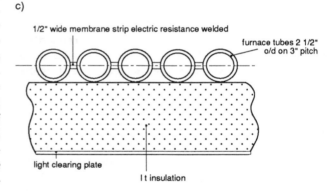

Figure 3 Water cooled furnace wall construction: a) stud tube; b) tangent tube; c) membrane tube panel (monowall).

heated downcomer tubes. The front wall and floor of the furnace are refractory lined. The horizontal U-tubes of the superheater are connected to vertical inlet and outlet headers. Baffles are fitted inside the headers, requiring the steam to make several passes through the tubes, thus achieving the high steam velocity necessary to ensure safe tube metal temperature in service. Oil burners are fitted in the refractory front wall of the furnace and, on leaving the boiler, combustion gases pass over further heat recovery surfaces such as economiser (heating feedwater) or air heater (heating combustion air). Steam sootblowers are fitted to give means of on load cleaning of boiler, superheater and further heat recovery tubes.

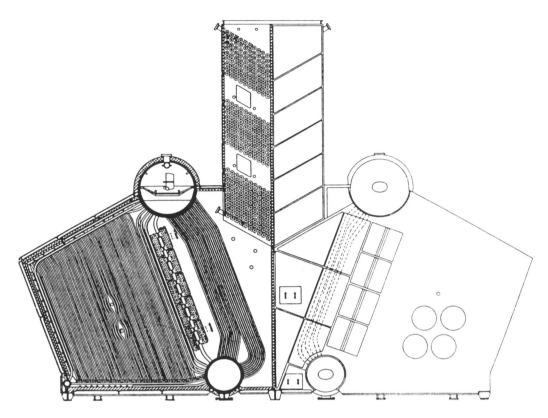

Figure 4   Foster Wheeler D type boiler.

a)

b)

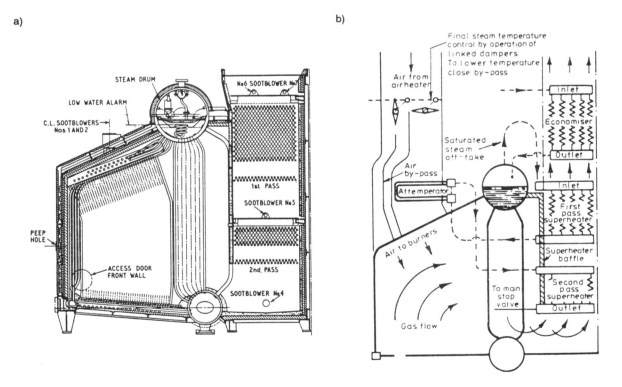

Figure 5   Foster Wheeler ESD I type boiler: a) sectional view; b) superheater and attemperator arrangement.

ESD I and ESD II type boilers

In an attempt to combat the problems experienced with the early 'D' types, Foster Wheeler introduced the External Superheater D type in which the basic construction methods remained as for the D type but the superheater was removed to a position behind the generating tube bank which was reduced in depth. This resulted in a reduced steam generating surface, an increased superheater surface and an increase in heat recovery surface beyond the boiler. Finding itself in a cooler gas temperature zone compared to the D type, the superheater exhibited a much greater rate of change of steam temperature with load and for this reason steam temperature control was adopted, even though design final steam temperature was only 450°C. In the mark I version (Fig 5) steam temperature control was by means of a steam-combustion air heat exchanger and in the mark II by damper control of gas flow over the superheater (Fig 6).

ESD III type

The ESD I and II designs still contained a good deal of refractory material in the furnace zone and very many expanded tube joints and gaskets. It was seen that maintenance could be reduced if these were reduced in extent or eliminated. In the ESD III the furnace was much enlarged and the bi-drum radiant approach appeared with the adoption of complete water cooling and burners mounted in the furnace roof. This increase in radiant surface reduced the need for a large generating tube bank which, in this design, reduced to eight rows in staggered formation, formed from the lowest metre or so of the four rows of tubes separating the furnace from the superheater. The superheater was further enlarged, permitting wide gaps between the tubes. Steam temperature control, now used because of more advanced steam conditions, was achieved by use of a steam-boiler water heat exchanger located in the upper drum (Fig 7).

Refractory was still not eliminated, but was largely shielded from direct radiation by close pitched furnace wall tubes. Many expanded joints also remained. The superheater tubes, being arranged parallel to the drum axis, tended to be long, requiring intermediate support along their length, and this proved to be troublesome in service. Further steps were taken to address these matters and an improved version of the ESD III (Fig 8) used gas tight, all welded monowalls in place of refractory lined casings behind tangent tubes for the furnace, and extended monowall construction to the superheater pass. The number of rows of tubes between furnace and superheater was reduced from four to two and the superheater was now aligned at right angles to the drum axis, the resulting shorter tubes not needing intermediate support.

a)

b)

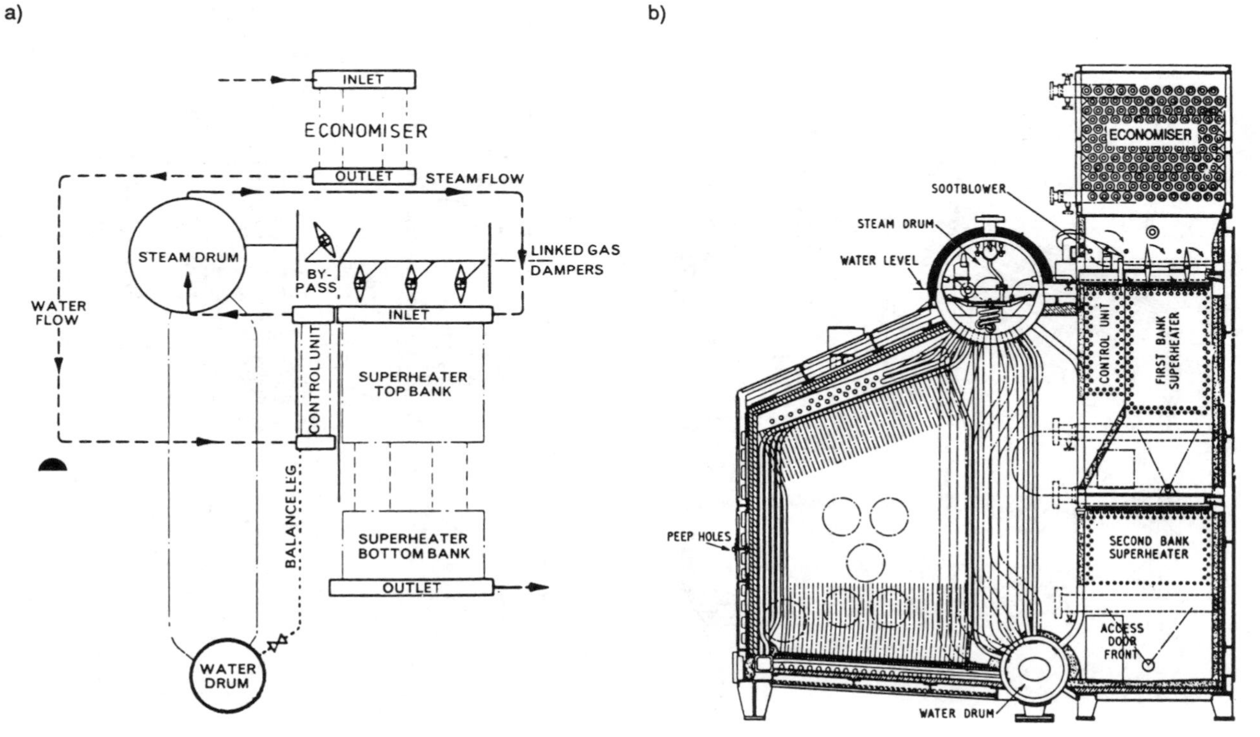

Figure 6 Foster Wheeler ESD II type boiler: a) flow diagram; b) sectional view.

a)

b)

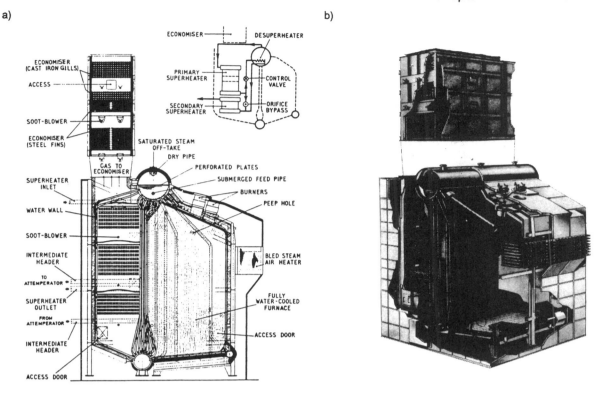

Figure 7 Foster Wheeler ESD III type boiler: a) sectional view; b) internal view.

a)

b)

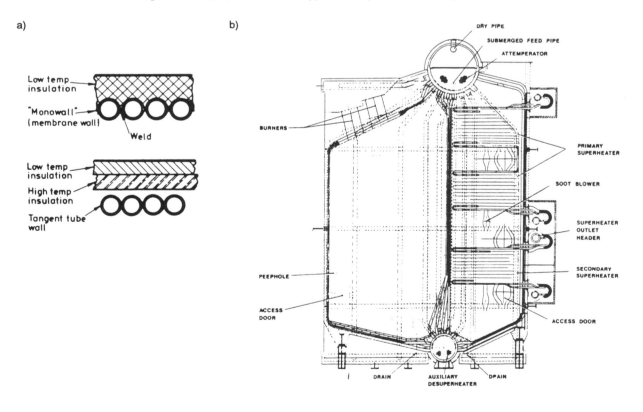

Figure 8 Foster Wheeler ESD III type boiler: a) alternative furnace tube arrangements;b) later type showing mono-wall construction.

ESD IV type

With final stage development of the ESD series we arrive at the single drum radiant boiler with complete monowall enclosure and monowall division between furnace and superheater. This further halves the number of tubes between furnace and superheater so that the lower ends of all the tubes forming the side walls and the division wall can now be accommodated in a header with all welded connections. Both refractory and steel casings are eliminated and the steaming economiser appears to compensate for loss of generating surface elsewhere (Fig 9).

DSD type

To cater for those shipowners who stated a preference for two drum boilers of more conventional design, the DSD (double superheater D type) offered several advantages over the D type or even the ESD I–III. A fully water cooled monowall enclosure system could be used with burners mounted in the furnace roof giving good distribution of hot products of combustion to the vertically aligned superheater tubes. The primary and secondary superheater sections were behind a three row furnace exit screen and were virtually self supporting, needing only to be located relative to adjacent boiler tubes. It was further claimed that the propensity for deposits to form would be reduced on vertical tubes and any that did would be more readily removed. Ample access around the superheaters was provided for this purpose. A conventional generating bank of small bore tubes was provided, with external unheated downcomers, and additional, external feeders supplied water from the lower drum to the bottom headers of the water wall circuits (Fig 10).

ESRD type

Achieving the maximum efficiency from steam plant at sea requires the adoption of the reheat cycle and for this a special boiler type is needed. In the reheat cycle steam, after passing through the superheater and HP turbine, is taken back to the boiler and reheated before returning to the intermediate and low pressure stages of the turbine. At sea, this is the sequence followed when in the ahead mode, but when manoeuvring astern or when steaming in harbour, reheated steam is not required. Under these conditions the reheater tubes will not receive a cooling flow of steam and so other means of protection are required.

The ESRD is constructed in a manner similar to the

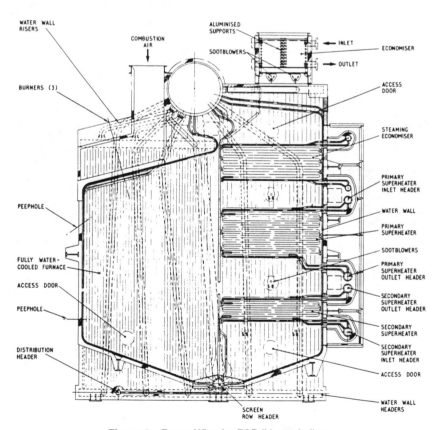

Figure 9 Foster Wheeler ESD IV type boiler.

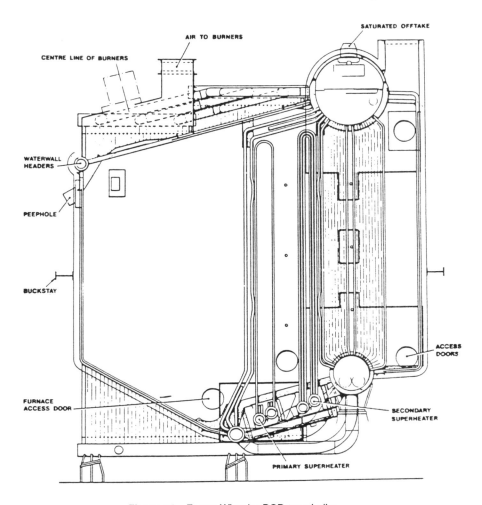

Figure 10 Foster Wheeler DSD type boiler.

ESD IV except that the convection passage containing the superheaters is divided into two parallel paths by a further monowall (Fig 11). Superheater surfaces are deployed in both paths but reheater surface is installed in one path only. The gas flow over the two paths is controlled by dampers at the exit from each path, so that the gas flow to the reheater, and thereby the reheat steam temperature, can be controlled (Fig 12). In astern or harbour operation the dampers above the reheater path are closed. Cooling air is admitted to the space between the top of the reheater and the closed dampers, and passes downwards over the reheater, joining the combustion gases which have crossed part of the superheater beneath the reheater, and exiting through a small permanent opening in the division wall. It joins combustion gases there, flowing upwards in the parallel path across economiser tube surfaces and out to further heat recovery equipment, used to ensure a high boiler efficiency at all times. Superheated steam tempera-

ture is controlled interstage by the use of a steam-boiler water heat exchanger in the boiler drum.

Babcock

Integral furnace type

This is essentially similar to the Foster Wheeler D type, the initial design of both being in the USA. Differences between them are confined to detail and to specific proprietary features. For example, Babcock boilers of that time used studded tubes in the furnace walls with the spaces between studs and between adjacent tubes packed with plastic chrome ore. This was an excellent refractory material but lacked mechanical strength and so 12 mm round studs of varying length were electric resistance welded to the furnace wall tubes to reinforce and support the refractory. This proved a very durable construction but in time it became difficult to obtain spares worldwide wherever ships called in for repairs. Eventually bare

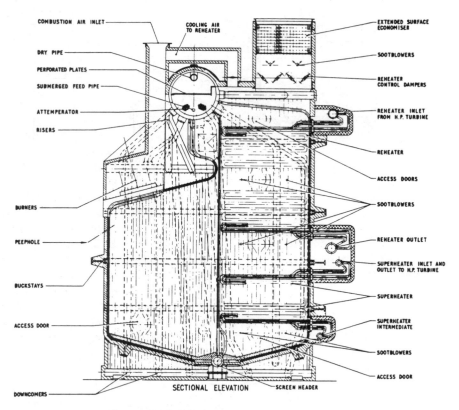

Figure 11   Foster Wheeler ESRD type boiler.

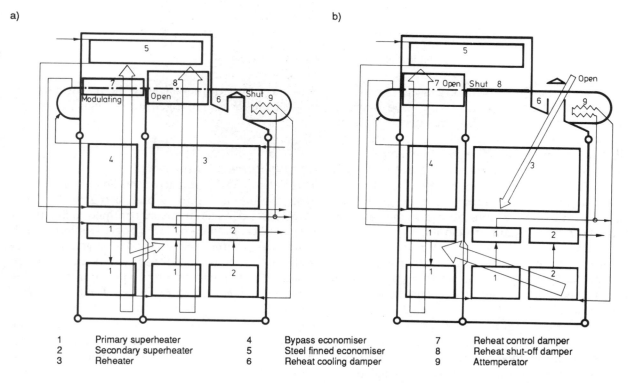

1	Primary superheater	4	Bypass economiser	7	Reheat control damper
2	Secondary superheater	5	Steel finned economiser	8	Reheat shut-off damper
3	Reheater	6	Reheat cooling damper	9	Attemperator

Figure 12   Gas flow through ESRD boiler: a) ahead operation; b) astern operation.

tubes on a tangent pitch were used, as in the D type. All Babcock boilers incorporate patent steam separating cyclones in the steam drum through which the steam/water mixture from the heated tubes is caused to pass. Inside the cyclones a vortex is formed creating a significant separating force causing steam free water to exit at the bottom and dry steam to leave at the top. These, together with a conventional slotted dry pipe, ensured dry steam to the superheater and steam free water to the downcomer tubes. As already observed the latter ensures a brisk circulation whilst the former was found to be effective over a very wide range of drum water level and practically eliminated all risk of scale build up inside the primary superheater tubes. To assist separation of steam and water in Foster Wheeler boilers, arrangements of perforated plates were used, although on occasion a form of cyclone was adopted with a horizontal axis as opposed to the vertical arrangement used by Babcock (Fig 13).

It was normal on Babcock boilers to find combustion equipment of Babcock design and a wide range was available. Foster Wheeler boilers were fitted with equipment from other burner makers, and sometimes Babcock burners were used. When fitted with economisers, those parts exposed to feed water at temperatures above about 140°C would, on Babcock boilers, be of Babcock design. This would be of mild steel construction, the tubes having oval section studs, electric resistance welded on. This design was originally used by the US Navy during the war, when it was difficult to obtain tubes with aluminium fins. Foster Wheeler had an economiser with CI gills shrunk onto mild steel tubes and a similar arrangement was also used by Babcock for economisers where the water temperature was below 140°C .

Selectable superheat and M10 types
Following its successful use in frigates for the Royal Navy, Babcock introduced into merchant service the selectable superheat boiler which was similar to the integral furnace type except that the convection pass was divided into two parallel paths by means of a wall of studded tubes and plastic chrome ore. The superheater was arranged on one side only of this gas tight division. Dampers at the outlet of each path enabled the gas flow over the superheater to be

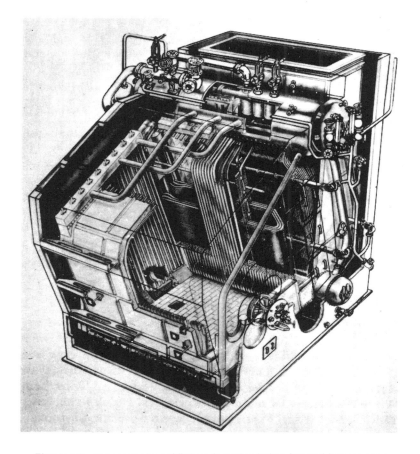

Figure 13 Cut-away view of Babcock marine boiler, integral furnace type.

controlled. The range of control obtained in this way was wide, and admirably suited the requirements of the Royal Navy. In merchant service less control range was permissible, and so some of this was sacrificed in an attempt to overcome operating difficulties which the selectable superheat boiler (Fig 14) shared with the integral furnace design. By arranging that the division wall did not start until after the first four rows of superheater tubes these could then pass over the whole depth of the boiler, the additional surface so obtained permitting a wider tube spacing in this sensitive, high temperature zone. This variation was marketed as the M10 type.

Babcock MR type

The MR boiler was introduced in response to marine industry demands for boilers to exhibit the highest possible efficiency and the lowest possible maintenance. It is a single drum radiant boiler of all welded construction in which all exposed refractory and all expanded joints and gaskets were eliminated. The membrane tube panel enclosure walls, in which adjacent 63 mm od tubes were joined by welding in a 12 mm wide mild steel strip, provided water cooling and gas tightness. The large fully water cooled furnace had a roof sloping at 5 deg to the horizontal,

enabling the oil burners to be attached normal to the roof and yet fire down the long vertical axis of the furnace. These units were, with the use of the steam atomising burners, able to achieve complete combustion within the furnace with as little as 3% excess of air, and an efficiency in excess of 90.7% on the gross calorific value was recorded when the units were fitted with rotary regenerative air heaters, reducing the temperature of the funnel gases to 116°C. In the convection passage the widely spaced superheater tubes were aligned at right angles to the drum axis so that the products of combustion produced by the row of burners in the furnace roof were evenly distributed across the whole width of the superheater. This encourages effective use of the heating surface and minimises risk of hot spots due to maldistribution, which could adversely affect tube temperature. The lowest possible superheater tube temperature was further encouraged by arranging the primary superheater, containing the cooler steam, below the secondary, both being connected so that the steam progresses upward in parallel flow with the products of combustion. Interstage attemperation and control of superheat is achieved by a steam-boiler water heat exchanger in the drum. This single drum radiant boiler has a drum diameter of at least 1.5 m and it was possible to accom-

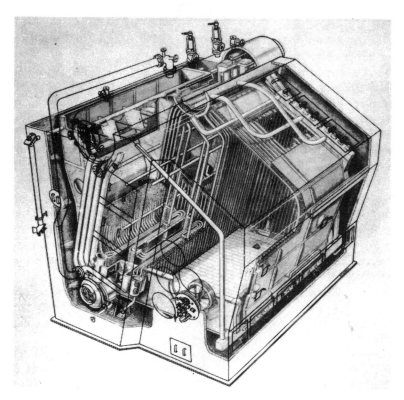

Figure 14   Cut-away view of Babcock marine boiler, selectable superheat type, showing a single furnace and two sets of dampers for adjusting the gas flow through the superheated and saturated sections of the boiler.

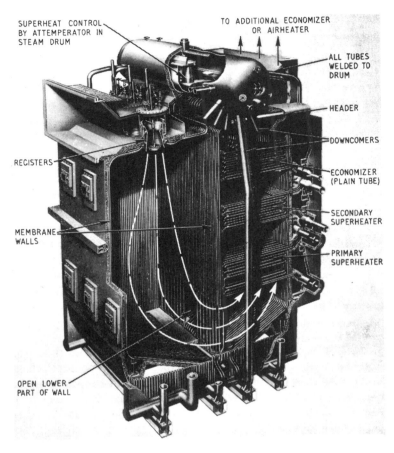

SUPERHEAT CONTROL BY ATTEMPERATOR IN STEAM DRUM

TO ADDITIONAL ECONOMIZER OR AIRHEATER

ALL TUBES WELDED TO DRUM

HEADER

DOWNCOMERS

ECONOMIZER (PLAIN TUBE)

SECONDARY SUPERHEATER

PRIMARY SUPERHEATER

REGISTERS

MEMBRANE WALLS

OPEN LOWER PART OF WALL

Figure 15   Babcock MR type boiler.

odate, in addition to the attemperator, a desuperheater for the provision of steam for auxiliary purposes (Fig 15).

M12 type

As already mentioned, preference for two drum boilers was sometimes stated and there were ships that did not provide space, notably headroom, for the radiant boilers then being used extensively in VLCCs and container ships. It was to meet such situations that Babcock offered the M12, a bi-drum unit with primary and secondary superheaters and a fully water cooled furnace similar to the Foster Wheeler DSD type. A fully water cooled furnace with membrane wall tube panels or tangent tubes backed with refractory and steel casings could be chosen, and the burners could be mounted on the roof or in the furnace front wall. The double superheater was arranged with the primary upstream of the secondary in the furnace exit gas stream, each being arranged with multiple steam passes with the hottest pass in parallel flow. Ample gas side access spaces were provided and steam temperature control was

achieved by interstage attemperation (Fig 16).

M21 type

In order to simplify construction and to introduce a degree of standardisation, the M12 was replaced by the M21 type, a bi-drum unit giving a choice of features such as:

    A single superheater;
    B double superheater;
    C tangent tubes, double casings;
    D membrane tube panel enclosures;
    E roof mounted burners;
    F front wall mounted burners;

and these could be combined ACE, or ACF, or ADE, or ADF, or BCE, or BCF, or BDE, or BDF. Each of these eight alternatives could be met with the same basic layout of the main boiler parts with the same overall dimensions simplifying drawing and ordering requirements (Fig 17).

MRR type

In 1963 a power plant design study instigated by the Esso Petroleum Company produced a set of marine

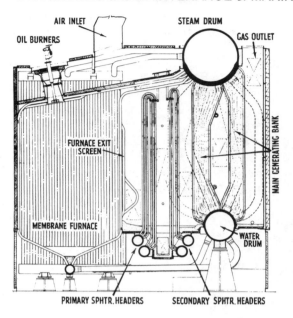

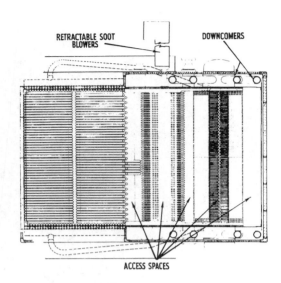

Figure 16   Cross-sectional elevation and plan of Babcock type M12 boiler.

propulsion machinery based upon the reheat cycle and which incorporated many novel features aimed at combining high efficiency and low maintenance. Out of this work came the Babcock MRR reheat boiler from which the straight cycle MR was soon to follow. The MRR is similar in construction to the MR except that the convection passage is divided into two parallel paths by a membrane tube wall, the gas flow over which is controlled by dampers located at the top, or gas outlet end of each path. Primary and secondary superheater surfaces are arranged in each path. The reheater is above them in one path and in the other is an economiser with bare tubes connected so that any steam generated rises upwards with the water flow into the steam drum to be separated in the cyclones. The division wall is completely gas tight and the superheater surfaces are so proportioned that when the reheater path dampers are closed the small gas flow leaking through them is cooled by the superheater to a temperature well below the normal reheater tube operating temperature so that no damage to the reheater can occur when reheat steam is not flowing. In normal, ahead steaming, modulation of the dampers controls reheat steam temperature without significant disturbance in main steam temperature, which is, in any case, controlled by an attemperator inside the boiler drum (Fig 18).

It will be noted that a degree of similarity exists between the various designs of the two major British boiler designers and this will be seen to further apply when reviewing the products of the other international majors. Differences in detail do occur and are the result of individual designers' attempts to overcome operational difficulties in a continuous battle to reduce the need for maintenance, improve efficiency and increase competitiveness. A significant step in this direction was taken during the latter part of the 1970s, when Stal Laval, in co-operation with Babcock, developed a very advanced propulsion system (VAP). Steam was generated at 125 bar or higher depending upon the shaft power of the set and at a temperature

Figure 17   Babcock M21 type bi-drum boiler.

a)

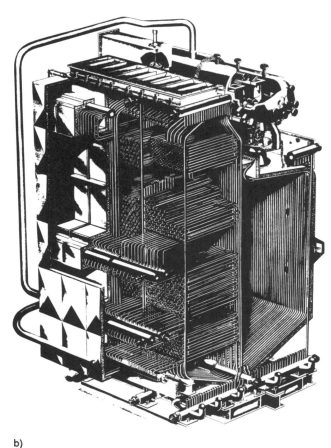

b)

of 500°C by a standard MR boiler and then raised to 600°C in a separate superheater immersed in an oil fired fluidised bed of graded sand. After expanding through the HP turbine the steam was to be reheated to 600°C in a second oil fired fluidised bed built in battery with the first and then returned to the IP and LP turbines. The combustion environment of the fluidised bed was intended to permit the achievement of 600°C or even higher without the problems afflicting conventional superheater and a full scale experimental fluidised superheater operated by Stal Laval at Orebro in Sweden proved this to be so. The turbine and gearing developments were also demonstrated to the technical press. By the time this was all ready for the market the diesel designers had forged further ahead and the demand for steam ships was in decline so that no VAP plant entered sea service.

Combustion Engineering

V2M–8

The V2M–8 is a bi-drum boiler of the integral furnace type with a vertical superheater, with all welded furnace walls or with tangent tubes backed with refractory lined steel casings. Advantages claimed by the manufacturers include: the superheater is positively drained at all times regardless of the attitude of the ship; slag accumulation on the superheater tubes is minimised; and the general layout of the unit is such as to avoid pockets where explosive gas mixtures could accumulate, thereby ensuring effective purging prior to lighting up. Provision can be made for firing in the roof, front or side of the furnace (Fig 19).

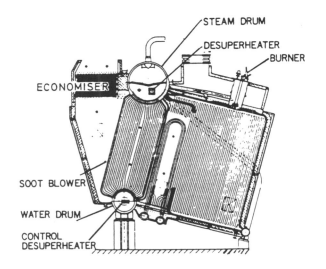

Figure 18   a) Babcock MRR reheat boiler; b) arrangement of convection chamber.

Figure 19   Combustion Engineering V2M–8 boiler.

V2M–9

As boiler plant in general began to demonstrate improved reliability shipowners showed increased interest in the single main boiler ship philosophy. A single boiler, used in place of two boilers, would require less space, but could still have the same capacity. It could have a very large furnace so as to give a greater residence time affording the opportunity for improved combustion compared to two smaller units. Better access for maintenance would be more easily obtained and initial cost would be reduced. The radiant boilers previously described all exhibited these advantages and Combustion Engineering responded by taking a basic D type boiler and extending the furnace downwards and beneath the unit. This layout necessitated supporting the boiler unit at its mid height so reducing movement of the upper and lower extremities due to thermal expansion. Stability when mounted in the moving platform of a ship at sea was also improved. A double superheater and welded furnace walls were employed and the firing platform was beneath the lower boiler drum.

A modification employed a tangential firing system, with burners mounted in each of the four corners aligned tangential to a circle at the furnace centre. This gave increased turbulence and a longer spiral flame path before the products of combustion impinged upon relatively cool boiler and superheater tubes (Fig 20).

V2M–8–LTG

The boiler and superheater are as for the V2M–8 but an additional furnace chamber is added on the side of the boiler generating bank remote from the main furnace and superheater. This additional reheat furnace is provided with oil burners and the horizontal tube reheater is arranged above its outlet. In normal ahead mode products of combustion, from oil burned in the main furnace in sufficient quantity to achieve the desired degree of superheat, pass over the superheater and main generating bank entering the reheat furnace, where the balance of the fuel is burned raising the gas temperature by an amount sufficient for the reheater duty needed. In harbour, or when manoeuvring astern, the burners in the reheat furnace are secured, and the products of combustion then reach the uncooled reheater tubes at a temperature low enough to avoid causing them damage (Fig 21).

V2M–8–divided furnace

A further derivative of the V2M–8, this reheat unit has the main furnace divided by a membrane wall (Fig 22). Each of the two furnaces so formed are

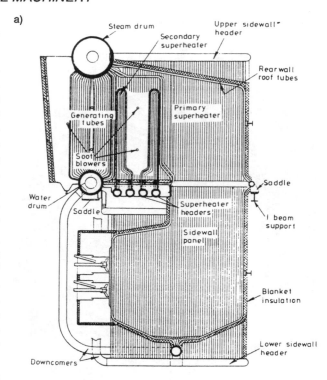

a)

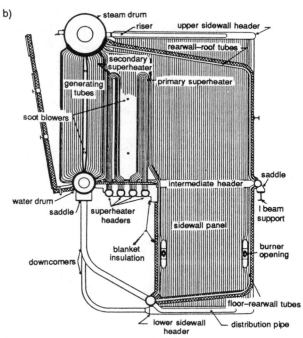

b)

Figure 20   a) Combustion Engineering V2M–9; b) later version with tangential firing arrangement.

provided with oil burners mounted on the roof. The products of combustion from one of these furnaces pass over reheater tube surfaces arranged at one end of the boiler whilst from the other furnace the gases pass over superheater tube surfaces at the other end

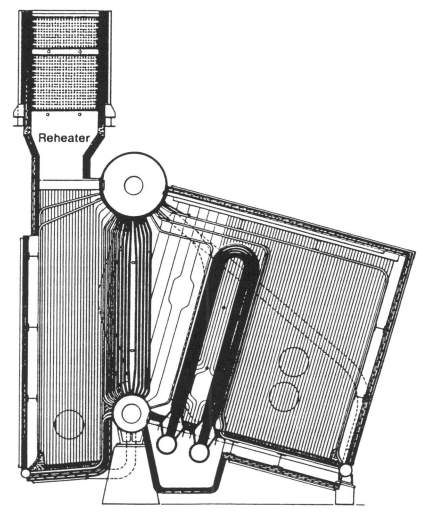

Figure 21   Combustion Engineering V2M–8 LTG reheat boiler.

of the boiler. Both gas streams combine before passing over the main bank of generating tubes. Differential firing in the two furnaces gives control of reheat steam temperature whilst the superheat is controlled by attemperation between stages of the double superheater. All welded furnace enclosure walls are used and the superheaters and reheater are all arranged in the near vertical position with horizontal inlet and outlet headers beneath.

Kawasaki Heavy Industries

BDU type

This is a basic bi-drum integral furnace boiler, the Kawasaki version having a double horizontal tube superheater, and front fired furnace constructed with tangent tubes backed with refractory lined steel casings (Fig 23). The bottom ends of the furnace exit screen tubes terminate in a separate header fed with water from the lower drum. The bottom headers of the front, rear and side furnace walls are fed by unheated downcomers from the steam drum. Steam temperature is controlled by attemperation with a heat exchanger in the steam drum and auxiliary steam at a reduced temperature is provided by a desuperheater in the lower drum. The steam circuit associated with steam temperature control incorporates a control valve and a fixed orifice in a bypass line. Care is needed in sizing the orifice since if the control valve is wide open and the orifice is too large insufficient steam will pass to the attemperator and the final steam temperature may exceed safety levels. Conversely, should the orifice be too small the control valve will be closed in to establish the correct steam quantity to the attemperator and drum steam pressure may exceed the working level. A more sophisticated system would utilise a second control valve in place of the orifice with means provided to

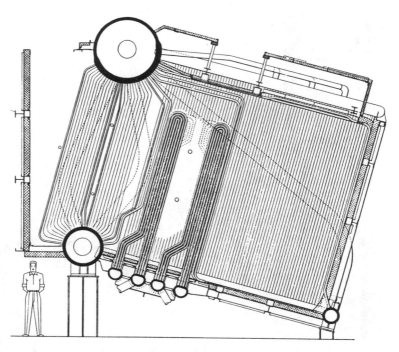

Figure 22   Combustion Engineering V2M–8 divided furnace reheat boiler.

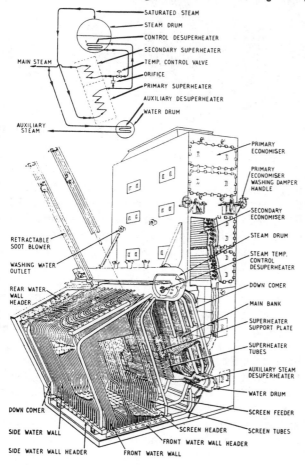

Figure 23   Kawasaki BDU boiler.

prevent it from being completely closed. The two valves under the influence of the steam temperature controller would operate in sequence to control the steam temperature even if operating conditions drifted away from design values. This avoids down time which may be required to change the orifice plate.

UF type

This is a radiant type boiler unit with fully water cooled furnace and convection passage enclosure walls and is very similar in arrangement and construction to the radiant designs of the British boilermakers, having primary and secondary superheaters with interstage attemperation (Fig 24).

UM type

In conformity with boilermakers elsewhere Kawasaki also offered a bi-drum unit incorporating modern construction methods with welded connections between tubes and headers wherever possible (Fig 25). The whole unit is enclosed in membrane wall tube panels and the oil burners are arranged in the furnace roof. There is an all welded vertical U-tube superheater immediately behind the furnace exit screen and generally simple tube shapes are used throughout the unit. The superheater construction is novel in that the U-tubes are made up into panels by being welded to stub headers at their ends (Fig 26). These are given a prior pressure test in the factory and then

a)

b)

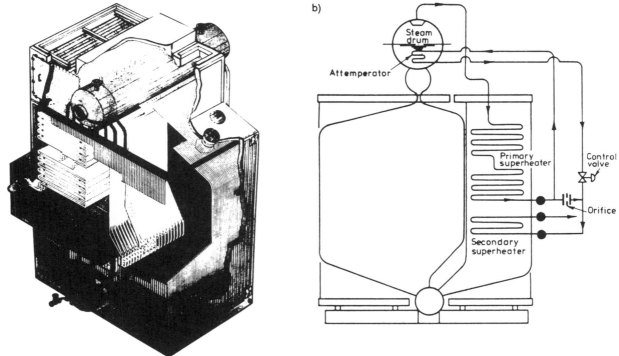

Figure 24 a) Kawasaki UF boiler; b) superheat control on UFE and UFC boiler.

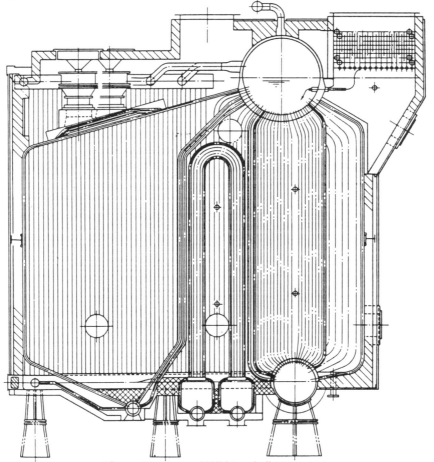

Figure 25 Kawasaki UM type boiler.

a)

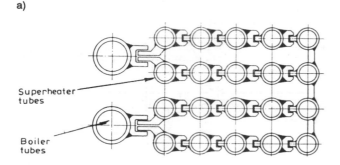

b)

Figure 26 a) Method of locating superheater tubes from boiler tubes; b) panel construction of Kawasaki superheater.

connected to the main headers by welded connecting tubes. As with the vertical tube superheater proposed by all the boilermakers offering this type of boiler unit the main support of the tube bundle is taken on the main headers at the bottom. Location and guidance of the superheater tubes is obtained by means of heat resisting alloy steel castings welded to adjacent boiler and superheater tubes. The designatory letters defining Kawasaki boilers are supplemented by an 'E' if the final heat recovery is by economiser or by a 'G' if final heat recovery is by a gas to air heater; the UM type thereby becoming UME or UMG.

UFR type

To provide for the adoption of the reheat cycle Kawasaki modified their UF type by arranging for the convection passage to have three parallel paths (Fig 27). As other boiler makers had done they divided the main convection passage into two parallel paths by means of a membrane tube wall with superheater surfaces on either side but reheater surface on

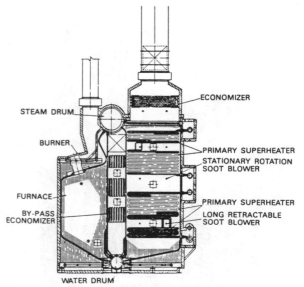

Figure 27   Kawasaki UFR and UF reheat boiler.

one side only. As a departure from previous designs they introduced a third convection passage between the furnace and the main divided passage (Fig 28). This third or bypass passage contains economiser surface. Dampers at the outlet of the three convection paths could be adjusted to control reheat and superheat in the normal ahead mode. As usual when operating astern or in harbour the dampers above the reheater are closed. In this design a double damper arrangement is used and the space between them can be pressurised with air to effectively seal the dampers preventing gas flow over the reheater. Since some

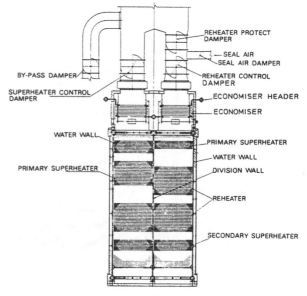

Figure 28   Bypass economiser system of reheat boilers.

a)

b)

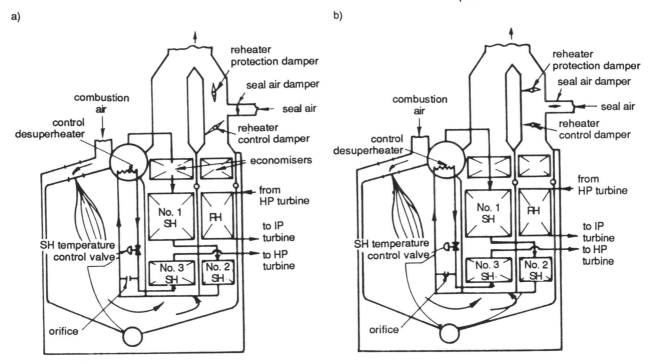

Figure 29 Kawasaki UTR reheat boiler: a) reheat condition; b) non-reheat condition.

gas always passes through the bypass passage, less heat is available for superheating and reheating. To compensate, the reheater is brought into a slightly hotter zone and additional superheater surface provided, with some primary surface above the reheater.

UTR type

A more simple solution to the problems posed by reheat were obtained by Kawasaki when they introduced this unit in which the bypass passage is eliminated (Fig 29). The resulting design, although exhibiting the same constructional detail as the UFR type, controls reheat and superheat generally in the manner adopted by the British boilermakers.

ANCILLARIES

Superheaters

With modest pressures and temperatures it was usually found sufficient to connect superheater tubes to the headers by expanding the tubes into tube holes in the header using a revolving mandrel expander. By revolving the tapered mandrel, rollers were forced against the tube bore, expanding it and squeezing the tube material against the metal of the header. The tube holes could be plain or were sometimes machined with one or more grooves. The tube end was also belled by an additional belling roller in the expander. As pressure and temperature advanced, difficulties were encountered with leaking at the expanded joints and in some cases this was countered by first expanding the tube and then running a light sealing weld around the tube end inside the header before lightly re-expanding. Each of these construction methods necessitated the provision of sufficient access handholes in the headers to permit the expanding and welding operations to be carried out. These handholes had to be sealed off for steaming and it was usual to have an oval or circular plug pulled up on the inside onto a gasket with a strongback and nut on the outside. Making and keeping these tight added to the maintenance load and became problematical as pressure and temperature levels increased. In some cases these plugs could also be sealed with a light weld bead which was machined off when access to the header was needed.

It became clear that to improve steam cycle efficiency steam pressure and temperature would rise to the highest practical values and that maintenance would only be reduced by adopting all welded construction. The difficulty presented by this was to ensure that all welded arrangements provided good access for repair at sea, should it become necessary. Constructing the boiler ashore meant that the sequence and location of the welding operations could be chosen to facilitate the making of welds of 100% quality. In a repair situation the welding work neces-

a)

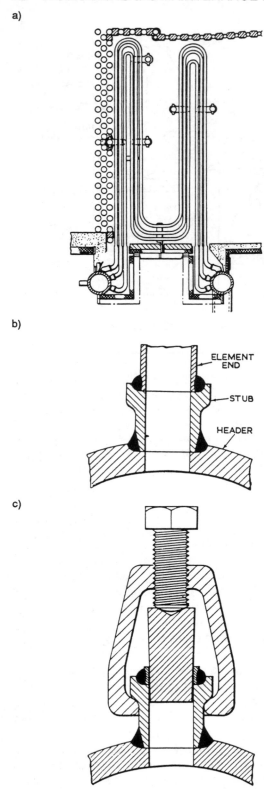

b)

c)

Figure 30   Melric joints applied to the superheater of a Babcock and Wilcox selectable superheat boiler: a) arrangement of superheat header and element; b) detail of melric joint; c) method of blanking off from outside of header in event of element failure.

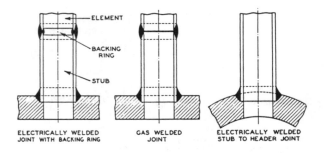

Figure 31   Methods of attaching superheater elements.

sary had to be accomplished in the space and time available. Some of the first all welded superheaters adopted a fillet weld connection between the superheater tubes and stubs previously welded to the headers in the factory and stress relieved prior to construction.

Figure 30 shows the 'melric' joint of this type. The advantages claimed include ease of making the fillet weld joints between tube and stub in the space available and the opportunity of increasing this space by bifurcating two tubes to one stub thereby doubling the pitch of the stubs.

Improved welding techniques and the use of inert gas shielding led to wider use of butt welded joints the connection between tube and header being via a stub previously welded to the header and stress relieved (Fig 31). The stub for these butt welded types was merely a short length of tube of appropriate material. These could be made of varying length and could be either straight or bent to suit the detail arrangement.

Where the design of boiler was such that an external welded joint was not possible (e.g. Fig 17) a method was devised for making an internal pressure weld between the tube end and the inside of the header. The need for stress relieving this joint was obviated by a factory applied weld deposit layer of a lower grade material to the inside of the header local to the tube hole, to which the tube end was fused with a full pressure weld. This process required special skills and was confined to those high temperature parts of the superheater where it was essential. A truly all welded arrangement was not practicable by this means. The Kawasaki UM design (Fig 25), includes an all welded superheater in a bi-drum boiler unit. If temporary plugs are fitted in the tubes connecting the stub headers to the main headers in such a layout, failure of one tube results in the loss of a whole panel of tubes.

There are cases where butt welds can sometimes

be made possible by combining two or three tubes into one stub by the use of bifurcation or trifurcation pieces. The space between the stubs can thereby be increased, creating better access for welding. When using this method care must be taken not to join together tubes having significantly different resistance to flow and/or heat absorption otherwise some tubes may receive insufficient steam flow.

Steam temperature and superheater tube temperature both vary throughout the steam path through the superheater. For metal parts outside the gas passage, such as the headers, the metal temperature is the same as the steam temperature within. For the tubes inside the gas passage the metal temperature must be assessed taking into account all possible variations in value, and the most adverse combinations of gas flow, steam flow and gas temperature. Only after a careful analysis of those factors is it possible to achieve maximum economy by minimising use of the most expensive alloys. The four materials in common use are; mild steel; ½% molybdenum; ½% molybdenum–1% chromium; and 1% molybdenum–2¼% chromium. Each of these has a maximum useful working temperature determined by the onset of rapid oxidation but in practical applications the stress resisting capabilities at the working temperature will determine choice of material. If too low a grade is chosen the allowable stress will be low and therefore the required tube thickness will be high. This tends to raise the metal temperature further and if this significantly affects the allowable stress then the time has passed for a change of material. There are, of course, more exotic alloys than those listed but it is rare to find that they are needed in marine boilers. One exception might be for naval applications where the high ratings used in a warship may make it desirable to consider a 12% chromium alloy. Oil fired units are subject to high temperature corrosion from fuel constituents, the major cause being the presence of vanadium and sodium in the fuel which form low melting point complex sodium/vanadium compounds with oxygen and sulphur oxides from the flue gas. The corrosion mechanism is very complex and has been subjected to considerable research. The corrosive effects can be minimised by keeping superheater tube and gas temperatures as low as possible, and for this reason, when fired with residual type oil fuel, boilers with conventional superheaters are limited to a final steam temperature between 525°C and 535°C. LNG ships must also be able to burn oil and steam temperature is similarly limited. Experience ashore shows that when coal is the fuel, steam temperature may be safely raised to 565°C.

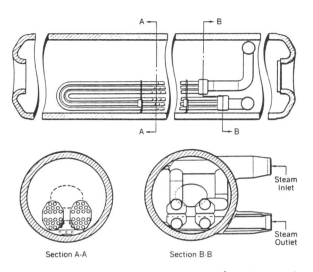

Figure 32 Babcock and Wilcox drum type surface attemperator.

Attemperators and desuperheaters

Each of these devices is a heat exchanger designed to remove heat from superheated steam. In the case of an attemperator this is usually accomplished at an intermediate stage of a superheater in order to control the final steam temperature and to protect the secondary stage of the superheater from excessive temperature. A desuperheater, however, may be used to reduce the temperature of a quantity of steam from the superheater outlet to as low as 3°C above the saturation temperature. Two types of heat exchanger may be found, ie surface type or direct contact type. The former is the most common for attemperators in view of the risk in the direct contact type of introducing impurities into the superheater. Since the cooling medium is feed water a direct contact attemperator is only used if feed water of the highest purity can be assured. This is less important for the desuperheater as it is situated downstream of the superheater. Where surface type desuperheaters are used the outlet temperature would be about 30°C above saturation temperature.

The construction of attemperators and desuperheaters is similar; only the duty differs. Surface types consist of a bundle of straight or bent tubes connected at their ends to inlet and outlet headers, the whole installed below water level inside a boiler drum with connections from inlet and outlet headers taken through the drum shell or drum end (Fig 32). To avoid thermal shock of the relatively heavy drum plates due to the high temperature steam passing into or out of the heat exchanger these connections are made so that the steam passes through a thermal sleeve (Fig 33). The space between the inner and

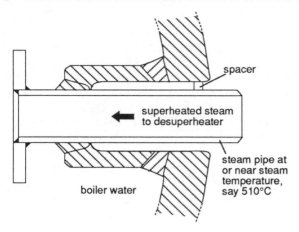

spacer

superheated steam
to desuperheater

steam pipe at
or near steam
temperature,
say 510°C

boiler water

Figure 33   Thermal sleeve.

outer parts of the sleeve is preferably open to air rather than to boiler water so as to avoid the risk of this annular space becoming concentrated with boiler water salts leading to corrosion.

Although similar in construction and function the essential difference between surface type attemperators and desuperheaters is that the former must be designed so that the steam passes through with a minimum drop in pressure so as to minimise boiler design pressure and thickness of the pressure parts. The steam from a desuperheater is usually used for auxiliary purposes and is not needed at high pressure, so that higher steam speed and pressure loss in the tubes is acceptable. Sometimes if desuperheaters are operated with a steam flow very much lower than the design capacity, the leaving steam temperature will approach saturation temperature and some condensation may form in downstream piping. To avoid this the pressure reducing valve commonly found in desuperheated steam circuits may be positioned upstream of the desuperheater so that the saturation temperature within is well below that in the drum. Since the steam leaving temperature cannot be below drum saturation temperature the leaving steam remains superheated.

Spray type units are arranged external to the boiler and have been used as desuperheaters at sea for many years. Their use as attemperators has only gained support following the introduction of more sophisticated water treatment regimes associated with modern high pressure marine boilers (Fig 34). A suitable length of pipework containing the steam whose temperature is to be reduced is substituted by the body of the unit which contains a spray nozzle arranged concentrically within. Feedwater at feed pump pressure is supplied to the spray nozzle from which it issues in a fine mist of water droplets which

rapidly enter into heat exchange with the steam thereby reducing its temperature. A liner is fitted so as to prevent spray water impingement on the hot walls of the body of the unit and a reasonable straight length of piping downstream is arranged to permit complete evaporation of the water before meeting any pipe bends.

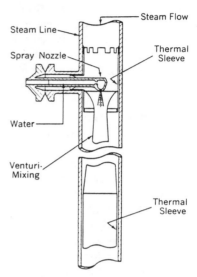

Steam Flow

Steam Line

Spray Nozzle

Thermal Sleeve

Water

Venturi-Mixing

Thermal Sleeve

Figure 34   Spray attemperator showing thermal sleeve.

Economisers

The gas temperature leaving a boiler cannot be reduced much below 30°C above the saturation temperature and in radiant types a much higher leaving gas temperature is usually found. So that an acceptable degree of efficiency can be obtained and fuel consumption reduced as much as possible further heat recovery surfaces are needed so that the gas temperature at the funnel may be as low as practicable. To carry out this further heat exchange, surfaces such as economiser and/or air heater are commonly used.

In many radiant boiler types economisers are also found arranged integrally within the boiler unit and in this location they consist of a number of multi-loop elements of plain tubes connected at their ends to inlet and outlet headers. Since they are fed with water leaving any external economiser fitted and since they are situated in a hot gas temperature zone and are required to perform a considerable heat exchange duty a portion of the water pumped through them may be converted into steam. These steaming economisers are arranged so that water enters the lower header and the steam/water mixture leaves from the top header and thence to the steam drum where the steam and water separate.

a)

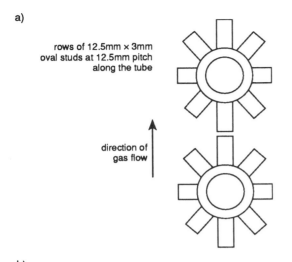

rows of 12.5mm × 3mm
oval studs at 12.5mm pitch
along the tube

direction of
gas flow

b)

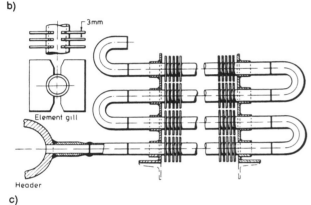

3mm

Element gill

Header

c)

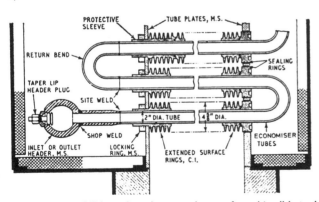

PROTECTIVE SLEEVE

TUBE PLATES, M.S.

RETURN BEND

SEALING RINGS

TAPER LIP HEADER PLUG

SITE WELD

2" DIA. TUBE   4⅛" DIA.

SHOP WELD

ECONOMISER TUBES

INLET OR OUTLET HEADER, M.S.

LOCKING RING, M.S.

EXTENDED SURFACE RINGS, C.I.

Figure 35 a) Mild steel stud economiser surface; b) mild steel plate fin economiser surface; c) cast iron gill economiser surface.

Used externally to the boiler for further heat recovery economisers are found in cooler gas zones and are fed with water at temperatures around 116°C or 185°C depending upon whether the feed cycle includes high pressure feed heaters after the de-aerator. In either case the economiser consists of a number of sinuous multi-loop elements of extended surface tubes connected at their ends to inlet and outlet headers. The extended surface is obtained by a variety of means such as resistance welded mild steel studs or plate fins, or by shrunk or cast iron gills (Fig 35). The former is lighter and enables a greater heat exchange for a given volume but is suitable only for those parts of the economiser surfaces where the water temperature within exceeds around 140°C. Since the coefficient of heat transfer on the water side is very much higher than on the gas side the tube temperature will not differ from the water temperature by any great amount. A tube surface temperature of 140°C is necessary to minimise the formation of weak acid due to condensation of water vapour and sulphuric acid from the products of combustion. At lower temperatures these could produce an acid concentration likely to cause vigorous attack on mild steel surfaces, due to the presence of sulphur in the fuel. The actual dewpoint temperature is dependent upon the proportion of the sulphur in the fuel which is oxidised to sulphur trioxide during combustion, the amount of moisture in the combustion air and the hydrogen content of the fuel. It is difficult to determine in service and the figure of 140°C is given as a guide which experience shows to be adequate for most situations. The operator can increase his margin of safety by attending to the quality of combustion and operating with a minimum of excess air. A combination of all mild steel and cast iron protected surfaces (Fig 36), is frequently found in external economiser arrangements on boilers associated with feed cycles having no high pressure feed heaters. When high pressure feed heaters are used the higher feed water temperature leaving them usually permits all mild steel economiser surfaces. This is not the case if the high pressure feed heater is arranged in series with the economisers. Then feed water from the de-aerator enters the economiser with cast iron protection from which it returns to be further heated in a high pressure feed heater going on to the all mild steel section of the economiser. This rare arrangement permits a high boiler efficiency without using gas/air heaters and retains the advantage to cycle efficiency of bled steam high pressure feed heating. The arrangement is, however, inferior in efficiency to the cycle using a maximum of bled steam feed heating and final heat recovery by means of a gas/air heater.

Regardless of the type of surfaces used in the economiser it is now common practice for these to be constructed with all welded connections between tubes and headers. These latter have inspection facilities which are also welded. Sometimes these are arranged so that, if necessary in an emergency, the closure can be made without welding (Fig 37).

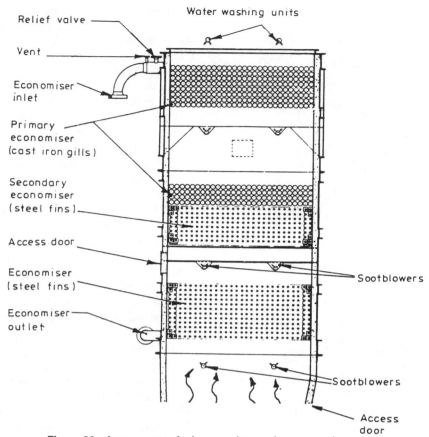

Figure 36   Arrangement of primary and secondary economisers.

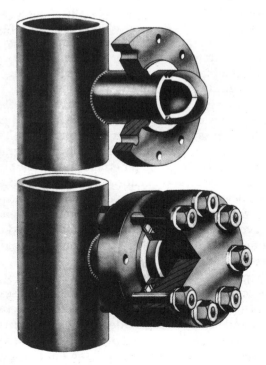

Figure 37   Inspection nipple.

Air heaters

An economiser can only economically reduce the funnel gas temperature to about 20°C above the inlet water temperature and so when high pressure feed heaters are used an acceptable boiler efficiency requires the use of a gas/air heater for final heat recovery. Three types of gas/air heater have been used at sea, namely:

Plate type

Usually of cast iron with integral fins on both air and gas sides.

Tubular type

Usually with plain mild steel tubes but on rare occasions glass tubes have been used.

Regenerative type

With either revolving or stationary heat transfer matrix.

The plate type consists of a number of cast iron plate modules bolted together and assembled so as to provide alternate air and gas passages. In passing through these the air and gas are exposed to fins cast

Figure 38 Cast iron plate type gas/air heater.

integral with the plates thus increasing the effective heating surface. The fins are required on both sides of the plates since the coefficients of heat transfer of air and gas are of the same order. When cast iron is used it is to combat the corrosive effect of weak sulphuric acid in the same way that cast iron gills are used to protect mild steel economiser tubes. Cast iron is reputed to be more resistant to this form of attack than mild steel although there is some controversy on the matter it sometimes being suggested that it is the greater mass of cast iron which confers a longer service life. However that may be, a great deal of cast iron is used in final heat recovery heat exchangers and generally acceptable results obtained (Fig 38).

Air is normally supplied to an air heater at a temperature of around 38°C and therefore certain of the metal parts are going to be at a temperature where corrosion is a serious risk. Considerable difficulties have been experienced with tubular air heaters where mild steel tubes were perforated after only 6 months in service. The modern tubular air heater is arranged with air passing through horizontal tubes, the products of combustion passing upwards over them. The tubes are expanded into tube plates at either end and the air trunking arranged so that the air makes two or more passes through the tubes. For maximum heat recovery air inlet is at the top so that air progresses through successive passes in a generally downwards direction in counter flow with the flue gas stream (Fig 39). The coolest tube temperature and the area usually found to suffer most from acid attack is therefore at the inlet end of the first air pass tubes and the tube plate nearby. To lessen the risk in this area the tube

plate is insulated on the air side and the tubes are extended into the inlet air trunking by 300 mm or so. In this first length of tube, inlet turbulence locally increases the air side heat transfer coefficient and should this occur within the gas passage the tube temperature is depressed even further. As an alternative a short ferrule can be inserted into the inlet end of the tubes separating the locally enhanced heat transfer coefficient from tubes in contact with flue gas. Another method is to preheat the incoming air at the expense of a reduced performance or an increase in heating surface to counteract the reduced mean temperature difference between gas and air.

Other attempts to overcome the corrosion problem in tubular air heaters include the use of glass tubes. These are completely resistant to attack from sulphuric acid but need special arrangements to seal them into the steel tube plate which is still prone to suffer. Also glass tubes must be carefully handled at all times and are easily damaged during any cleaning or maintenance operations. The most widespread practice was to use mild steel tubes with a coat of vitreous enamel; in effect glass coated steel tubes. These had mixed success, dependent largely on the quality and completeness of the enamel. Although more robust than glass tubes any imperfection in the enamel coating was avidly sought out by the acid which then rapidly perforated the tube beneath. Nevertheless there were many applications showing significant advantage over plain mild steel tubes and there was the bonus feature that the smooth enamel coating reduced the tendency for gas side fouling.

If a tubular air heater is required to reduce the gas temperature by 50% of the difference between the temperature of the incoming gas and incoming air it would be very bulky and heavy. A rotary regenerative air heater for the same duty would probably be less heavy and would occupy much less space and, in spite of having moving parts, might be preferred. In modern ships with radiant boilers even larger air heater duties are found requiring the gas temperature to be reduced by up to 75% of the difference between incoming gas and air temperatures. These larger duties would be impracticable for the recuperative tubular or plate type air heaters and in consequence the regenerative air heater has an established place at sea.

The regenerative air heater is either of the revolving matrix type based on the Ljungstrom design or of the fixed matrix type. In the former a closely packed matrix of specially corrugated plates is slowly revolved so as to pass through the gas stream and be heated and then through the air stream where its heat content is delivered to the air (Fig 40). In the latter, slowly revolving air hoods cause the gas and air

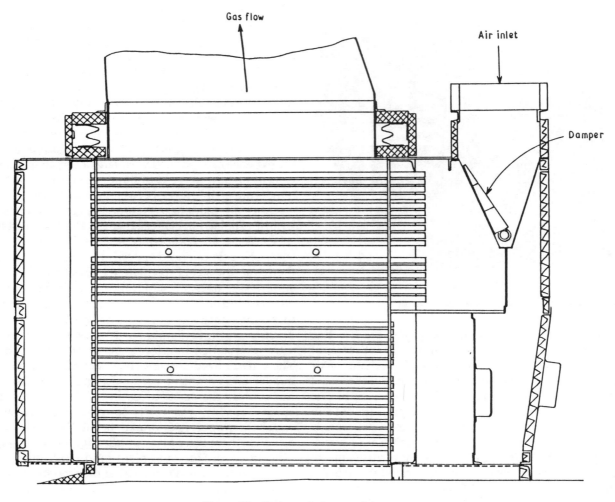

Figure 39   Horizontal tube gas/air heater.

stream to pass sequentially over the matrix giving the same effect of transferring heat from gas to air (Fig 41). The material forming the matrix cycles in temperature, reaching a low value whilst air is passing. On then entering the gas stream there is a tendency for condensation to occur resulting in some acid attack. In a regenerative air heater this would ultimately result in a loss of performance and eventual partial blockage of the fluid passages with corrosion products. Serious difficulty has been avoided by the adoption of enamelled elements forming the matrix and satisfactory service life has been obtained. In the type having a fixed matrix the upper or coolest portion of the matrix is often manufactured in a glazed ceramic honeycomb, also with very good results. Since rotation is involved with either design each will include sliding seals to separate air and gas streams. For efficient operation these must be maintained and properly adjusted at all times. Since the combustion air is always at a greater pressure than the flue gas

there is a tendency for air to leak across the seals into the gas stream and to recognise this the capacity of the forced draught fans is adjusted accordingly. Any seal leakage greater than that allowed for results in a loss of efficiency due to overloading the fan or, worse, a shortage of combustion air at the burners.

When final heat recovery is accomplished by economisers it is still possible to have heated combustion air. This is desirable as it confers two advantages. Hot combustion air is certainly beneficial in support of good combustion but in addition it provides a boost to the steam cycle efficiency by using bled steam in a steam air heater. This device is a heat exchanger in which mild steel or cupro-nickel tubes are connected at their ends to inlet and outlet headers. The tubes have closely pitched extended surface finning applied on the outside over which the combustion air is passed (Fig 42).

Bled steam is admitted via the inlet header and condenses within the tubes giving up its superheat

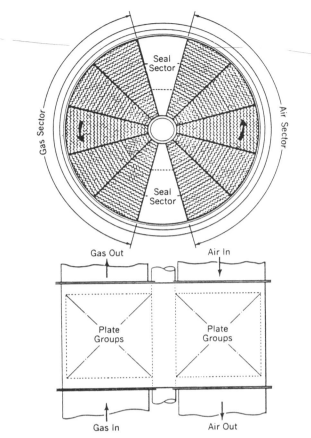

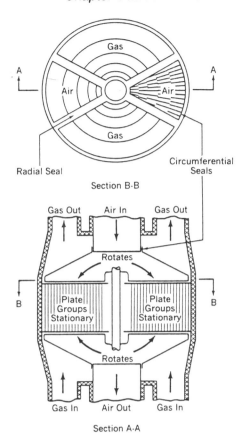

Figure 40 Diagrammatic arrangement of rotary regenerative air heater (vertical shaft arrangement) with gas and air counterflow.

Figure 41 Arrangement of counterflow regenerative air heater with stationary plates.

a)

b)

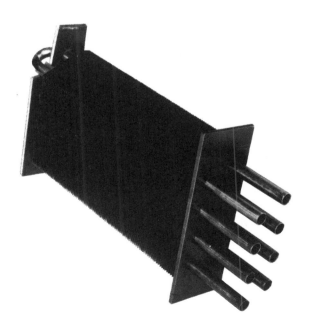

Figure 42 a) Mild steel steam air heater surface; b) cupro nickel steam air heater surface.

and latent heat to the combustion air. A certain amount of cooling of the condensate is also sometimes included. The outlet header is connected via a steam trap to the drain system. These compact heat exchangers are normally found on steam ships operating with a steam cycle which excludes high pressure feed heaters and are also sometimes used as air preheaters upstream of gas/air heaters for reasons previously mentioned.

Sootblowers

Cleanliness is all important in the operation of heat exchangers including boilers and all the ancillaries described. For boilers, economisers and gas/air heaters which are exposed to products of combustion some form of on load cleaning is necessary. The most common method involves the regular use of sootblowers in which superheated steam is discharged onto the heating surfaces, driving off any deposits. It will be appreciated that part of the sootblower is itself exposed to the products of combustion and this must be taken into account when choosing the sootblower type and materials of construction.

In its simplest form a steam sootblower consists of a headpiece, including a valve, mounted external to the heat exchanger. Extending from this into the gas passage is a tube or lance fitted with nozzles through which the steam discharges. An electric or pneumatic motor attached to the headpiece causes the lance to rotate and when the nozzles come into a position where the discharge of steam will impinge on the area to be cleaned a cam operated valve opens in the head to admit steam from the sootblowers steam piping system. As the lance continues to rotate, bringing the nozzles clear of the heating surfaces, the cam allows the steam valve to close. In such a sootblower the lance is permanently in the gas passage and, apart from a small quantity of purge air admitted to prevent combustion products from entering the head, is uncooled when not in operation (Fig 43).

In early bi-drum convection bank boilers such sootblowers fitted in the superheater zone experienced a very short life due to the ravages of temperature and corrosion. As a result the superheater area suffered severely from fouling and blockage of the gas passages making it necessary to use high pressure water washing off load. To alleviate these difficulties superheaters were arranged to accommodate retractable sootblowers. These allow the lance to be withdrawn when not in operation so that the lance is only exposed to hot gases whilst a cooling flow of steam is passing through. These sootblowers possess a more powerful cleaning action, better able to deal with the deposits which the chemistry of the fuel ash at high temperatures causes to be bonded to the heating surfaces and is more difficult to remove than dusty, sooty, deposits found elsewhere. In operation the lance revolves and traverses across the gas passage whilst steam jets pointing sideways at the end of the lance clean a spiral path. When fully inserted the

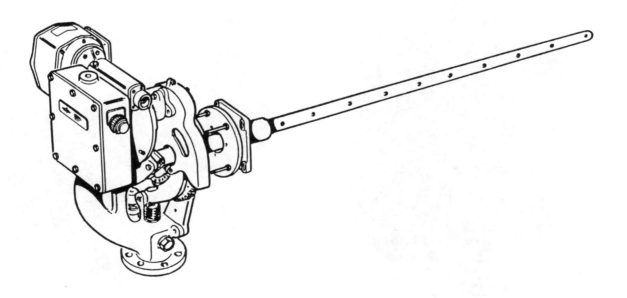

Figure 43   Multi-nozzle, rotating element sootblower.

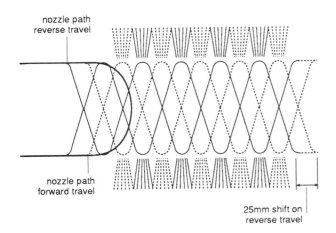

Figure 44 Rack sootblower cleaning pattern.

lance withdraws after making a half turn so that the outward spiral cleaned is out of phase with the inward enabling the whole area to be exposed to the cleaning effect of the steam jets (Fig 44). The head of

At lower temperatures, and by choosing suitable materials for the lance, fixed head rotating element sootblowers can give good service. The arrangement of nozzles (Fig 46) along the length of the lance is chosen to suit the location of the lance in relation to the heat exchanger tubes. If the lance is aligned normal to the tubes across the tube bank and is in close proximity to them multijet nozzles are pitched to correspond with every third lane or so between the tubes whereas if the lance runs parallel to and in line with the tube axes it can be located at a distance where the tube bank subtends an arc of 90 deg to the lance and fewer nozzles can be used.

Since all fresh water used aboard ship has to be made, and that supplied for makeup to the boiler must be further treated with chemicals to ensure a high degree of purity, the use of steam for sootblowers can prove expensive. In the past, use has been made of sootblowing systems where the operating and cleaning medium was compressed air. In modern ships, and with the residual type fuels currently

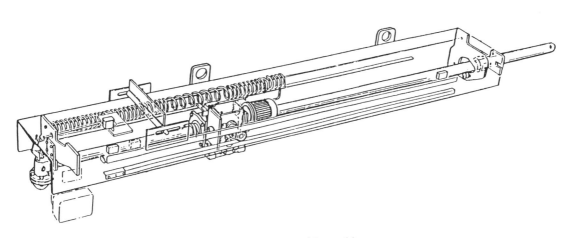

Figure 45 Long retractable sootblower.

the sootblower is supported on steel work outside the boiler and the lance is traversed along a rack with the steam being supplied through a telescopic tube (Fig 45). Retractable or rack type sootlowers, so called because of the rack traversing mechanism, have proved extremely successful in hot gas zones due to their improved life span and superior cleaning effect. They are naturally more expensive than the simple, fixed head, rotating element blowers and they occupy a good deal of space outside the boiler. For these reasons their use is confined to those areas where the simpler type has not proved satisfactory and that is basically in areas where the gas temperature exceeds 750°C.

available, steam is now universal. All of the sootblowers provided for a boiler unit, including its final heat recovery system, are connected to a permanent system of pipework outside the boiler. This pipework

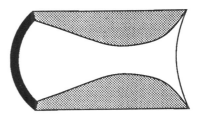

Figure 46 Supersonic nozzle.

is normally isolated and is put under steam only when the sootblowers are to be operated. This will be at a frequency dictated by operating conditions; typically once every watch. It is necessary, therefore, to carefully warm through the piping system prior to operating the blowers, ensuring that all condensate is fully drained. Control systems are now common which will cause the sootblowers to operate sequentially and as necessary the operator can programme the controls to omit some blowers from the sequence or to repeat some as local conditions may require.

FUELS

The vast majority of steam ships will currently be fuelled with a residual type of oil which is likely to be of high density and viscosity. The reception and storage of this aboard ship is of importance with regard to successful boiler operation and reference should be made to Chapter 4. Oil is fed to the boiler via pumping and heating equipment so that the oil arrives with the correct viscosity and energy for the atomising system in use. The pipe system conducting the fuel is arranged so that prior to lighting up, adequately heated oil can be recirculated providing a supply at suitable conditions as soon as light up is attempted. Flexible connections between the burner front manifold and the individual burners must be kept as short as possible to limit the amount of cold oil within. In addition the pipe system will include fuel flow control valves actuated by the automatic combustion control system, isolating valves, quick closing valves actuated by safety devices such as low water level and individual burner shut off valves.

The choice of combustion equipment and design of combustion chamber are complementary to the attainment of the three 'T's—time, temperature and turbulence—to a degree necessary for good combustion. Time is required for combustion air and fuel to mix and to burn completely within the confines of the combustion chamber. Modern marine boiler plant provides for this with larger furnaces than were previously found. Its most advanced form is in radiant boiler designs with roof mounted burners firing down the long vertical axis of the furnace with an outlet to one side at the bottom.

High temperature is needed to vaporise the fuel and to ensure rapid ignition. Most combustion equipment incorporates some form of bluff body to create a low pressure area and recirculation zone to draw back some of the atomised and ignited fuel into the path of incoming fuel spray, creating a stable area

of high temperature. Turbulence is necessary to aid mixing of fuel and air so that complete combustion can be achieved without the need for more air than that required to consume the combustibles carbon, hydrogen and sulphur. The arrangement of the air admission apparatus is important. The apparatus comprises the air inlet trunking, the windbox containing the air registers and the air registers themselves controlling the air to each burner. The design of the furnace chamber is also of some importance as, for example, in the Combustion Engineering tangentially fired furnace and in other cases where arches or similar projections have been made into the furnace with the object of encouraging turbulence. Generally speaking such devices have proved unnecessary as shown by the success of radiant boilers where sufficient time and turbulence have been obtained with burners firing, substantially, vertically downwards. Simple furnace shapes and circular air register designs are widely available.

Of further importance for efficient, complete combustion of heavy fuel oil is the design and performance of the fuel atomiser. There are a number of systems available involving the energy either contained in the pressurised fuel itself or in a separate atomising agency. Using the pressure of the fuel is the oldest and simplest method, but since oil flow rate through the atomiser is proportional to the square root of the oil pressure, a very high maximum pressure is required if a large turn down is needed. Oil pressure at 70 bar or more has been used but a value of 20 bar is much more common. This will only allow a turn down to 70% of maximum oil flow at an oil pressure of 10 bar, below which atomisation is seriously impaired. In this case in order to reduce the boiler output below about 70% of maximum, burners have to be shut down in sequence and relit when load increases again. At one time such a practice was common and great skill was achieved by firemen in anticipating the number of burners needed on each occasion. With modern, automatically controlled plant where there may be no-one on the firing platform it is necessary from a safety aspect to have all burners firing at all times. This means that a turn down of at least 10:1 is desirable otherwise at very low steam demand it may be necessary to dump excess evaporation to the condenser with consequent fuel wastage. To achieve a very high turn down ratio without using excessive maximum oil pressure requires an atomising system where the energy in a separate atomising medium is used. One such system utilises a spinning cup rotated at high rev/min by an electric motor (Fig 47). Oil is fed at low pressure onto the inside face of the cup, the spinning action of

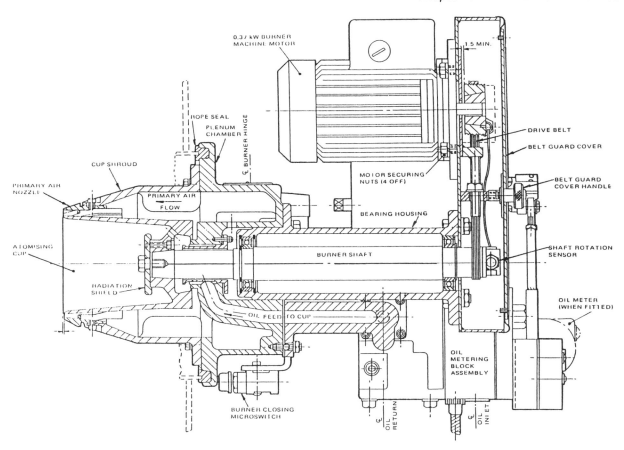

Figure 47 Spinning cup burner.

which causes the fuel to progress down the slightly conical surface and shear off the rim in a fine spray. Sufficient energy for atomisation is provided by the electric motor for all rates of oil flow. Another system uses a separate atomising fluid. Steam is the usual choice when available although when lighting up before steam becomes available compressed air may be used. Steam at 10 bar or so is used with a maximum oil pressure of about 20 bar. The steam and fuel mix within the atomiser just prior to the point of discharge, where the energy released by the steam shears the fuel into an extremely fine mist (Fig 48). This

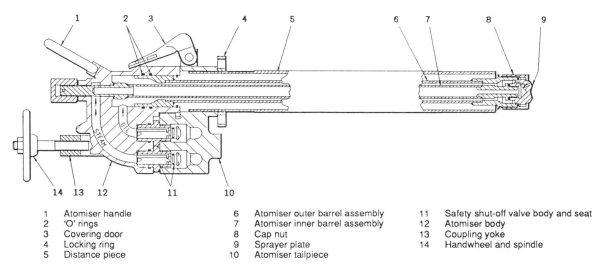

1	Atomiser handle	6	Atomiser outer barrel assembly	11	Safety shut-off valve body and seat
2	'O' rings	7	Atomiser inner barrel assembly	12	Atomiser body
3	Covering door	8	Cap nut	13	Coupling yoke
4	Locking ring	9	Sprayer plate	14	Handwheel and spindle
5	Distance piece	10	Atomiser tailpiece		

Figure 48 Y-Jet steam atomiser.

provides a simple system with no moving parts. Operation with a constant steam pressure and a varying oil pressure gives adequate turn down with the high quality atomisation necessary for complete combustion of heavy oil fuel with a minimum of excess air.

Natural gas as a fuel at sea will be found on ships designed to transport liquefied natural gas in insulated tanks. Since it is carried at virtually atmospheric pressure the liquid gas must be cooled to about –180°C, any heat leakage into the cargo resulting in some 'boil off'. The degree of boil off will depend on the design of the tanks, the tank insulation, the nature of the voyage and weather conditions. This will be collected, heated and compressed then fed to the boiler through special gas burners, providing steam for all purposes. It is a requirement to always burn a pilot quantity of fuel oil and so if steam demand is greater than can be met from the boil off gas the oil quantity is increased. Use of gaseous fuels requires

special care with regard to safety aspects and the requirements in this respect are covered by the classification societies. Most boiler types would be suitable for use with natural gas, the main consideration being that there should be no risk of pockets of explosive gas mixtures forming within the unit and that no such mixtures should leak into the machinery spaces. Top fired radiant boilers would appear to be less acceptable in this respect but this has not proved to be the case as arrangements are made to vent the top of the furnace into the uptakes via the division wall (Fig 49). This is in any case desirable even with oil fuel firing, as in certain circumstances small pockets of combustibles could accumulate in that zone. Prevention of leakage into the machinery spaces can be achieved by use of all welded enclosure walls or by double casings with combustion air between. Fuel lines to the burners are double pipes with inert gas in the annulus at a pressure greater than the fuel gas, which will be about 1 bar. A ventilation hood con-

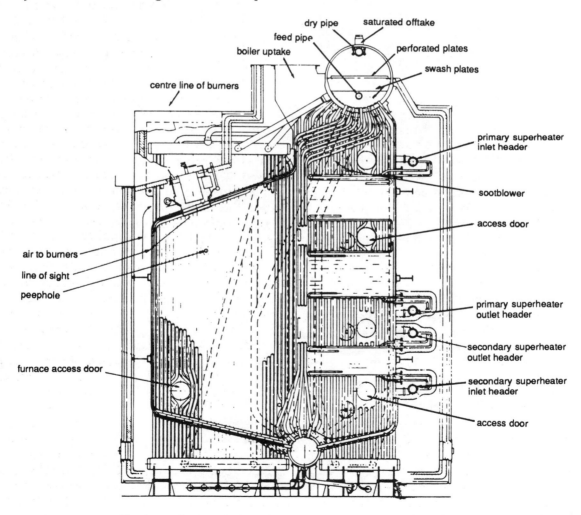

Figure 49 Foster Wheeler ESD roof-fired monowall oil/natural gas boiler.

nected to an extractor fan is arranged above the firing platform so that there is a continuous sweep of air across the burner zone for discharge outboard with gas detection devices.

During the 1980s a number of coal fired ships were built. There was much speculation concerning how best to deal with this renewed interest in a fuel which had lost favour when oil first became plentiful and cheap. The predominant means of burning coal ashore was established in central power stations where the coal was pulverised to a fineness of 70% less than 75μ and fired in a burner which could also handle oil fuel as a support fuel. Translating this to the marine environment presented problems as the grinding mills were bulky, heavy and susceptible to vibration. Indeed it was not clear whether the ship would adversely affect the mills or vice versa. An alternative was to pulverise ashore and bunker in this condition. This would have required the bunkers to be kept under inert gas as coal in a finely divided state presents a spontaneous combustion risk.

At the same time great interest was being shown in combustion of coal in a fluidised bed. This had potential advantages for burning coal at sea in so far as combustion residues could be more easily dealt with and a wider range of coal types consumed. However, there were but few examples of this technology in use ashore and marine industry was not ready to adopt any process so important to the success of the ship if it had not already gained acceptance elsewhere. This left industrial experience ashore, of which there was a great deal where coal was burned on mechanical stokers. Bearing in mind the likelihood that coal quality would vary between bunkering ports and that a good response to changes in load demand was a requirement, the favoured choice for use at sea soon became the spreader stoker.

For a spreader stoker the coal must be bunkered with a specific size spectrum; ideally one third between 19 mm and 12 mm, another between 12 mm and 6 mm and the third between 6 mm and 0 mm. In practice some variation on this is permissible and, depending upon ash content, maximum size may approach 32 mm and up to 50% may be less than 6 mm. The coal is projected into the furnace by a number of rotor feeders fitted with vanes which distribute the coal over the grate, the larger pieces falling at the rear and pieces of reduced size progressively toward the front or feeder end. In operation the finest coal particles will burn in suspension above the grate whilst those pieces falling to the grate burn there. As the grate traverses from the rear toward the front (feeder end) the largest pieces falling at the rear spend longer in the combustion zone than the smaller

pieces falling nearer the front and in this way, by adjusting the grate speed, only spent ash is discharged over the front end of the grate into an ash pit. The grate is made up of fire bars, suitably pierced for the passage of combustion air. These are carried on endless chains passing over sprockets mounted on shafts, one of which is driven by electric or hydraulic means. Primary combustion air passes upward through the grate and provision is made for the admission of secondary air through a number of ports situated above grate level in the furnace boundary walls. Response to changes in load demand is made by adjusting the rate of coal feed to the rotor by varying the stroke of a reciprocating feeder or the speed of a chain feeder (Fig 50).

Although the provision of secondary air above the grate is designed to create turbulence in this region, to encourage complete combustion of particulate fuel in suspension, and volatile matter driven off the grate, it must be realised that it is much more difficult to achieve complete combustion with coal than with fluid fuels such as oil or gas, and it will be found that much particulate matter will be carried from the furnace and through the boiler by the gaseous products of combustion. Some of this particulate matter will contain combustible material and, in order to maximise combustion, efficiency arrangements are made to separate the heavier particles from the gas stream and to re-inject them onto the grate through a series of grit refiring nozzles above the rear end of the grate. The major part of the combustible material is contained in these larger particles and so the remaining particulate contamination in the gas stream is separated out and collected for disposal. This is done by centrifugal means by passing the gas stream through a multicellular dust collector. A collection efficiency as high as 95% is possible, but the remaining 5%, consisting of the finest particles, may still be too great a quantity to be permitted by some harbour authorities. For this reason it may not be possible to burn coal in harbour. To cater for this situation, oil burners may be fitted in one of the furnace walls, well above grate level so that sufficient protection for the grate is given by a layer of ash left on when coal firing is ceased. These burners are also used to assist in lighting up and getting the coal fire started on the grate.

Boilers designed to burn coal at sea have to achieve a high efficiency and low maintenance, just as is the case for oil fired boilers. To be sure of meeting these goals the fuels to be used must be known at the design stage. The variation in coal quality and specification is far wider than for oil bunkers and whereas oil fired plant can be compared on the basis of a standard oil

a)

b)   c)

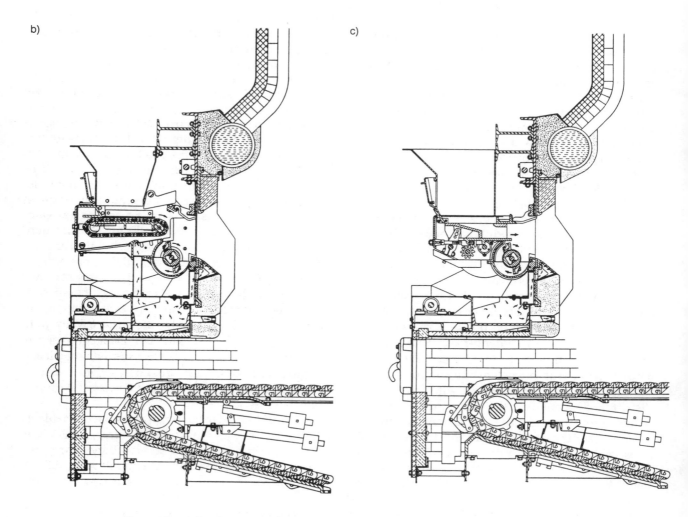

Figure 50   a) RotoGrate spreader stoker; b) chain coal feeder; c) reciprocating coal feeder.

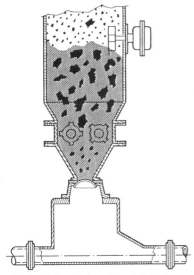 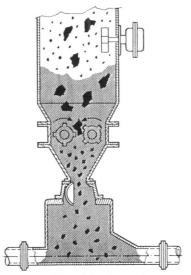 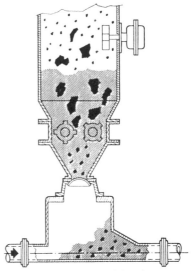

1. Accumulation—Fine ash and clinker is allowed to accumulate above the closed dome valve. Fine material falls through the stationary ash breaker and larger lumps are stored above. When adequate clinker and ash is gathered the level probe signals the dome valve to open and the ash breaker to start.

2. Breaking—The ash breaker continues cycling to deposit ash and broken clinker through the dome valve into the conveying chamber where it is allowed to build up through the dome valve to the ash breaker.

3. Conveying—While the ash breaker is preparing the material for conveying and the conveying chamber becomes full, the dome valve will close and initiate a conveying cycle. High pressure air enters the conveying chamber in a controlled manner that produces a dense phase conveying action. During breaking approximately six conveying cycles take place until the accumulation of material above the ash breaker is consumed.

Figure 51   Pneumatic ash handling system.

fuel specification, such as that proposed by the Society of Naval Architects and Marine Engineers, no such standard basis exists or is likely to exist for coal fired plant. The performance and efficiency of coal fired plant relates to a specified coal. Since the nature of marine operations implies that coal bunkers may be taken from more than one source it follows that details of these sources and the nature of the coals they provide must be established at an early stage so that the coal handling, coal firing and ash handling equipment may be properly designed.

The many characteristics of coal are all important but moisture, volatile content, and amount and nature of ash are particularly so. Moisture content has a bearing on the storage and handling arrangements and influences efficiency and combustion air temperature. Volatile content has a bearing on the design heat release per unit grate area. There must be a sufficient quantity of ash to protect the grate, say not less than 5%, but a high ash coal is clearly not a good proposition as a large inert content in the bunkers constitutes a loss of cargo revenue. Ash is also important in terms of its chemical nature which is very complicated. Heated ash does not melt at any sharply defined temperature but starts to soften at a substantially lower temperature than that at which it becomes molten. If the ash particles carried along by the gaseous products of combustion are not cooled be-

low the softening temperature before they leave the combustion chamber, they will stick to any downstream surface against which they may impinge and a severe fouling problem will result. In many cases it is the low ash softening temperature which dictates the size of the furnace. There has been a great deal of research into the behaviour of coal ash, resulting in methods using a detailed ash analysis to predict the effect of burning coals containing them, with very good prospects for avoidance of high temperature

Figure 52   Section across Redler conveyor.

slagging in the furnace zone as well as low temperature fouling. If only for this reason, prior knowledge of the coals to be bunkered and details of their ash is vital.

Coal and ash handling aboard ship are processes which must be given attention as they will significantly affect the success of the ship. Wherever the coal is stored, it has to be transported to a ready use day bunker local to the boiler. From there the coal feeds by gravity to the feeder/stokers mounted on the furnace front. It is now possible to transport coal through pipes using compressed air as the motive means. In this way dust free transfer of coal from any storage bunker to the day bin is accomplished with a minimum space requirement and without segregation or degradation of the coal.

A somewhat similar system is available for dealing with the residues of combustion which are normally collected in hoppers beneath the grate and at other strategic locations (Fig 51). Such fuel and ash

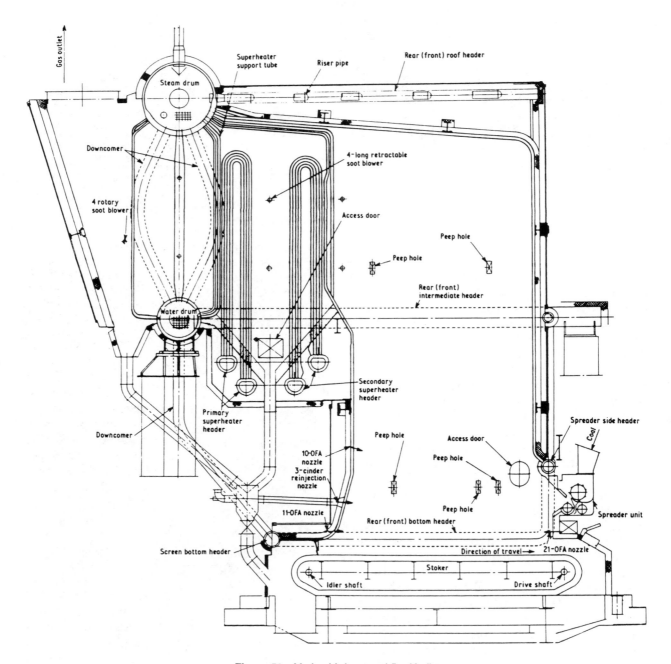

Figure 53   Marine bi-drum coal fired boiler.

handling systems can be fully automatic, with level sensors in the coal bunkers and day bin determining when coal is to be forwarded and when to switch from an empty bunker to the next full one. Similarly the ash hoppers have level detectors to initiate the ash discharge sequence. Where necessary the ash can be broken down in size by breakers integral with the conveying equipment and taken either to an overboard discharge or to an onboard storage facility depending upon the ship's trading pattern. As an alternative to pneumatic systems it is also possible for shipowners to choose all mechanical conveying arrangements giving similar facility to those described above (Fig 52).

For operation with a minimum of maintenance and operational difficulty the boiler must be designed to achieve as near complete combustion in the furnace zone as is possible. Just as with oil firing the requirements of time, temperature and turbulence also apply. This means a large furnace is needed to provide time and to minimise particulate carryover. Temperature on and near the grate is achieved by

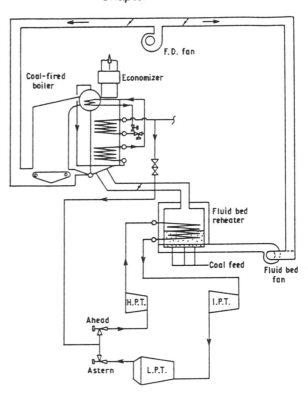

Figure 55 Coal fired very advanced propulsion.

limiting the primary air supply through the grate to that recommended by the grate designer and turbulence to encourage mixing and rapid combustion of particulates and volatiles above the grate is provided by the introduction of secondary air. The cooling surfaces in the furnace must be sufficient to cool the gaseous products of combustion to a level below the ash softening temperature and the convection gas passages must be arranged so that the gas velocity between the tubes of the superheater, economiser and generating surfaces is not so high that erosion becomes a problem. A detailed ash analysis will yield information concerning its abrasiveness which will enable the boiler designer to ensure that this requirement is met. Practical boiler designs include bi-drum types, similar to that shown in Fig 53 or developments of the radiant boiler, similar to that shown in Fig 54, as proposed by Babcock.

Many other arrangements for coal fired ships have been considered, including the use of pulverised coal and fluidised bed combustion, but development of these to a practical application stage was forestalled when oil bunker price levels fell, rendering coal less attractive. Further work in this interesting field remains for the future, although little development would be required to achieve the reheat coal fired plant of Fig 55.

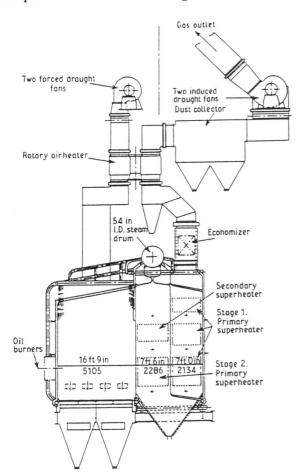

Figure 54 Babcock marine radiant coal fired boiler.

CONTROL

The unmanned machinery space is common today and the operators have the benefit of an air conditioned control room from which to monitor the operation of the plant. This has been made possible by the steady development and acceptance of automatic controls. Initially the impetus for this was generated by a desire for improved plant efficiency compounded later by a need to reduce manning levels. Control systems may be pneumatic, electronic analogue or electronic digital microprocessor based. Full details of available equipment are beyond the scope of this chapter, but either type can be arranged to operate basic boiler functions such as combustion control (i.e. steam flow), feedwater control (drum level) and steam temperature control. Further complete oil/gas burner management systems are available matching the operation of the combustion equipment to the load duty of the boiler and having safety monitoring and automatic start up incorporated.

For boiler pressure control a closed control loop or feed back system is employed, where the actual boiler steam pressure is measured and compared to the input demand signal or desired value of pressure. The difference between these, the error signal, is used in a controller to reduce the difference between the demand and actual values of pressure to zero, by adjustment of the heat input to the boiler (Fig 56). The controller can provide an output signal to the fuel valve which is proportional to the error signal, with integral and derivative action as deemed necessary, depending upon the nature of the plant. This is set up by the control engineer during commissioning. Proportional only control results in a steam pressure offset from the desired value. This offset may be

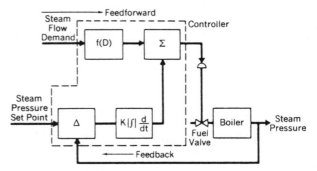

f(D) = Calibration for feedforward action

Σ = Summing action

Figure 57 Feedforward-feedback control.

reduced in value by increasing the relative proportional gain which could lead to undamped oscillation of steam pressure if a steady state fuel valve position is not achieved. Integral action added in the controller will result in elimination of the offset at the expense of a slower response time, taking longer to achieve stable steam pressure, but at the desired value. Stability and response may both be improved by adding derivative action or rate control. This causes a movement of the fuel valve, the size of which is proportional to the rate of change in steam pressure.

In a closed loop control system the controlled variable has to deviate from its set point before any corrective action is initiated by the controller. To increase the promptness of the response, the feed back system is combined with a feed forward system. In the boiler pressure control case this introduces a signal from a steam flow transmitter which enables detection of a boiler load change before the steam pressure has time to respond. This feed forward action immediately positions the fuel valve according to a calibration curve of steam flow versus fuel flow produced by the boiler designer. Should the calibration be exact no steam pressure error will develop so the feedback loop will have no work to do. Shifts in calibration due either to original errors or changes in plant condition cause a steam pressure variation which is then corrected by the feedback loop trimming the fuel valve position (Fig 57).

For complete combustion control adjustment of fuel flow only is insufficient, as combustion air must be supplied in step with the fuel. To achieve this, the fuel flow demand signal also acts upon the control drive for the forced draught fan, either operating discharge dampers or inlet vanes, varying the air delivery of the fan in the same sense as the variation in fuel flow. The air flow is determined from a measure of the windbox-to-furnace differential pressure,

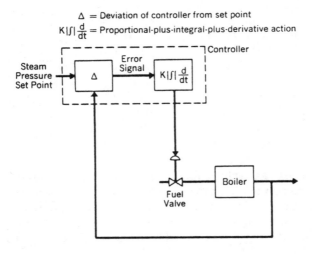

Δ = Deviation of controller from set point

$K|\int|\frac{d}{dt}$ = Proportional-plus-integral-plus-derivative action

Figure 56 Proportional-plus-integral-plus-derivative control.

or from a venturi at the fan inlet trunking or some similar means, whilst fuel flow is obtained from the pressure drop over an orifice in the fuel line. Signals representing these quantities are compared to a calibration for the fuel in question and any error signal resulting is used to trim the fuel valve as necessary. Cross limiting devices are employed to ensure that on upward load changes the fuel rate does not increase faster that the air flow, whilst on downward load changes the fuel rate decreases faster than the air flow. In other words, air leads fuel on upward load change, but fuel leads air on downward load change.

Steam temperature control is obtained by comparing the measured value of the variable with a desired value signal input from a hand control station. The difference in these signals is modified with proportional and integral action to provide a signal which causes adjustment to the attemperator valves or the gas flow dampers as appropriate. Some anticipatory effect may be achieved by taking a signal from the primary superheater outlet steam temperature and using this as feed forward action.

In a water tube boiler where the water content is low in relation to its steam output, good feedwater control is essential. A simple single element control loop compares the actual drum water level with the desired level input by a hand control station, and applies proportional and integral action to the difference, giving an output signal acting to change the position of the feed valve (Fig 58). Swell and shrink which occurs when boiler load is changed will, with this system, result in wide drum water level varia-

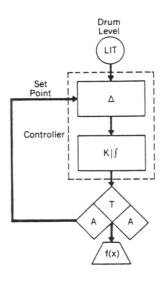

Figure 58 Single element feedwater control.

tions and a long time to restore water level to the set point. Improvement in this respect can be achieved with two element control. This includes a feed forward loop using steam flow measurement to initially shift the feed water control valve in the correct direction with the level difference signal finally restoring water level to the set point. In this way feedwater flow is maintained proportional to steam flow. The drum level signal corrects for any imbalance in water input versus steam output caused by deviation in the feed water valve position–water flow relationship, and provides necessary transient adjustments to cope with the 'shrink and swell' characteristics of the boiler (Fig 59). In cases where severe and rapid load changes may be experienced, and where the availability of the boiler is critical to the safety of the ship, such as in single main boiler applications, three element feed water control gives even greater accuracy. In this the signal from the summer in a two element control, i.e. the feedwater demand signal, is compared with a feedwater flow signal, and the difference, with proportional and integral action added, is the flow demand signal in a three element system (Fig 60). Three element feedwater control systems can be adjusted to restore a predetermined water level at all loads, or can be adjusted to permit water level to vary with load so that a nearly constant amount of water is maintained in the boiler.

With oil or gas fired boilers the fuel is of sensibly constant specific energy so that fuel flow is a measure of heat input and can be used to indicate a demand for combustion air. Coal, on the other hand, varies widely in specific energy so that, for coal fired boilers, the control system uses steam flow to indicate a demand

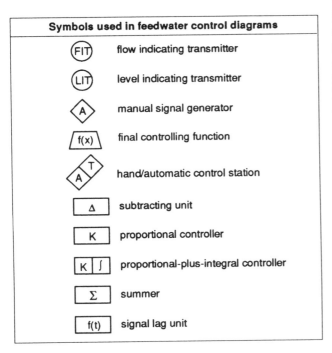

Symbols used in feedwater control diagrams	
(FIT)	flow indicating transmitter
(LIT)	level indicating transmitter
A	manual signal generator
f(x)	final controlling function
T / A	hand/automatic control station
Δ	subtracting unit
K	proportional controller
K ∫	proportional-plus-integral controller
Σ	summer
f(t)	signal lag unit

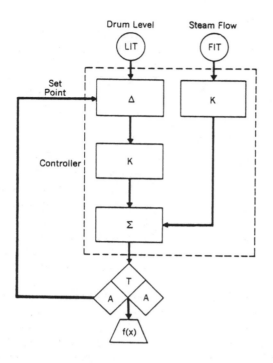

Figure 59   Two element feedwater control.

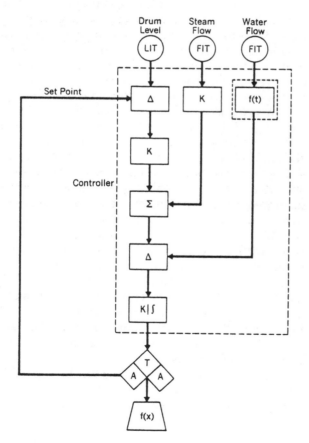

Figure 60   Three element feedwater control.

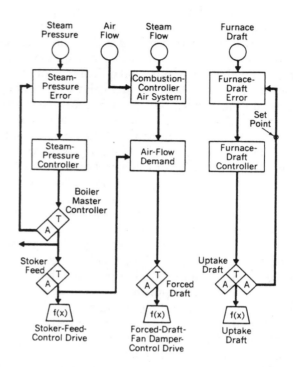

Figure 61   Combustion control for a spreader-stoker fired boiler.

for combustion air. Also, since it is difficult to seal the stoker and coal feeders into the furnace, it is necessary to carry a small depression in the furnace, say –6 mm wg, and this is achieved by an induced draught fan controlled by a furnace draught loop. The control layout for a stoker fired boiler then appears as in Fig 61.

The usual arrangement for ships' machinery is to have boiler following control. The boiler is assigned responsibility for control of steam pressure to the turbine, and load control is the responsibility of the turbine. The demand for load change goes directly to the turbine control valves, positioning them to achieve the desired load. Following a load change, the boiler control modifies the firing rate to reach the new load level and restore steam pressure to its normal operating value. Load response can be very rapid since the stored energy in the boiler is used to provide the initial change in load.

There are many refinements to control loops and many combinations providing the ability to achieve bridge control with unmanned or periodically unmanned machinery spaces (see Chapter 7, *Automation and Control*).

AUXILIARY BOILERS

Apart from water tube boilers used for main propulsion purposes, there are a number of designs at sea

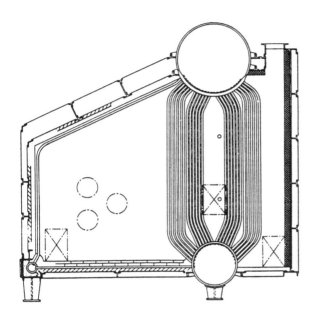

Figure 62   Foster Wheeler type D4 water tube boiler.

which are used for a variety of auxiliary purposes including, in some cases, emergency propulsion. Many auxiliary boilers are found on motor ships, where they may not always receive care and attention to the expert degree that would be expected on a steam ship. For this reason, and also due to the relat-

ively short periods when they may be fired, these boilers are of simple and robust construction, usually of the bi-drum integral furnace type with simple tube shapes such as the Foster Wheeler D4 (Fig 62) or the Babcock M11 (Fig 63). These boilers may be required to deliver saturated steam or, as shown in Fig 64, a superposed superheater in the uptake allows for a small degree of superheat.

Due to the intermittent operating routine to which these boilers are subjected, and due to the fact that returning condensate may bring particulate matter and/or oil from the steam consumers, feed and boiler water conditions may not always reach appropriate standards of quality and internal deposits followed by tube failure can result. Vigilance, and proper maintenance of filters and steam systems can minimise these risks, but some owners have avoided them by adopting the indirect fired or double evaporation system. In this the boiler consists of two parts; a high pressure portion and a low pressure portion. The former is similar to the D4 or M11 and is direct fired, operating on a closed cycle on the water side. Once filled with high quality water it only needs occasional topping up to replace any slight leakage which may occur. The steam produced is led to the low pressure portion which is supported above the fired boiler. It consists of a pressure vessel containing a tube bundle

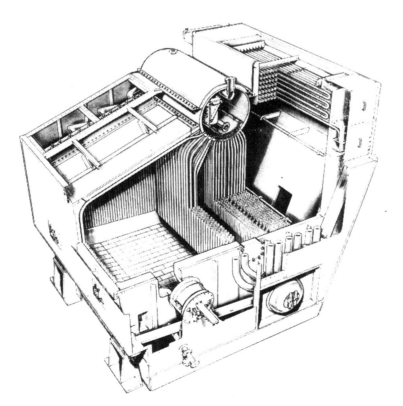

Figure 63   Babcock type M11 water tube boiler.

through which the steam generated by the high pressure portion is passed. The heat given up by the condensing high pressure steam generates steam at a lower pressure from the water surrounding the tube bundle within the low pressure vessel. The low pressure steam is used to supply the auxiliary services and the high pressure condensate returns by gravity to the high pressure boiler. In this case it is less important that some of the auxiliary services may be dirty because the worst that can happen is that the secondary tube bundle becomes fouled and the production of low pressure steam is reduced. Risk of tube failure is virtually eliminated since the highly heated tubes in the combustion zone are only exposed to the high quality closed circuit water. Boiler units of the double pressure or double evaporation type are available from many suppliers worldwide, one typical design being the Aalborg AT4, Fig 64. This shows the secondary or low pressure section arranged above the primary high pressure section and connected thereto by welded steam and condensate pipes. The tube bundle within is connected to inlet and outlet headers which are welded into the drumhead. The primary high pressure section is of bi drum construction and is fired by a simple rotary cup burner. Products of combustion leave from the side of the furnace at floor level and pass in a generally longitudinal fashion over tubular generating surface connected between upper and lower drums. Beyond the generating surface the combustion gases transit a

Figure 65 Low pressure reboiler.

superheater arranged in the uptake. The low pressure steam is thereby superheated to some degree before delivery to the auxiliary consumer and this is very useful in ensuring that wet conditions do not

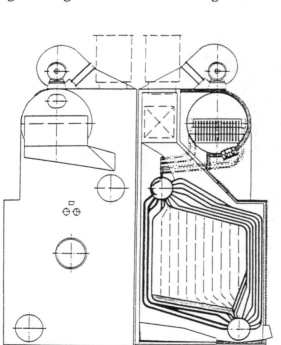

Figure 64 Aalborg AT-4 boiler.

Figure 66 Babcock M11M type boiler.

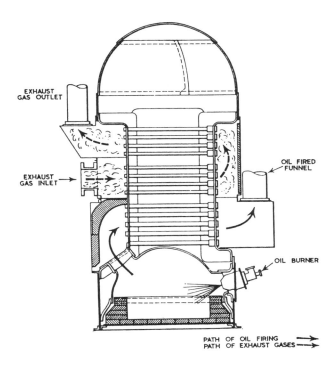

EXHAUST GAS OUTLET

EXHAUST GAS INLET →

OIL FIRED FUNNEL

OIL BURNER

PATH OF OIL FIRING →
PATH OF EXHAUST GASES →

Figure 67 Cochran composite boiler.

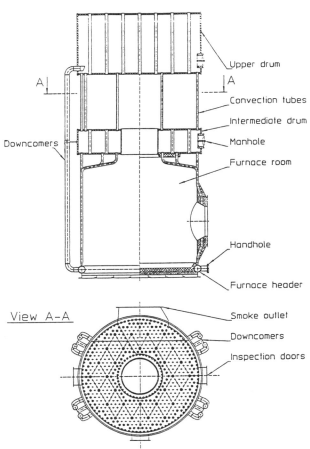

Upper drum

Convection tubes

Intermediate drum

Manhole

Furnace room

Downcomers

A | | A

Handhole

Furnace header

View A-A

Smoke outlet

Downcomers

Inspection doors

Figure 69 Aalborg AQ9 boiler.

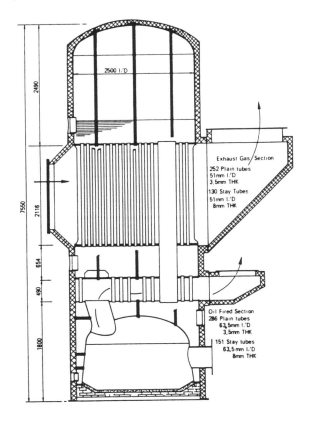

2500 I./D

2490

7550

2116

654

490

1800

Exhaust Gas Section

252 Plain tubes
51mm I./D
3.5mm THK

130 Stay Tubes
51mm I./D
8mm THK

Oil Fired Section
286 Plain tubes
63,5mm I./D
3,5mm THK

151 Stay tubes
63,5mm I./D
8mm THK

Figure 68 Aalborg AQ5 composite boiler: working pressure 7 bar; oil fired section heating surface 75m²; exhaust gas section heating surface 200m².

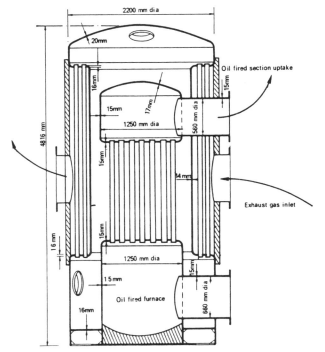

2200 mm dia

20mm

16mm

15mm

17mm

1250 mm dia

560 mm dia

Oil fired section uptake

15mm

4816 mm

15mm

14 mm

Exhaust gas inlet

16 mm

15mm

1250 mm dia

1.5mm

Oil fired furnace

16mm

15mm

660 mm dia

Figure 70 A G Weser composite boiler.

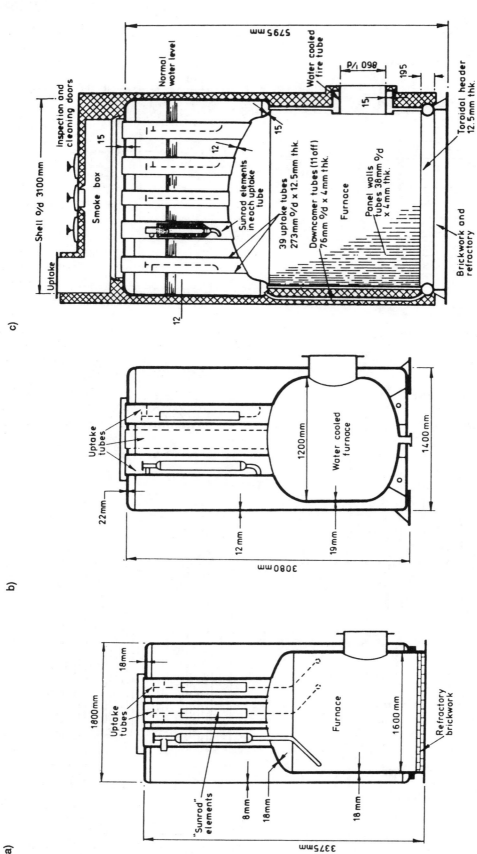

Figure 71 Sunrod boilers: a) CPD25 type, working pressure 7.5 bar, evaporation 2500 kg/h; b) CPD12 type, working pressure 8 kg/cm²; c) CPH140 type, working pressure 7.5 bar, evaporation 1400 kg/h.

exist when steam is passing to machinery remote from the boiler.

The Babcock M11 can also be supplied in dual pressure mode when it is connected by steam and condensate pipes to a reboiler, which is a low pressure vessel fitted with a tube plate and a high pressure head (Fig 65). The high pressure steam enters this head and passes through the U–tubes connected to the tube plate. It condenses within, the condensate draining from the tubes and out of the bottom of the high pressure head beneath the baffle, returning to the M11 by gravity.

With the advent of single main boiler steam ships, notably VLCCs, the auxiliary boiler had the role of emergency propulsion. So that this unit should have the same standard of construction as the all welded radiant boilers then used for main propulsion, much welded construction and use of membrane tube panel enclosure walls was adopted as typically shown by the Babcock M11M (Fig 66). This could be roof fired or front fired with steam atomising burners, and could deliver saturated steam or superheated steam up to about 350°C from a superposed superheater, and could operate at steam pressures up to the same level as the main boiler as necessary. Auxiliary boilers of this type could also be fitted with heating coils in the lower drum accepting bled steam or desuperheated steam. These coils could be sized to generate low pressure steam for auxiliary duties at sea or could be smaller, sufficient to maintain the boiler at a bar or so pressure ready for instant firing. In either case, the boiler would be in readiness to supply emergency propulsion steam with a minimum delay. Such emergency steam connected to a suitable stage of the main turbine provides get-u-home power in the event of loss of the main boiler, and prompt supply of this power would be needed if the emergency occurred with the vessel in close company with others, or in bad weather in restricted waters. Obviously, when using a boiler in this way to supply low pressure auxiliary steam great care would be needed to maintain water side cleanliness, since on occasion it would also be directly fired.

Many ships need only small amounts of steam at low pressure, and in these cases water tube boilers can prove uneconomic. Of the variety of proprietary designs of fire tube or tank type boiler, many are composite, including sections for diesel exhaust gas heat recovery as well as for direct firing. In the Cochran boiler (Fig 67), the products of combustion and exhaust gases pass through separate sets of tubes immersed in the boiler water. These tubes are expanded into tube plates which form part of the boiler pressure shell. With the Aalborg AQ5 (Fig 68) the gas streams pass horizontally over the outside of vertical tubes expanded into tube plates forming part of the boiler pressure vessel, in such a way that boiler water flows upwards throughout the tubes. Large downcomer tubes complete the circulation system. Larger Aalborg vertical fired tube boilers such as the AQ9 (Fig 69), have water tube furnace enclosure walls and external downcomers. A G Weser produced a boiler unit where the products of combustion pass through tubes surrounded by boiler water whilst diesel exhaust passes over tubes through which boiler water passes (Fig 70). A design similar in principle came from Howaldtswerke.

The Sunrod oil fired boiler combines a fire tube and a water tube by arranging the latter inside the former. The water tube surface is extended by having steel pins electric resistance welded on its outer surface. The furnace is arranged either as a water cooled shell with a refractory floor or as a completely water cooled shell. In the largest sizes the furnace walls are of water tube construction (Fig 71). In each case a number of fire tubes of large diameter extend upwards from the furnace top to a tube plate forming the top of the pressure shell. Inside each of these is arranged a water tube with extended surface. The top and bottom of each water tube is connected through the wali of its fire tube into the water space of the boiler (Fig 72).

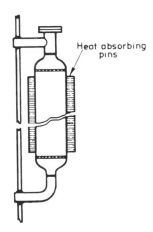

Heat absorbing pins

Figure 72 The Sunrod patent element.

The small boilers described, normally supplied as packages complete with burners, pumps, fans, mountings and controls, are generally of the vertical type which is economical of deckspace. Horizontal type packaged boilers may also be found, typical of which is the Cochran Chieftain (Fig 73). The horizontal boiler shell has a large diameter cylindrical furnace tube, from the rear end of which a number of fire tubes extend forward to the front tube plate. A smoke

Figure 73   Cochran Chieftain boiler.

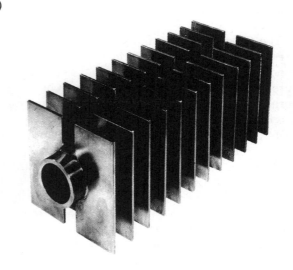

a)

b)

c)

Figure 74   a) Mild steel extended surface; b) cast iron sleeve extended surface; c) Sunrod patent finned form.

box at the front returns the products of combustion into a further set of fire tubes extending between front and rear tube plates, so that the combustion gases exit into an uptake at the rear end. The whole is mounted on a base frame complete with all ancillaries.

EXHAUST GAS HEAT RECOVERY

Since most vessels, whether propelled by steam turbine or diesel engine, can find use for steam in ships' services, it was natural that the diesel designers should seek to use some of the 35% of the heat in the fuel otherwise discharged to the stack to generate steam. A useful supply of steam can be obtained and the efficiency of the plant is given a significant boost. The heat supply to the heat recovery boiler used to generate this steam consists of a large volume of relatively low temperature gas. Consequently the mean temperature difference between exhaust gas and the water boiling within the boiler tubes is low, so that large amounts of heating surface are needed. To minimise the bulk and weight of the boiler arranged above the engine, extended surfaces are used, the heat exchanger taking on the appearance of an economiser as used for final heat recovery on fired boilers. Indeed the suppliers of economisers also supply the heat recovery equipment. The usual arrangement has a bank, or banks, of sinuous tubes connected at each end to headers, the whole arranged within an insulated casing. The type of extended heating surface used varies with the manufacturer and is shown typically by Fig 74. An exception to the use of extended surface is seen in the exhaust gas unit of La Mont design which uses a stack of closely pitched spirally wound plain tubes connected to vertical inlet and outlet headers (Fig 75).

The heat recovery unit may be supplied with a steam and water drum when arranged as an independent unit for forced circulation, or sometimes for natural circulation. The most common arrangement is to have the unit circulated by a pump and connected to a separate oil fired boiler. The circulating pump draws water from this, and the steam/water

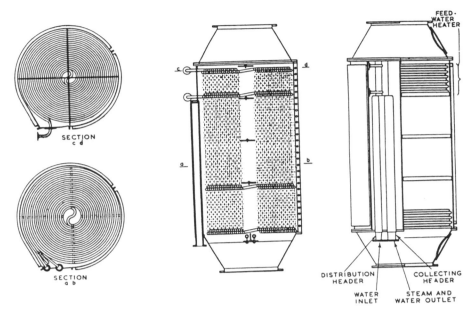

Figure 75 La Mont exhaust gas economiser.

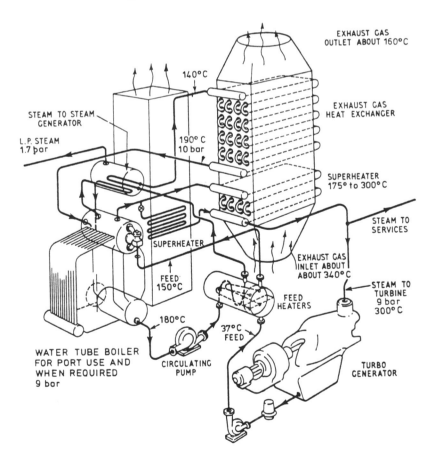

Figure 76 Typical arrangement of exhaust gas heat exchanger circulating into water tube boiler which acts as steam receiver at sea and can be fired in port or when required. Steam is supplied at 9 bar superheated to 340°C for turbo generator and other services, also steam, at 1.7 bar for heating and domestic use.

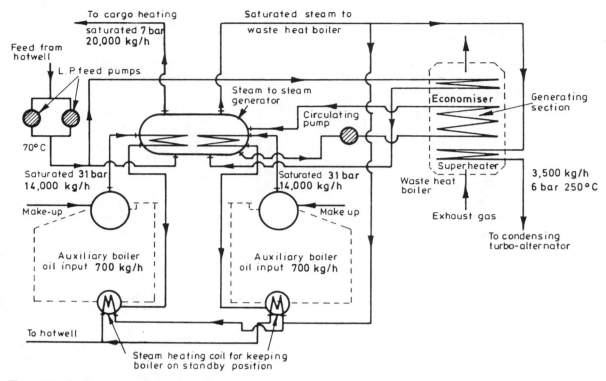

Figure 77   Auxiliary steam system for motor vessel embodying closed circuit w.t. auxiliary boilers, steam to steam generators, waste heat boiler and turbo alternator.

mixture leaving the heat exchangers is separated in the drum of the oil fired boiler, and the steam taken therefrom. At sea the main engine exhaust is used to generate steam, which at the same time keeps the oil fired boiler warm having a preservative effect. In harbour when the main engine is shut down the oil fired boiler is flashed up to produce steam as required. If, at sea, the steam generated from the diesel exhaust is insufficient to meet demand, then the supply can be supplemented by firing the auxiliary boiler (Fig 76). Similar arrangements are possible when the oil fired boiler is of the double evaporation type, the exhaust gas heat recovery unit then being circulated from the LP section (Fig 77). It is not normally necessary to make any attempt to control the output of the exhaust gas unit. If, at sea, the demand for steam is less than that generated, the pressure in the system will rise. This reduces the mean temperature difference between gas and water in the tubes so reducing heat transfer and the rate of steam generation. It is, however, a simple matter to fit a gas bypass so that, should pressure tend to rise too much, a damper opens, allowing gas to bypass the heating surfaces.

Such heat recovery and auxiliary steam systems can be very simple or very sophisticated depending upon the nature of the vessel and the steam demand on board. Improvements in the overall efficiency of the main engine have led to a decline in the temperature of the exhaust gases so that more complicated arrangements are made in order to extract the maximum amount of heat. Heat recovery systems may be found to include superheaters, dual pressure generating sections, feedheating, steam to steam generation and dump condensers for additional control.

OPERATION

Boilers of all types are subject to extremely hazardous conditions involving very high temperatures, abrasive and chemically aggressive fuel constituents and the ever present risk of lax operating procedures brought about by over confidence engendered by the inherent robustness and reliability of the plant. Vigilance is essential at all times and the prime consideration is cleanliness of both gas and water sides of the various sections of the boiler plant so that the boiler operates efficiently and with low maintenance.

A high efficiency is obtained when heat losses are low. A major heat loss occurs in the products of combustion exhausted to atmosphere via the funnel. This is minimised by keeping heating surfaces clean and operating with a minimum of excess air so that the temperature and quantity of the exhaust gases is as low as possible. A further loss is due to the latent heat of moisture formed during combustion from the hydrogen in the fuel but there is little of practical value to be achieved by the operator. Finally there are radiation and unburned losses. The former may be contained by keeping all insulation in good order and the outside surface of the boiler unit as clean and bright as possible. Unburnt losses can be kept to a small value by proper maintenance and care in operation of the combustion equipment.

The necessary care begins with receipt of the fuel on board. In the case of oil the precautions given in Chapter 4 should be observed. With coal it is necessary to establish that a suitable size spectrum is achieved and that water content is not excessive. The fuel must reach the point of combustion in good condition. For oil fuel, settling tanks provide a ready use quantity of oil which may be kept at a suitable pumping temperature for a sufficient time, for any water or other residue to settle out. From here it is taken through suction strainers by the pumping and heating unit, which is arranged in duplex form so that 100% standby pumping and heating capacity exists. Steam heating is used in service, although a separate small capacity electric heater and pump is used for lighting up from cold. From the pumping and heating unit, the fuel oil is further filtered before entering the pipework leading to the firing front. This pipework is arranged in a complete loop back to the suction side of the pumping and heating unit, to enable the whole system to be brought up to working temperature by circulating hot oil before attempting light off. Connections from this pipework to the individual burners and their control valves must be as short as possible to minimise the amount of cold oil injected into the furnace during the first attempt at ignition. The arrangement of the pipework should be such that no dead legs or loops occur where sludge deposits may accumulate, and the heating of the oil should be closely controlled at all times. It is customary to exercise this control so that the viscosity at the burners is at an optimum value for the particular type of atomiser in use. This may be done by temperature, knowing the temperature-viscosity characteristics of the fuel, or directly by means of a viscometer.

For coal the transfer from storage bunker to day bunker should be by means which does not cause degradation of the size spectrum, and the outlet from the day bin should be by means not likely to cause segregation to occur across the width of the stoker. All of the storage and transfer equipment for all fuel types should be kept in good working order.

Combustion equipment needs special care since inadequate combustion conditions caused by badly serviced combustion equipment can lead to serious long term difficulties downstream. With oil firing, regular cleaning and inspection of the atomiser tips is an essential safeguard. Poor atomisation occurs with dirty, partially blocked or misshapen orifices. As soon as wear is detected, the sprayer tips should be replaced with new and the old discarded. This should apply to all burners of a group, which should all have sprayers of equal size and quality at all times. The burner barrel must be set up correctly within the air register, i.e. centrally disposed and with the atomiser in the correct axial location. The swirler or impeller should be firmly attached to the burner carrier tube and in its correct axial location. The air register doors should be free to operate and provide unrestricted passage when open. The correct settings for the combustion equipment should all be clearly specified by the manufacturer.

The air supply arrangements must also be in order. The suction of the forced draught fan should not be impeded, and the trunking should be clear, particularly following any maintenance which may have disturbed those parts. The closely pitched heating surfaces of a steam airheater can also be blocked easily, and should be inspected for cleanliness at intervals and cleaned as soon as necessary. Any dampers in the forced draught air trunking should be checked to ensure that they are in the correct position and that the blades and spindles have not parted company. Sometimes, baffles are used in the windbox to obtain the correct, even air distribution between the several registers, and an occasional check that these have not shifted is worthwhile.

Similar remarks apply to the air supply trunking and forced draught fans on coal fired boilers. Primary air enters beneath the stoker through the fine ash hopper. A check that all is clear in this region should be made. Some stokers will have separate air compartments controlled by dampers, whereby air distribution along the length of the grate can be adjusted. A check on the condition and setting of these dampers is advisable. Secondary air systems involve high pressure secondary air fans, which may take their suction from the hot forced draught air trunking, and deliver to a duct system encompassing the front and rear of the furnace, ending in a number of branches to the individual secondary air nozzles which pierce the furnace wall. Distribution of secondary air in this duct system may be adjusted by means of dampers which should be correctly set.

Although spreader type stokers are not prone to serious clinker formation, a regular furnace inspection is desirable to establish that combustion proceeds in good order. Observation by television cameras has been proposed but until there is wide adoption of such systems the recommendation is for a regular local inspection. If clinker formation is detected then the fire tools provided should be used to prevent clinker growing to a size which may cause jamming of the grate. Correct tensioning of the grate should be observed and any lubrication of moving parts attended to. There may also be cooling air and water supplies to the coal feeder equipment and these must be kept operational.

Assuming that good combustion conditions with a minimum excess of air are achieved, there should be no tendency for severe fouling to occur. Fuels used will, however, vary within a certain range, and contain many undesirable impurities, certain combinations of which will increase the tendency to fouling which must be countered by regular use of sootblowing equipment. For this to be successful the sootblowers must themselves be maintained in correct working order, and any deterioration corrected before it leads to problems within the boiler. This involves checking the condition of the lances and steam nozzles and ensuring that the blowing arc during which steam is admitted is correctly aligned with the heating surfaces. The air purging arrangements should be checked to avoid corrosion due to ingress of combustion products when not in use. Further, a check should be made that the sootblower lance is obtaining steam at the appropriate pressure as specified by the designer. This will be adjustable at each sootblower head. At intervals, when the plant is shut down for maintenance and survey, the cleanliness of all gas side surfaces can be inspected and, if necessary, water washing carried out. Very high pressure water washing equipment is available for this task, and, if embarked upon, it should be carried through to a conclusion which leaves all surfaces clean and deposit free. If this is not done, any small amount of deposit remaining, now devoid of any soluble matter, will be baked on during subsequent operational periods and will need severe mechanical attack for removal. If left on it provides a good key for a further rapid build up of new deposit. This is particularly so in high temperature zones and the extra care and effort necessary to achieve a good result will be well repaid.

Water side cleanliness is no less important to a good service life from a boiler as it has already been observed that even very thin layers of scale inside heated tubes soon lead to temperatures which can cause tube failure. It is therefore most important to ensure that water conditions within the boiler are adjusted by the addition of water treatment chemi-

cals, avoiding scale formation and promoting corrosion free conditions within the whole boiler, steam and condensate systems. Feedwater entering the boiler should pass through a fine microfilter to remove particulates which may have been picked up in the pre-boiler system. After several years operation, or more frequently should there be any accident or interruption in proper treatment, it may become necessary to clean the water side of the boiler. With modern, all welded designs, the use of chemical cleaning has come into vogue. This must be approached with caution and the services of a properly qualified chemical cleaning team should be used. Since cleaning is accomplished by circulating weak acids around the affected parts it is essential that thorough flushing and subsequent passivation procedures follow the cleaning stage. Passivation ensures that the water side surfaces receive a protective layer of magnetite, and follows all water side cleaning operations, even those occurring prior to commissioning when the task is to remove millscale and other small debris resulting from construction. The actual treatment used for boiler water conditioning varies with operating pressure since, in general terms, the higher the pressure the greater the degree of water purity required. For the highest pressures, volatile treatments are used, limiting the amount of dissolved solids in the boiler water and avoiding the need to continuously blow down a small quantity of water from the boiler drum to control the solids content of the water. Care is needed to avoid a build up of particulate matter in the lower parts of the boiler which, if left unchecked, could impede circulation. To avoid this it is customary, on shutting down and after extinguishing burners, to briefly operate manually the blow down valves from the lower headers.

Lighting up is a process during which accidents are likely to occur. Apart from the obvious precautions of making sure that the gas passages are clear, all access doors are closed and that there is water in the boiler, the first requirement is to ensure that there is no fuel or fuel vapour anywhere within the setting which could give rise to an explosive situation. A visual inspection of the furnace is followed by a few minutes purge by running the forced draught fan with all air registers open. Following this fan speed is reduced and air registers are closed, except on the first burner. Having circulated hot oil to the furnace front, the first burner is inserted into its firing position, the igniter energised and the fuel valve opened. The following few seconds is a trial for ignition period, during which the burner should ignite and a signal be received by the flame scanning device.

Should light off not occur during this period the burner is secured and the sequence restarted with a further air purge. With the first burner safely firing with a lighting up capacity atomiser, pressure raising begins. At this stage the boiler stop valve is closed, the drum and superheater vents are open, the superheater and steam range drains are open and the superheater circulating valve is open. This last is found in a small bore pipe leading from the superheater outlet to atmosphere, its purpose being to permit a cooling flow of steam through the superheater until the boiler goes on load. The pressure raising period is a hazardous one for the superheater and requires that the firing rate be limited, so that, with the small steam flow allowed, the superheater tubes do not become overheated. Pressure should begin to rise after the first hour or so and until this point no steam is available to cool the superheater, so during this initial period great care is taken not to overfire. Thereafter, with a steady firing rate, usually specified by the designer, the pressure will rise so that the saturation temperature in the boiler increases

at the rate of 1°C per minute, so avoiding any risk of stresses induced by any substantial temperature differential in any area of the boiler pressure parts. The typical lighting up chart (Fig 78), shows how the pressure will increase at a faster rate as time passes by until full boiler pressure, in this case 62 bar, is reached in a little over 4 hours. This chart also indicates the status of the various vent and drain valves during the lighting up period. Steam temperature should also be monitored so that the circulating valve is not needlessly left wide open, but is trimmed in to conserve water and aid pressure raising. This valve is finally closed when the boiler takes load.

When the main engine is ready to take steam, the boiler stop valve would have been opened to warm through the lines and the remaining burners are ignited. Thereafter the fuel oil pressure is varied, causing the firing rate to match the steam demand by maintaining constant boiler steam pressure. On modern plant, burner management and boiler control is achieved with automatic devices and it is only necessary for the operator to satisfy himself that this

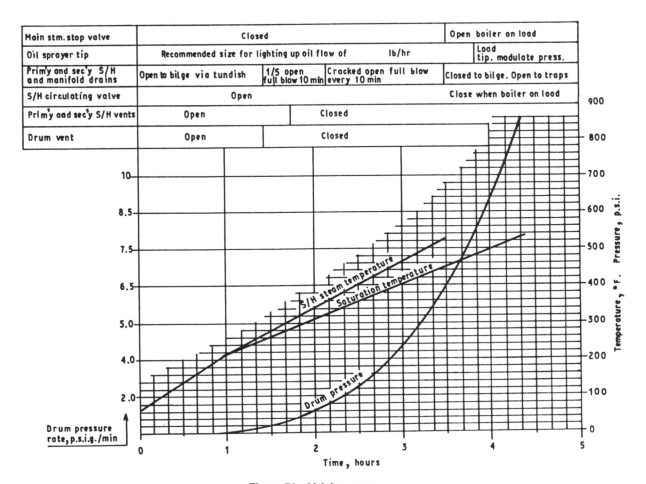

Figure 78 Lighting up curve.

equipment, the built in alarms and safety cut outs are operational, and to engage the system according to the maker's instructions. The automatic controls will take care of all manoeuvring situations and steady load operation at sea, during which it is only necessary for regular checks to be made on safety devices such as low water level alarms and low low level trips, which extinguish the burners when water reaches a dangerously low level. There is an established routine for blowing down water gauge glasses, and it is as well to extend this to include a check on all alarm and safety cut out devices since such equipment, if seldom called into play, has been known to fail to operate when an emergency arises. If, during any emergency, steam pressure falls back well below the set point, care is needed, following resolution of the problem, not to regain pressure too quickly. For safety of the superheater, fuel flow and steam flow should be in balance. When regaining pressure, fuel flow must be greater than that needed for the existing steam flow. This excess firing rate will elevate the superheater tube temperature and must therefore be limited. It will be satisfactory if the rate of regained pressure does not exceed the rate of pressure rise existing at the end of the lighting up period, as shown on the lighting up chart.

Cleanliness of the heat recovery surfaces after the boiler can often be judged by observing the gas pressure differential above and below. Any significant rise in this value should be attended to. Whilst good combustion conditions will minimise the risk, deposits allowed to accumulate in this area are a fire risk and, should fire take hold undetected, it can prove impossible to control and can wreck the heat exchanger, or even the whole boiler (Fig 79). There is plenty of evidence of soot fires leading on to hydrogen fires where the metal parts of a boiler burn in steam, releasing hydrogen which burns in air, these two combustion effects continuing in an unstoppable manner until either the steam or the metal is exhausted. Sometimes, due to tube failure in an economiser if the individual tube cannot be isolated, or if the failures are of a multiple nature, it becomes necessary to make an emergency bypass of the economiser on the water side. Ordinarily, the gas temperature in this zone will not be sufficiently high to cause any distress to the metal parts, but there will be a fire risk due to the overheating of any deposits on the tubes. Sootblowers should therefore be operated prior to operation with the economisers bypassed, a suitably reduced firing rate should be established and the gas temperature into and out of the bypassed unit monitored, the plant being shut down at the first sign of untoward readings. Such events are also known to

Figure 79 Damage caused through hydrogen fire in finned tube type economiser.

have occurred in diesel exhaust gas boilers and, apart from keeping them clean, a sensible precaution with this equipment is to leave the circulating pump running, after the engine is shut down, to cool down the unit and to ensure that air is not admitted until cooler conditions prevail. The only cure is prevention.

These operating principles apply to all boilers, although for simpler auxiliary types the procedures may be somewhat less complicated. In any event it is wise to follow the manufacturer's instructions for all boiler types.

WATER TREATMENT

Probably the single most important factor concerning safe, efficient and reliable operation of boiler plant is the maintenance of correct water conditions appropriate to the particular installation. Since raw water is insufficiently pure for use in boiler plant water treatment is used to produce the desired water conditions.

Each class of boiler unit, whether it be high pressure main propulsion or low pressure exhaust gas heat recovery plant, has its own set of desirable water conditions. It goes beyond the scope of this chapter to detail these, but BS 1170 will provide the necessary information. The recommendations of the equipment supplier or specialist water treatment chemical supplier should be observed and followed at all times. The principles and methods of treatment of the working fluid apply, in general, to all installations.

It is worth pointing out that a problem at one point in the feed/boiler/steam/condensate system can cause serious problems at another; e.g. corrosion in the feed system will result in the corrosion products being transported into the boiler with possible deposition and tube failure from either over heating or sub-deposit corrosion.

The history of present marine boiler water treatment can probably be said to have been started on a more logical basis by the work of Commander Solberg of the US Navy Department in the 1930s. Cdr Solberg carried out considerable experimental work producing artificial scales and testing the effect of various chemicals on them. One of the most effective mixtures he found at controlling scale formation was a combination of sodium carbonate, sodium phosphate and starch. The mixture was known as US Navy Compound. Its use was extended to the Royal Navy in world war II, where it was known as boiler compound navy or BCN for short. This type of treatment, containing as it does a combination of phosphate and alkali in the correct proportions to deal with evaporated seawater make–up, and starch for sludge conditioning, formed the basis of marine water treatment for a number of years. It was only in the 60's and 70's that more modern forms of treatment were developed to deal with higher boiler pressures and heat fluxes.

The objectives of feed water treatment and chemical control can be listed as follows:

1. Prevention of corrosion/deposition within the boiler itself.

2. Prevention of corrosion/deposition of the feed and condensate systems.

3. Prevention of damage to machinery due to impure steam being generated.

4. Prevention of outage time due to failure of the boiler or its associated equipment.

5. Reduction of time for repair or maintenance.

6. Maintenance of a safe operating environment for personnel.

The following paragraphs highlight the water treatment regimes necessary to achieve satisfactory conditions within the boiler and pre-boiler systems, and conclude by detailing some of the problems which may result if these conditions are not regularly maintained.

Sources of water
General
Boiler feed make-up water is usually obtained from either evaporated seawater or shore water and, in the case of some low pressure units, raw shore water. The quality of shore water varies considerably and it is recommended that evaporated water be used in all cases where possible.

Evaporated waters
These are produced by distilling fresh water or seawater. A single effect evaporator should produce water containing about 1mg/l dissolved solids and not more than 3 or 4 mg/l. The water will still contain considerable quantities of dissolved gases such as oxygen and carbon dioxide.

Shore waters
There are two classes of dissolved salts in shore water that are important to boiler operation; calcium and magnesium salts (i.e. hardness); and others which consist mainly of sodium salts. The hardness salts potentially form scale in a boiler whereas the sodium salts do not.

Feed water
General
The feed water to the boiler will comprise returned condensate plus a small amount of make-up feed. The make-up is required to make good any losses from the cycle, such as boiler blowdown and small steam leaks etc. The following points should be noted in connection with feed water quality.

Hardness salts
For all but the lowest pressure boilers there should be no detectable hardness in the feed water. Hardness can contaminate the feed water either from evaporator priming or condenser leakage. Any contamination detected should be rapidly found and corrected, as hardness may cause scale formation within the boiler and tube failure from overheating.

pH value
The pH value of the feed should be controlled within a certain range to minimise corrosion of the pre-boiler system and thus avoid problems that these corrosion products cause in the boiler. The normal range of feed pH is 8.5–9.2 (the pH may be increased to 9.2–9.5 for those feed/condensate systems that do not contain cupreous material). The range 8.5–9.2 is wide and an operating level is normally determined by trial and error as that which gives the minimum

pick–up of iron, copper and nickel. Experience indicates that this is usually 9.0–9.1. This pH is achieved by continuous addition of a suitable alkali to the feed. In low pressure boilers, and those not using the feed as spray water for attemperation or desuperheating purposes, it is permissible to use a non-volatile alkali such as caustic soda; but it is much more common to use a volatile alkali. Hydrazine, which is primarily dosed as an oxygen scavenger, is an alkali and does contribute to an increase in pH level. At high temperatures hydrazine thermally decomposes to ammonia, which then returns with the condensate and also raises the pH,

$$3N_2H_4 \rightarrow 4NH_3 + N_2$$

To achieve the desired level it may be necessary to dose either additional ammonia or a neutralising amine such as cyclohexylamine or morpholine. These amines also have the beneficial effect of neutralising any carbon dioxide present.

Dissolved gases
Dissolved gases are present in the feed water coming either from the make-up water or returned condensate. The principal gases are oxygen and carbon dioxide, the presence of which can cause corrosion of the feed, economiser, boiler and condensate systems. Both mechanical and chemical means are employed to remove the gases. Medium and high pressure boilers invariably have a mechanical deaerator, which will reduce levels to typically 0.005 mg/l oxygen. In systems with an open feed tank the levels of oxygen can be minimised by maintaining a high temperature.

Iron, copper and nickel
These three metals or their oxides are the most common metals found in feed water although there may be small quantities of others such as zinc, aluminium etc. The proportion and quantities of these metals is determined by the materials of construction and also the chemical environment, e.g. a high pH and high oxygen level will give rise to a high copper level. At the pH of the feed these metallic oxides are particulate in form and thus can be removed by filtration. Cartridge type filters are often installed for high pressure boilers.

Conductivity
Conductivity gives a good indication of water quality or the level of dissolved solids present. Conductivity measuring equipment is simple to use and reliable. The routine measurement of conductivity, preferably on a continuous basis will show up any feed water contamination such as condenser leakage or evaporator priming.

Silica
Silica can cause the deposition of very insulating scales in a boiler. At high pressures, i.e. above 40 bar, silica has an appreciable volatility in steam. However, it is not normally a problem when evaporated sea water is used as make-up because silica is present at a low level in sea water. Shore water can have high levels of silica.

Oil
Oil contamination can be very damaging to a boiler. Slight contamination can be dealt with by the conditioning chemicals but in general all steps should be taken to prevent its ingress.

Treatment chemicals
There are a number of forms of boiler water treatment that can be used depending on the operating pressure and type of boiler. Many specialist water treatment chemical suppliers have their own proprietary products and their recommendations for the application of these products should always be followed. The recommendations of boiler suppliers should also be followed. The following notes give the important features of the most commonly used treatments.

Caustic/phosphate
This treatment is based on the maintenance of reserves of both caustic soda and phosphate in the boiler water. The chemical reserves give the required alkaline environment to prevent corrosion and protect against the ingress of hardness salts. Calcium and magnesium salts will be precipitated according to the following reactions.

$$3CaCl_2 + 2Na_3PO_4 \rightarrow Ca_3(PO_4)_2 + 6NaCl$$

$$MgCl_2 + 2NaOH \rightarrow Mg(OH)_2 + 2NaCl$$

In order to prevent salts being precipitated in the feed system the chemicals are preferably added directly to the boiler. The precipitated salts are removed by blowdown.

Congruent phosphate
Caustic soda at high concentrations such as can be formed beneath deposits can cause serious and rapid corrosion of boiler steels. It has been shown that concentrating a solution of tri-sodium phosphate to the point of dryness does result in free caustic soda being formed. It is for this reason that congruent or

coordinated phosphate was developed. The pH and phosphate levels are controlled by dosing a mixture of di- and tri-sodium phosphates so that even a solution concentrated to dryness theoretically contains zero caustic soda. There are, however, disadvantages with this form of treatment and it is not suitable for conditioning all boiler waters for the following reasons.

1. More sophisticated control is necessary with very narrow limits being imposed for both pH and phosphate.

2. The alkalinity buffer against acid chloride attack is reduced. Thus if it is not possible to maintain low chloride levels, it is recommended that the conventional caustic/phosphate treatment be reverted to.

Polymers

Specific water soluble polymers are used for coagulation, dispersion and to prevent scale and sludge formation. The action of certain polymers is to prevent scale formation by magnesium and calcium salts by forming a non-adherent sludge. One of the most common polymers used in this treatment is a polyacrylate, used in conjunction with either sodium hydroxide or sodium hydroxide/sodium phosphate.

The polymer treatment prevents scale deposition and minimises sludge formation. It may also loosen any scale already present in a boiler. It is therefore preferable to introduce such a treatment to clean boilers only, otherwise troubles might be encountered through the exposure of leakages at places where scale has been loosened, i.e. tube expansions etc., or blockage of tubes by the detached scale.

Oxygen scavengers

Common chemicals continuously added to the feed for scavenging oxygen are sodium sulphite and hydrazine which react with oxygen according to the following equations:

$$2Na_2SO_3 + O_2 \rightarrow 2Na_2SO_4$$

$$2N_2H_4 + O_2 \rightarrow 2NH_3 + 2H_2O$$

The use of sodium sulphite is restricted to boilers operating at pressures up to 40 bar. Above this pressure the sulphite decomposes to give acidic products. Hydrazine has no such restrictions, although its present day usage is declining because of its toxic nature. There are a number of proprietary products available which do not have this disadvantage.

Amines

Amines are used to protect against corrosion. There are two distinct classes.

Neutralising amines

They are steam-volatile, and are used to neutralise carbon dioxide in steam, condensate and feed systems. The common amines used are cyclohexylamine and morpholine, or combinations of the two.

Filming amine

These do show a neutralising tendency, but their essential function is to protect by forming a molecular water-repellent protective film on metal surfaces and thus prevent corrosion. Octadecylamine is a commonly used filming amine.

Antifoams

These are complex organic compounds of high molecular mass and should be applied according to the supplier's instructions. They are effective at reducing carry over due to foaming and thus improving steam purity. For safety reasons it is recommended that they are only used as an additional safeguard and are not used to allow total solids to rise higher than would be allowed without their application.

Steam purity

Many marine boilers provide steam for turbines and it is important that good quality steam is produced. This requires the correct installation of drum internals and selection of the appropriate boiler water conditions. Boilers with only rudimentary drum internals will require lower concentrations to be maintained in the boiler water than otherwise would have been necessary.

Sampling

The first requirement to be able to control feed and boiler water conditions is to obtain representative samples. For all sample locations, where the medium to be sampled is above 60°C it is necessary to fit a cooler. This is for both protection of the operator from scalding and to prevent a proportion of the sample flashing off as steam, which would give falsely high test readings. Where boiler water sampling is fitted with an internal collection pipe it should be checked that the pipe is remote from the feed discharge. Otherwise contamination of the sample with feed water will give falsely low test readings. It is essential when taking a sample that the sample be run to waste for sufficient time to flush out all lines and the collection container.

It is beyond the scope of this chapter to detail the methods of analysis. Details of commonly used test methods can be found in BS 1170, 'Treatment of water for marine boilers'. Further test methods can be found in BS 1427 and BS 2690. A number of treatment chemical companies have simplified methods for their own proprietary products.

There is a trend towards the greater use of continuous on-line instrumentation such as pH, conductivity and sodium analysers. Modern analytical instruments are reliable and robust, making them suitable for ship-board use. Fitted with high or low alarms the advantages of early warning of dangerous conditions is obvious.

Troubles associated with water treatment

Failure to maintain adequate water conditions can have serious consequences for boiler operation. The main types of failure can be categorised as follows.

Overheating
This can be divided into short and long term.

Short term
This type of failure can result from either a loss of feedwater, when it is usual for a large number of tubes to be affected, or blockage of an individual tube when the damage is confined to the blocked or partially blocked tube. The feature of this type of failure is that the tube swells, and the failure is thin edged, purely because the metal overheats and becomes plastic. The internal pressure causes the material to expand like a balloon to the point of failure. There is one exception to this and this is a short water failure in the presence of copper. The copper reaches its melting point and a thick edged rupture results from intergranular penetration.

If a short water failure is taken to the extreme the metal becomes so hot that the water present dissociates into hydrogen and oxygen and the heat produced in the oxidation of the steel is sufficient for a self sustaining hydrogen fire to be started and which will continue as long as water is being fed to the boiler.

A further possible cause of short water failure which occurs in superheaters is by priming when a slug of water blocks a few tubes for a short period of time but sufficient for these tubes to overheat and possibly fail.

Long term
These arise as a result of internal deposits or oil contamination reducing heat transfer, causing overheating and blistering of the tubes. Small longitudinal splits develop around the blister, and through the peak of the blister the metal thins, and finally fails as a 'creep rupture'. The presence of oil tends to make

this happen very much more quickly than with other types of deposit. This type of failure can also occur in the steam circuits. Here the problem (assuming that the design is correct) can be due to the use of the wrong material. More often, it is caused by excessive operational temperatures either continuously or by a number of short term temperature escalations e.g. during start-up or soot blowing.

All these failures can be termed 'creep' and can be recognised by a heavily oxidised layer and a thick edged failure with numerous small longitudinal cracks adjacent to the point of failure.

Corrosion
Once more this general heading can be split into two distinct types.

Pitting
To complicate matters this can be further subdivided into several categories.

1. Dissolved gas i.e. oxygen or carbon dioxide bubbles, cling to the metal surface, setting off a vigorous corrosion reaction. The pits are characterised by being sharp edged and having no corrosion products present. The time to failure can be very short.

2. Scab pitting is much the same as the above, and is caused by high oxygen and low pH. Characteristic are hard scabs of corrosion product.

3. Soft scab pitting is caused by droplets of water adhering to the surface during storage or shutdown. The corrosion products are soft and reddy in colour.

4. Acid pitting is caused by either poorly carried out acid clean or sea water contamination and is characterised by the base of the pits having a larger area than the entry.

On-load corrosion
On-load corrosion is probably not as prevalent now as it was a few years ago, as we appreciate the causes more fully, but nevertheless is one of the most common causes of failure in medium and high pressure boiler plant. The principal cause is a deposition of metallic oxides within the furnace. The oxides of iron and copper are transported into the boiler and may be the result of corrosion in the condensate/feed system or generated within the boiler itself. For example, high oxygen and low pH can cause corrosion of the eceonomiser and the resulting corrosion products end up in the boiler. These corrosion products, which at the pH in the boiler are largely particulate in

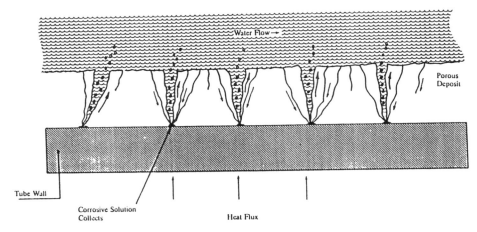

Figure 80 Salt concentration by 'wick boiling'.

nature, tend to bake out in the areas of highest heat flux i.e. on the furnace side of the tube in an area around the furnace at or slightly above the burners. The deposit changes the form of boiling from nucleate to wick boiling. Nucleate boiling is the normal production of steam bubbles at the tube surface in a clean deposit free tube. Figure 80 shows the wick boiling process where boiler water enters the deposit through fine pores and is drawn down to the metal surface by capillary action. Evaporation takes place at this surface with the steam escaping through larger pores. The evaporation causes concentration of boiler salts and may reach a level of many thousands times the concentration in the bulk fluid as there is no flow at the metal surface to flush the salts away. The concentrated boiler solution rapidly attacks the boiler steel. The deposit has an insulating effect and the temperature rise accelerates the rate of attack. The tube thins, often over a considerable length, and eventually fails.

In severe cases corrosion process goes a stage further and a more catastrophic failure occurs. Hydrogen is produced in the process and this can diffuse into the metal. The hydrogen reacts with the carbon of the metal and methane is produced under extreme pressure. This destroys the metal structure and the metal becomes weak and brittle. The failure is often extremely violent with sections of tubing blowing out. It is most important that the oxide deposits are removed before this process is initiated and for this reason a regular chemical cleaning is recommended.

Wastage

General wastage on the water side is extremely rare but can be caused by marginal water conditions. It is more normally associated with the gas side.

Corrosion associated with stress

For the sake of completeness it is worth while mentioning these although the occurrence on marine boilers is rare. Under this heading we have fatigue type failures where alternating stress eventually gives rise to failure. This process is accelerated if there is a corrosive environment, i.e. corrosion fatigue. If thermal cycling is present then it becomes thermal fatigue.

Caustic embrittlement or gouging is no longer the problem that it was with riveted drums etc., but it is still occasionally found at tube expansions. The mechanism is a combination of the residual stress in the expansion joint and a high caustic concentration as a result of leakage at the expansion joint.

BIBLIOGRAPHY

1. BS 1170, 'Recommendations for treatment of water for marine boilers', HMSO (1990).
2. BS 1427, 'Routine control methods of testing water used in industry', HMSO (1989).
3. BS 2690, 'Methods of testing water used in industry', HMSO (1989).
4. Milton, S.H. and Leach, R.M., *Marine steam boilers*, Butterworths, 4th edition, 1980.

Acknowledgments

The author is indebted to Mr Malcolm Macrae of Babcock Energy Ltd for the notes on water treatment.

Chapter 2
Marine Steam Turbines

D G Nicholas

INTRODUCTION

The aim of this chapter is to describe typical steam propulsion machinery in terms of the engineering principles involved in its design. Typical values are given for loadings, operating temperatures and pressures etc., but the information provided in the operating manuals for a specific set of machinery must always take precedence.

TYPE OF CYCLE

The term 'cycle' is used to describe the overall thermodynamic process in which heat is converted into mechanical power. The aim in designing the cycle is to strike the best compromise between cost, reliability, ease of maintenance and efficiency.

The most basic steam cycle consists of a boiler, turbine and condenser with extraction and feed pumps to return the condensed steam to the boiler. For a given set of inlet steam conditions the efficiency can be improved by the use of reheating, which is discussed later in this section, by the use of feed heating and by utilising different methods of driving auxiliaries such as the electrical generator and the feed pump.

The feed water is heated by steam 'bled' from various points in the turbine and the final feed temperature is established by the saturation temperature of the highest pressure bleed. The latent heat of steam represents a large proportion of the total heat of the steam and the principle of feed heating is to bleed off a proportion of steam after it has performed work in the turbine and use it for heating the feed water whereby the loss of latent heat from the cycle to the condenser cooling water is reduced. Obviously with less steam flowing completely through the turbine,

the power output is reduced, but the efficiency of the cycle can be increased by 9% or 10% as shown in Fig 1, which also illustrates that there is an optimum final feed temperature for each inlet steam pressure. In addition, it can be shown that it is better to gradu-

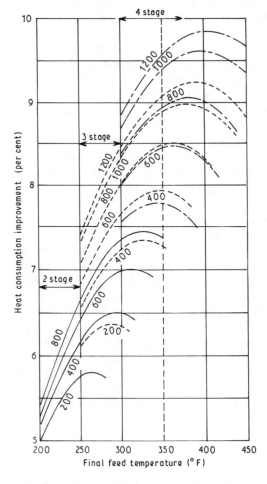

Figure 1 The reduction of heat consumption by the use of feed heating.

a)

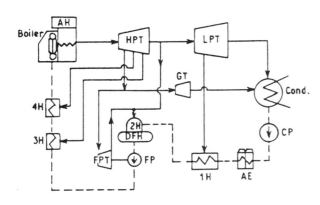

b)

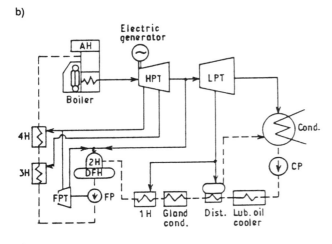

c)

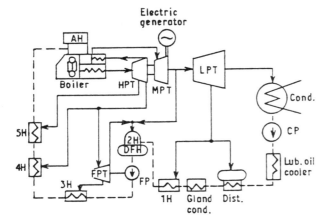

BOIL: boiler
GENE: electric generator
AH: air heater
HPT: high pressure turbine
MPT: medium pressure turbine
LPT: low pressure turbine
COND: condenser
CP: condensate pump

LO CLR: lub oil cooler
DIST: distiller
GLA-CON: gland condenser
H: heater
FP: feed water pump
DFH: deaerating feedwater
          heater
GT: turbo generator

Figure 2   Three types of steam cycle.

ally heat the water in stages by extracting small quantities of steam from several points on the turbine, and Fig 1 also illustrates that with increasing steam conditions the optimum improvement in efficiency is achieved with a greater number of heaters.

Three typical cycles are illustrated in Figs 2 a, b and c. The cycle in Fig 2a includes a non reheat, two cylinder turbine with four stages of feed heating, including a combined deaerator heater. It will be noted that the turbines driving the feed pump and the generator receive steam bled from the HP turbine. The reason for this is that low powered turbines cannot make efficient use of the high pressure main inlet steam, and it is better to make effective use of this steam in the main HP turbine before bleeding it off at a lower pressure for driving the auxiliary turbines. The feed pump is driven by a back pressure turbine and its exhaust steam is added to steam bled from the HP/LP cross-over point to supply the deaerator heater.

Figure 2b again shows a cycle with a non reheat, two cylinder turbine with four stages of feed heat, but this time the generator is mechanically driven from the main turbine and the absence of air ejectors indicates the use of a rotary air pump. In the search for efficiency the condensate is used to cool the lubricating oil and so pick up the heat resulting from the mechanical losses in the gearbox and the turbine bearings. As in the previous case, heaters 3 and 4 are located after the feed pump and are termed 'high pressure' heaters because of the high water pressure to which they are subjected, whereas the heaters downstream of the feed pump are described as low pressure heaters.

To avoid corrosion in the boiler, it is necessary to remove any dissolved air from the feed water and a deaerator, or a direct contact heater, is used for this, in addition to providing a stage of feed heating. To obtain effective release of the air, the condensate must be at the saturation temperature corresponding to its pressure and broken up into droplets. This is achieved in a direct contact heater by spraying the condensate into the shell to a series of drip trays which provides direct contact between the droplets and the heating steam bled from the turbine. The shell is also used to provide a reservoir of feed water which connects to the feed pump suction.

The system also includes a distiller to produce pure water for the boiler and the condensate retrieves most of the heat used in the distillation process. A further addition is a gland steam condenser which saves the heat otherwise lost from the steam leaking from turbine shaft glands and control valve spindles.

Figure 2c illustrates a cycle in which a reheat turbine is used. As the inlet steam conditions are

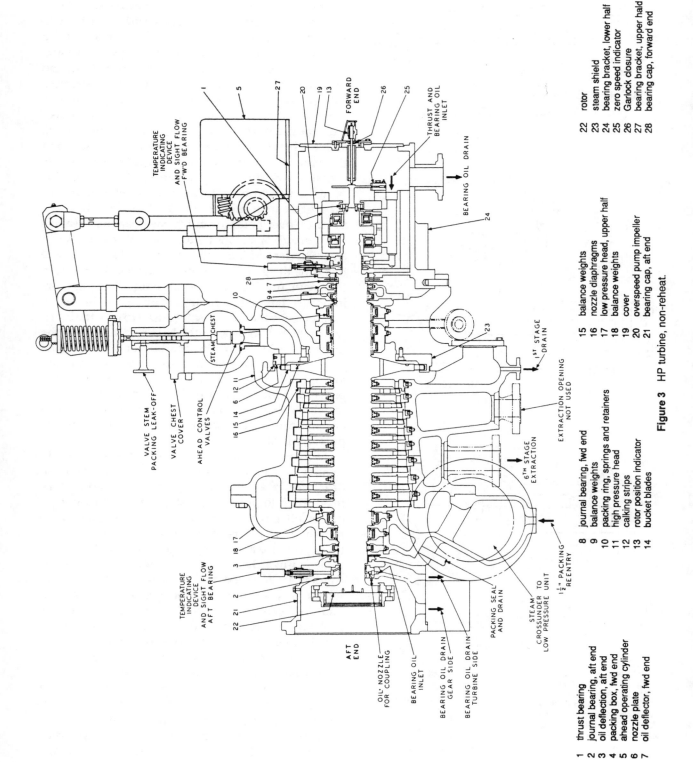

1 thrust bearing
2 journal bearing, aft end
3 oil deflection, aft end
4 packing box, fwd end
5 ahead operating cylinder
6 nozzle plate
7 oil deflector, fwd end

8   journal bearing, fwd end
9   balance weights
10 packing ring, springs and retainers
11 high pressure head
12 calking strips
13 rotor position indicator
14 bucket blades

15 balance weights
16 nozzle diaphragms
17 low pressure head, upper half
18 balance weights
19 cover
20 overspeed pump impeller
21 bearing cap, aft end

22 rotor
23 steam shield
24 bearing bracket, lower half
25 zero speed indicator
26 Garlock closure
27 bearing bracket, upper half
28 bearing cap, forward end

Figure 3 HP turbine, non-reheat.

usually significantly higher than for non-reheat systems, there is an increase to five stages of feed heat with three HP heaters, indicating a higher final feed temperature. Otherwise the system is identical to Fig 2b.

REHEAT AND NON-REHEAT TURBINES

The majority of turbines in service are of the non-reheat type and operate with inlet steam conditions circa 60 bar/510°C.

In the case of reheat turbines the steam is returned to the boiler for reheating, usually to its original inlet temperature, after it has expanded through the HP cylinder. The reheated steam then returns to the turbine to complete its expansion in the intermediate and low pressure cylinders.

Typical steam conditions are 100 bar/510°C/510°C with the second temperature indicating the reheat temperature. The reason for using reheat is to improve efficiency and a system working on the conditions quoted would give a fuel rate 4–6% less than for typical non-reheat systems, with turbines of similar output.

Figure 3 illustrates a typical non reheat HP turbine in which the steam will expand from the inlet conditions given above down to about 6.5 bar and 230°C in the HP cylinder, the final expansion to vacuum taking place in the LP cylinder.

Figure 4 shows a combined HP/IP cylinder as used on some reheat machines. It will be noted that the HP and reheated IP steam enter the cylinder at a mid point with the two inlet belts adjacent to each other. The HP and IP sections of blading on either side are of opposite hand. This arrangement is adopted in order to obtain reasonably uniform thermal gradients in the cylinder and the inlet temperatures of 510°C reduce gradually to about 330°C at each end as the steam expands in the HP and IP sections of the cylinder.

The corresponding steam pressures are 100 bar at inlet reducing to about 22 bar at the end of the HP section prior to returning to the boiler for reheat, and about 5 bar after expansion in the IP section.

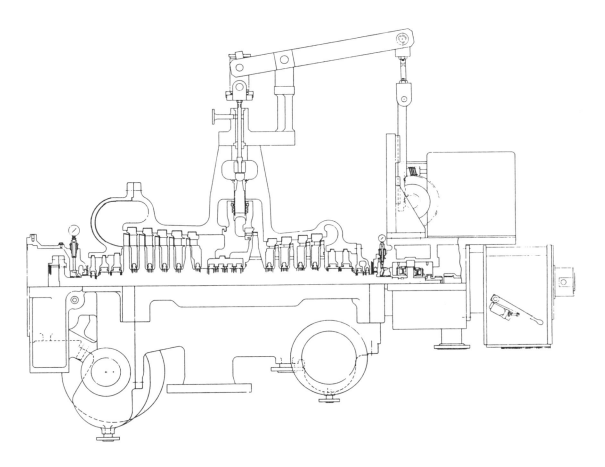

Figure 4 Reheat HP/IP turbine.

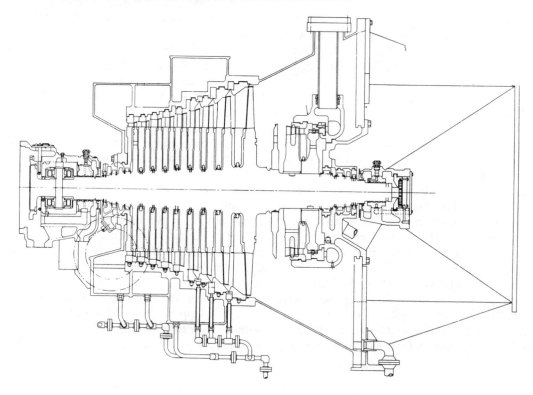

Figure 5   LP turbine with axial exhaust.

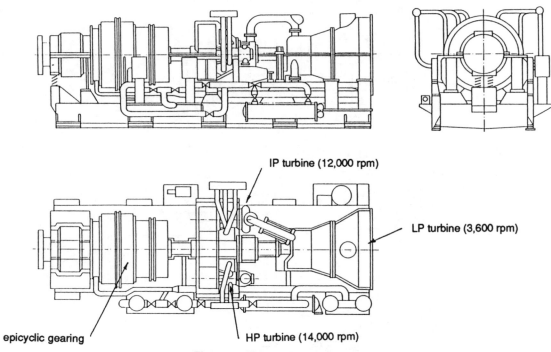

IP turbine (12,000 rpm)

LP turbine (3,600 rpm)

epicyclic gearing

HP turbine (14,000 rpm)

Figure 6   Three cylinder reheat turbine.

Figure 5 shows an LP cylinder which can be used in either the non-reheat or reheat systems.

Figure 6 shows an arrangement of a reheat turbine with separate HP and IP turbines. This has many fundamental advantages. The individual turbines will have gradual thermal gradients from inlet to

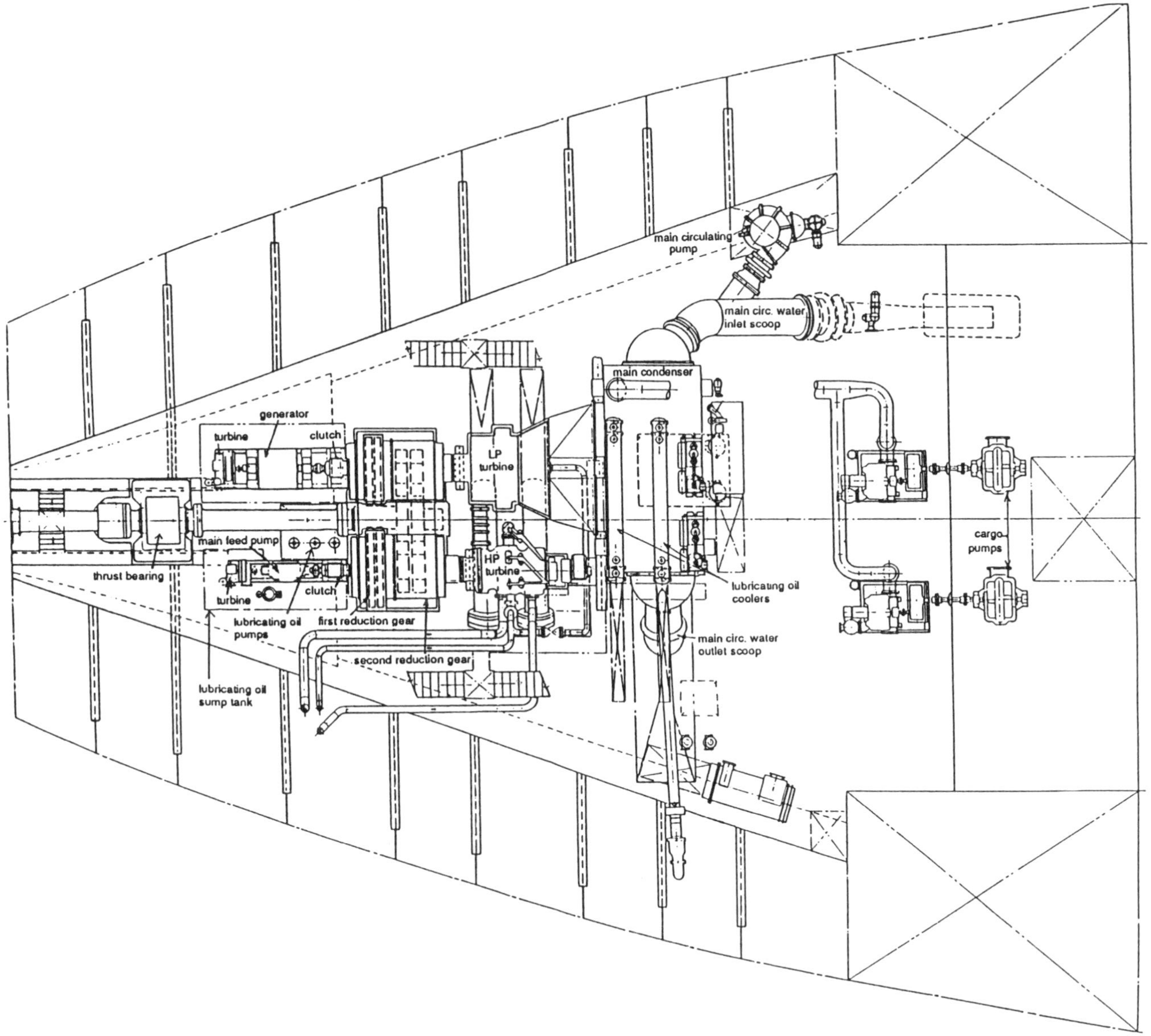

Figure 7 Plan arrangement of propulsion machinery.

exhaust and can be made dimensionally very small, particularly if high steam conditions are employed when the specific steam volume is small. This small size minimises thermal stress, which is size related, and makes the machinery easier to operate than turbines having a combined HP/IP cylinder. The latter have a long rotor with large hub diameter, which takes longer to warm through and requires more care at start-up to avoid gland rubs.

For efficient operation there is an optimal relationship between the speed of the steam issuing from the nozzles within the turbine and the speed of the rotor blades upon which the steam jets impinge, which is explained in a later paragraph. In order to achieve this correct blade speed in small diameter turbines the rotational speed has to be increased. For example, an HP turbine having a mean diameter of the blade ring of 250 mm would have a rotational speed of about 14,000 rev/min at rated power.

ARRANGEMENT OF THE PROPULSION MACHINERY IN THE SHIP

A typical installation is shown in plan in Fig 7. This installation shows a cross compound reheat turbine having a combined HP/IP cylinder and an LP with axial exhaust and in-plane condenser. The term 'compound' means that there are two cylinders HP and LP and 'cross compound' refers to a side by side arrangement of the cylinders.

It will be noted that the main feed pump is driven via a clutch from the HP turbine input shaft to the gearbox, this giving an appropriate rotational speed for the pump of about 6,500 rev/min. If the main engine is not running, or is manoeuvring, the pump can be declutched and driven by a small independent turbine.

The generator is also mechanically driven from the main engine by a clutched connection to the LP turbine input shaft to the gearbox, the rotational speed at the normal ship operating speed being 3,600 rev/min to give 60 Hz with a 2 pole generator. Again, an auxiliary turbine is provided to give an independent drive for the generator when required.

The alternative to the use of these mechanical drives for the feed pump and generator is to use individual turbine drives, but these low power machines would be far less efficient than making use of power produced by the main engine.

A separate main thrust bearing is shown, but sometimes this is incorporated in the gearbox.

The cooling water for the condenser is provided by a scoop during normal service and this is supple-mented by a motor driven pump for start up and when manoeuvring.

Air and incondensible gases are removed from the condenser by an air pump which is located on the condenser top.

The DC or direct contact heater (see *Condensers and Feed Heaters,* page 90) is located at a high level. This heater deaerates the condensate and also acts as a feed storage vessel from which the feed pump draws. The reason for its high location is to provide an adequate pressure at the feed pump suction to prevent steam flashing and cavitation taking place since the water temperature at this point will be about 145°C, the saturation temperature of the heating steam supplied to the DC heater. The first and second stage low pressure heaters and gland condenser are positioned on the end of the condenser and the two high pressure heaters are located underneath the turbines.

Key blocks locate the condenser, which has to be allowed to slide and accommodate thermal expansion.

The lubricating oil tank with the pumps mounted on it is located just aft and adjacent to the gearbox and at a sufficiently low level to allow effective oil drainage from all the turbine bearings. The oil coolers are mounted on the condenser top.

TYPES OF TURBINE

There are two basic types of turbine designated 'impulse' or 'reaction', and they differ in the way in which they convert the kinetic energy in a jet of steam into a torque upon the rotor.

The boiler converts the chemical energy in the fuel into a combination of pressure and thermal or internal energy in the steam. Both types of turbine then make use of this energy by allowing the steam to expand progressively through a number of 'stages' as the pressure reduces from the inlet condition to the vacuum created in the condenser into which the turbine exhausts. For a given combination of inlet steam conditions and exhaust vacuum an optimum proportion of the energy in the steam can be converted into useful work by the turbine blades and the designer's aim is to obtain this maximum efficiency at the rated output. He achieves this by choosing the appropriate number of stages, as this establishes the proportion of the energy in the steam which is released at each stage in the form of kinetic energy in the jet of steam issuing from the nozzles. The fewer the stages the higher will be the steam velocity at the nozzle outlets.

Each stage consists of a circle of fixed blades or nozzles which produce jets of steam which impinge on to the rotor blades and the steam flows through the passages formed between the blades.

A stage in an impulse turbine

Figure 8 illustrates vectorially the path of the steam as it leaves the nozzles with a velocity of C_0 and with the rotor blade velocity u. The steam has a velocity of C_{RI} relative to the blade. The stage design ensures that the angle of direction of C_{RI} exactly suits the entry angle of the blade at rated power, but at lower powers C_0 and u will change so the angle of C_{RI} will change resulting in a lower stage efficiency.

The steam leaves the blade with the relative speed C_{R0} and the angle of exit will correspond to the leaving angle of the blade profile. When the blade velocity u is added vectorially, the absolute velocity of the steam is seen to be C_2 which is designed to be moving in the correct direction to cleanly enter the next stage nozzles without losses. The velocity of the steam leaving the blade C_{R0} will be less than the relative inlet velocity C_{RI} due to the effect of friction from

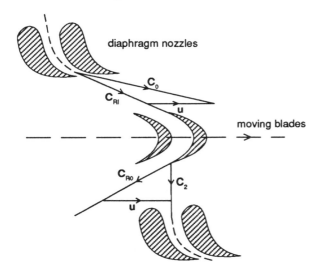

Figure 8   Vector diagram for an impulse stage.

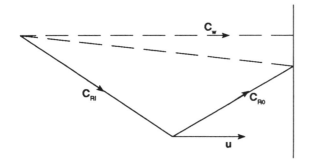

Figure 9   Vector diagram showing the velocity of whirl.

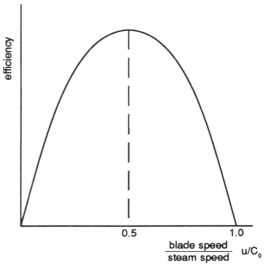

Figure 10   Variation of impulse stage efficiency with u/C_0 values.

roughness or fouling of the blades.

The torque imparted to the blades results from the change in momentum of the steam in the same direction as the blade. This component of the change of steam velocity is shown vectorially in Fig 9 and is called the velocity of whirl C_W and if the flow of steam through the stage is M then

$$\text{force exerted on the blade} \ = \ MC_W$$
$$\text{and the power developed} \ = \ MC_W u.$$
$$\text{The stage efficiency} = \frac{\text{work on blades}}{\text{energy in steam}} = \frac{MC_W u}{\frac{1}{2}MC_0^2}$$
$$= \frac{2uC_W}{C_0^2}$$

Allowing for losses it can be shown, as in Fig 10, that the maximum efficiency is achieved when the ratio 'blade speed/steam speed' approaches the value 0.5, and the designer will incorporate the appropriate number of stages to achieve this.

A stage in a reaction turbine

In this case the force on the blades is achieved by the reaction established as the steam accelerates through the blade passages. The acceleration is obtained through half of the stage pressure drop taking place in the moving blades. The other half occurs in the fixed blades and this accelerates the steam so that it forms a belt of steam rotating at a speed equal to that of the moving blades so that it can then enter the blade passages in a shock free manner.

Thus only half of the available stage energy is utilised to generate a force on the moving blades and so for the same blade speed two reaction stages are required to replace one impulse stage. This is a major disadvantage of reaction turbines for marine use, where a compact design is needed, not only to minimise the space required by the machinery, but also to shorten the bearing centres to give short stiff rotors which are easier to operate and are less disturbed by thermal transients. Also, because half of the pressure drop of the steam takes place across the moving blades, these have to be sealed to minimise leakage and so maintain efficiency. Small running clearances are called for which are difficult to maintain in marine service.

For these reasons most modern marine turbines are of the impulse type, but it should be noted that these are not pure impulse in the sense that the whole pressure drop takes place in the stationary nozzles, as in fact the best stage efficiencies are obtained with some pressure drop across the moving blades. Typically, the proportion of energy in the steam designed to act on the reaction principle increases through the machine from about 5% at the first stage to 50% at the last stage. This means that even with 'impulse' turbines there will be a pressure drop across the moving blades, but this will be much smaller at the high pressure stages than for reaction turbines and running clearances can be greater.

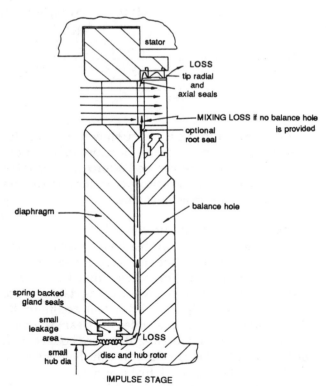

Figure 11 Leakage losses.

In expanding from 62 bar/510°C to a vacuum of 711 mm Hg, the specific volume of steam increases from 0.055 m^3/kg to about 37.5 m^3/kg depending upon the degree of wetness at the exhaust, and the flow area of the nozzles and blades in each stage of the turbine is designed to match the quantity, speed and specific volume of the steam at that point. It will be noted that even with the quite moderate inlet steam conditions quoted above, the steam expands at the exhaust to a volume 700 times greater than at inlet, and in order to give adequate flow area the last stage blades of a 24 MW turbine operating on these conditions would be about 430 mm long, with an overall diameter to the blade tips of nearly 2 m.

SOURCES OF LOSS OF EFFICIENCY

The designer will have aimed to achieve maximum efficiency by achieving the correct blade speed to steam speed relationship, but he will also aim to minimise the losses which can occur in the turbine. The most significant ones are given below.

Leakage losses (Fig 11)

These are minimised by ensuring that leakage paths are small compared to the flow area through the blades and nozzles. The leakage paths are:

a.   Steam which leaks past the diaphragm or interstage glands instead of passing through the nozzles.
A running clearance has to be provided so some leakage is inevitable and is allowed for in the design, but if the interstage glands become excessively worn, large losses can result. This is because this leakage steam rejoins the jet of high velocity steam leaving the nozzles before it enters the moving blades and the loss results from the effect of the leakage steam having to be accelerated up to the jet speed and thereby reducing its value.

b.   Steam which leaks past the moving blades.
Marine turbines usually use a single axial clearance between the blade shrouding and the face of the diaphragm, shown in Fig 12a, but in high reaction designs additional radial baffles might be used, as shown in Fig 12b.

Blade and nozzle losses

Losses are involved as the steam flows through the blade and nozzle passages and these are related to the wetted surface and the shape of the cross-section of

a)

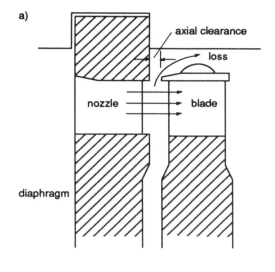

b)

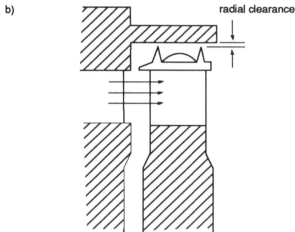

Figure 12 a) Axial; and b) radial seals for moving blades.

the passage. The areas of the roof and platform of the passage remain constant regardless of height and so these losses increase as the blades become shorter. Turbine design rules usually exclude the use of blades shorter than some prescribed size.

The losses will be increased if the surfaces of the blades and nozzles become rough in service or become covered by deposits from the steam. Great care must be exercised in removing deposits and the best method is to use a water blast containing a very fine grit.

Partial admission losses

The flow area at any point in the turbine is proportioned to match the volume and velocity of the steam at that point, but at the high pressure end of the turbine the volume may be too small to enable the

designer to make use of a full 360 deg ring of nozzles, bearing in mind the limitation of a minimum blade and nozzle height referred to in the previous paragraph. If the full 360 deg annulus is not used this is termed partial admission and losses occur as a result of the high velocity steam at the ends of the active arc entraining with 'dead' steam. Designers accept these partial admission losses in order to provide well proportioned passages in line with the previous paragraph.

CONSTRUCTIONAL DETAILS OF A TYPICAL TURBINE

General arrangement

The usual arrangement of the turbine is as a two cylinder machine as shown in Fig 7 with a high pressure (HP) cylinder and a low pressure (LP) cylinder located side by side with the outputs feeding through flexible couplings into a gearbox (a cross compound turbine). The power developed by each cylinder is usually about equal to allow the best optimisation of the gearbox.

From consideration of earlier paragraphs on the design requirements to achieve the best turbine efficiency it will be apparent that the best solution is to employ a small diameter high speed HP turbine, whereas the LP turbine will require long blades which will limit the speed to give acceptable levels of centrifugal stress. For a 24 MW turbine the HP turbine would have a blade/nozzle ring diameter of about 500 mm and a rotor speed of about 6,500 rev/min, whereas the LP rotor speed would be about 3,500 rev/min. The cross compound arrangement allows the designer to select these differing speeds, and in some cases when maximum efficiency is being sought with high steam conditions, triple reduction gearing is used for the HP turbine, and also, in the case of reheat turbines, for the IP turbine. This allows very high rotor speeds of 12,000 rev/min to 14,000 rev/min to be employed with the very small diameter turbines necessary to give good efficiency with very high pressure steam.

After expanding through the HP turbine the steam passes to the LP turbine via the cross-over connections which will have a flexible bellows to allow for the difference in expansion of the HP and LP cylinders as they heat up to normal working temperature. If an IP turbine is included the steam connections will be HP to IP and then to the LP.

The turbines are supported on seatings formed within the bottom structure of the ships hull. One end

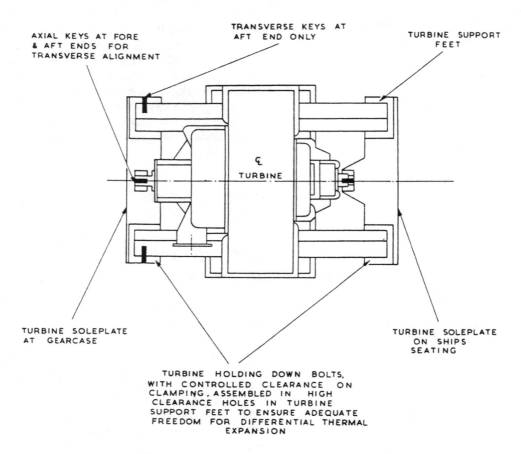

Figure 13 Arrangement of alignment keys, LP turbine.

of the turbine will be made a fixed point by the use of a dowel on the turbine centre line or else by a combination of transverse and axial keys as shown in Fig 13.

Turbine casings

HP and IP casings are made from low alloy steel castings and the material must have adequate temperature/strength and creep properties for the inlet steam temperature employed.

It must be appreciated that the strength of the steel at the operating temperature may be half that at the ambient temperature. Thermal stresses are set up during the period of warming through and working up to full power, and might cause cracking although the designer will have minimised this danger by making the casing as symmetrical as possible and avoiding sharp cornered recesses.

Design of the main casing joint

The main joint between the top and bottom half casings must be designed to avoid danger of leakage because if a leak occurs the 'wire cutting' action of the steam will rapidly make it worse. The flanges must be perfectly flat with a good surface finish and the joint is made metal to metal with the addition only of a thin smear of a good graphite compound.

The bolting is designed to counteract the steam pressure in the casing opening the inner edge of the joint, but since the effect of temperature is to cause the stress in the bolts to relax and reduce with time, the initial tightening of the bolt has to be great enough to allow for this. Typically, the manufacturers will call for the bolts to be tightened to give 0.15% strain and this will give an adequate residual stress after 30,000 operating hours to still hold the inner edge of the joint closed (Fig 14). If the turbine was continuing in service the bolts would require tightening. Small bolts are 'flogged up' or tightened with torque increasing spanners, but bolts larger than 60 mm are usually made hollow to allow the insertion of an electric heating element. After making it finger tight, the bolt is heated up to temperature and the nut rotated a calculated angle to achieve the required force in the bolt. This can be checked by measuring the bolt extension after it has cooled.

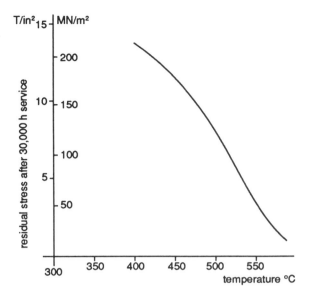

Figure 14 Stress relaxation of main joint bolts with temperature.

In order to maintain the correct alignment of the top and bottom half casings a number of the flange bolts will be 'fitted' bolts and identified to their holes, or else dowels might be used.

Location of the casing

An important aspect of the casing design is the location to the bearing pedestals by vertical and horizontal keys as shown in Fig 15. The casing is supported as closely as possible to its horizontal centre line to avoid vertical expansion causing a loss of concentricity between the casing and rotor.

This is necessary because, in order to minimise steam leakages and maintain efficiency, the HP and IP turbines will operate with small radial running clearances of about 0.3 mm between the rotor and the stationary components. The rotor is located by its bearings and the keys locate the casing to the bearing pedestals. Their job is to maintain the casing concentric to the rotor whilst allowing free thermal expansions to take place as the metal temperatures increase from ambient to full working temperature.

Because of the high temperatures, the HP and IP casings will suffer some degree of thermal distortion, particularly during start up. If the bearing pedestals were rigidly attached to the ends of the casing, these distortions could cause misalignment of the journal and thrust bearings and the usual practice is to support the casing with paws (sliding feet) which extend from the casing joint flanges as seen in Fig 15.

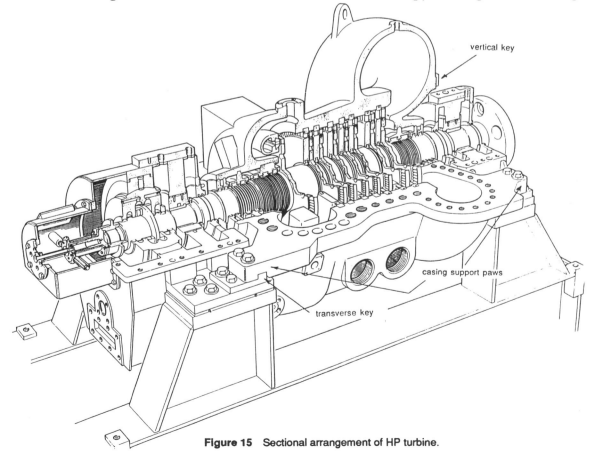

Figure 15 Sectional arrangement of HP turbine.

Low pressure casing (Fig 16)

The LP casing is usually fabricated from mild steel plate and as the operating temperatures are low very little stress relaxation will take place in the main joint bolting under normal ahead steaming conditions.

The exhaust chamber has to be a rigid structure to withstand the atmospheric load of nearly 11 tonnes/m² under vacuum conditions.

The astern turbine element is located in the LP exhaust space, the reason being that under vacuum conditions only a very small loss is caused by the 'windmilling' of the astern blades when the ship is moving in the ahead direction.

The highest temperatures are experienced in the LP cylinder during prolonged astern running as a result of the windmilling action of the long ahead blades under these conditions. In particularly severe cases the high temperature can cause such distortions of the casing that the main joint opens causing air to leak in and lower the vacuum, which worsens the windmilling effect and a deteriorating snowballing situation develops which can only be improved by stopping engines and going ahead at moderate power levels to cool things down.

Turbine rotors

The HP and LP rotors are manufactured from very high quality monobloc forgings of low alloy steel. The HP rotor material is chosen to give good strength and creep properties at the high inlet steam temperatures. The LP rotor material is of high strength to withstand the high centrifugal stresses generated by the long last row blades and it also has to avoid any tendency for brittleness at the relatively low temperatures which exist at this exhaust end of the machine.

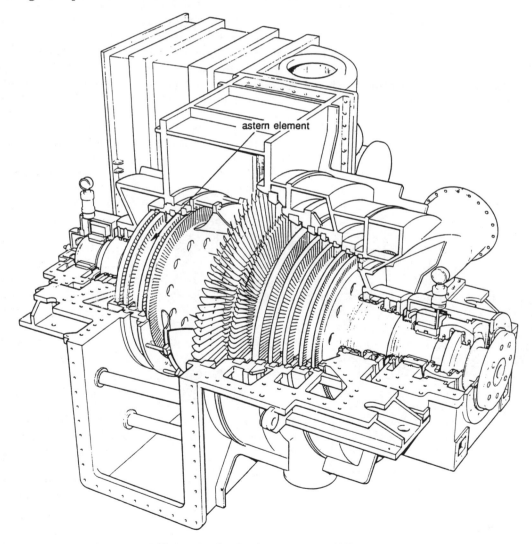

astern element

Figure 16   Sectional arrangement of LP turbine.

The rotors are described as 'monobloc' as the discs or wheels which carry the blades are integral parts of the forging and not the separate shrunk-on components which were necessary in earlier times when it was not possible to make the forging large enough to machine the rotor 'out of the solid'. Problems sometimes arose in service by these discs becoming loose during temperature transients, changing position, and causing the rotor to lose its original balance and so vibrate.

Critical speeds/rotor response

A major design aim is to ensure that no 'critical speeds' occur in the normal speed range. Strictly, the term 'critical speed' should apply only to the theoretical concept of a rotor having rigid supports. The critical speed is then the speed which is in resonance or coincides with a natural frequency of the rotor, which in turn depends on the distribution of weight along the rotor and its stiffness. In practice the rotor is supported upon the oil film in its bearings and this has two major effects. The oil films act as springs and lower the speed at which resonance occurs, in addition providing damping in the same manner as the hydraulic shock absorbers on a motor car suspension system. The effect is shown in Fig 17.

Theoretically, the rigidly supported rotor will develop an infinitely large amplitude of vibration at its critical speed. When running in journal bearings it will be seen that the speed at which resonance occurs has reduced and also most importantly the damping effect of the bearing limits the size of the vibration amplitudes. Turbine designers calculate the dynamic characteristics for the rotors using a complex computer programme and produce response curves like curve (b) to indicate the amplitudes of vibration which would be produced if the rotor became unbalanced at different positions along its length. Curve (b) shows two speeds at which limited peaks of vibration occur and this results from journal bearings having different stiffnesses in the vertical and horizontal planes. Responses can occur at other higher speeds as the rotor vibrates in various ways or modes and the various peaks are described as 1st, 2nd, 3rd criticals etc. in ascending orders of turbine speed.

In practice turbines are designed to ensure a very low response to imbalance and quite often it is impossible to detect the peaks shown on curve (b).

Turbine blading and diaphragms

Blades

The turbine blades convert the energy in the steam to mechanical power and to minimise the losses re-

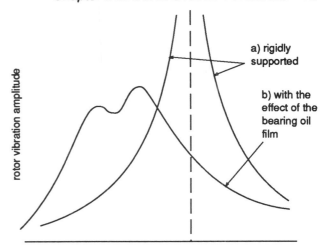

Figure 17 Rotor vibration response/critical speed.

ferred to earlier it is essential that they are in good condition with a high surface finish. Boiler deposits can precipitate out onto the blades, usually at a point in the expansion where all superheat has been lost and the steam is approaching the saturated condition, and these deposits can have a very serious effect upon the turbine performance. The emphasis must be upon maintaining a very high level of feed water purity and monitoring the turbine steam continuously for dissolved solids.

Apart from their effect upon turbine efficiency these contaminants are corrosive and can cause blade failures due to the stress corrosion effect upon highly stressed blades.

Types of blades and roots

Various types of blades are illustrated in Fig 18, and the difference between a first stage blade (5) and a last stage blade (1) again indicates the enormous expansion in volume of the steam as it passes through the turbine.

The blades are attached to the rotor disc by various types of blade root, the choice being dictated by the size of the centrifugal stress which will vary according to the rotational speed of the turbine and the size and weight of the blade.

Blades (3) and (4) in the illustration are short blades fitted to an HP turbine of conventional design running at about 6 500 rev/min and the blade root is a fir tree or straddle type. All HP turbine blades are fitted with a band of stainless steel shrouding riveted to the blade tips by a riveting tang formed integral with the blade. Blades (2) and (3) are fitted in an LP turbine running at 3 600 rev/min and it will be noted that the larger blade (2) has three sets of locating

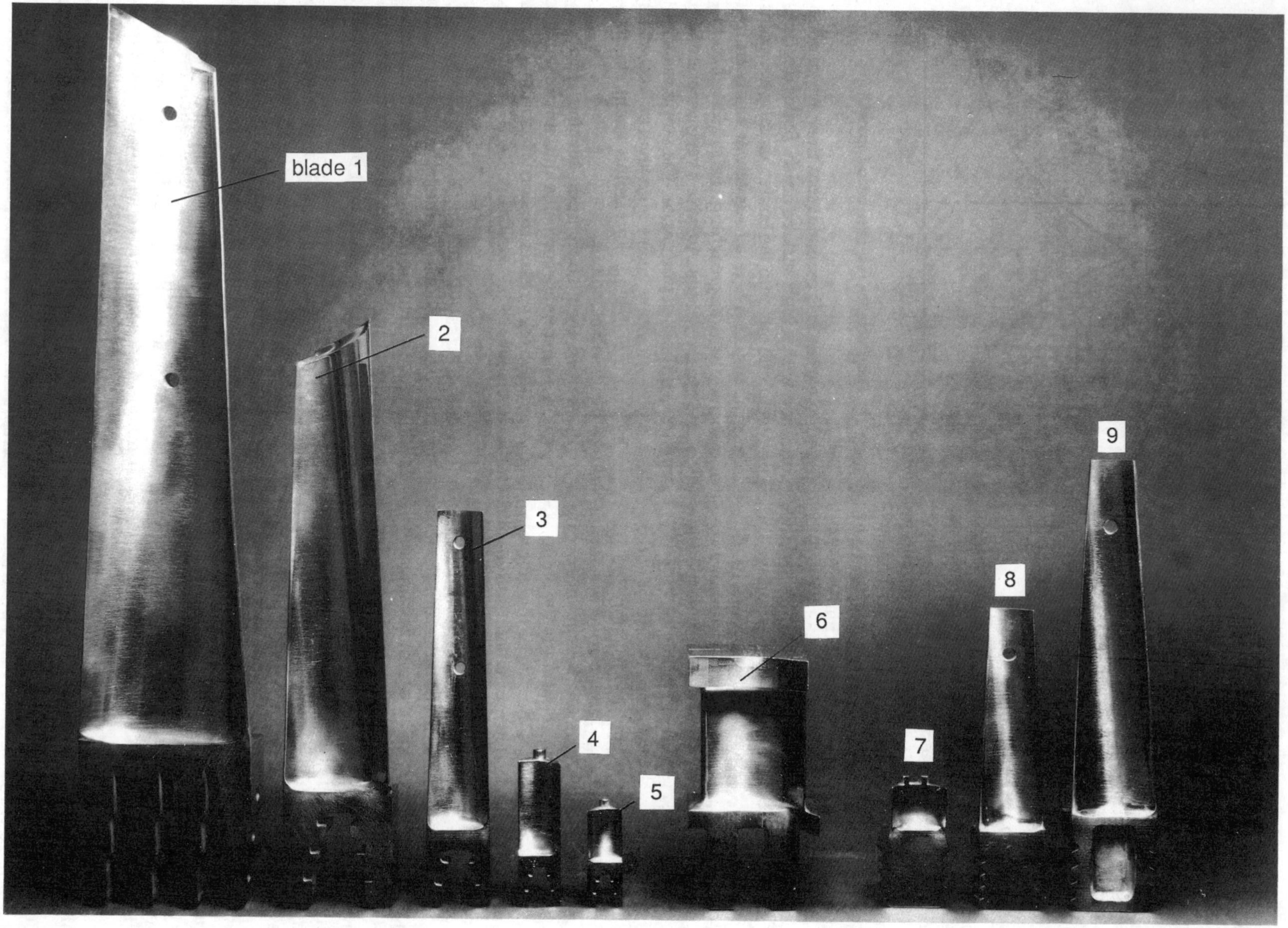

Figure 18 Examples of turbine blades.

lands in the root compared to two sets in the smaller blades because of the higher centrifugal stress set up by the longer blade.

The large last blade (1) is heavy and has a tip speed approaching 500 m/s when the LP turbine is running at its maximum speed of 3 600 rev/min. In this case a multi-forked root is used in which the very high centrifugal force is resisted by a number of axial pins (three in this case).

The two types of root are further illustrated in Fig 19, which also shows how the fir tree rooted blades are entered onto the rotor by means of a blade 'window' which is closed by a special closing blade having a pinned root.

Very high speed turbines could use the serrated roots used on blades (7), (8) and (9), but the blades may even be machined integral with the rotor if the stresses are too high for any type of root to cope with.

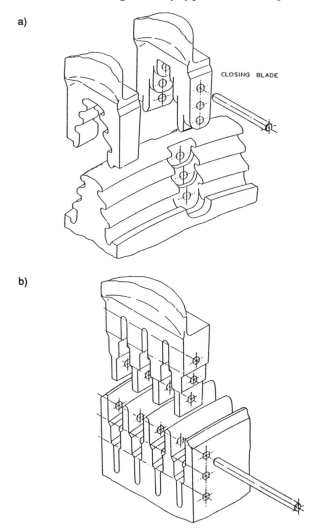

Figure 19 Runner blade root fixings: a) fir tree root; b) multifork root.

Blade (6) is an example of a relatively short blade which is subjected to such high steam stresses that it has to be made very wide and the resulting high weight called for the use of a multifork root.

Blade vibration

The blades have to be designed to avoid any vibration resonances throughout the operating speed range. This is achieved partly by the proportions of the blades themselves—the relationship of the blade height to its chordal width. A long, slender blade will have lower natural frequencies than a short wide blade. In addition the blades can be joined together in groups, by means of shrouding in the case of blades (4), (5) and (7), these blades having a tang formed on their top band which is used as a riveting attachment for the shrouding band. Blades (1), (3), (8) and (9) have drilled holes through which lacing wire can be fixed while the blades are being located on the rotor. Various numbers of blades can be grouped together to give the required vibration characteristics.

The shrouding band also provides an axial and sometimes radial seal against steam leakage as discussed earlier.

Blades are manufactured in various grades of 12%–13% chrome steels to give the required property depending on the position of the blade in the turbine. Good high temperature strength and resistance to creep is required at the HP turbine inlet end whilst high strength is required for the highly stressed long LP blades.

The high tip speed of the LP last blades, coupled with the fact that the steam will be significantly wet at this stage means that they have to be protected against water droplet erosion. Erosion shields made of wear resistant material such as stellite are brazed to the outer section of the leading edge.

Diaphragms

Each stage of the turbine consists of a circle of fixed nozzles and a row of blades attached to the rotor. The first stage nozzles are contained in a nozzle plate which forms the end wall of the steam inlet belt of the turbine cylinder and all the other sets of stage nozzles are located in diaphragms.

The typical features of a diaphragm are shown in Fig 20 from which it will be seen that the nozzles are contained in two half rings which fit into the top and bottom halves of the turbine casing. There is a significant pressure drop across the diaphragm and an interstage gland minimises leakage of steam which bypasses the nozzles and represents a loss as described in the section *'Sources of loss of efficiency'*. This gland has to be centralised to the rotor accurately and this is done by adjustment to the side keys, which also support the diaphragms, and to the top and bottom keys.

The diaphragms are located in grooves machined in the casing. The pressure drop acting upon the face areas of the diaphragms generates a considerable force which holds the diaphragms against the downstream faces of the casing grooves. The diaphragms are usually given a considerable axial clearance in the grooves to prevent them becoming jammed in by an accumulation of boiler deposits, and each half is then located in the grooves by 3 or 4 adjusting pegs (see Fig 20). Diaphragms are distorted in service by the pressure drop across them

and the maximum deflection of about 1.5 mm takes place at the joint face adjacent to the gland bore.

To prevent the top half diaphragms dropping out when the top half cylinder is lifted they are fitted with retaining plates which are screwed into recesses in the top half main joint face.

Radial keys are fitted into the mating joint faces of the two diaphragm halves to minimise steam leakage at this joint.

The last 2 or 3 LP diaphragms may be made of high grade cast iron such as meehanite or spheroidal graphite types of iron, this choice of material being made to

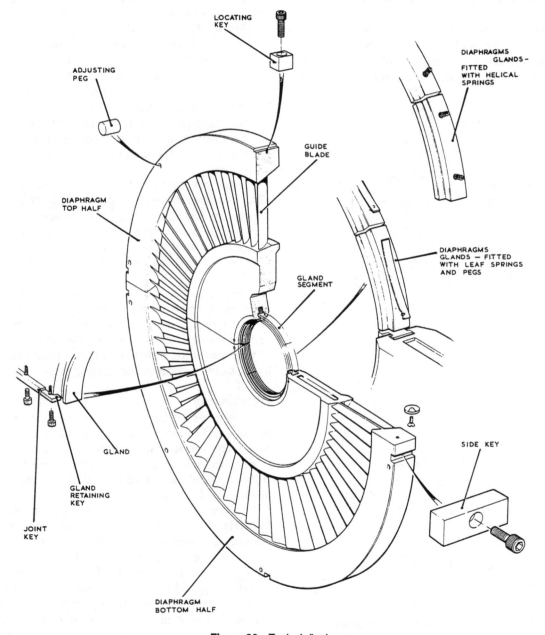

Figure 20   Typical diaphragm.

provide the best resistance to water droplet erosion from the wet steam.

All the other diaphragms are made of steel of various grades to suit the operating conditions from molybdenum vanadium steel at high temperature locations to plain carbon steel where the temperature is below 400°C.

Couplings

Flexible couplings are used on the drive shafts transmitting the turbine output to the gearbox. They have to be capable of absorbing misalignment caused by hull movements and the expansions of the turbine supports and the gearbox and also of accepting axial expansions of the turbine rotor. The alignment instructions usually make allowance for these expansions, for example by making the cold setting of the turbine end coupling higher than the gearbox coupling if it is calculated that the upward expansion of the gearcase is greater than that of the turbine supports at full working temperature. If membrane type couplings are used they might be pre-loaded in the cold state to allow for subsequent rotor expansion.

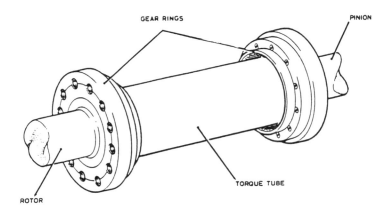

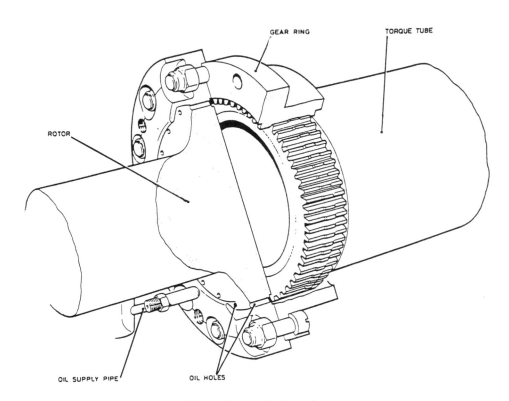

Figure 21 Toothed coupling.

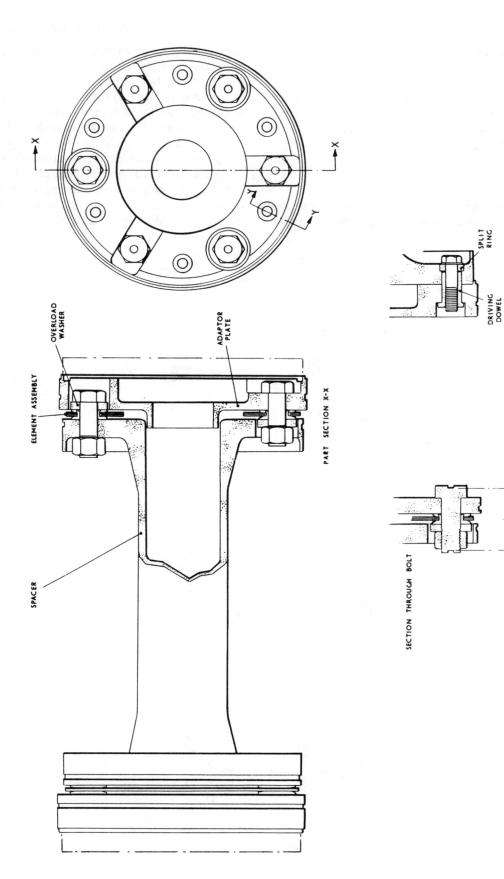

OVERLOAD WASHER

ADAPTOR PLATE

ELEMENT ASSEMBLY

SPACER

PART SECTION X-X

SPLIT RING

DRIVING DOWEL

SECTION 'Y Y'

SECTION THROUGH BOLT

A

Figure 22 Membrane coupling.

The couplings may be either the toothed or membrane type illustrated in Figs 21 and 22 respectively. The latter use packs of thin stainless steel laminations to transmit the drive and provide the flexibility to absorb misalignment.

Membrane couplings have two main advantages in that they do not require lubrication and they maintain an accurate location of the quill shaft centre relative to the turbine rotor, so avoiding imbalance.

Gear couplings can be prone to fretting at the tooth contact positions and care must be taken to ensure that lubricating oil sprays are accurately positioned. Sometimes centering rings are used to ensure the concentricity of the quill shaft.

Bearings

Two basic types of bearings are employed—journal bearings in which the turbine rotors rotate and thrust bearings which absorb the steam thrust upon the rotors and locate them accurately in their casing.

Journal bearings

The principle of action of a plain journal bearing is illustrated in Figs 23a and b.

Figure 23 shows the formation of an oil wedge which generates a pressure to balance the weight of the rotor. Usually oil is supplied to both sides of the bearing at the horizontal centre line, the oil inlets being supplied from an annular chamber in the bearing housing, which connects to the oil supply at the bottom of the housing. The nominal bearing loading is the proportion of the rotor weight supported by the bearing divided by the plan as projected area of the bearing, and a typical value would be 10.5 kg/cm². The actual oil pressure in the oil wedge will be higher than that, as the effective area of the wedge is less than the projected area of the bearing and oil will squirt from this high pressure zone on either side of the bearing. A proportion of the oil carries over to mix with the fresh cool oil entering the bearing and flows around the top of the journal, mixing with further fresh oil before re-entering the oil wedge.

The oil film will have a minimum thickness of approximately 0.04 mm to 0.05 mm when the turbine is running at its rated speed, but at lower speeds the film becomes thinner and there is a danger that at speeds below about 50 rev/min no oil film will be created and the bearing will provide only boundary lubrication and heavy wear will result. This emphasises the need for the oil and the bearings to be kept scrupulously clean if scoring of the bearings and journals is to be avoided. Also a good surface finish is essential on both bearings and journals. Deep trans-

verse or circumferential scores will form leakage paths from the oil wedge and reduce the load carrying capacity of the bearing.

Figure 24 illustrates a typical journal bearing which consists of a top and bottom half housing, 1 and 2, into which fit the bearing shells, 3 and 4. The latter are usually made of steel lined with a 0.75 mm layer of white metal, although occasionally aluminium tin might be used. The thickness of the white metal is chosen to provide an adequate depth to absorb foreign particles whilst avoiding too great a thickness as this reduces its fatigue strength. Aluminium tin can give twice the fatigue life of white metal and yet have a similar hardness to white metal and so be equally compatible with the journal.

High operating temperatures will reduce the fatigue life of whitemetal and the aim should be to operate with bearing metal temperatures not exceed-

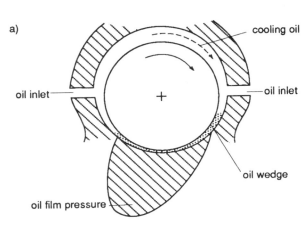

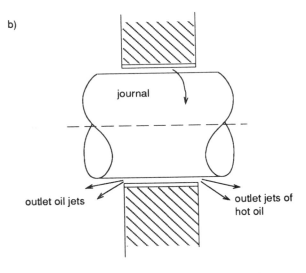

Figure 23 The working principles of a journal bearing.

Table 1 **The effect of temperature upon the strength of bearing whitemetal.**

	Ambient temperature	150°C
Brinell hardness	31/32	7/8
Ultimate tensile strength	87.26 MPa (5.65 ton/in²)	40.16 MPa (2.6 ton/in²)
Fatigue strength (20 x 10⁶ reversals)	34.81 MPa (5050lb/in⁴)	13.79 MPa (2000 lb/in²)

ing 130°C. Table 1 illustrates the effect of temperature upon the strength of white metal.

The total diametric clearance of the bearing is usually in the range of 0.2 mm per 100 mm diameter. A bigger clearance gives cooler running as it allows more oil to flow across the top of the journal, but too big a clearance can result in the turbine running with greater amplitude of vibration. The reason for this is that a proportion of the 'damping' referred to in the rotor critical speed section is provided by the oil constrained between the top of the journal and the top half of the bearing and a large clearance reduces this damping effect.

It will be noted from Fig 24 that the bearing is located in its housing by four pads. These can be adjusted by removing or adding shims in order to realign the turbine rotor in its casing. Care must be taken to ensure that after such an adjustment the clearances between the pads and the housing are minimal, not more than 0.02 mm, or else there will be a danger of vibration.

Bearing stability

Under some circumstances journal bearings can become unstable causing the rotor to vibrate at a frequency slightly less than half its running speed with a characteristic throbbing sound and this condition is described as an 'oil critical', oil whirl or oil whip. It is more likely to occur with lightly loaded high speed bearings and when the oil is cold.

If it persists a remedy can be to machine a circumferential groove in the centre of the bearing, in effect dividing the bearing into two short bearings which are inherently stiffer, with greater resistance to oil whirl.

Bearings must be a tight fit in their housings-any slackness will result in vibration and the fit must be carefully checked using leads or plastic gauges.

Other types of bearing

Problems of bearing stability are more severe with high speed machines and so the HP and IP turbines which have relatively lightweight motors and run at speeds of 6 000 rev/min or much higher, often use one of the following types of bearing.

a. Lemon bore bearing

The vertical diametral clearance is half the horizontal

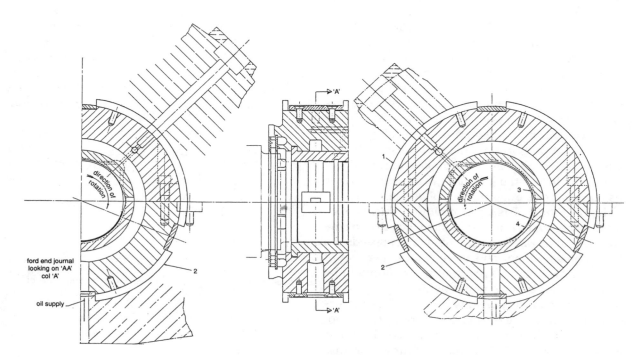

Figure 24 Typical journal bearing.

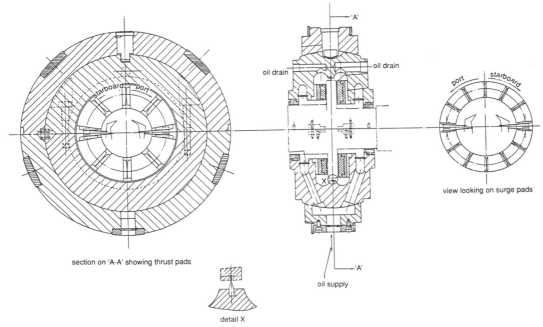

section on 'A-A' showing thrust pads

detail X

view looking on surge pads

oil supply

Figure 25 Typical thrust bearing.

clearance i.e. radial clearances at the top and either side are equal. The effect is to produce a hydrodynamic film in the top half of the bearing which provides a stabilising force on the journal.

b. Tilting pad bearings
The bearing comprises a number of pivoted individual pads, lined with white metal, each of which will generate a hydrodynamic oil film. The forces generated by these oil films locate the journal and make this type of bearing the most inherently stable of all types.

c. Offset halves
The top half bearing is laterally displaced relative to the bottom half and this has the effect of generating a hydrodynamic oil film in the small clearance side of the top half which provides a stabilising force on the bearing.

Thrust bearings
An axial thrust is developed on the turbine rotor as a result of the pressure drops across the moving blades giving a higher pressure on the upstream side of the turbine discs or wheels than the downstream side and also due to a similar effect at the shaft end glands where pressure drops occur and there are changes in the rotor diameter. The higher the levels of reaction used in the design the higher the thrust load. Designers aim to achieve a moderate level of thrust which gives a specific loading on the thrust bearings of about 10.5 kg/cm^2.

A typical thrust bearing is illustrated in Fig 25 and this shows the arrangement of a set of pads on either side of the thrust collar, usually described as the main and surge pads respectively. These pads are usually made of steel, faced with white metal, and can tilt as shown in Fig 26 under the action of the oil movement set up by the thrust collar as it rotates. Also shown is a typical oil film thickness and movement of the pad as it tilts in order to illustrate how small these are and hence how important it is to maintain the cleanliness of the oil and also to ensure the accurate alignment of the thrust bearing to the thrust collar. An error of 0.025 mm from one side of the thrust collar to the other would give twice the film thickness for the pads

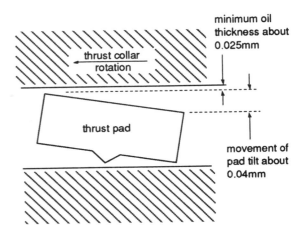

minimum oil thickness about 0.025mm

thrust collar rotation

thrust pad

movement of pad tilt about 0.04mm

Figure 26 Oil film thickness for a tilting pad thrust bearing.

on one side of the bearing and because of the characteristics of these tilting thrust pads, would result in these pads only carrying a small fraction of the load carried by the pads operating with the small clearance. This is the reason most installations use a spherical location for the thrust bearing in the bearing pedestal to allow it to align itself to the thrust collar and so provide a reasonably equal loading of the thrust pads.

Turbines operate with quite small axial clearances between the rotor and casing and the two sets of pads, one on either side of the thrust collar provide the necessary location of the rotor. Typically a total axial clearance of 0.25 mm to 0.40 mm is specified depending on the size of the bearing. This clearance cannot be made too small or else the surge pads will generate an excessive thrust which is added to the normal load being carried by the main pads. If the clearance is too large the surge pads can become unstable which can cause fretting and wear of their pivots.

Adjustable liners are provided behind the main and the surge pads and these are used both to adjust the axial position of the rotor to give the correct running clearances in the casing and also to adjust the axial clearance in the thrust bearing.

Glands

The turbine glands have two main functions.

1. To minimise leakage from the shaft ends and between stages during normal running.

2. To seal the ends of the rotors when raising vacuum.

It is not possible to totally seal the rotating shafts and the presence of a running clearance means that some leakage of steam will always take place. This is minimised by having a number of baffles which have a small radial clearance, usually of the order of 0.25–0.40 mm, with castellations on the rotor to form a number of restrictions. This arrangement gives rise to the name labyrinth gland. This can be seen in Fig 27 which illustrates typical gland assemblies which are located at the inlet and exhaust ends of an HP turbine. It will also be seen that the gland is divided into a number of sections, four at the inlet end and three at the exhaust end, and that external connections are made to the spaces (called pockets) between these sections. The function of these connections can be seen in Figs 28a and 28b which illustrate the conditions in a gland system at standby and at full power.

The outer pockets are connected to a small gland steam condenser which maintains them at a slight vacuum, about 50 mm water gauge below atmospheric, in order to prevent any steam leaking into the engine room.

The adjacent pockets connect to the gland steam receiver which is maintained at a pressure just above atmospheric (to prevent any air leaking into the system) by control valves which either feed steam to the receiver or else leak it off to the main condenser. Under standby conditions it will be seen from Fig 28a that 0.12 kg/s of steam is being supplied and this is used to 'pack' both the HP turbine and LP turbine glands to maintain the vacuum. When running at full power a considerable quantity of steam, 0.289 kg/s, leaks from the inner pocket of the inlet end gland and as this steam is at full inlet temperature it is used to contribute to the turbine output by being passed back into the turbine. In this case it rejoins the turbine at the HP exhaust and combines with the main flow of steam in the LP turbine. The gland condenser maintains the outer pockets at a slight vacuum and the adjacent pockets direct leakage steam to the gland receiver as also does the equivalent pocket in the LP turbine inlet end gland. A vacuum exists at the LP turbine exhaust so packing steam is always required by the astern end LP turbine gland and this is supplied from the gland steam reservoir. Surplus steam is passed to the main condenser under the control of the reservoir pressure control valve.

It will be noted from Fig 27 that the gland rings or segments are located against a shoulder by a spring and can be pushed radially outwards from their normal position. During start-up conditions considerable thermal gradients can be set up in the casing which can cause distortions greater than the radial clearance at the glands and the rubbing which results would cause severe local heating and bending of the rotor if the glands were solid and immovable rather than spring supported. Additionally the glands are manufactured from materials which give the minimum heating effect when rubbed. These are commonly nickel aluminium bronze, or, occasionally, carbon when the operating temperature is less than 425°C, and a high chrome iron (17% Cr) at higher temperatures.

The interstage glands fitted in the diaphragms are of similar design, but require many fewer baffles as the interstage pressure drops are only a fraction of the pressure drop across a shaft end gland.

Gland clearances are measured by removing the top half casing and rotor and inserting lead wire across the baffles at the top and bottom positions and measuring the thickness of the indentations after the rotor and top half casing have been dropped back into position. Clearances are taken by long feeler gauges at either side. Temporary wedges are used to

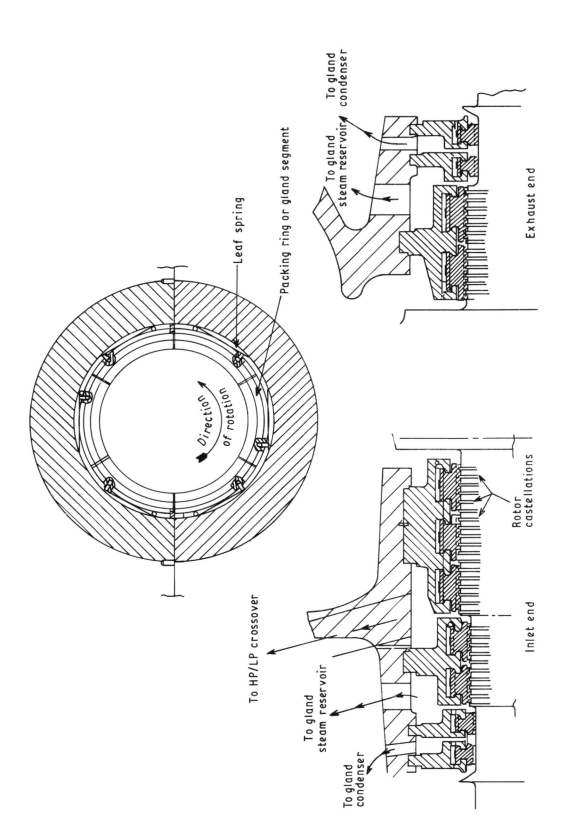

Figure 2.7 Rotor glands; gland diagram.

Leaf spring

Packing ring or gland segment

Direction of rotation

To gland condenser

To gland steam reservoir

Exhaust end

Rotor castellations

To HP/LP crossover

To gland steam reservoir

Inlet end

To gland steam reservoir

To gland condenser

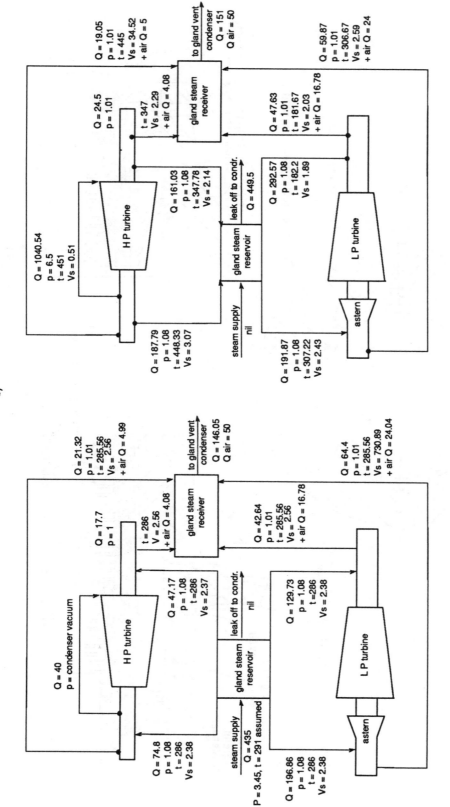

b)

Q = quantity, kg/h
p = pressure, bar
t = temperature, °C
Vs = specific volume, m³/kg

Figure 28 a) Gland system at standby conditions; b) gland system at full power conditions.

Q = quantity, kg/h
p = pressure, bar
t = temperature, °C
Vs = specific volume, m³/kg

a)

hold the spring loaded gland segments against their locating shoulders when these clearance checks are being made.

TURBINE CONTROL

There are two basic ways of controlling the steam to the turbine.

Throttle control

This utilises a single valve to control the flow of steam through the complete power range. This means that if a ship operates at low power for significant periods of time the steam entering the turbine has been heavily throttled and this adds to the losses involved in running at a point well removed from full power for which the turbine will have been designed.

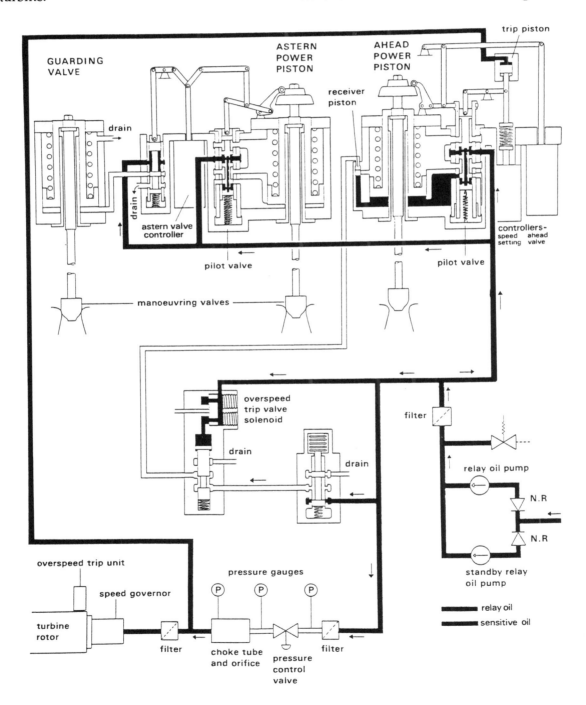

Figure 29 Control system for throttle valve.

Nozzle control

In this case the inlet nozzles to the HP turbine are divided into groups with each group supplied from its own individual control valve. In this case the valves are closed sequentially as power is reduced so that throttling only takes place on the steam being supplied to one group of nozzles so minimising the losses. The most efficient way of operating at reduced power is at a so called 'nozzle point' where one or more of the nozzle valves are completely closed to give the desired reduction in power, but those remaining in service are all fully open.

Control systems

A typical control system for a throttle controlled turbine is shown in Fig 29. The ahead, astern and guarding valve are all located in an integral chest

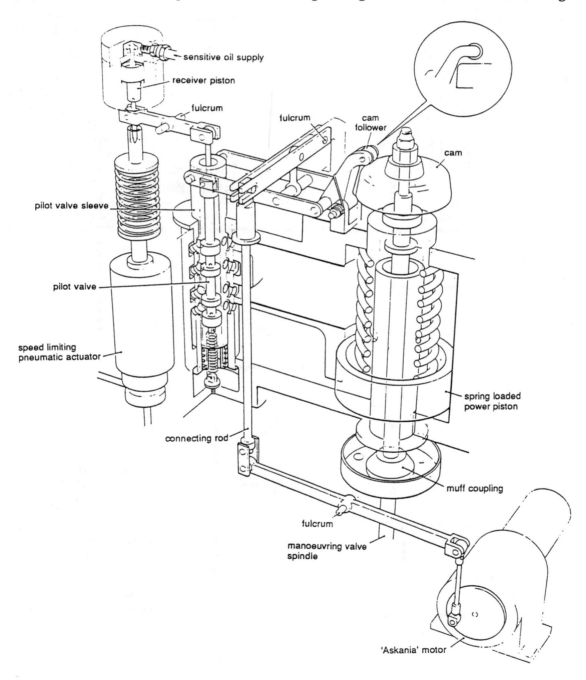

Figure 30   Typical arrangement of valve gear (ahead).

separate from the turbine and connected to it by steam pipes connecting to the ahead and astern turbines respectively. The guarding valve is either open or closed and is a safeguard against steam being admitted simultaneously to the ahead and the astern turbine. It is normally closed and only opens when the signal is received for the astern valve to open.

In the case of single screw ships there would usually be a provision for emergency steaming whereby if a problem had arisen with the HP turbine, this could be decoupled from the gearbox and a temporary steam connection made from the steam chest to the LP turbine.

All the valves are of the single seating diffuser type-the diffuser being the tapered section downstream of the valve which enables an efficient pressure recovery to be made from the kinetic energy produced as the steam passes the valve seat at high speed.

The valves are actuated by hydraulic servos supplied with oil from a module consisting of motor driven positive displacement pumps, and filters giving fine filtration. The servos are linked to the ship's bridge control system by an actuator which moves a pilot valve which in turn lets high pressure oil into or out of the servo cylinder to open or close the steam valve. In the scheme illustrated there is a linkage between the pilot valve and the servo spindle which is designed to improve the overall control characteristics by providing an approximate linear relationship between the input actuator movement and the speed of the ship. This linkage is better illustrated in the isometric sketch. Fig 30 and this also shows the use of a stepper motor as the link with the ship's control system. A neater method would be to use a linear electric actuator.

The sketch also shows the speed limiting actuator which protects the turbine from over speeding if a coupling should fail or the ship's propeller should come out of the water in rough seas. A speed governor is shown in Fig 31 and this provides the sensitive oil supply to the speed limiter.

The system diagram also shows an overspeed trip which gives the final protection against overspeeding the turbines by trip closing all the steam valves if the speed exceeds a set value.

This overspeed trip valve is solenoid operated and is triggered by the signal from a solid state electronic

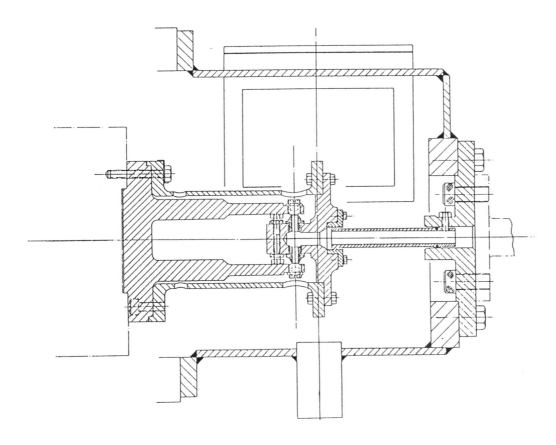

Figure 31 Governor used for speed control of turbines.

overspeed trip unit. To avoid the inconvenience of spurious trips the overspeed trip unit has three independent circuits which sense the turbine speed by means of pick-ups mounted in the turbine pedestal, and receiving a speed signal by the pulses produced by a toothed wheel. A trip is initiated only if two out of the three circuits indicate that the tripping speed has been reached.

In the case of nozzle governed turbines the ahead turbine will be controlled by a number of control valves, usually between four and eight, located in a steam chest which is an integral part of the HP turbine. These valves may be operated by various means such as individual hydraulic actuators, or by a camshaft which is rotated by an electric or hydraulic motor, or a barlift mechanism. The overall control scheme would follow similar lines to those described above for the throttle control system.

Control valves

Figure 32 illustrates a section through a typical control valve and its enclosure called a 'chest', which have various design features, introduced to overcome operational problems.

The steam chest is subjected to rapid temperature rise during start-up and every attempt is made to minimise the likelihood of cracking by employing large radii at corners and a constant section thickness.

The combined valve seat and diffuser is manufactured in a Moly-Van material with stellite facings on the seating area to resist steam cutting at small valve openings. The location of the valve seat into the steam chest has a degree of flexibility designed into it. The reason for this is that the large mass of the chest compared to the seat results in different rates of expansion during the warm up period and without some flexibility some crushing of the material beyond the elastic limit would take place and the seat would become loose.

A major problem in the design of steam valves is the danger of damage due to steam buffeting. In severe cases this can cause very high frequency vibration which results in extremely rapid wear of the valve spindles. The design features to combat this phenomena are the fitting of a flow straightener around the valve, radial keys to locate the valve and the use of hardened nitrided valve spindles and spindle bushes, both of which would be made in nitralloy material.

The force required to open a single seated valve can be very large as it is established by the full inlet steam pressure acting upon the area within the contact circle on the seats. In order to reduce this a balancing effect is obtained by the use of a pilot valve,

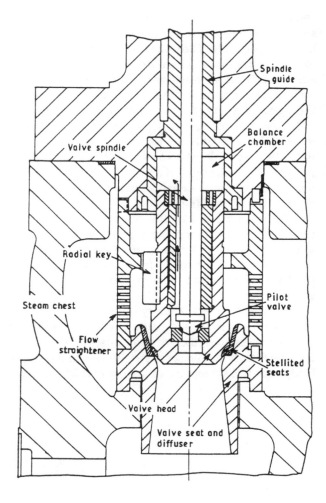

Figure 32   Section through marine propulsion turbine control valve and steam chest.

formed at the end of the valve spindle, which connects a balance chamber, positioned above the valve, with the steam pressure which exists downstream of the valve seat. Thus the first movement of the valve spindle establishes a state of pressure balance before the main valve lifts off its seat and significant amounts of steam start flowing into the turbine.

Some steam leakage takes place between the valve spindle and its bushes and leak-off connections are provided to direct this into the turbine gland steam system.

MONITORING AND DATA LOGGING OF THE TURBINE

Various operating parameters are continuously monitored to maintain safe operation and to maximise the efficiency of the propulsion plant.

Suitable measuring sensors are usually installed to measure HP shaft thrust wear; LP shaft thrust wear; HP shaft eccentricity; LP shaft eccentricity; differential expansion HP turbine; differential expansion LP turbine; bearing pedestal vibration.

Note

1. Shaft eccentricity is a measurement of the orbit in which the turbine shaft is rotating.
2. Differential expansion relates to the different rates at which the turbine rotor and casing expand because of the differences in mass and surface area.

The output signals from all the above may be fed to direct reading instruments in the control room or else fed into a computer data logging system. In the latter case the readouts could be obtained either as a print-out or else as a display on a screen in which the current reading would appear superimposed on a schematic of the propulsion plant. Additional data such as vibration levels, oil and bearing temperatures, steam temperatures and pressures at various points in the cycle, CW temperatures, shaft speed and power etc. can all be fed into the data logging system and called up for display on the screen in schematic form by inputting the appropriate code on the keyboard.

A typical control and monitoring panel is shown in Fig 33.

The turbine can be tripped by means of a solenoid trip valve which drains signal oil from the control valve operating mechanism resulting in rapid closing of the steam valves. This trip can be initiated by one of the following.

Figure 33 Panel for the control and monitoring of the machinery.

1. The turbine overspeeding above a set limit, usually 10% above the normal maximum.

2. The loss of bearing oil pressure.

3. The loss of condenser vacuum.

4. Thrust bearing failure.

5. Other factors, such as high vibration, or rotor differential expansion, could be arranged to trip the turbine if required by the owner and/or the turbine supplier.

Turbine alarms

An alarm and annunciator panel might be provided which will give an audible alarm and an illuminated indication of the cause for the alarm being initiated. Alternatively the alarm system can form part of the computer data logging and control system in which case the fault identification would appear on the VDU when an alarm is initiated.

CONDENSERS AND FEED HEATERS

Condensers and feed heaters are used to increase the efficiency of the propulsion plant. The condenser reduces the back pressure against which the turbine works to an extremely low level, typically within 50 mm of mercury of the absolute vacuum, increasing the power output for a given inlet steam flow and so increasing the efficiency. In thermodynamic terms the condenser lowers the temperature at which heat is rejected from the cycle and this increases the fundamental efficiency of the cycle. The reasons why feed heating improves the efficiency were given earlier.

Constructional and design features of condensers

Most marine condensers are of the axial in-plane type as shown in Fig 7 showing the general arrangement of the machinery in the ship. The condenser can also be located beneath the LP turbine exhaust and this arrangement is sometimes used for VLCC machinery where there is no limitation on the height of the plant. This type of condenser is illustrated in Figs 34 and 35 which show longitudinal and cross sections of a typical example and also serve to show the design features common to all condensers.

It is undesirable to suspend the whole weight of the condenser and the entrained cooling water from the LP turbine on the structure would need to be made very much stronger to avoid an unacceptably large vertical deflection. Thus, underslung condensers usually either have spring supports as shown in Figs 34 and 35, or else they can be mounted solidly on seatings with a flexible bellows connection to the LP turbine exhaust.

Spring supports are designed to cope with the raqnge of vertical thermal expansions which can occur in service.

The cold setting procedure is laid down by the manufacturer, and usually consists of adjusting the height of the condenser after filling with cooling water by means of jacking screws provided on the spring bases. The aim is to establish a prescribed gap between the top flange of the condenser and the corresponding flange on the turbine exhaust. When the flanges are pulled together when making the joint a calculated proportion of the weight of the condenser is transferred from the springs to the turbine. The reason for doing this is to enable the springs to be able to absorb the maximum downward thermal expansion which can occur, which will be under the emergency operating condition when vacuum has been lost and the condenser casing has become very hot. If the springs had been incorrectly designed or set a large upward force could result under these conditions which could lift the LP turbine with obvious hazardous effects.

The disadvantages of using a solidly mounted condenser with a connecting bellows are:

1. The bellows could fail and cause loss of vacuum.

2. The turbine is subjected to an additional vertical load when vacuum is established and this is equal to

turbine exhaust area × atmospheric pressure

This is a significant load and is approximately 10,500 kg/m^2.

The condenser consists of a welded steel shell into which flows the exhaust steam from the turbine. Several thousand tubes, usually of about 25 mm diameter, pass through the shell as shown in the illustration, and these are arranged in a specific pattern decided upon by the designer. The cooling water flowing through these tubes removes the latent heat of the steam, so achieving the condensation process, but this also releases air and traces of other incondensable gases. These incondensable gases can congregate inside a badly designed condenser masking some of the tubes and preventing the full vacuum being achieved. The pattern in which the tubes are arranged is designed to assist in the removal of these gases. In the illustrations it will be seen that the tubes are arranged in two large groups called tube bundles.

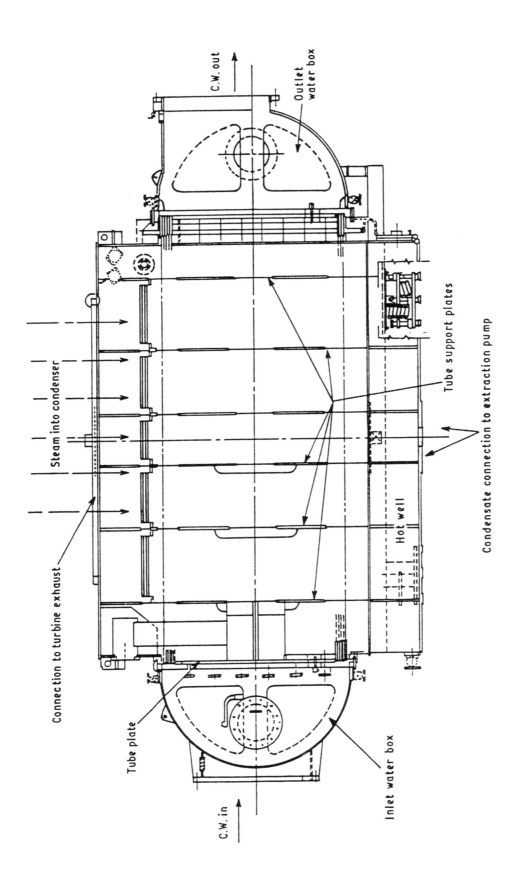

C.W. out

Outlet water box

Tube support plates

Condensate connection to extraction pump

Steam into condenser

Hot well

Connection to turbine exhaust

Tube plate

Inlet water box

C.W. in

Figure 34 Longitudinal section through condenser.

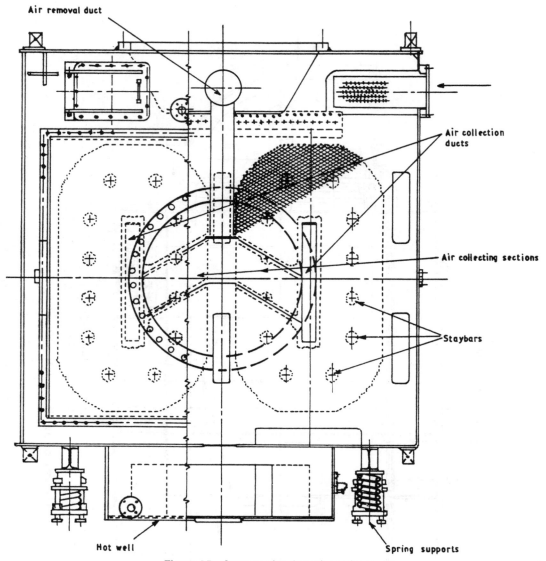

Figure 35   Cross section through condenser.

In the centre of each bundle is an air collection duct which runs the whole length of the condenser and air is driven into these ducts by the steam flowing radially into the bundles. At the left hand end of the condenser (longitudinal section) these ducts connect to an air removal duct after passing through a batch of tubes which are screened from the steam in the condenser by baffle plates and act as an air cooling section. By cooling the air its volume is reduced and the air pump or air ejectors are made more effective.

Both ends of each tube are located into a tubeplate, usually made in rolled naval brass, and bolted to each end of the condenser shell. The tubes are expanded into the holes in the tubeplates by the use of rolling tools or else by high pressure hydraulic equipment. If the same material is used for the tubes and the tubeplate they can be welded using specialised automatic orbital welding heads.

The tubes have to be capable of withstanding the corrosive action of sea water, particularly when it is polluted, and a common choice of material is aluminium brass which has a good reputation in marine applications. The effect of erosion is minimised by limiting the velocity of the water in the tubes and Table 2 gives the allowable water velocities for five commonly used tube materials.

If tubes become partially blocked with debris the local water velocity may exceed these limits and cause erosion of the tubes. Another danger is that polythene sheet might be drawn into the cooling water intakes and block off a section of the tubeplate, so causing an increase of water velocity in the unaf-

Table 2 Allowable water velocities.

Material	Typical wall thickness (mm)	Maximum velocity (m/s)
Admiralty brass	1.2	2.0
90.10 Copper nickel	1.2	3.0
7.30 Copper nickel	1.2	3.5
Titanium	0.7 or 0.5	5.0
Stainless steel 316	0.7	4.0

fected tubes. The condenser will have been designed to make full use of the maximum allowable velocities listed in Table II as the heat transfer on the water side of the tubes is greatly improved by increases in water velocity. On the other hand, increased velocity will require more power to drive the cooling water pumps and an economic balance has to be aimed for.

The steam enters the condenser at high velocity bringing with it water droplets; at the end of the expansion in the turbine about 10% of the steam will have condensed into water. Quite often a protective grid is fitted, to prevent erosion of the top layers of tubes from the high speed impingement of these water droplets.

The high steam speed can have another effect which is to cause vibration of the tubes in a similar manner to the 'singing' of telephone wires in a high wind. The tube support plates, sometimes called sagging plates, are arranged so that the natural frequency of the tubes over the span between the support plates is higher than can be induced by the steam flow.

The support plates have another function which is to increase the strength of the condenser shell in resisting the vacuum collapse pressure which amounts to 11 tonnes for every square metre of shell surface.

At the end of each condenser, waterboxes are provided to which are connected the cooling water inlet and outlet pipes. The prime function of the waterboxes is to obtain an even distribution of water flow through all the tubes. They are welded fabrications in mild steel protected from corrosion by a rubber lining or an internal coating such as a coal tar epoxy paint. Inspection doors are provided to allow regular inspection of these protective coatings and also to investigate any suspected tube to tubeplate joint leaks. If any leaks are found, special 'bungs' are available to blank off the affected tubes since salt

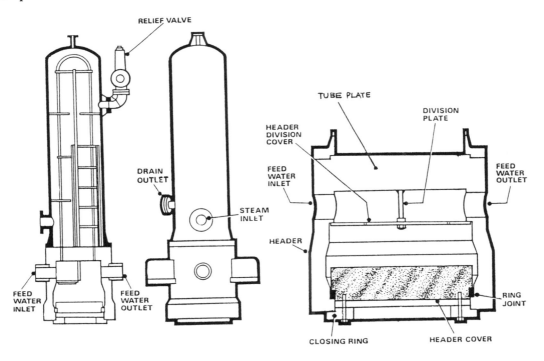

Enlarged section of
High Pressure Forged
Header with self-sealing
Joint.

Figure 36 High pressure heater.

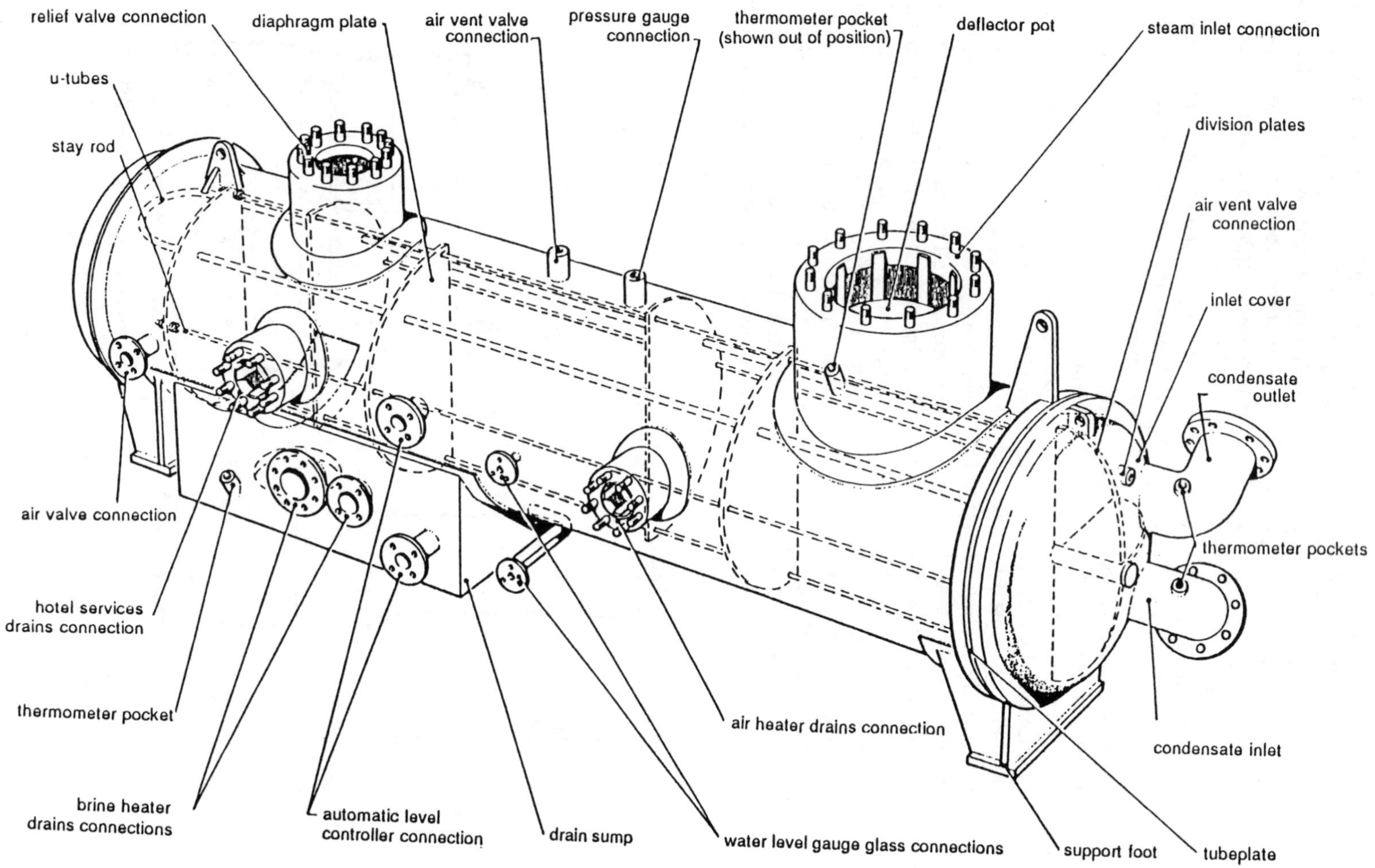

steam inlet connection

division plates

air vent valve connection

inlet cover

condensate outlet

thermometer pockets

condensate inlet

tubeplate

support foot

deflector pot

thermometer pocket (shown out of position)

air heater drains connection

water level gauge glass connections

pressure gauge connection

air vent valve connection

diaphragm plate

relief valve connection

u-tubes

stay rod

air valve connection

hotel services drains connection

thermometer pocket

brine heater drains connections

drain sump

automatic level controller connection

Figure 37 LP heater and drain cooler.

water leaks into the condensate will have a disastrous effect upon the boiler. The feed water purity is continuously monitored and problems with the condenser would be indicated by the associated alarm.

Constructional and design features of feed heaters

Type of cycle (page 60) described different types of steam cycle used for propulsion systems involving the use of three different types of feed heaters; low pressure, high pressure and direct contact deaerator heaters. The constructional details of these differ considerably as will be seen from the following descriptions.

High pressure heaters

The water side of these heaters operates at the discharge pressure from the boiler feed pump and this

accounts for the basis of the design, a typical example of which is seen in Fig 36. The feed water connects into a strong forged header and the tube bundle is formed in a 'U' configuration with tubes expanded and welded into the tube plates. The thickness of the tube plates and the header walls indicate the high operating pressure.

The feed water is heated by the steam bled from the turbine and this steam is cooled and condensed so that its latent heat contributes the major part of the heating action. The feed water leaves the heater at the saturation temperature corresponding to the bled steam pressure and the bled steam condensate is drained to a lower pressure heater where some of its sensible heat can be recovered.

Low pressure heaters

The water side operates at the discharge pressure from the condensate extraction pumps and these

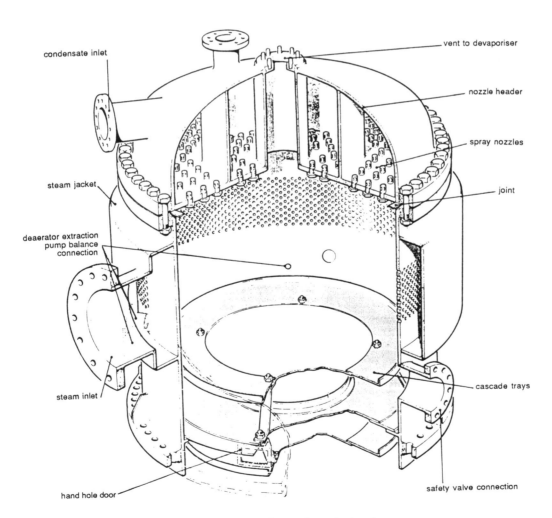

Figure 38 S-type deaerator head.

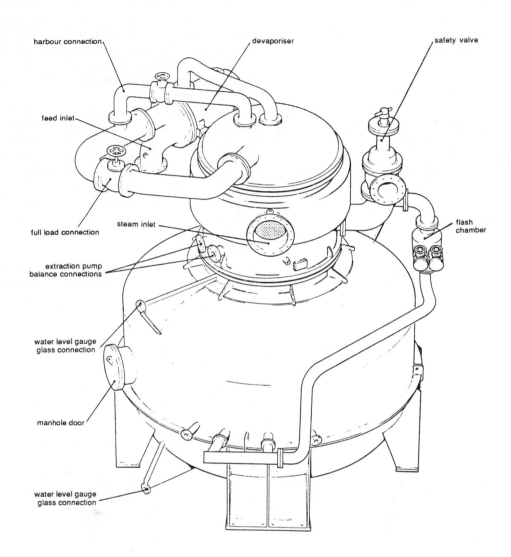

Figure 39 Deaerator head and storage tank.

heaters are of relatively light construction as shown in Fig 37. Steam bled from the turbine has to enter via a deflector pot which prevents direct impingement onto the heater tubes of water droplets entrained in the wet, low pressure steam.

It will be noted that the heat contained in various drains from hotel service steam, steam air heater if fitted, brine heaters etc., can be recovered by directing them into the LP heater. The major heating effect is from the latent heat of the bled steam.

Direct contact deaerator heater

This type of heater has the dual action of removing air which has been absorbed into the condensate as well as providing a contribution to heating the feed water.

The principle of action was referred to in *Type of cycle* and Fig 38 illustrates a deaerator head equipped with multiple nozzles which spray the feed water into direct contact with the heating steam, which is bled from the turbine. The air and incondens-able gases which are released are drawn off by a small fan from a vent in the top of the deaerator head. Cascade trays help to break the water up into droplets as it falls. The deaerator operates with a steam pressure above atmospheric to prevent any possibility of air leaking in, and the feed temperature at outlet is the saturation temperature corresponding to this pressure.

The deaerator head is normally fitted to a feed storage tank as shown in Fig 39 and the suction to the boiler feed pump connects to this tank.

GEARING

The wide range of operating speeds for propulsion turbines will have been noted from earlier descriptions in this chapter and typical values are as follows.

HP turbine	6 500 rev/min
LP turbine	3 600 rev/min
High speed HP turbine	14 000 rev/min
High speed IP turbine	12 000 rev/min.

These turbine speeds have to be reduced to propeller speeds of about 140 rev/min for fast container ships and 80 rev/min for VLCCs and large bulk carriers. In achieving these speed reductions, enormous torques are developed at the low speed end of the gearbox and the tooth contact forces are correspondingly very large. The basic problem in gearing design is achieving a uniform distribution of these forces along the face width of the tooth. If the designer is unsuccessful, severe pitting of the tooth surfaces results from the drive being concentrated on a shorter length of tooth than was intended.

Minute distortions of the teeth will totally change this critical load distribution along the face width of the teeth and the manufacturer has to allow for the bending and twisting of the gears and pinions which takes place in service, together with differences in temperature between the gear and the pinion. In addition temperature differences will exist along the face width of the teeth. The hottest point of a single helical gear is at approximately one third of the face width and this will cause the gear to adopt a barrel shape.

In order to counteract these effects the manufacturer carries out 'tooth corrections' which aim at ensuring an even load distribution when the gear is running under its normal operating conditions. It will be appreciated from all this that any adjustments to the gearing must only be carried out by suitably experienced and knowledgeable personnel.

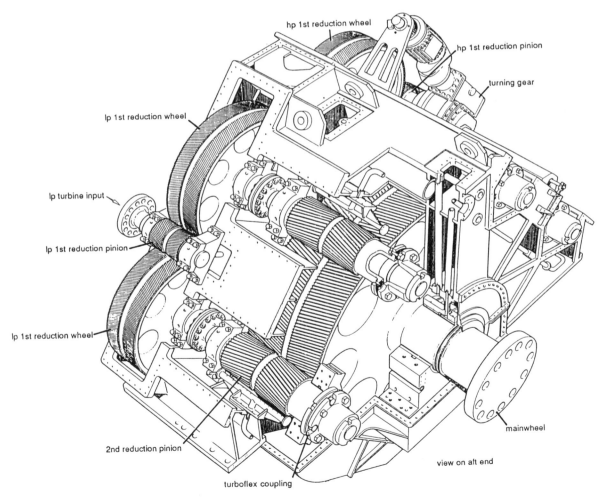

Figure 40 Locked train gearbox.

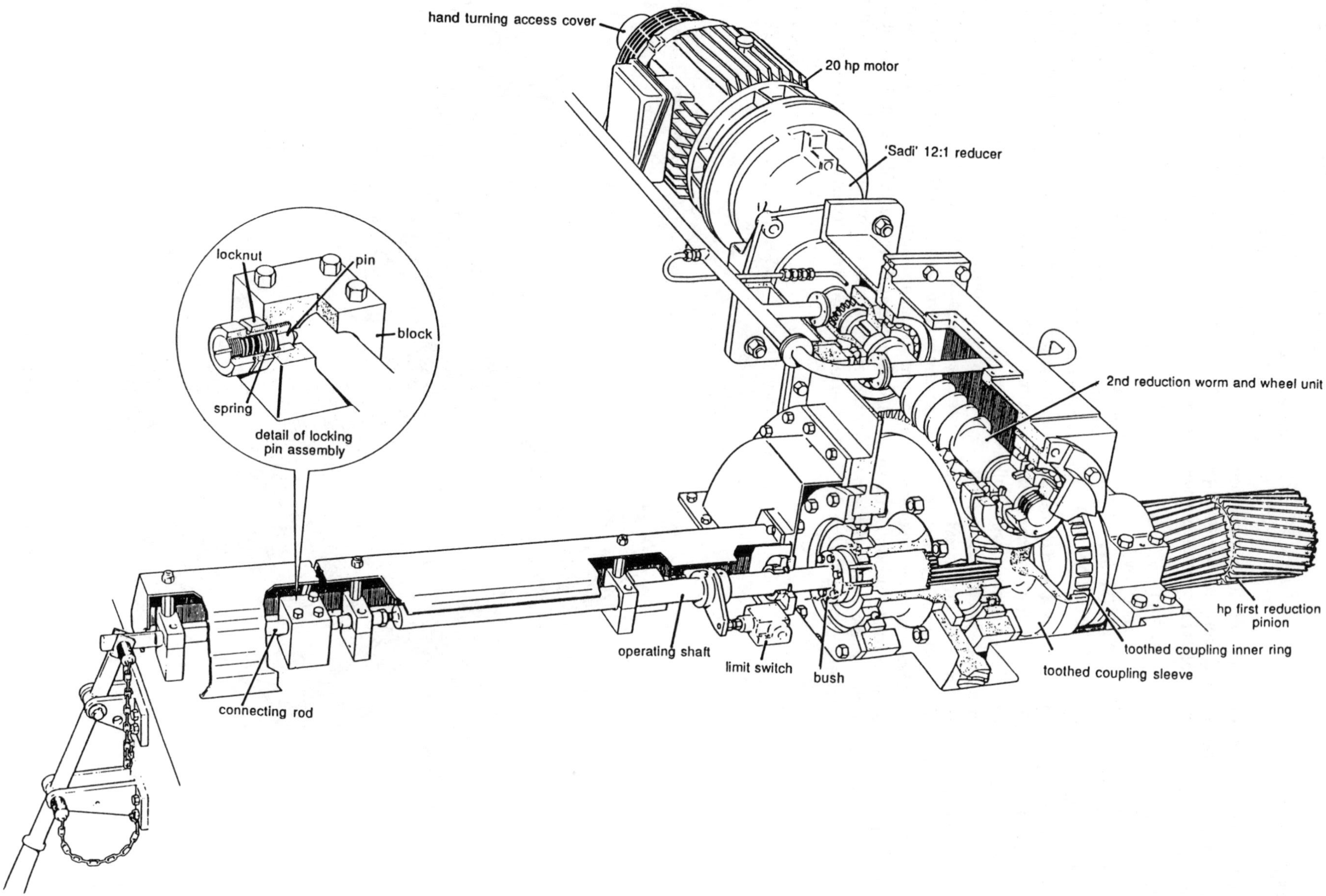

hand turning access cover

20 hp motor

'Sadi' 12:1 reducer

2nd reduction worm and wheel unit

hp first reduction pinion

toothed coupling inner ring

toothed coupling sleeve

bush

limit switch

operating shaft

block

pin

locknut

spring

detail of locking pin assembly

connecting rod

Figure 41 Turning gear.

Types of gearbox

Two types have emerged as the most suitable for marine propulsion, these being the locked train type or else the epicyclic gearbox. Both types make use of hardened and ground gears although the low speed wheel in a locked train gearbox may be through hardened meshing with hardened and ground pinions.

Locked train gearboxes

The arrangement of a typical example is shown in Fig 40. The inputs from the HP and LP turbines should be noted, the inputs being by flexible couplings as described in the section *Turbine bladings and diaphragms* (page 73). Each input pinion meshes with a pair of first reduction wheels, thus splitting the drive so that four second reduction pinions mesh with the main wheel. Thus the tooth meshing forces represent only a quarter of the total torque being transmitted.

The connections from the first reduction wheels to the second reduction pinions are torsionally flexible quill shafts which pass through the centres of the hollow secondary pinions. This feature reduces any variation in the load sharing between the four secondary pinions. Also, the quill drive connects to the pinion through a flexible coupling and this allows the pinion to adopt a correct meshing alignment with the main wheel without being disturbed by any distortions of the gear case.

When setting up the gearbox the flexible couplings are freed from the quill shafts by an oil injection process and all the pinions are rotated into mesh contact taking up all the backlash in the normal direction of rotation. The oil injection pressure is then released, re-fixing the couplings to the quill shafts and ensuring that all four pinions take up the drive simultaneously and hence share the load equally.

The bearings are pressure lubricated in the usual way and the teeth are lubricated and cooled by oil sprays which apply the oil immediately after meshing has occurred.

When a turbine is shut down in the hot condition it needs to be rotated slowly to prevent thermal distortions taking place. The 'barring' or turning gear which provides this rotation is an auxiliary, motor driven worm reduction gear mounted on the gearbox and can be brought into mesh with one of the input pinions or first reduction wheels. Suitable protection is provided to prevent any attempt to do this when the machinery is rotating under steam (Fig 41).

Epicyclic gears

A double reduction epicyclic gearbox is shown in Fig 42. The turbine input is via a toothed coupling to the

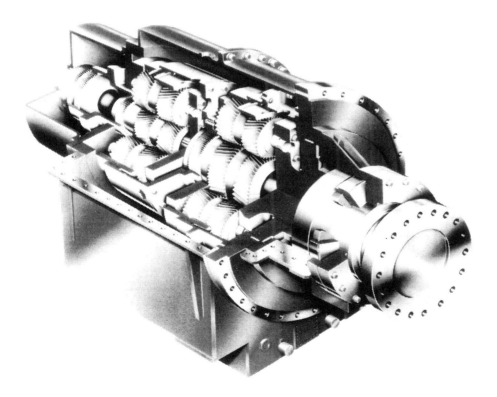

Figure 42 Double reduction epicyclic gearbox.

sun wheel of the first reduction gear and the drive passes through the planet wheels to the annulus. The annulus assembly rotates and connects to the sun wheel of the secondary reduction gear which has a fixed annulus and the output coupling is driven by the planet gear carrier.

Epicyclic gears offer big advantages over other types in terms of lightness and compactness. Tooth loadings are reduced by splitting the drive through a number of planet gears usually between 3 and 5. Various methods are employed to achieve a uniform distribution of load along the face width of the tooth. In the case of the gearbox shown in the illustration a flexible annulus is utilised, which provides a limited movement to allow the planet wheel and annulus teeth to align themselves accurately. This gearbox also incorporates the main thrust bearing.

LUBRICATING OIL SYSTEM

Oil is required for the thrust and journal bearings of the turbine and gearbox, for the gearing lubrication and cooling sprays and for the main propeller shaft thrust bearing. A typical system arrangement is shown in Fig 43 which incorporates motor driven pumps for

starting and emergency back-up, and an engine driven, normal duty pump. The drive for the latter would usually be taken from an intermediate shaft in the gearbox. Further emergency supply is provided by the gravity tank which is maintained in a fully filled condition by an orificed connection to the oil supply mains from the pumps. Oil will be supplied automatically to the bearings for a limited period from this tank if all the pumps fail.

The oil coolers and filters are duplicated with isolating and changeover valves provided to allow maintenance on the shut down unit. The pressure drop across the filters is measured to indicate when cleaning or a change of element is required and the temperature drop across the coolers will give an indication of when they require cleaning.

A centrifugal separator is often used with a connection from the bottom of the oil tank, to remove any build up of water in the oil.

TURBO-GENERATORS

These are usually self contained machines with ratings in the range of 400–2 000 kW and a typical 1 000 kW set is shown in Fig 44. The condenser is integrated

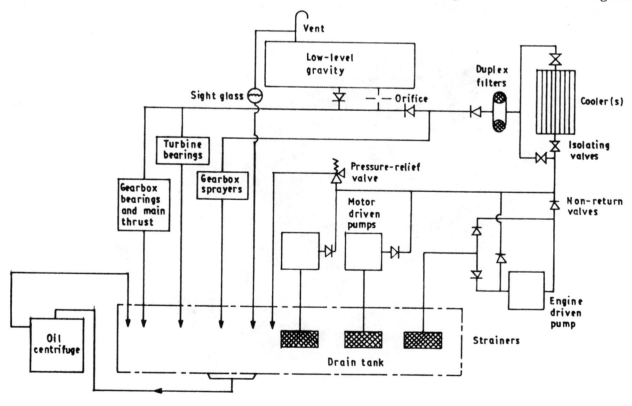

Figure 43   Lubricating oil system.

Figure 44   1000 kW turbo-generator.

into the bed frame and the latter also acts as the oil tank, with the oil filters and cooler mounted on it.

The turbine would run at speeds in the range 9,000–12,000 rev/min driving a 60 Hz 1,800 rev/min generator through either an epicyclic or side pinion gearbox.

All the turbine components are smaller, but similar to those described for the main propulsion turbines, but an essential difference exists with the control system as the speed has to be maintained constant to close limits in order to maintain the electrical system frequency.

The steam valves are opened and closed by hydraulic servo mechanisms called control valve actuators, a version of which is shown in Fig 45. The governor produces a signal oil pressure, which raises or lowers a pilot valve against a spring, and the latter admits or releases high pressure control oil to or from the servo. The steam valve is attached to the bottom beam of the actuator. The mechanism has to be able to repeat the valve position for a given signal oil pressure from the governor accurately. If a variation of more than 0.1 mm exists, it is unlikely that good governing will be achieved. If problems are experienced and the electrical frequency is fluctuating or 'hunting', the problem will lie either with the governor itself or will be due to scoring of the actuator pilot valve or the sleeve in which it operates. This type of damage would have to be very carefully removed,

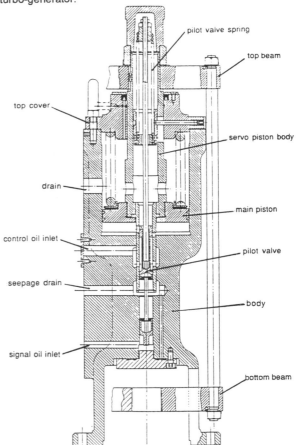

Figure 45   Inlet governing valve actuator.

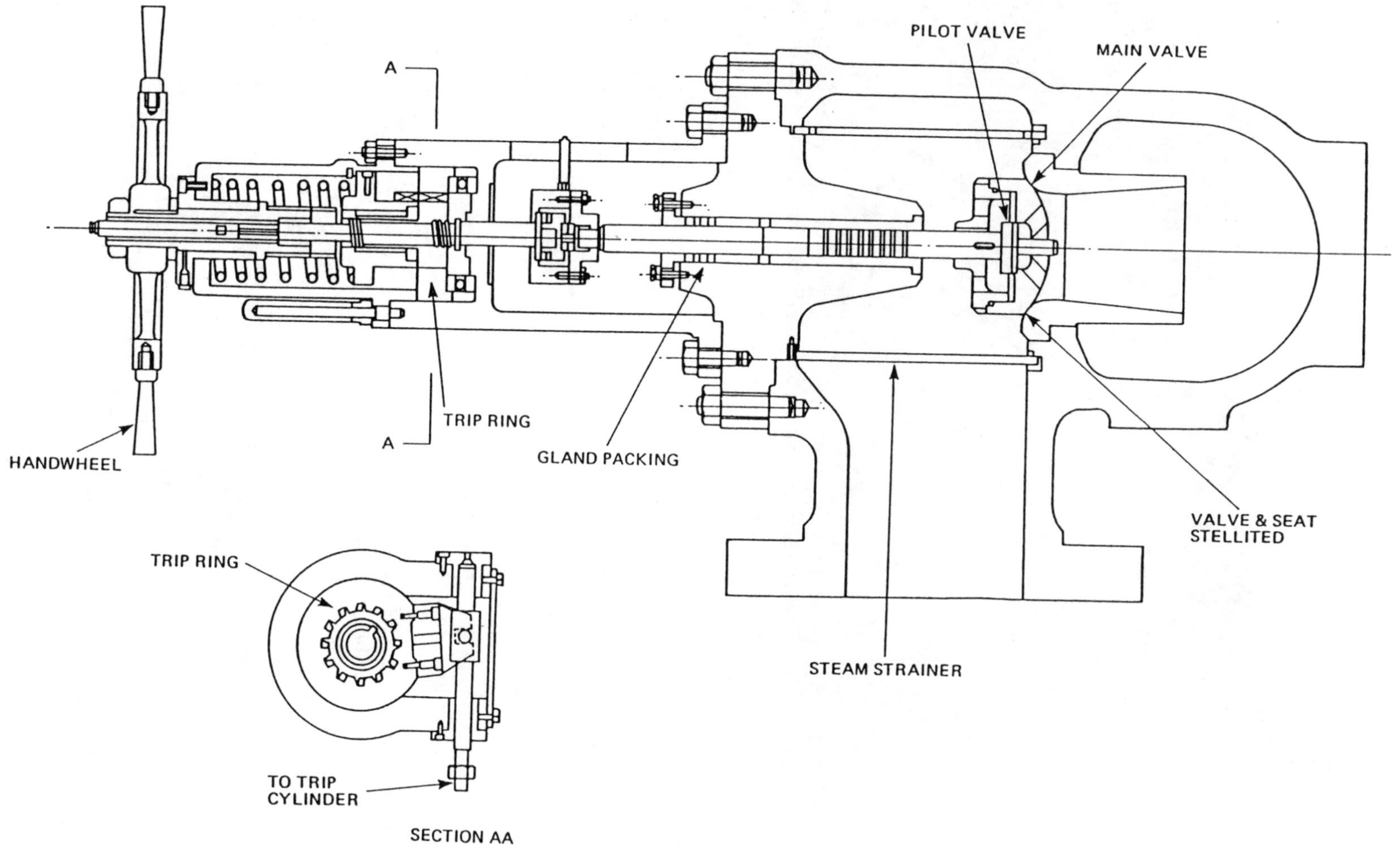

VALVE & SEAT STELLITED

MAIN VALVE

PILOT VALVE

STEAM STRAINER

GLAND PACKING

TRIP RING

A

A

HANDWHEEL

TRIP RING

TO TRIP CYLINDER

SECTION AA

Figure 46 Stop valve assembly.

the final operation being the use of metal polish or a fine lapping compound to achieve the high surface finish and low friction that is essential.

Another very important aspect of turbo generators is the protection against overspeed, as an electrical fault may instantly remove the load from the turbine and this will result in very high rates of acceleration taking place. To avoid a disastrous overspeed which can result in the disintegration of the turbine and generator rotors, the steam valves have to close within a fraction of a second of the loss of load. An overspeed trip unit is fitted to the turbine rotor. This usually consists of an eccentric ring restrained by a spring. The spring will move out from its normal position if the turbine speed reaches 110% of its normal value, operating a trip valve. This valve dumps the control oil which, in addition to causing the control valves to close, also causes the trip cylinder to operate. Figure 46 shows the stop valve assembly and the trip arrangement which allows a powerful spring to close the valve when the trip cylinder operates. This whole sequence of events is designed to take place so quickly that the maximum speed rise of the turbine is limited to about 15%.

If more than one turbo generator is installed in the ship and if a diesel generator is also fitted, it is necessary to ensure that when they are operating in parallel they share the overall electrical load. This will only be achieved if each governor has a closely similar droop characteristic—the speed change from no load to full load is equal for each generator in the ship's system. If proprietary governors are fitted these usually have a droop adjustment facility, but problems can arise if the governor is manufactured by the turbine or diesel engine builder as these usually have a fixed droop characteristic which can only be changed by fitting a different governor spring or else by changing a signal oil orifice.

TURBINE OPERATION

Turbine operation is based upon the principle of obtaining maximum reliability for the propulsion plant, minimising the amount of maintenance work that is required, and maximising the operating efficiency.

Safeguarding reliability

The following are sources of damage to steam plant.

Water erosion
Considerable amounts of water are condensed during start-up, the latent heat of the condensed steam being absorbed in heating up the pipework and turbine casings to their working temperature. The steam main should be gradually pressurised and warmed through using the blow-down drain until the full rated pressure is obtained at the turbine stop valve, with at least 50°C superheat before admitting steam to the turbine. The turbine should then be warmed through, with vacuum established and gland steam applied, by sequentially opening and closing the ahead and astern valves for short durations just sufficient to cause the shaft to rotate, all turbine casing drains being open. This warming through procedure would be incorporated into an automated start-up system, as would the rate of build up of power from a cold start. If the machinery has been in service within 12 hours or so there would be no need to follow this routine.

Thermal stress
The greatest danger of excessive thermal stresses being imposed on the turbine with subsequent damage in the form of cracks, is likely during start-up from cold. The aim is to warm through gradually, following the manufacturer's instructions.

An important aspect to understand is that heat transfer through a wetted surface will be 30 to 40 times greater than through a dry surface and this very rapid heating can cause high thermal stress and distortion in the turbine casing. If, for example the turbine is on low power, a vacuum will exist within the turbine through the LP cylinder and up to the first few stages of the HP turbine which will be the only stages producing power. If the throttle valves are suddenly opened to obtain a large increase in power output, the pressure distribution inside the turbine is changed dramatically so that much higher pressures are established in the HP turbine reducing to a vacuum only in the last few LP stages. The inside walls of the turbine casing would have initially been dry and at the saturation temperature corresponding to a vacuum, which would be significantly lower than the saturation temperature of the high pressure which has been established suddenly. The cold metal surface initiates condensation and the subsequent wet conditions promote very high rates of heat transfer, with the risk of distortion and cracking referred to earlier.

Vibration
One source of serious vibration is a rotor becoming bent, and a bend of only 0.04 mm is sufficient to cause rough running. A rotor can have either a temporary or a permanent bend.

A temporary bend is created if a rotor is allowed to

remain stationary in a warm or hot turbine. Thermo-syphon effects in the space inside the casing result in the top becoming hotter than the bottom and this results in the rotor becoming bent in a convex upwards shape. The condition can be eliminated and avoided by always ensuring that the rotors are barred round if the casings are hot.

A permanent bend can result from heavy gland rubs, although modern glands are designed to mini-mise the damage caused by rubbing. A rub is caused either by attempting to run with a rotor having a temporary bend as described above, or else because the casing has distorted as a result of attempting to increase power from cold too rapidly with the result-ing effects described in the previous paragraph. The effect of a rub is to cause intense local heating of the rotor which causes the bend to increase and create a snowballing worsening of the situation with the ro-tor rotating in a 'skipping rope' mode. The situation can only be avoided by rapidly reducing power on the first onset of vibration and attempt to roll out the bend by running the turbine at no more than 400 rev/ min.

Vibration may also be the result of damage to the rotor blades or shrouding, the loss of blades or shrouding, or to bearing instability.

Damage to journals and thrust bearings

The section on bearings described the small dimen-sion of the oil films established in the journal and thrust bearing, the result of which is that virtually any foreign matter in the oil will cause scoring which can reduce the effectiveness of the bearing in estab-lishing an oil film. Thus a cumulative effect can take place which can lead to a bearing failure. The point to be observed is to maintain scrupulous cleanliness whenever any part of the oil system is opened up.

Maximising efficiency

To maximise efficiency the aim is to run the plant in the manner intended by the designer. The inlet steam conditions should be kept at the prescribed values as should the vacuum. Any fall off of the latter can lose about 4% in efficiency for every 25 mm loss of vacuum. There is no gain in operating at a vacuum better than the designed value as the turbine last stage of blades cannot take advantage of the lower pressure and the expansion to the lower pressure will take place in the condenser with no contribution of additional power.

Any throttling at the turbine control valves should be minimised. If the turbine has multiple control valves the ship should be operated at a power level which allows all the valves in service to be virtually fully open. If the turbine has a single control valve some designs provide separate small groups of inlet nozzles, each controlled by a manual isolating valve. These groups can be brought into service as required to maintain the service speed, depending on the cleanliness of the hull. This avoids the main valve operating in a throttling mode when the hull is clean, in order to allow the reserve of power needed to maintain speed with the hull in a fouled condition.

Bled steam pressures should be maintained at the design values. If the stage pressures show significant variation it is likely that the turbine blades have either become coated with boiler salts or else have suffered some degree of damage. In either case the flow area through the blades has been reduced and this causes the change in pressure distribution in the turbine.

As the condenser cooling water and the conden-sate and feed water pass through the various stages of feed heating, temperature rises should be moni-tored to ensure that the tubes are not fouled and in need of cleaning.

Chapter 3
Marine Diesel Engines

P Durham

INTRODUCTION

'Engineering' is the application of scientific principles to practical ends such as the design, construction and operation of efficient and economical structures. By understanding the reasons behind design features and manufacturing techniques, marine engineers can operate their engines with a greater depth of understanding of the loadings, both mechanical and thermal. A full understanding of the engine as a whole, and as individual components or systems, makes the ship's engineer a more competent and self-reliant operator. This chapter aims to provide an insight into the individual components of an engine, highlighting the design criteria and how they inter-relate with the other components in the engine to provide a reliable and operational whole.

BEDPLATES

Bedplates are the 'foundation' of the engine, without the support of which the shaft alignment in particular, and engine structure as a whole, would inevitably be lost.

The original bedplate design followed the practices involved in the steam reciprocating engines, but it soon became apparent that the magnitude of the forces generated inside a diesel were substantially greater than those in a steam engine, and of a different nature, with the consequence that bedplates had to be developed which would accommodate the 'cyclic' peak pressures, and at the same time maintain the alignment for these longer engines. As power weight ratios became more competitive, the fabricated bedplate evolved to provide a light but strong and stiff foundation. The fabricated bedplate has subsequently undergone several refinements.

The traditional basic structure of two longitudinal girders tied together with transverse girders has stood the test of time. There have been some modifications to accommodate the ever increasing mean effective pressures (mep); a consequence of the ongoing search for greater powers whilst still minimising weight. The classic transverse girder structure is shown in Fig 1.

Figure 1a shows an end view (looking fore and aft). Fig 1b shows a longitudinal section through the transverse girder and indicates how the bearing saddle is supported. The arrows indicate the forces imposed upon the bearing by the firing forces in the engine. These forces come through the running gear (piston, crosshead, con-rod, and crankshaft), and are both cyclic and fluctuating in nature. The bearing saddle requires very substantial support to withstand these forces, especially as both peak and mean effective pressures increase.

The top and bottom plates of the longitudinal girder are substantially thicker than their supporting plates, because they are the ones upon which the longitudinal and transverse alignment of the engine

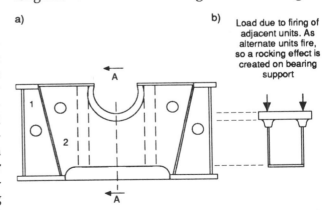

Figure 1 Structure of bed plate: section through bedplate and section (A-A) through transverse girder.

depend. It is therefore necessary for there to be adequate thickness in these plates to allow for a final machining across them once the whole bedplate is assembled, thereby recovering any distortion that may have occurred during the fabrication process. This machining, performed in a huge milling/planing machine, that both spans and travels the length of the bedplate, leaves the bedplate ready to accept, and align on its upper face, the rest of the engine structure. The lower face provides a flat surface for the mating of the supporting chocks.

The chocks are used to compensate for the natural unevenness of the tank tops and in so doing give the bedplate a seating as close as possible to the stiff and flat bed where the engine was originally built and tested. The tank tops are, by their very nature, not necessarily flat, and so, in compensation, the chocks used have to be hand fitted to provide the level base required for the bedplate. To reduce the cost and time required for the fitting of these chocks, the tank tops, instead of being spot faced by local machining, are now frequently fitted with prepared pads welded *in situ*. These plates provide a machined surface to which the chocks can be more readily matched.

Matching is a job requiring great skill and practice if the chocks are to be fitted accurately and in such a way that fretting is avoided as far as possible. Fretting is the process which occurs when a slight oscillatory movement takes place between two surfaces under load; the result being the abrasion of surface material. Initially on a microscopic scale, 'fretting' can progress to such an extent that there is a complete loss of grip between the two surfaces. Wearing proceeds so that slackness and unacceptable movement occur. Since fretting produces an irregular (non-flat) surface it is a difficult situation to rectify or recover, other than by machining flat and true again. In some instances, grinding the surface with 'mandrills' has been an effective palliative, but access below the bedplate precludes either of these operations (unless the whole engine is dismantled and the bedplate raised to give access).

For this reason it is essential that the chocks fitted must have the maximum surface contact with the tank top and the underside of the bedplate. Any 'peaks' on the chocks will soon be compressed out by fretting and loading so that the chock will become slack, and the alignment of the bedplate, and hence the crankshaft, will be impaired. Misalignment of the crankshaft can lead to many problems, the least of which could be damage to the white metal bearings, and the worst of which could be cracking of the crankshaft ultimately leading to fracture. During any part of the above there is the potential for a crankcase explosion; a situation that must be avoided at all costs.

The chocks are carefully hand scraped and fitted at their relevant location and the engine pulled down onto them using 'holding down bolts', the latter having undergone several changes over recent years.

Many engineers at sea will now have had experience with the synthetic resins used as a chocking material. These resins come as a pourable fluid into which is mixed a hardening agent. The fluid can then be poured into preformed retaining dams under the engine bedplate, setting without any contraction in dimension. All that is required is a tolerance for a small amount of compression which occurs when the engine is hardened down. Greased dowels, or similar, are used to protect the bolt holes from filling up with the liquid resin. Being impervious to oil, sea water and mild acids, the resin is an ideal and simple alternative to the steel/cast iron chocking traditionally used. There is a reduction in fitting time, skilled labour is not required, nor are machine flat surfaces, and as the resin gives 100% contact there is a potential for reduction in the incidence of fretting.

The area of the resin chock is, naturally, larger than that used for the metallic chocking and may cover several holding down bolts at a time. There is also a slight internal resilience in the material, not apparent in cast iron, which gives the resin a very small ability to absorb or dampen vibration transmission.

It is easy to see that the adoption of long studs to hold down the bedplate has led to greater elasticity in the stud, in such a way that the chock is held in compression even as the surfaces bed into one another. To provide further security of grip the holding down bolts invariably carry a necked section with outside diameter (od) smaller than the diameter at the root of the threaded sections. The potential for failure at the root of a thread is thus alleviated. As with all such studs (piston crown, cylinder head, tie bolts and so on), the necked section should never be marked or damaged. Any scratch, pop mark or surface flaw can lead to the localising of stresses that can lead to fatigue failure. The origin of the failure is frequently easily traced to the surface damage previously mentioned. The studs are therefore fitted as illustrated in Fig 2, from which it can be seen that sleeves are used to allow the adoption of long studs, the exposed threads being protected from impact damage by metal caps. Lock nuts are no longer favoured because they give a false sense of security; whilst they may appear tight and apparently satisfactory in a cursory check, it is possible that fretting may have occurred, leading to a lack of 'dimensional accuracy', so that the grip of the nuts is lost, even

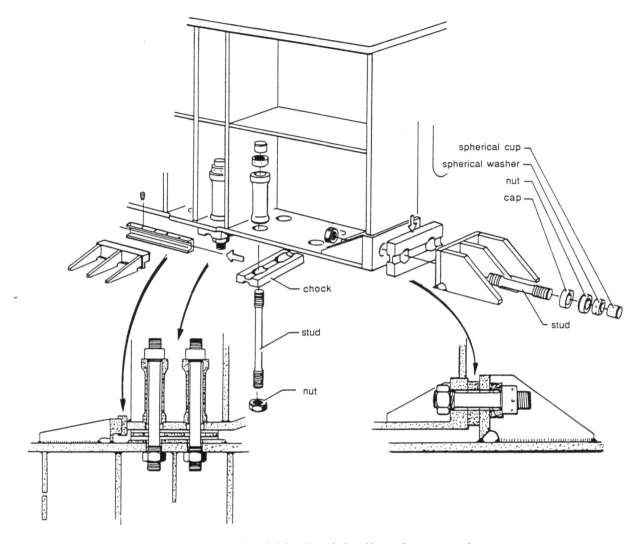

spherical cup
spherical washer
nut
cap

chock

stud

stud

nut

Note: • long holding down bolts with cast iron spacer tubes
        • chocks placed on steel pads, with bevel of 1:100 on both
        • where such bevel is greater than 1:100 spherical washers and nuts
          are used at lower end of bolt
        • side chocks, bevelled 1:100, are fitted from aft end on both sides
        • fore and aft chocks fitted from above with 1:100 bevel

Figure 2   Fitting of studs in bedplate.

though they remain tight against each other. A single nut with some form of locking built in or tab washer is to be preferred. It is more easily tested and less likely to give a false impression of tightness.

The whole system of chocking is designed to give the bedplate, as nearly as possible, the alignment originally provided on the test bed. To produce this in the engine room, the bedplate is landed onto temporary chocks, which are adjustable so that the bedplate alignment can be modified (using piano wires, optical telescopes, or laser beams) to as close to the original condition as possible. It is at this point that the metallic hand fitted chocks or the epoxy resin chocking is fitted. Once this is achieved the temporary chocks are removed.

The longitudinal girders of the bedplate are constructed to provide adequate longitudinal stiffness to the structure so that the crankshaft alignment is maintained. Problems arise as ships' structures become lighter (to improve their cargo carrying competitiveness), in that they also become more flexible. Such problems do create difficulties for the engine builder/designer who has to make every attempt to ensure that his bedplate remains longitudinally rigid under all service conditions. With this in mind, the ship's engineer must recognise the need for maintenance of bedplate alignment. He should check for slack or loose bolts and chocks at regular intervals, whilst appreciating that the slackness of an individual chock may not alone cause alignment problems. It may, in conjunction with other engine operating conditions, lead to bearing failure or bearing wear down. Overloading of the engine collectively or on one or more units, together with loose chocks, which separately may not be of sufficient magnitude to damage the engine, may collectively lead to some form of bearing/shaft failure.

The fact that a problem within any part of the engine system may be caused, not by a single component, but by the interaction of several minor inconsistencies, should be borne in mind by the engineer as he attempts to analyse or diagnose a particular condition.

The longitudinal girders are tied together by 'transverse girders' to make the bedplate. Until recently, these were of two plate construction, as shown in Fig 1.

The two plates are placed at the extremities of the bearing saddle so that they carry the firing loads of the adjacent units with as little longitudinal deformation of the saddle alignment as possible. To further strengthen the plates, mutual support is provided by stiffening tubes welded into the two cheek plates. Successful as these supports were for many years, the ever increasing demand for power with as little weight as possible has led to more failures, predominately under the bearing saddle, but also along the sealing welds. It should be appreciated that the 'box-like' structure of the transverse girder, Fig 1b, is difficult to fabricate without there being an in-built weakness (notch) in the closing weld. Because of this, and other allied needs to provide a strong transverse girder, cast steel units are now the norm for larger engines. Figure 3 shows a recent form of this structure.

The diagram clearly shows how the firing forces transmitted into the crankshaft, and thence into the bearing and saddle, are transmitted via the stiffening webs directly to the ends of the tie bolts. Although these cast transverse girders are, by nature, heavier than their predecessors they are immensely strong and can take the increased loading without deformation or failure. Thus, the crankshaft alignment is maintained, even though powers have increased with consequent higher bearing loading. The firing forces that press down on the bearing saddle also attempt to push up the cylinder covers, the net effect being to put the whole of the engine structure into tensile loading. Tie rods pass through the engine structure and are tensioned in such a way that, even during peak powers, the structure of the engine, from transverse girder to the top of the jacket, is held in compression. The tie rods have to be strong and capable of withstanding cyclic stressing due to the firing forces. To provide this as safely as possible they will be designed with the same protections as mentioned earlier for studs. Similarly, they will need to be uniformly tensioned, preferably hydraulically, to the designed loadings. Any uneven loading, including excessive loading of these tie rods, can result in their failure, either by fracture or by fretting at the ends where their nuts seat on the jacket casing and under the transverse girder.

During firing the transverse girders are subjected to a bending moment, as the the saddle is pushed down by the crankshaft and the tie rods are pulled up. To limit this bending effect and consequent distortion of the bearing housing, the tie rods are positioned as close as possible to the centreline of the shaft. This, in turn, causes problems in the arrangements for holding down the top cover of the bearing. One manufacturer overcomes this by using jacking bolts from the inside of the A-frame as shown in Fig 4. This allows the tie bolts to be placed very close to the bearing and thereby reduces the bending effects across the transverse girder. Other manufacturers achieve similar protection by using two top keeps held in place by smaller studs offset from the transverse centreline of the tie bolts (Fig 3).

The search for increasing powers and, possibly more importantly, fuel economy has led to the development of the super long stroke engines with stroke bore ratios of 2.5:1. Such engines require large throws from the crankshaft. To accommodate these, if the traditional double plate box type longitudinal girders were to be used, the bedplate would need to be much wider. However, a solution has been devised such that the increased throw is accommodated, to a large extent, within the bedplate itself. This has been made possible by making the bedplate much deeper than previously and then by using single plate longitudinal girders. These reduce the overall width of the engine and keep the weight down. In addition, the shaft centre line has been dropped and the horizontal forces generated by the crankshaft and its running gear are thus taken directly into the transverse girder instead of along the line of the interface between the A-frames and the bedplate.

Such a design can be seen in Figs 3 and 4. In both cases the transverse girders are designed to carry the stresses generated as the engine operates. Many

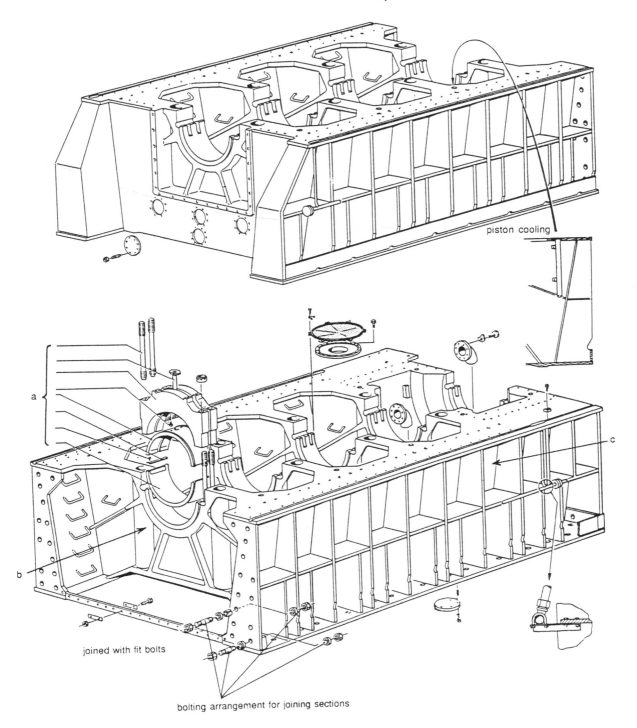

piston cooling

a

c

b

joined with fit bolts

bolting arrangement for joining sections

Figure 3 a) Two main bearing caps with associated shell bearings, holding down arrangements and oil supply; b) cast transverse girder (with radial webs); c) single plate longitudinal girder, with substantial ribs.

container ships and tankers now have engines with stroke bore ratios in excess of 3.5: 1. Whilst the stroke is lengthened, the engine height is maintained by shortening the connecting rod. The same principles as above apply for the bedplate.

The longitudinal girders are substantially supported by both horizontal and vertical ribbing, both providing strength and stiffness to the 'mono-plate' structure. Access to all webbing is possible so that the integrity of all the welding is assured (Fig 3).

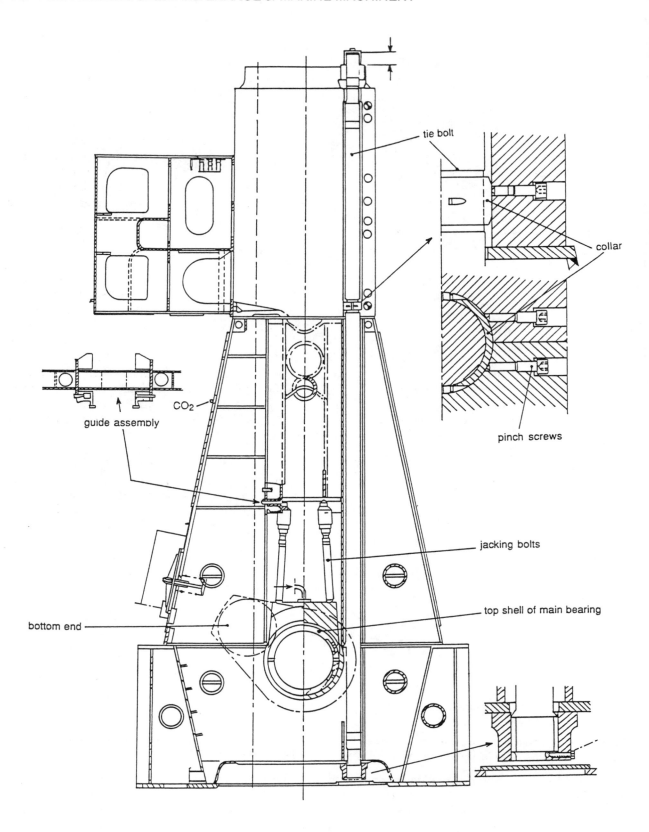

Figure 4   Transverse section of engine, showing jacking bolts inside A frame.

CRANKSHAFTS

At some time, and in varying degress, the crankshaft is exposed to all forms of mechanical stressing. On the larger engines the crankshaft has, for many years, been manufactured by forging, from a single billet, the combined 'webs' and 'bottom end' comprising one 'throw'. These were then assembled into the composite structure of the crankshaft by 'shrink fitting' the relevant main bearing journals between each throw. These shrink fits, in the region of 1/600 the shaft diameter, used to be achieved by heating up the web and then entering the pin when the required expansion had taken place. However, with this method there was the possibility that slight products of oxidation, created by the heating, might become trapped in the interface such that the integrity of the grip was marginally reduced. To avoid this, liquid nitrogen or similar cooling agents have recently been adopted to cool the pin sufficiently for it to be entered into the web. These 'shrink' fits create quite substantial crushing forces on the pin which lead to similar magnitude tensile stresses around the bore of the hole in the web. The distribution of these is such that a series of concentric circles can be drawn, linking together stresses of the same magnitude, usually referred to as 'hoop' stresses. To ensure that there is no discontinuity to these hoops, the fitting of dowels or keys along the interface, between pin and web, should be avoided. These stresses, imposed during the manufacturing process, will be an inevitable part of the crankshaft loading for the rest of its life. In operation the shaft will be subjected to stresses over and above these inherent residual stresses. Their combined effects must therefore be considered and allowed for in design strength. In an attempt to separate the effects of these two stresses it has become common practice for the ends of the main bearing journal to be 'swollen' to a larger diameter in way of the shrink fit. This then means that the region in which the maximum hoop stresses are concentrated is removed from the area where the web applies the main turning moment to the pin. It is essential that there is a generous radius between these two diameters. In some cases the finely machined radius may be 'cold rolled' to further improve its resistance to cracking, thereby providing the crankshaft with greater integrity.

A diagrammatic view of the distribution of the hoop stresses is shown in Fig 5.

The more obvious forms of mechanical stressing that the crankshaft is subjected to are torsional stressing and bending stressing. Torsional stressing, being a result of the forces applied by the connecting rod to the bottom end, varies in magnitude with both the changes in cylinder pressure and the angle of thrust applied by the connecting rod during the power stroke. The compression stroke, acting as a resistance to turning, further compounds this variation in torque, so that, were the shaft not adequately dimensioned, early fatigue failure through cyclic torsional stressing would be likely to occur.

'Torsional' vibration indicates a situation where an applied turning moment causes the shaft to 'wind up' (twist along its length) and then unwind again as the stiffness of the shaft re-asserts itself over the applied torque.

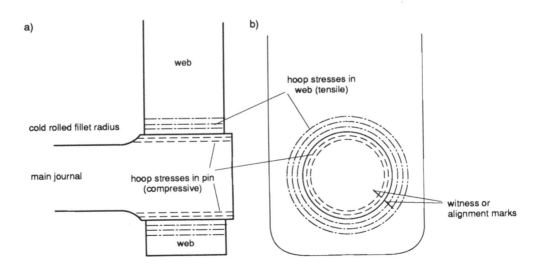

Figure 5   Distribution of hoop stresses: a) longitudinal section through shaft and web; b) end view on shaft and web.

There is a limit beyond which any shaft (and indeed any component) subjected to a cyclic stress will fatigue and fail. For this reason torsional stressing beyond the design value should be avoided. This, in turn, means that overloading of one or more units must be avoided, as must any cylinder pressure distribution that is away from the norm. In direct drive diesel engines, the ability of the propeller to absorb torque influences the torsional stresses within a crankshaft system (and the line shaft system). Should any imbalance (broken or bent blades for example) occur in the propeller the engineer should be aware that the resultant reaction in the engine will aggravate the torsional stresses already in it.

The bending stresses generated within the shaft system are easy to visualise, especially if one main bearing is lower than it should be (due to wear, or lack of support from chocks). The firing forces will deflect the shaft into the housing causing the shaft to bend, which in turn causes the fibres at the outside surface of the curvature to be put into tension whilst those on the inside are compressed. Throughout the revolution these stresses are reversed, leading to a cyclic stressing that may lead to fatigue failure, particularly if there are flaws on the journal that may act as crack initiation centres. The most obvious of these are any drillings in the shaft, made to provide lubrication passages. Naturally, the area around such holes is subjected not only to the torsional effects but also to the bending stresses mentioned above. In an attempt to make the holes accept these loadings, they are provided with generous radii and have as smooth and consistent a surface finish as possible. Though torque is a function of radius, and hence the maximum torque is felt at the surface of a shaft, there will be torque transmission of some value throughout the depth of the shaft, so it is important to maintain reasonable surface finish over the full depth of the oil hole. Any surface inconsistency within the hole may lead to crack propagation in the shaft which could work its way through the whole shaft.

Apart from torsion and bending stresses, the shaft will also be subjected to shear forces, particularly over the tdc position, where the piston rod, connecting rod and webs are in alignment and the turning moment is negligible. At this point in the cycle, the crank throw is thrust downwards creating a shearing effect on the two main journals. However, a large part of the load (discounting the crosshead) will go into the bottom end bearing. Though designed in every way to absorb this, the bottom end bearing will be subjected to a bending force whilst being supported by the webs. The latter are thus put into compression and must be designed with adequate strength to withstand this loading, especially as later in the stroke these webs are put into tension, albeit of a much lower magnitude.

The combined effect of the above peak loading is the generation of a stress concentration on the under side of the bottom end pin where it meets the web. For this reason a generous radius is formed around the pin blending it into the web to give as smooth a stress distribution as possible. This radius does, however, reduce the load carrying area available for a given width between webs. It is for this reason that many shafts are now made with the radius set back into the web, thereby giving protection (in terms of stress distribution) whilst still providing a full width pin.

Another and major method of providing strength against the above stressing is that of producing crankshaft throws with continuous 'grain flow'. This means that a billet of steel is forged into the shape of the crank throw so that the original centre of the billet (of an inherently weaker grain structure than that at the surface, as a result of the slower rate of cooling at the centre, where larger and therefore weaker grains form) follows the centre ground of the webs and bearing. This in turn means that the finer, and therefore stronger, grain structure is maintained along the surface of the throw, giving strength to the highly loaded areas.

It is normally accepted that the shrink fit will only slip in service if exceptional stresses are imposed on the crankshaft system.

Attempting to start the engine when a cylinder is partially filled with fluid may cause slip. Fluid may have accumulated above the piston because of leakage from piston, jacket or valve cooling, or it could be fuel from a leaking fuel injector. There must be sufficient liquid (virtually incompressible) so that the piston rising towards tdc is restricted in movement and the crankshaft continuing to turn causes the slip to occur. The unit resisting movement is the one at which the slip is most likely to take place. Normally only one such shrink fit is affected by slipping. The amount of displacement can be seen by checking the alignment marks (witness marks, Fig 5). Previous experience has shown that the amount of damage to the relevant mating surfaces is negligible so that the original degree of grip will not be lost.

Naturally, the movement of one web relevant to the rest of the engine will have an effect on the timing and balance of the engine. The overall effect is related to the degree of twist and the location, along the crankshaft, at which the slip has taken place. A small amount of twist may well be accommodated within the engine, perhaps with some minor adjustments made to the fuel timing. A large amount of slip would need further assessment and it is likely that some form of recovery should be attempted. Before that, it is important to consider the number of units, and those which are affected by the slip. That is to say the 'slipped' unit will not be the only one out of phase (unless it is the end unit of an engine). To determine which units are affected, work from the cam shaft drive to the slipped unit. All units 'beyond' this point are adversely affected.

The following systems may be affected to a greater or lesser degree by the slip.

1. Fuel timing
Usually recoverable by adjustment of the pump or cam.

2. 'Breathing' of the engine (aspiration)
The regular sequence of breathing from the scavenge space will be changed by the displacement of the crank which controls the point at which the piston uncovers the ports. This can only be recovered by realignment of the crank system. In extreme cases of slip the irregular breathing may result in the surging of the turbocharger and possibly the vibration of the scavenge spaces themselves.

3. Exhaust
The timing of the exhaust will have altered due to the change of phase that occurs between the crankshaft and the cam shaft over the affected units. The exhaust timing will be affected so that the turbocharger may well surge and vibrations of the uptake piping may occur. In mild cases the cams may be adjusted to return to an acceptable operating condition. Where the twist is large it will be necessary to realign the slipped shrink fit.

4. Balance
The disposition of weights will have been altered throughout the crankshaft system, with an adverse effect on its static and dynamic balance. The 'critical' speed will have altered and unacceptable engine vibrations may be set up, affecting chocking and other mountings throughout the engine.

Perhaps the simplest approach to assessing the acceptability or otherwise of a slipped shrink fit would be to run the engine and monitor the areas mentioned above. This should be done judiciously and subsequently at regular intervals thereafter. If any of the conditions mentioned above are, or look likely to become, unacceptable then recovery of the slip is essential. Whenever possible and convenient, the repair should be carried out at a shiprepair facility. If this is not possible, there are several recorded precedents for recovery procedures.

1. Chill as far as possible the crank pin (dry ice etc.).

2. After several hours of cooling, warm up the web by applying a broad flame over a wide area.

3. Lock the journal against rotation (remove shims and harden down the keep).

4. Jack the web back into position. (Mount the jack on wooden battens to protect bedplate structure from a high and localised load).

5. Erect a stop above the web, to prevent overshooting the desired position, before applying jacking force.

6. The fitting of dowels is not recommended; they upset the hoop stresses mentioned earlier and, being 'driven' in, also lift the surfaces apart and thereby reduce the frictional grip essential to the shrink fit.

7. Record the affected unit in the engine log, ensuring that the witness marks are regularly checked initially, after just a few running hours and then after every voyage or extremely heavy weather, where possible.

Adequate precautions must be taken against fire, contamination of lubricating oil, and unexpected engine movement and so on. Such a repair should not be undertaken by ships' staff without referring to the engine builders and the superintendent engineer.

Crankshafts should be checked for the following.

a) surface damage of journals by:
    i. scoring by impurities in lubricating oil or particles embedded in white metal.
    ii. corrosion (usually apparent as discoloration), possibly from weak acids caused by oxidation of lubricating oil (weak); bacteria in oil; products of combustion (trunk engines).

b) cracks at fillet radii, oil holes or other areas where stress concentrations occur.
Caused by cyclic torsional stresses; crankshaft misalignment (worn main bearings or loose chocks); overloading of the engine.

c) slipped shrink fit (check witness marks).
Caused by liquid in cylinder during starting; propeller collision with submerged object; extreme and sudden overloading of a unit or units (possibly as a result of a major fault in the fuel injection and timing system).

d) ovality.
This occurs infrequently but is a problem that primarily concerns the bottom end journal, though

in extreme cases the mains and even the crosshead pins may be affected. It is caused by a combination of reduced effectiveness of lubricating oil and the directional thrust of the connecting rod, which is at a maximum somewhere around 45 deg after tdc, with a result that the journal wears oval. The amount of ovality in line with and at 90 deg to the maximum thrust should be checked. Usually the maximum ovality that can be carried is in the region of one-quarter the working clearance of the bearing, any more would begin to affect hydrodynamic lubrication. Ovality can be recovered to acceptable conditions by *in situ* grinding.

One of the most important and radical changes of recent times has been the production of crankshafts by 'welding' together pre cast or forged sections of shaft. This process, accepted by all the major classification societies and regulating bodies, has the advantage of eliminating the need for a shrink fit. The procedure is simply to forge a throw, similar to that described earlier though this time with sections of shaft formed at the lower end of the webs. These 'stubs', when welded to the adjacent throw form the main bearing journals. The welding techniques employed are such that these shafts are more than able to withstand the variations in stress mentioned above. As there is no longer any need to provide a depth of material around the pin, in which to absorb the hoop stresses, these shafts are much lighter in structure than the traditional shrink fit shafts.

Deflections

Deflections are readings obtained from between the webs of individual crank throws as the crankshaft is rotated. Standard procedure is to fit a dial gauge between the webs, usually as close to the shaft circumference as possible (at opposite side to throw), and set to zero when crank throw is as close to bdc as possible. Turning the crankshaft slowly and taking a reading at every 90 deg thereafter will provide top and bottom readings indicating the state of the shaft alignment in the vertical plane, and port and starboard readings indicating the state of alignment in the horizontal plane. Figures 6 and 7 show the effect of low and high bearings on deflection readings. It should be noted, however, that the readings from one unit alone do not enable the shaft alignment to be assessed. It is only from an overview of the interrelationship of all units that the lie of the shaft can be interpreted. The readings of an individual unit may point to a problem being present but they will not determine the cause. Also, although a set of deflec-

tions will indicate, when correctly translated, where misalignment is occurring, it is imperative that a set of wear down readings is also taken. An excessively worn bearing will inevitably give shaft misalignment. Only when the wear down readings have been taken, and satisfactory adjustments to the worn bearings have been made, should any attempt be made to rectify any misalignment indicated by deflections.

A simple but effective check on the validity of a set of deflection gauge readings is the 'complemental check'. That is, the top plus bottom readings should be roughly equal to the port and starboard readings added together. Any large discrepancy in this should

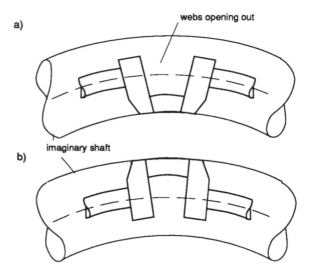

Figure 6   Throw at a) bdc, and; b) tdc, showing the effects of 'low' bearing (i.e. causing reduction in reading from bdc to tdc).

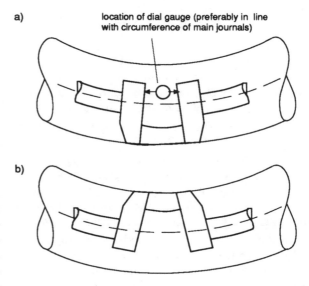

Figure 7   Throw at a) bdc, and; b) tdc, showing the effects on deflection readings of a 'high' bearing (i.e. deflection gauge increases in reading from bdc to tdc).

prompt the taking of another set of readings from the unit(s) concerned. The error in the recorded values may have come from a misread gauge or a wrong transcription.

Should the same readings be found then it is more than likely that there is some major misalignment in the bedplate, not just in the horizontal plane as is the norm, but also in the vertical. The bedplate is probably twisted! Thankfully, such conditions are very rare and, more often than not, the bedplate is disturbed in the horizontal plane alone. If the main bearings are in satisfactory condition then the support of the bearing housing is suspect. This may be the failure (cracking) of the fabricated transverse girders or perhaps the loss of support, locally, of the bedplate itself or cracked, broken, worn or missing chocks. In extreme cases it may be the upsetting of the tank top caused perhaps by hogging and sagging in heavy weather, grounding, collision, and so on. It may even be due to a combination of factors, any one of which alone may not affect the engine alignment. Consider the combined effects of two or more of the following: slightly worn chocks, trim of vessel; cargo distribution throughout length of vessel (or ballast distribution); temperature of tank plating immediately below engine (to obtain the most relevant and representative readings, take deflections as close to the normal running temperature of engine as is possible); and overhanging weights (flywheels, detuners, etc.).

The turning gear should also be considered. In turning the engine it must overcome the static friction of the running gear. With today's more flexible shafts there is a large possibility that the crank system may be 'wound up' a little. This twist could distort the readings adjacent to the turning gear. To check for this, stop the turning gear at each reading and back it off the teeth of the flywheel. Any change in the deflection gauge indicates that the shaft was being twisted, and the readings with the turning gear backed off are the valid ones. It is also possible for incorrect readings to be recorded because the shaft is not seating into the main bearing housing. This phenomenon is predominant in medium and high speed engines where the shaft is much stiffer and the running gear much lighter than those of a slow speed engine.

The shaft 'spanning' a bearing will provide a better set of deflections than when the engine is running and forcing the shaft into the bearing seat, and so bending or 'deflecting' the shaft. To check that this is not happening, use 'Swedish' type feeler gauges to determine whether the shaft is seated on the bearing. If it is not, then remove the main bearing shims and pull the bearing keep down as each deflection gauge

reading is taken. The reading taken when the shaft is pulled down is the valid one. It gives a picture of the bending that the shaft undergoes as the engine runs. Such a condition rarely, if ever, applies to a slow speed engine.

The following steps should be taken before attempting to take the readings.

1. Check that no-one is working on the propeller or in the vicinity. This does not imply that readings should be taken in dry dock. On the contrary, readings taken there do not reflect the natural lie of the ship when she is afloat. The alignment at that time is enforced by the line of the 'keel blocks' and as such bears no resemblance to the natural deflection of the floating vessel.

2. Check that no-one is working inside the engine, on crossheads, or in cylinders etc.

3. Check that all hanging bars or pins are removed and that lifting gear, chain blocks and engine room crane are not attached to any of the running gear.

4. Open all indicator cocks.

5. Whenever possible, use a gauge that shows negative readings under compression and positive on expansion.

6. Watch amperage as the engine is turning to get an idea of resistance to turning. Any sudden changes in reading should be investigated immediately.

CYLINDER LINERS

Cylinder liners are, almost without exception, cast components which at first sight appear to be cylindrical units of no great complexity. However, even though their shape is simple the materials from which they are made are not quite so basic. For many years a good quality cast iron was used in their production. More recently, the worsening quality of fuels has given rise to greater wear rates. This has led to improvements in the liner material quality, to resist wear and to provide the liner with as long a life as possible. In alloying any material there is such a quantum leap in costs that no operator or owner must consider the benefit worthwhile before he buys in such components. In the case of cast iron for cylinder liners the improved qualities required are those of resistance to wear and in particular to corrosion, which occurs as a direct result of the sulphur compounds frequently associated with many modern residual fuels. Chromium, vanadium and molybdenum are some of the more common metals introduced into the cast iron to improve these properties. A more fundamental reason for using cast iron, as opposed to steel, say, which would provide a tough and more crack resistant liner, is the 'self-lubricating' property of cast iron.

This self-lubricating property is a result of the 'graphite' in the matrix (structure) of the cast iron. The graphite is available in two broad groups; flake, and nodular or spheroidal graphite. Both forms provide the iron with self-lubricating properties, although the flake form tends to have slightly better capabilities than the nodular in that respect. However, the nodular graphite in the matrix does not generate the stress raising centres that are more inherent to the flake graphite, so nodular cast iron provides a slightly tougher iron, more resistant to crack formation but slightly less effective as a lubricant than the flake type. The decision as to which type to use is a rather complicated mix of the following considerations; cylinder liner loading conditions, with respect to gas pressures; piston ring speed; diameter of liner; service duties; and the types of fuel to be used. It is to be understood that there must be a great deal of compatibility between the materials used for the liner and those used for the rings, because mismatching of these two components in hardness and self-lubricating properties would very quickly generate wear rates that would be unacceptable. Discounting chrome plated liners (very unusual on large bore liners, possibly because of the loss of integrity around ports, where rings may 'peel' the plating off, and certainly because of the expense of plating such large components) it can be seen that the ring, always in contact with the liner and therefore wearing continuously, needs to be harder than the liner.

The ring also has to flex to suit the ever changing contours of a worn liner so nodular graphite would be more suited to the manufacture of rings. Liners, on the other hand, usually well supported by jackets, steel support bands or even cylinder heads, do not need to have the greater resistance to flexing and so flake type graphite is usually adopted to maximise their self-lubricating properties.

To produce a liner with a homogeneous (evenly distributed) mix within its matrix, the casting is spun about its own axis as it is solidifying and cooling so that the centrifugal forces generated hold the different constituents of the alloy in position and produce a more dense and uniformly structured casting.

A self-lubricating material is needed because of the difficulty in lubricating the ring pack as it moves up and down the liner surface. The flash point of lubricating oil, broadly speaking, is around 210°C. The temperature at the opening of the exhaust is frequently at least twice this, so any oil exposed to this temperature will, at the very least, begin to carbonise. The lighter elements will start to vaporise, leaving the carbon base, which does not lubricate the ring pack as effectively. It is evident that the lubrication of the ring pack over the tdc of the unit will be particularly difficult, due to the higher pressures as well as the elevated temperatures in that region. These pressures force the rings out onto the liner surface so there is little likelihood of there being an adequate oil film between the ring and the liner. Even under the best conditions, the oil film in a liner is rarely thick enough to ensure total separation of the two materials. Over tdc, therefore, the self-lubricating properties of the liner compensate for the reduced effectiveness of the normal cylinder oil supply. This indicates why the greatest wear can be expected over the top part of the cylinder liner. Lower in the stroke, not only does the temperature fall, but the ring to liner wall pressure reduces with the reduction in cylinder pressure.

It is also normal to find that the wear is directional. That is to say, the wear around the cylinder liner top occurs more in a port and starboard direction than in the fore and aft mode. In large bore engines this may well be as a result of the rolling of the vessel and the piston therefore lying on first one side and then the other. In medium speed engines the same wear pattern exists, primarily due to the thrust of the connecting rod. That is, as the piston is pushed down under the power stroke there will be a reaction by the piston skirt against the cylinder wall. The direction of thrust is reversed during the compression stroke so that the liner tends to wear oval. The guides in a crosshead engine take this same thrust from the connecting rod, thereby relieving the piston from such transverse loading. That is the reason for the employment of crossheads in large engines. Were it not for them, this reaction thrust would have to be carried via the piston onto the liner. Apart from the phenomenal and unacceptable loading that this would impart to the piston, skirt and liner, the piston skirt would not be able to accommodate a 'gudgeon pin' of adequate load carrying capability. Broadly speaking then, the liner tends to wear into an oval shape that opens out towards the top of the cylinder liner. Other wear patterns that may occur are possibly due to uneven cooling of the liner, simply through an inadequate coolant supply, or because of changes in section through the liner (bossing for lubricating oil quills etc) so that there is a change in the heat transfer rate through that section.

It is important to recognise that such unevenness of heat transfer can affect wear rates not only because the liner expansion differs at these points, but also because the strength of the liner material itself will change with temperature, getting weaker and less wear resistant as temperatures rise. Elevated temperatures also adversely affect the protection given by the lubricating oil.

One of the main forms of wear is the so called 'microseizure' (mz). This is described in the section *Piston Rings* (page 133).

Another form of wear is generated by acidic corrosion of the liner surface. This can usually be traced to an attack by sulphuric acid. This acid is formed from the sulphur dioxide generated during combustion. The amount of acid formed is therefore directly related to the amount of sulphur present in the fuel during combustion. In an attempt to combat this in the early days of diesel engines, the jacket temperatures were lifted, the idea being to reduce the amount of acid condensing out at the 'dew point'. Effective as this was, it did not eliminate the problem and, over the intervening years, cylinder lubricants have been developed with elevated reserves of alkalines to combat the acid attack. One of the major problems is the difficulty in matching the alkaline reserve to the sulphur content in the fuel. Sulphur content varies according to the field the oil came from, and will vary from bunker station to bunker station, and quite frequently vary at one terminal, as supplies come from different refineries. A quantifying scale has been developed to indicate the reserve of alkalinity within an oil, called the 'total base number' (TBN) or, more frequently now, the 'base number'. A high number (70) indicates a high alkaline reserve so a fuel with a sulphur content of 3% is best matched by a cylinder oil with a TBN of 70. At the other end of the scale a TBN of 10 may be considered adequate for a sulphur content of 1%. The 'matching' of TBN to sulphur content is difficult. It is not easy to determine the sulphur content of the fuel being used, as it may have been loaded on top of previous bunkers, and economics make it impossible to carry a wide selection of TBN cylinder oils. It is up to the operators of the vessel to provide an oil that has a TBN roughly compatible with the average sulphur content found in the bunkering stations that the ship visits. Of more immediate concern to the ship's engineer are the adverse effects of using an oil with a TBN too high or too low for the fuel being burned.

If the TBN is too high for the sulphur content of the fuel being burned the excess reserve will not be used and may well burn out to deposit upon the piston top as a greyish white compound. This deposit may cause problems by either absorbing the cylinder lubricating oil, thereby leading to increased mz, or, if in a harder form, actually scraping off the cylinder lubricating oil and once more increasing mz and wear.

If the TBN is too low for the sulphur content of the fuel, the acids formed by a process of condensation of the original SO_2 will attack the liner and corrosive wear will accelerate again. It is also possible that a wear known as 'cloverleafing' may occur. This generates a wear pattern that, very roughly, looks like a clover leaf. In simple terms, all that happens is that the oil leaving the injection point in the liner, and being successively spread over the liner, has its TBN reserve gradually diminished the further away it gets from the injection point. That is, the neutralising of the acid adjacent to the hole is good, but as the base reserve diminishes the acid can become more active so that outside the protected zone acid attack can ensue. This produces an irregular circumferential wear pattern in the liner so that the rings are unable to conform to it totally. Where the rings cannot seal against the liner (in the heavily corroded areas) blow past will occur, such that:

a) the rings are locally overheated and begin to lose their tension;

b) the liner surface is overheated locally and begins to lose its strength (wears more easily); and

c) cylinder lubricating oil is burned off the liner wall and wear rates go up.

Cloverleafing is a situation that should be avoided wherever possible.

Primarily, lubrication of a cylinder liner provides protection for the ring pack. The oil, as indicated above, neutralises the acids, lubricates the rings, cools the rings by heat transfer through to the wall of the liner, and helps to carry particles away from the ring's landing surfaces. The timing and location of the injection ports is discussed a little under the section on piston rings. The oil protects the liner against acid attack and wear in general, much as it does for the rings. To help distribute the oil from the injection point, sloping grooves are sometimes ground into the liner surface, the overall height of which should be deeper than a ring so that oil can still gain access to the ring pack even if injection occurs with a ring immediately over one of the injection holes. These grooves should have adequate radii to encourage oil distribution, and not to act as scrapers.

Wear rates are difficult to specify. Much depends on:

a) the quality of the materials (i.e. ring and liner) and their compatibility with one another;

b) the quality of fuel being used and, equally importantly, the quality of combustion (atomisation, penetration etc.);

c) the effective distribution of the correct quality and quantity of cylinder lubricating oil;

d) the loading of the engine running temperatures and pressures (even today, raising the jacket water temperatures 'slightly' can reduce the amount of sulphuric acid attack).

One of the more important developments in recent years, as far as large bore engines are concerned, has been 'bore cooling'. This accepted procedure has found applications in almost every cooled component within the engine: fuel injectors; cylinder covers; exhaust valve housings; and, very commonly, cylinder liners. The arrangement can be seen in Fig 8. The principle is to cool the inner surface of the liner adequately and without weakening it. Improved cooling could be achieved by reducing the wall thickness. This would then either fail under present engine loadings or require some form of strengthening sleeve to be fitted around it. The latter, made of steel, would have to be shrunk on, and is not a satisfactory long term solution. However, the material of the liner can be increased in depth so that it is strong enough to resist the firing pressure and then, providing that bore cooling is adopted, the correct inside surface temperatures can be maintained. The carefully machined passages are brought close enough to the inner surface to be able to carry the heat away, but not so close that the structure of the liner is weakened.

As the refineries extract more usable components from the crude oils, the quality of the oil left over (residual oil) becomes poorer. The difficulty in burning the residual oil cleanly compounds the wear problems discussed above. In some exceptional cases refineries have 'strained' their processes so much that some of the catalysts (alumina and silica) have carried over with the residual fuel. The extreme hardness of these elements has led to disastrous wear rates in liners and rings and fuel pump barrels. Fortunately, such events are rare and a more normal wear rate of less than 0.1 mm per thousand hours should be expected on the larger engines, with much less on medium and high speed engines (partly because they are burning cleaner fuels). Many guide lines are provided for the maximum wear acceptable (such as 0.7% of the cylinder bore), but consultation with the maker's manual should be the first priority. Generally speaking, a maximum wear value will soon reveal itself; rings begin to break more quickly; blow past occurs causing dirty scavenge spaces (and possibly fires); there is a loss of compression and reduction in power, with the likelihood of black smoke and elevated exhaust temperatures; and the rate of wear accelerates.

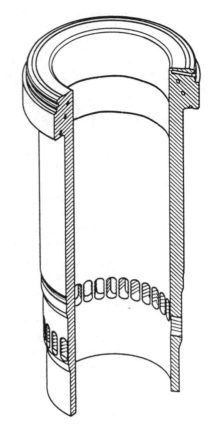

Figure 8   Bore cooled cylinder liner.

Regular measurement of liner wear is essential, so that a pattern of wear rate can be established, from which the expected useful life of a liner can be determined. The ship's engineer should be able to plan where and when he can have the worn liner drawn and replaced with a new one.

Unless some form of deformation has occurred, or the liner has become badly scaled on its outside surface and is jammed in the jacket, removing a cylinder liner should not be a difficult task. Usually the proprietary lifting gear is all that is required. In any case, the engine room crane should never be used to 'pull' a liner out. The crane is for lifting designated weights; not pulling against an unquantifiable load. In extreme cases of liners jamming, when even hydraulic jacks fail to move them, the last resort may be to collapse them by chain drilling them longitudinally (or burning them out), taking care not to damage the landing ground for seals. In some smaller liners the use of dry ice (or similar) to cool and shrink the liner slightly may help. Replacement of the liner is fairly straight forward once the correct alignment for lubricating oil quills etc. has been achieved. However, the rubber sealing rings should be treated with caution. Rubber, synthetic or otherwise, is virtually incompressible, so rings of too large a cross sectional area may prevent a liner from seating smoothly. Forcing such a liner down into position will only create stressing at the ring groove area. This may not reveal itself as a problem immediately, but the stresses, subjected to running loads of temperature and pressure, may, in time, cause cracking. It is reasonable practice to drop the 'bare' liner into the jacket to check its size, and then, all being well, the rubber rings can be fitted. Any resistance to entry is then related to the rings and corrective action can be taken. (Some engines with exhaust ports as well as scavenge ports carry copper based rings immediately above and below the exhaust ports to protect the rubber rings from attack by the exhaust gases. These soft metal rings bed into the jacket as the liner is fitted. The above procedure should therefore not be adopted. When fitting them it is important to ensure that correctly sized rubber rings are fitted every time.)

CYLINDER COVERS

The design of a cylinder cover is very complex, particularly where a large valve operates through its centre. In some of the earlier loop scavenged engines, cylinder covers were simpler components, with a central fuel injector and then pockets for starting air, indicator cocks etc. In those cases the head was often cast iron with some form of steel backing ring to absorb the bending forces created as the head was tightened down. In later designs the head was a solid steel forging of immense strength, the cooling passages of which were formed by the bore cooling process described above.

In 'uniflow' type engines, the central exhaust valve may cause problems of stress distribution, and in particular the effective cooling required of the valve seat. Because the centre of the head is taken up by the exhaust valve, it becomes necessary to fit two or more fuel injectors around the cover. These pockets also present problems in terms of strength and cooling. In simplistic terms, the head can be considered to be a top plate supported by a cylindrical wall that is in turn sealed by a lower plate forming the top of the combustion chamber. As the head is tightened, the top plate is put into a load that attempts to bend it across the supporting walls. Cast iron, not being good at resisting bending stresses, is therefore not particularly suitable for this plate (hence the use of steel rings in earlier models). The pulling down of the top plate puts the side walls into compression. The closing plate may be domed, for strength and to help form a better shaped combustion chamber. As the

engine fires, the lower plate tends to lift the head, causing further compression of the side walls and increased bending of the top plate. The insertion of valve pockets into such a structure aggravates the situation further, particularly when the massive exhaust valve of present engines is used. A typical modern head is shown in Fig 9.

The complex passage ways used to achieve adequate cooling of the valve seat can be seen in Fig 9. The valve stem is fitted with vanes, which cause the valve to rotate as the exhaust gas, released at high velocity, passes over them. Because of the use of the 'air spring' there is very little resistance to rotation. The valve, still spinning as it closes, tends to knock any deposits from the products of combustion off the valve seat and face, so that the seat life and effective seal are extended. Were such products not cleared from the seat they may become hammered into and across the face, providing a leakage pathway for the high pressure gases. This would be enlarged by the so called 'wire drawing' process so that the valve seal would be lost and cylinder pressures would not be maintained. Such a process is progressive, and further deterioration of the valve seat would take place until the reduced quality of combustion, with reduction in power and increased liner wear and so on, would reach an unacceptable level.

The ship's engineer, for his own benefit, should always ensure that the head is tightened down evenly. This not only prolongs the life of head bolts and improves the life of the head seal but may prevent distortion of the cylinder liner. A head tightened in an imbalanced way may force the liner into an incorrect attitude as a result of the unequal forces on its top lip. (Were this to occur there could be a change in the wear pattern and rate.)

The heads of medium speed engines are very much more complicated, with multi valve heads being common. One problem common to all heads is that of obtaining adequate and effective cooling. It is not correct to think that large cooling passages solve the heat transfer problem. It is the area exposed, the thickness of the material through which the heat is passing and, not least, the speed of coolant over the area that is important. Nor is the formation of steam in these areas unacceptable, assuming that steam is formed as a design feature and not simply because there is an inadequate flow of water. From a 'ph' (pressure–enthalpy) diagram it is clear that when water is raised to its boiling point (relevant to the system pressure), it is able to absorb a great deal of heat (latent) at the same temperature before being superheated. However, a problem with steam formation is the possible deposition of any anti-corrosion

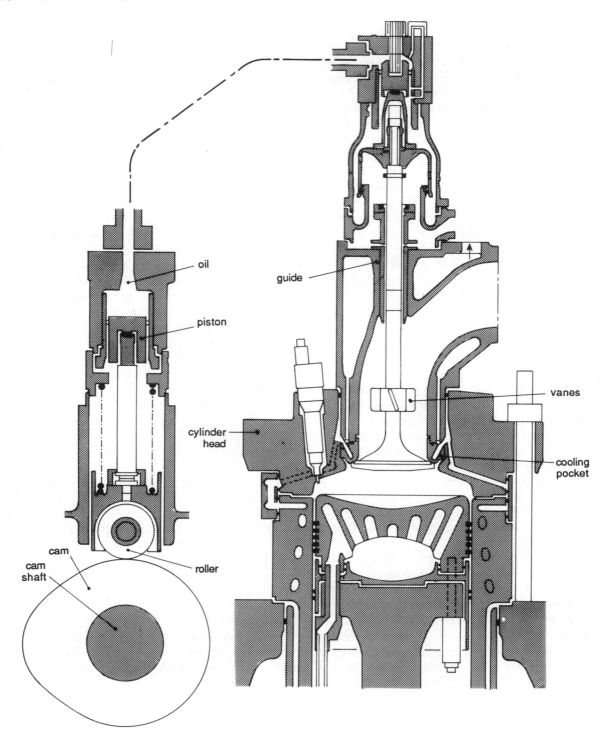

Figure 9   Typical modern head, showing bore cooled cylinder liner and cylinder cover with valve seat cooling included.

additives used in the circulating water. These may impair heat transfer with consequent localised over-heating. The system should therefore be kept clean and the coolant maintained at the correct level of corrosion inhibitor. If this practice is followed the head should give long service without any problems developing.

FUEL

The quality of fuels provided for ships today has deteriorated, so combustion processes have to be regulated and monitored with ever increasing attention. As fuel qualities have deteriorated it is to be expected that they will include more and more elements that are either non-combustible or so difficult to ignite and burn that they form no useful part of the combustion process. In fact, they frequently deposit out as harmful substances where fuel pump and cylinder liner wear is concerned. The more aggressive of these are the compounds of vanadium, sulphur, and other chemicals natural to the oil. There are other contaminants that may be picked up by the oil from the refinery storage tanks or indeed the ship's tanks. These include water (salt or fresh), and other products, such as scale, from tank and pipe walls. In some cases the contaminants can be removed during purification of the oil on the vessel; water, solids and even a proportion of sodium can be removed. Unfortunately, the more oil-soluble ones, like vanadium and sulphur, are not removed through purification even if some degree of water washing is applied. It is worth noting that the aggressive nature of the vanadium products of combustion are further magnified when burned in the presence of sodium, particularly when the ratio of vanadium to sodium is greater than 3:1. The removal of sodium at the purification stage can thus be seen as a great benefit. Even though sodium may not be an original contaminant of the oil, it may be picked up by the oil from sea water or in lesser amounts from the salt laden atmosphere (possibly via the turbocharger). See *Chapter 4*.

The most important stage of combustion is the original ignition. Any fuel starts to burn (in the absence of some spark or flame) only when it is raised to a temperature greater than its self-ignition temperature (SIT), and, once ignited, the volatility of the fuel will then dictate the speed of combustion throughout the fuel. Temperature, in a compression ignition engine like the diesel, is transmitted to the fuel from the air in the combustion chamber, the air itself having being raised in temperature during the compression stroke. It is worth noting that the large bore engines have relatively low compression ratios, probably in the region of 11:1, when compared to medium speed engines where compression ratios of 16:1 or higher are not unusual. Higher compression ratios still are designed into high speed engines. The reason for such a low compression ratio in the bigger engines is the limit to which the piston crown and other components forming the combustion chamber can be loaded. That is, cyclic high loadings on such large

areas as the piston crowns will cause them to fail through fatigue, so the peak pressures have to be limited to more acceptable levels. This is achieved, whilst still developing a reasonable mean effective pressure, by limiting the compression pressure to as low a value as practicable. Any further reduction in compression ratio, and hence compression pressure, would not raise the temperature of the air sufficiently by the end of compression. The temperature of the air at the end of compression must be high enough to ensure certain and rapid heat transfer to the injected fuel.

To this end large engines should be circulated with heated jacket water prior to their being started, to ensure that during the first part of compression the air in the cylinder will absorb heat from the warmed cylinder liner, piston crown and cylinder cover. As compression continues there will be a natural increase in temperature due to the compression itself, and the terminal temperature of the compression will be much higher than that which could be achieved by simply compressing the air from scavenge temperature. Thus the 'warming' through of an engine is not purely to reduce the effects of thermal shocking which occur once the engine has started, but also, and probably more importantly, to ensure crisp ignition of the injected fuel. Once the engine is running the problem of ignition will be reduced, because the running temperatures of all the components will rise.

When the fuel is injected into the combustion chamber and travels through the hot, compressed air it absorbs heat. The friction that occurs between the injected fuel and the dense (compacted) air also helps to raise the temperature of the fuel to its SIT. The density of the air is important for another reason, allied in some ways to the first. By causing resistance to travel, it prevents over-penetration of the combustion chamber by the fuel droplets. Were the droplets to travel too far before being burned away they would impinge upon the cylinder walls, or perhaps the piston crown. The effect of the still burning fuel on the cylinder wall would be to burn off any lubricating oil film still adhering. The metal of the piston crown or cylinder wall does not burn, but gets so hot that the bonds in its structure are broken and it is gradually destroyed, creating a roughened surface. Reduced turbocharger performance can adversely affect the air density, as can slow steaming. In slow steaming, the speed of compression is, relatively, so slow that leakage of air from the combustion chamber via the ring pack is increased, the end result being that the temperature of the air at the end of compression will be lower than normal, and that the air density will be reduced. This explains why there were some severe cases of piston crown burning and liner wear in the early days of slow steaming. The adoption of slow steaming nozzles overcomes this problem to a large extent. These nozzles have smaller diameter holes in the injector tip than the standard nozzle, so smaller droplets are formed, which in turn cannot penetrate too far before being entirely consumed. The droplet size is governed by the pressure of the oil in the fuel injector and the diameter of the holes.

Usually referred to as 'atomisation', this process of droplet formation is crucial to the optimum combustion conditions. Droplets that are too large will take longer to burn completely so they will over penetrate the combustion chamber. Being large they may also take longer to absorb sufficient heat to reach their SIT. Alternatively, droplets that are too small will ignite readily, probably immediately on release from the injector. The fuel burning in the vicinity consumes the air in that region to form an inert cloud into which the remainder of the charge is injected. This results in poor combustion, which leads to the formation of carbon deposits around the fuel injector, the more volatile elements vaporising to leave a carbon deposit, as described earlier.

If combustion is to be clean, crisp and complete, a balance of the following factors must be achieved: adequate air at temperatures well above the SIT of the fuel; air at the correct density to aid ignition and control penetration; and the correct injector tip with orifices matched to the above conditions, so providing correctly atomised fuel.

One feature above all which should be considered by the ship's engineers is ignition delay (ID). The ID is the time period between injection into the combustion chamber and ignition of the fuel. As fuel quality has deteriorated over the years the ID has become longer, so that if no allowance were made for it, combustion of the fuel would be taking place far too late in the cycle.

Speed of compression is one of the features governing air temperature at the end of compression, but as the piston approaches tdc, it slows down. Also, the area of metal surrounding the combustion chamber will be large compared to the enclosed volume. The air temperature will be higher than that of the combustion chamber walls, so, because of the slower compression and low surface temperatures, the air temperature starts to 'reduce' as the crank covers those last few degrees to tdc. Thus, to maximise heat transfer from air to fuel, the fuel should be injected into the air when the air is at its highest temperature (heat flows from the hotter to the cooler body). Since this is just prior to tdc it becomes essential to always

inject fuel before tdc; allowing for the ID it should be injected even earlier.

Now consider the following. As the engine slows down, the air cools still further, so some form of compensation should be made to ensure that the fuel is injected as far as is possible into the air when the air is at its highest temperature. Engine builders and designers have developed the fuel injection technique commonly known as variable injection timing (VIT). This equipment, built into the timing mechanism of the fuel pumps, allows adjustment to be made to the fuel timing whilst the engine is running. The start of injection may be advanced or retarded as the case may require. Lengthening IDs require advancement of the point of injection.

Shorter IDs require the injection to be retarded. The VIT system often includes a mechanism that automatically advances the fuel setting as the engine is slowed down. This improves ignition qualities, as explained above, and in so doing improves fuel economy. This automatic advancement is usually available down to around 85% of service speed. To attempt it below that level could generate unaccep-

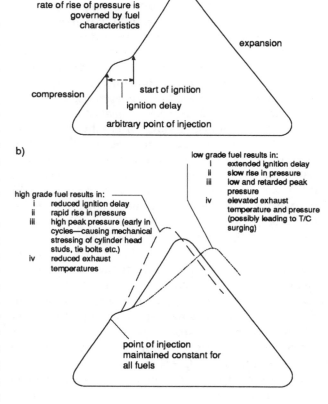

Figure 10 a) Normal draw card; b) normal card with effects of both good and poor quality fuel superimposed.

table bearing loads at the lower speed where, in any case, effective lubrication is beginning to fall off.

The point of maximum pressure in the cycle gives a good indication of the quality of fuel being burned. The maximum pressure will occur, or should occur, when the engine is correctly set up and burning an acceptable grade of fuel, at a designated number of degrees after tdc. With modern electronic monitoring of cylinder events this point can be determined quite accurately. If it is measured and found to be late, then it can be assumed that a poorer quality of fuel is being burned, and through the VIT linkage, the point of injection should be advanced. The converse also applies. Retarded ignition invariably results in lower firing pressures than normal.

High quality fuels with their earlier ignition cause high peak pressures. The use of a peak pressure can therefore be used to monitor the quality of a fuel, assuming that the original timing of the fuel pumps was correct (Fig 10).

FUEL PUMPS AND INJECTORS

Over the years there have been many forms of fuel pump and fuel injection systems. Present trends have settled, almost without exception, on the 'jerk pump' method, and by far the greatest proportion use pumps with the well known helix form of fuel regulation.

The previous section described why the fuel must be raised to the correct pressure and then accurately injected into the cylinder at a precise point. To achieve this, the oil could be pressurised into an accumulator and then released by controlling the opening of the injector (perhaps electronically, or through the timing valves of the common rail method). Alternatively, the oil can be rapidly raised in pressure over a very few degrees of crank angle, and the pressure thus developed can be used to operate the fuel injector. This, in essence, is the jerk system. Such a method creates enormous, and almost instantaneous, forces throughout the system. Consider the cam that generates the pumping effect. For such pressures to be developed quickly, the pumping face of the cam must rise rapidly from the base dwell surface. Then, as the pressure builds up, there will be a substantial back pressure onto this cam face. To carry these high loads without damage to either roller or cam, the cam face must be of adequate area and well lubricated.

The pump itself, in simplistic terms, consists of a ram carried in a matched barrel. There are return springs and racks etc. but the principle of the pump can be understood from these two components. The ram carries an accurately machined helical groove

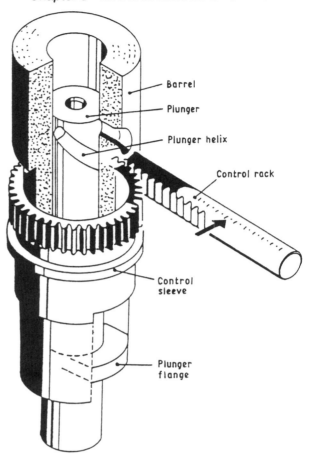

Figure 11 Fuel injection regulating mechanism.

cut into its flank (Fig 11). The top of the ram is flat (except in some of the more refined units), and as the ram rises up inside the barrel this top face will shut off the oil inlet ports that are machined through the barrel. Any fuel above the ram at this point will be subjected to rapid compression as the roller driving the ram is forced rapidly upwards by the cam. The oil is directed by high pressure piping to the fuel injector. The latter, set to some pre-determined lift value, will open and oil will flow into the combustion space. The end of injection is controlled by the helical groove. As the ram continues to rise, the helix will uncover the 'spill' port in the barrel and the pressure will rapidly drop, with the injector automatically closing as the pressure falls off. The quantity of oil delivered will depend upon the rotational position of the helix with respect to the spill port. If the top of the helix is in line with the port, no delivery will take place. Then, as the ram is rotated, the depth to the edge of the helix increases, as does the duration of injection. The start of injection, controlled by the top face of the ram, is therefore always at the same point, unless some form of VIT is fitted to the unit which allows vertical

Labels on figure: Barrel, Plunger, Plunger helix, Control rack, Control sleeve, Plunger flange displacement of the barrel. Raising the barrel delays the start of injection; lowering the barrel advances the start of injection. Such fine tuning can be adopted to deal with, and compensate for, changes in the quality of the fuel, and, in particular, variances in the ID characteristics of the fuel.

When the helix uncovers the spill port, pressure release occurs and there is a rapid back flow of fuel. To prevent this flow from evacuating, even partially, the fuel injector and its supply pipe, a non-return valve is fitted at the discharge of the fuel pump. This valve also serves to prevent oil from being drawn back into the pump as the ram returns, under spring pressure, for there will be a period during the return stroke, from the point where the helix closes off the spill port to the time when the upper face of the ram uncovers it again, when a suction will be developed above the ram (i.e. the reverse of the delivery period). This reduced pressure in the pump body could cause problems, were it not for the non-return valve, for any evacuation of the delivery pipe would mean that it would have to be 'refilled' on the next pumping stroke before delivery pressures could be realised again. This would interrupt the timing of fuel injection and is wholly undesirable. However, the closing of the non-return valve, although protecting the pipeline from partial evacuation, could in itself generate another problem. The valve, closing smartly, will halt the back flow of oil so suddenly that a reverse wave of oil may develop and, reflecting off the valve, travel back down the pipe to reopen the fuel injector. These shock waves are capable of reopening the injectors, not just once but several times. To prevent this and the problems that would ensue in the power stroke, and combustion in general, the non-return valve is fitted with a small collar just below the mitre seat. This collar, acting like a piston as the valve closes, draws a small volume of oil from the pipe line, which is sufficient to reduce the pressure therein so that any reverberating shock waves are of such a low magnitude as to be harmless.

There are many ways of setting the timing of these jerk pumps, with some manufacturers providing special measuring equipment to enable more accurate settings to be achieved. Without these, or any other knowledge of the pump, timing can be monitored by using the 'spill' timing procedure. This is achieved by turning the cam shaft until the roller of the pump in question is on the lower dwell of the cam circumference. The HP discharge pipe should then be disconnected (providing the oil supply has been shut off), and the discharge, non-return valve and its spring should be removed, cleaned and stored away carefully. Then a 'goose' necked pipe should be fitted

to the discharge of the pump. Fuel carefully released to the pump will run through the pump body and out through this goose neck into some receptacle. If the cam is now turned, slowly and carefully, the roller rising up the pumping flank of the cam will gradually lift the ram inside the barrel until it shuts off the ports and the oil flow will stop. Turning the shaft too quickly would cause the ram to rise and discharge the oil so that it may not be easy to distinguish the point at which the ports are covered. If the procedure is followed carefully, the cessation of oil flow from the goose neck, accompanied by a bubble forming at the pipe end, is clearly discernible. This represents what would be the start of injection under normal running. The angle at which this occurs can be read from the fly wheel or perhaps from the cam shaft protractor. Any adjustments to the timing of the individual pump can be made by raising or lowering the body (respectively retarding or advancing its timing). Simply advancing or retarding the cam shaft will simultaneously adjust all the pumps.

Jerk pumps do not necessarily have to be regulated by helical grooves. Some manufacturers use a plain ram, still operating in the jerk fashion (that is, pumping over a very short period of time), but regulate the start and end of injection by valves built into the suction and delivery sides of the pump. The opening period of these valves is regulated from the engine controls in a similar way to the rotation of the ram (by rack and pinion) in the helix type of pump. As with the helix type of pump the start of injection is always constant with the end of injection controlled by the spill valve, being variable according the load on engine and speed required. As before, differing fuel qualities may require earlier or later injection according to the relevant ID. This can be achieved by the use of an external linkage to the suction valve, the seating of which initiates the start of fuel compression and injection. Thus, VIT is easily achieved by causing this suction valve to seat earlier (for long IDs) or later (for short IDs).

Most of the problems associated with either kind of injection pump are generated by the use of low quality fuels which are both abrasive and corrosive. (See *Chapter 4* for information on fuel treatment.) Wear and tear on the finely machined rams and barrels is the most common area of failure, through scoring and/or seizure, although some valves on the suction sides of pumps have been known to suffer from cavitation damage.

The viscous fuels are usually heated to enable them to be pumped around the system more easily. This hot fuel causes the components of the fuel pump to expand so that they would seize if allowances were not made. When the pumps are cold, therefore, their working clearances are quite large, so the relatively cool diesel oil which may be used for manoeuvring will leak past the rams. Relevant protection should be taken to ensure that this leakage does not contaminate the lubricating oil serving the cam shaft. As the pump is changed over to heavy fuel the temperature should be increased slowly so that the correct working clearance is achieved when the oil is at the desired temperature.

SCAVENGING

Scavenging is only applicable to 2-stroke engines, and is the process of clearing from the cylinder any remaining products of combustion from the previous cycle. Air, at a low pressure, is introduced into the cylinder through scavenge ports which are opened shortly after the opening of the exhaust valve. The prior opening of the exhaust valve allows the exhaust gases to expand out of the cylinder, reducing the pressure in the cylinder to well below that of the scavenge air. Were that not the case, the air would not be able to 'clean out' the cylinder and recharge it with fresh air for the next cycle. The effectiveness with which the air clears the cylinder is called its 'scavenge efficiency' and is a comparison between the fresh air and the total of fresh air and any gases still remaining in the cylinder. Thus, in the case of 100% scavenge efficiency, all the gases have been cleared out and a completely new charge of fresh air is in the cylinder. (The comparable efficiency for a 4-stroke is the 'volumetric efficiency'; a comparison between the mass actually in the cylinder and the mass that the cylinder could contain at normal temperatures and pressures. In fact the 'volumetric efficiency' can be greater than 100% because of the effects of supercharging.)

All major engine builders now adopt a process of scavenging known as 'uniflow' which, as the name implies, operates by directing the air through the cylinder in one direction only. Such a system is easily capable of achieving 100% scavenge efficiency and is absolutely essential in modern long stroke engines. The main alternative to this system is 'loop' scavenge where the air/exhaust flow through the cylinder takes the form of a loop. This process, though it simplifies the design of the cylinder head etc., cannot get much above 95% efficient, and is even less efficient on long stroke engines. Loop scavenge, achieved by having both exhaust and scavenge ports in the liner, the opening and closing of which regulated by the piston, has been superseded by the uniflow process where only scavenge ports are used in the liner. In uniflow the ports are located at the lower end of the liner, uniformly around the circumference. It is quite common to have these ports 'angled' tangentially to the liner in such a way that the air passing through them develops a swirling characteristic that not only helps to clean out the liner, but also aids combustion. This is because the slow moving air coming from 'behind' the injector, carries the products of combustion away from the tip and simultaneously provides it with fresh air throughout the injection period. (This is known as downstream injection and is preferred when the air velocity is low. Upstream injection is used to advantage with high velocity air flows.)

Scavenging can be achieved providing there is an adequate flow of air into the cylinders from the 'scavenge spaces'. Increasing the pressure of this air flow not only helps with scavenging but, more importantly, increases the density of the charge air remaining in the cylinder. This process of increasing the air pressure and thereby the air density is called 'supercharging', and can be achieved by increasing the speed of the pumps/pistons etc. which are supplying the scavenge air.

Any mechanical drive taken from the engine to drive these pumps/pistons absorbs energy (power) from the engine. The main problem with such a process is the lack of response of such pumps to changes in load. When an engine is exposed to an increase in load, head wind or current for example, the engine will tend to slow down, causing a reduction in speed of the pumps supplying the air. Thus, just when the engine needs more air to burn the extra fuel injected to match the increase in load, the supply could decrease. The result is incomplete combustion, black smoke and all the other undesirable side effects of reduced combustion efficiency.

Turbochargers on the other hand, driven by the exhaust gases from the cylinder, respond directly to changes in load. As the fuel injection rate is altered to suit the load, so the mass (and therefore the energy within it) of the exhaust gas generated changes proportionately. This self-regulating ability of the turbocharger has improved the power outputs and versatility of the diesel engine.

Turbochargers are really superchargers driven by heat from the exhaust gas that may otherwise be wasted or lost. Thus not only is it possible to increase the charge air pressure, and through that combustion efficiency, but, by recovering heat from the exhaust gas, the overall thermal efficiency of the plant is also improved.

The effect of supercharging is 'to increase the air density in the cylinder, allowing a proportionate increase in the fuel injected and thereby give a corresponding increase in power output'.

To accept these increases in power, and the corresponding increase in mep and peak pressures, (though the increase in peak pressures is modified as far as possible by reducing the compression ratio as explained earlier) certain modifications need to be made to the engine.

To absorb the increased firing pressures and mep, the strength of the combustion chamber has to be improved, not simply by increased wall thicknesses as that would only reduce heat transfer, but by improved design. Piston crown design has advanced over recent years, one of the latest being the honeycomb design that combines effective cooling with great strength. Similarly, bore cooling has come into its own to allow the wall thickness to be maintained whilst still providing adequate and effective cooling.

The firing forces are carried through the piston down to the crosshead bearing and ultimately to the main bearings and transverse girders. It has become necessary therefore to improve the load carrying ability of these components, a process that is repeated each time a new model or modified engine comes on to the market. The crossheads in particular have undergone many refinements over the years, as have the transverse girders that are at present solid forged to provide adequate support and strength.

TURBOCHARGERS

Structure

In general, the modern turbocharger serves a system known as 'constant pressure charging', and one, or at most two, turbochargers per engine are all that is required. The more complicated 'pulse charging' system used on earlier engines and on some lower powered medium speed engines often needed three or more turbochargers. In the constant pressure system the pressure in the exhaust manifold leading to the turbocharger is virtually steady. That is, the pulses of energy that occur as the exhaust is released from the cylinder are absorbed in the large volume exhaust manifold so that, at the turbocharger, almost steady flow conditions exist. The pulse system used these pulses to improve the output of the turbocharger, but the system was extremely complicated and best suited to an engine with cylinder numbers that were multiples of three. The turbochargers of the constant pressure system operate under more steady flow conditions so the energy conversion of the turbine element is improved over the pulse system. There are many advantages of constant pressure over pulse. Constant pressure systems are now almost universally applied and this section will relate to such a system. Because

all units evacuate into a common exhaust manifold the turbocharger itself can be situated anywhere along the manifold to facilitate accessibility and provide easy egress to the engine room uptakes. Because of the enormous strides taken in the development of the turbocharger, facilitated by computer aided design and machining, the modern unit is able to put out adequate air quantities and pressures for a single unit to serve even the larger engines. However, makers or owners sometimes prefer to have two units as a safeguard, so that the engine can still steam on one unit should the other fail and require recovery.

Although turbochargers have improved in performance over the years, their basic construction has remained, until very recent times, when non-water cooled units have appeared.

Figure 12 shows the traditional structure of the turbocharger.

The bearings may take one of two forms; ball/roller or sleeve type.

Ball or roller

Ball races will be fitted at the compressor end to locate the shaft, and thereby fix the clearance between the casing and the blades of the compressor impeller (the most critical of clearances where performance is concerned, as any increase in clearance there would result in a rapid fall off in compressor performance, and too small a clearance would result in rotor to casing contact). The shaft is able to slide through the bearing at the turbine end of the unit where the relative expansion is accommodated in a roller bearing. Expansion between the casing and rotor occurs because of the elevated temperatures, and difference in materials of casing and shaft. The bearings are enclosed in resilient mountings to protect them from damage by vibration. The mounting is a housing fitted with small plate type springs that dampen vibration transmission, so that the the races receive some protection from impact damage by the balls or rollers (sometimes referred to as brinelling or false brinelling).

Sleeve type, white metal lined

These bearings provide, through their greater length, a stabilising influence on shaft alignment and longitudinal vibration. They tend to be adopted in the larger turbocharger, the thrust being taken by a face machined to provide the requisite oil wedges, similar to those formed in the classic tilting pad thrust block. In fact some models do adopt tilting pad thrust blocks. The clearance in these must be set so as not to interfere with the rotor to casing clearance mentioned above. Sleeve type bearings are usually sup-

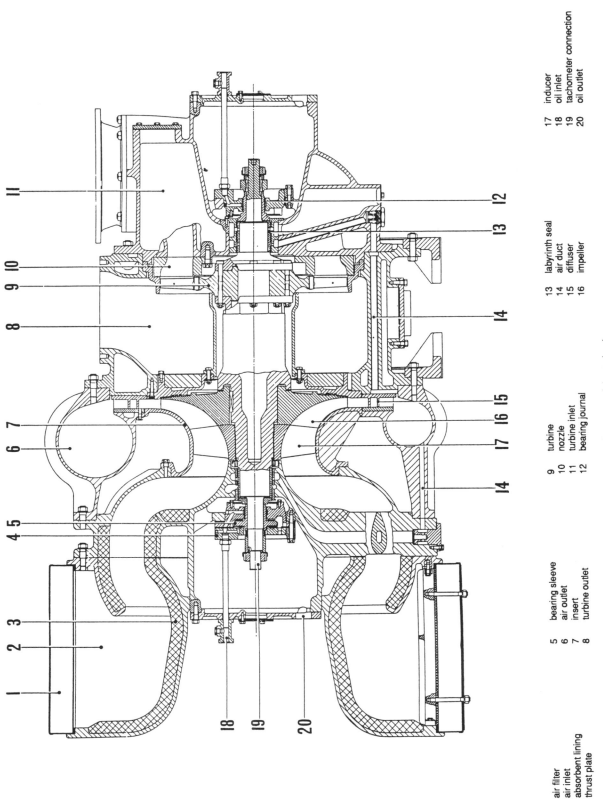

1 air filter
2 air inlet
3 absorbent lining
4 thrust plate

5 bearing sleeve
6 air outlet
7 insert
8 turbine outlet

9   turbine
10 nozzle
11 turbine inlet
12 bearing journal

13 labyrinth seal
14 air duct
15 diffuser
16 impeller

17 inducer
18 oil inlet
19 tachometer connection
20 oil outlet

Figure 12 Structure of the turbocharger.

plied with oil from an external feed. This supply, externally cooled, has a reserve supply (usually from some form of header tank) that protects the bearings during the run down period. That is, the engine may be stopped, perhaps because of failure of the main lubricating oil supply, but the turbocharger would run on for some time, and the bearings would still need lubricating during that time. Ball/roller races, because of their negligible clearance, require a cleaner oil and so are usually supplied from a supply integral to the turbocharger casing. In this respect they are self-sufficient, and will self-lubricate under the run-down conditions mentioned above (shaft driven gear type pumps or discs and scrapers).

Labyrinth seals are fitted just inboard of the bearings to seal the shaft against air leakage. To assist this seal and to help cool the shaft, particularly at the turbine end, the labyrinth is supplied with pressure air bled from the compressor discharge volute.

The compressor impeller has its leading edges machined into blades which induce a flow onto the main compressor radial vanes. The steepness and overall width of these vanes dictates the compression ratio and capacity respectively. Modern, superbly machined rotors are capable of providing compression ratios (delivery pressure/inlet pressure) of 4:1 or more. Such a value is adequate for the foreseeable future so 'two stage' turbocharging, with all its associated complexities, is not essential.

The impeller discharges high velocity air into the 'diffuser' ring, where the kinetic energy is converted into pressure energy. Diffuser rings are important components within the pressure development section of the turbocharger. Simply by changing one diffuser ring for another with different characteristics, the output pressure from a turbocharger can be altered to suit a particular engine so the diffuser is one of the simplest ways of matching the output pressure from a turbocharger to that required by a particular engine. Such matching can therefore be achieved without recourse to changing the shape or size of impeller or indeed the frame size of a given turbocharger. There are limits as to how much the diffuser ring can vary the turbocharger performance, but its capabilities should be borne in mind should any trouble be experienced with continuous surging or lack of scavenge efficiency.

The annular space between the impeller tips and the diffuser ring will be pressurised from the impeller discharge itself, so the air will attempt to 'leak' down the back plate of the impeller to gain access to the exhaust gas passages. To limit this, rather than stop it, a series of concentric grooves are machined into the back of the impeller forming a labyrinth type seal which regulates the leakage to an acceptable level.

The air passing down the back of the impeller is usually guided by a sleeve through which the shaft runs to the turbine disc. Thus, not only does the air seal the passage of exhaust gas, but the leakage also cools the disc. The disc forged into, or bolted onto, the shaft carries the turbine blading, which is usually fitted into the disc using the inverted 'fir tree' root method. This method of fitting allows the roots of the blades to expand into the disc (small clearances below the fir tree 'branches'), whilst still resisting the enormous centrifugal forces to which the blades are subjected.

The blades should be very slightly loose in their housing so that there are no residual stresses imposed on the root by fitting. Any such stress could cause early failure of the blade since the stresses created whilst running, including the thermal stress, are very substantial. Thermal stress develops as a result of the alternate flow over the blades of hot exhaust gas and then cool scavenge air. The same gases could contain corrosive elements as well as abrasive or scale forming substances. To reduce as far as possible the development of scale or deposits of any type, 'water washing' of the blades is frequently adopted. This process, injecting water into the gas flow just prior to the nozzle ring, is an attempt to dissolve the scale and at the same time clean the nozzles and blades by the impact effect of the water droplets. Such a procedure should be carried out to the guidelines set down by the manufacturer, the frequency of washing being dictated by the quality of the fuel and the effectiveness of combustion. Above all it should be appreciated that water washing should not be applied to a turbocharger whose previous history is unknown. It is possible, in such a case, that the removal of the soluble deposits could lead to the rotor being thrown out of balance. Thus water washing should be established from the outset, from new or after each overhaul, and the frequency between washings maintained, so that the chances of an unbalanced situation developing are diminished. Water washing is not an alternative to stripping the unit down for manual cleaning; it simply means that the operating efficiency of the unit can be maintained at a higher level between scheduled overhauls. It is interesting to note that some units use nut shells (graded, and toasted) for this purpose, their impingement effect taking off more than just the water soluble compounds.

The effectiveness of the above can be monitored from readings of pressures and temperatures taken throughout the system, both before and after cleaning. With clean fuels and good combustion the cleaning process is not as important, as the blades and nozzles will not foul up so quickly. The blades, made from highly corrosion resistant materials, are usually of the 'taper twisted' type. The taper reduces the mass of material towards the tips and in so doing reduces the stress on the blade root. This is subjected to high centrifugal forces as well as bending, the bending being occasioned by the variations in gas pressures flowing over the blades. To withstand these, the bottom of the blade is substantially radiussed into the root. To further support the blades, against both bending and vibration, they may be held together by a lacing wire or wires. This wire is not secured to each blade, but is threaded through neat fitting holes so that as the blade warms up into its 'desired' operating position, the wire, through expansion and centrifugal force, locks onto the blade.

The blades give each other mutual support and in so doing dampen down the vibrational tendencies. The 'twist' of the blade is intended to give it a better chance of matching to the gas inlet velocity and direction. The velocity from the nozzles will be fairly uniform across the radial depth of the nozzle, but the linear speed of the blade increases with radius so that the tips are travelling at a greater speed than the roots. The twist therefore helps to match the blade inlet angle to the relative velocity between gas and blade. This aids smooth gas entry to the blades, with consequent improvement in their operating efficiency.

The casings of turbochargers are made to match their service demands. They are of aluminium alloy, lightweight and corrosion resistant at air side, with cast iron at the higher temperature and water cooled turbine end.

Non-water cooled units have recently appeared. Higher thermal efficiencies of constant pressure charged engines have resulted in less heat being released from the engines to the turbochargers. In addition, the removal of heat from the turbocharger reduces its thermal efficiency and thus the heat available to the 'waste heat' boilers. The non-water cooled unit counteracts these and eliminates the corrosion problems of the inside surfaces of some of the water cooled units. Corrosion occurred where the circulating water cooled the plating down to such an extent that the internal surfaces were being cooled to below their dew point, with the resultant acidic attack.

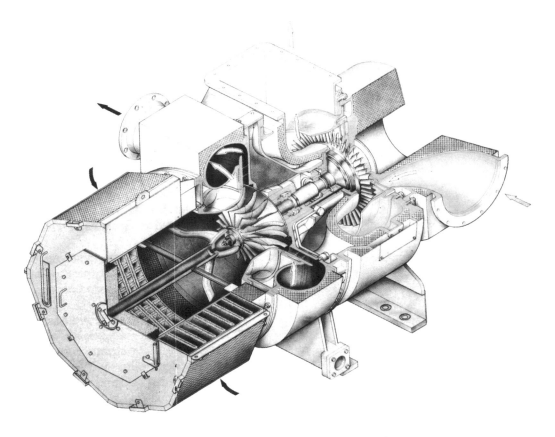

Figure 13   Napier-MET non water cooled turbocharger.

Another development, concurrent with the new wave of non-water cooled units, is the location of the support bearing between the compressor and turbine wheels. This is a better position for taking the rotor weight than the extremities of the shaft, where there is the potential for shaft whirl. The original reason for locating the bearings at the ends of the shaft was accessibility; much reduced in the new location. However improvements in design have improved accessibility again and, at the same time, extended the time periods required for the overhaul of such bearings. A typical non-cooled turbocharger is shown in Fig 13.

Surging

Surging (variously known as coughing, barking etc.) is a vibration of audible level emanating from the compressor end of the rotating element. The compressor, depending upon its speed at any particular time, can only discharge up to a given pressure. If for any reason the pressure in the scavenge space is equal to or higher than this discharge pressure, air will attempt to flow back through the rotating impeller. In essence this is like a centrifugal pump attempting to pump against a closed valve, but with the air compressors the back flow of air throws the rotating element into a vibration which produces the so called barking noise.

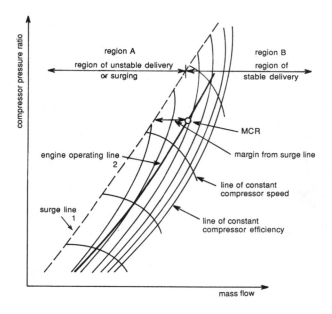

Line 1 is the pressure limit of the compressor. Above that pressure, at a given mass flow, air will attempt to flow back through the rotating impeller causing the heavy vibration and consequent noise called barking (surging).
Line 2 is the demand line of the engine, i.e. the pressure mass flow relationship at different rpm.

Figure 14 Compressor characteristic.

There are many causes of surging. It is usually engine initiated. The turbocharger should be matched to the engine's air consumption rate and pressure across the whole operating range; this being calculated before the engine is built and tested during the shop trials. 'Matching' can be understood from Fig 14.

Area 'A' shows that the engine is receiving air at a higher pressure than it needs for a given speed, and as a consequence surging will occur. Area 'B' is a stable zone where the engine and the turbocharger will operate in harmony. There should be a reasonable safety margin between the two lines (1 and 2) to allow for turbocharger fouling and general depreciation in engine performance before it enters the surge zone.

An engine travelling from one climate to another will be subjected to great variations in both air density and air temperature. In high temperature, low density climes, usually associated with the tropics, the engine will still have to achieve its rated performance. The turbocharger will be putting out the same volume of air as always but, because the air is less dense, the mass throughput will be reduced. For the turbocharger and engine to be able to provide adequate outputs under these conditions, it is necessary that they are initially provided with a slightly higher rating than is required in more temperate climes. This is referred to as 'de-rating'. Similar concepts are applied to engines that have to work at very high altitudes where once again the air density is reduced.

LOAD DIAGRAM

All engine builders provide diagrams for their particular models, from which various running conditions can be determined. The diagrams are assembled from information from engine tests taken under controlled conditions. The diagram for one engine of a range is then used as a standard for all other engines in that range.

Unfortunately there is no standardised format for these diagrams and the engineer must familiarise himself with the chart prepared for the engine with which he is working.

Figure 15 is a graphical representation of various brake powers against revs per min and mean effective pressure. Such a diagram may be used by the ship's staff to determine load/speed areas within which the engine can be operated safely. It should be appreciated that this diagram is not applicable to any particular make or range of engines but simply represents the way that some engine builders display these parameters.

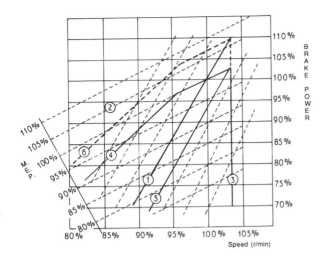

1 The propeller line through the maximum continuous rating point. Corresponding to 100% power and 100% revs, it in fact represents the engine loading as used on the test bed.
2. Lines of constant mean effective pressure.
3. Line represents the maximum permissible speed, only to be exceeded in an emergency.
4. Line provides a relationship between bmep and maximum continuous power against rev/min. Following this line normally ensures an ample excess of air for combustion.
5. Line represents the propeller line for a fully laden ship. Fouling of the hull will increase ship resistance such that this line will progressively move to the left of the diagram. Thus the area between lines 4 and 5 provides the limits for a normally loaded vessel. Above line 4 the engine is overloaded and it should only be run in this area for limited periods. It should not rise above line 6.
6. Line represents the maximum overload condition. Steaming in ballast would normally fall below line 5.

Figure 15 Load diagram.

There will also be different diagrams according to whether the engine is direct drive or driving through a cp propeller. Figure 15 refers to a fixed pitch propeller and assumes that the power output varies as the revs^3 and that the mean effective pressure varies as the revs^2.

INDICATOR DIAGRAMS

An indicator diagram traces out the pressure and volume relationships in the cylinder of an engine on rectangular axes, and it can be used to estimate the work done by the engine per cycle. The indicator must move a vertical distance proportional to the pressure in the cylinder and the drum, as it rotates, provides a horizontal motion proportional to the change in cylinder volume.

The indicator is connected to a screwed cock which is in connection with the combustion chamber of the cylinder being monitored. When the engine cock is opened, the cylinder pressure also acts on the piston in the indicator cylinder, causing it to rise. This ver-

tical movement is resisted by a spring, the strength of which is chosen to obtain a diagram illustrating the part of the cycle being investigated. The vertical movement of the piston is transferred to the pen mechanism by a parallel motion linkage.

The indicator card is held onto the drum with spring clips. The drum is rotated against an internal spring pressure by a special wire reinforced, non-elastic cord, which, being wrapped around the drum several times, is led to a linkage operated by a cam, the cam throw being proportional to the stroke of the engine.

When the cord is attached to the cam mechanism and the indicator cock is opened, a P-V diagram is obtained by lightly pressing the stylus onto the card. From the area of this diagram and the stiffness of the indicator spring it is possible to calculate the indicated power output of the cylinder:

$$ip = \text{average height of diagram} \times \\ \text{spring scale} \times \text{engine constant} \times \text{revs}$$

The average height of the diagram is found by measuring its area and dividing this area by the length of the card. The area can be found by using the mid-ordinate rule or similar, or by using a planimeter (an instrument used for tracing out and accurately measuring the areas of small diagrams such as from ordnance survey maps or plans of a factory etc.). The length of the diagram should always be the same as the throw of the cam but should be measured in any case as any deviation from the 'recorded' length indicates a fault with the indicator mechanism. Too long a diagram would indicate that the drum spring is, perhaps, not tensioned sufficiently and the drum is skidding beyond its warranted travel; too short and maybe the drum is incorrectly set up and insufficient rotation is occurring. Similarly, faults on the cord or pulleys may become apparent if the measured card length deviates from the original set length. The faults mentioned above may not be immediately apparent so it is always necessary to measure the length as a cross check.

The spring scale is marked on the spring itself and is a measure of the pressure required to compress the spring through a quoted length (6 bar to a cm, for example).

The engine constant is the stroke of the engine multiplied by the cylinder bore area.

Apart from taking 'power cards', the standard P-V diagram, the indicator may be used to take cards 90 deg out of phase (draw cards). A draw card is merely a diagram taken with the drum rotation advanced by 90 deg to the main piston of the engine. This allows the injection period to be spread out across the centre

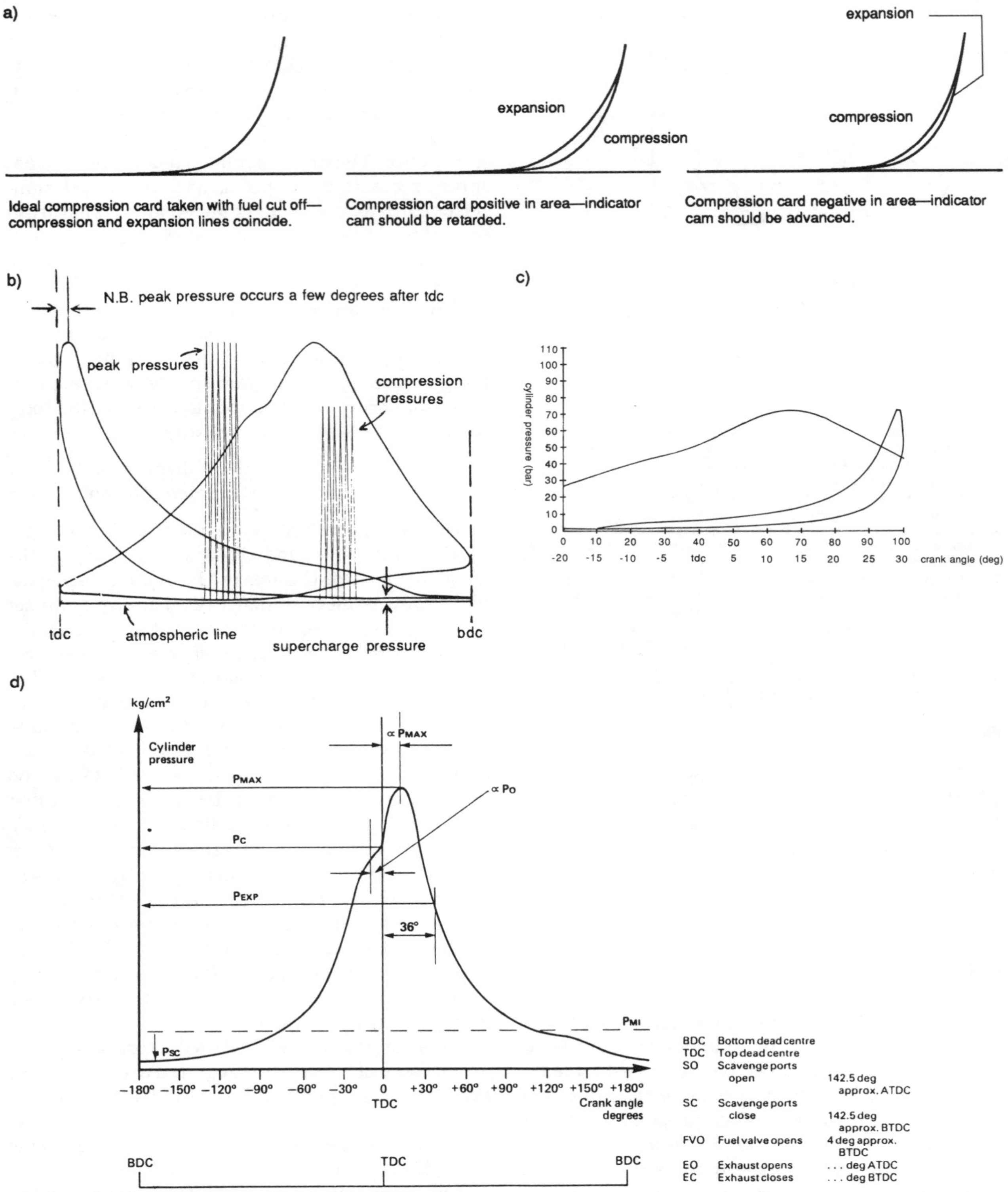
a)
expansion
compression
expansion
compression
Ideal compression card taken with fuel cut off—compression and expansion lines coincide.
Compression card positive in area—indicator cam should be retarded.
Compression card negative in area—indicator cam should be advanced.
b)
N.B. peak pressure occurs a few degrees after tdc
peak pressures
compression pressures
tdc
atmospheric line
supercharge pressure
bdc
c)
cylinder pressure (bar)
110
100
90
80
70
60
50
40
30
20
10
0
0 10 20 30 40 50 60 70 80 90 100
-20 -15 -10 -5 tdc 5 10 15 20 25 30
crank angle (deg)
d)
kg/cm²
Cylinder pressure
∝ PMAX
PMAX
∝ Po
Pc
PEXP
36°
PMI
Psc
−180° −150° −120° −90° −60° −30° 0 +30° +60° +90° +120° +150° +180°
TDC
Crank angle degrees
BDC
TDC
BDC
BDC Bottom dead centre
TDC Top dead centre
SO Scavenge ports open 142.5 deg approx. ATDC
SC Scavenge ports close 142.5 deg approx. BTDC
FVO Fuel valve opens 4 deg approx. BTDC
EO Exhaust opens ... deg ATDC
EC Exhaust closes ... deg BTDC

Figure 16 Indicator cards: a) set of compression cards (a compression card is taken with the fuel shut off in the unit in question—to highlight any faults, compression cards are best taken at a slow speed where compression discrepancies are magnified); b) typical power card with out of phase card taken on the same diagram; c) print taken from an electronic measuring device (pressures and their relevant angles are automatically printed onto the card; useful for checking the engine performance); d) trace of a power card taken over a full cycle with the card 'opened' out so that the compression curve appears to the left of the vertical (tdc) line and the combustion and expansion occurring to the right of the same line. This is a common way for electronic monitors to record events in the cylinder, again relevant pressures and angles may well be recorded on the print out.

of the card so that the combustion process can be examined more closely. (The combustion process is very compact and very little other than the peak or firing pressure can be told from a power card.)

The same spring is used for both power and draw cards, and can also be used to measure the compression pressure. It is best to do this with the engine running slowly, as slow compression highlights leakage that could be associated with worn liners, piston rings or even a leaky exhaust valve. With the fuel shut off the relevant cylinder, the compression card can be taken with or without the drum rotating. If the drum is pulled slowly around by hand as the indicator responds to rising cylinder pressure, a series of vertical lines will be drawn on the card. The average height of these lines will provide the compression pressure for that cylinder. If the drum is rotated as before, by the power cam, a single rising curve should be obtained, and the height is the compression pressure. If a double line appears on the card the cam drive system is either advanced or retarded with respect to the crankshaft (Fig 16a). This is usually sorted out by the engine builder, but, in time, a chain drive system may stretch and the resulting retardation of the cam shaft will show up as an open loop on a compression card. This loss of timing should be rectified immediately if efficient and economic running of the engine is to be maintained. Power cards taken when the cam shaft is not 'timed' correctly to the crankshaft will give false indications of power, and any adjustment of fuel timing to 're-cover' this timing will adversely affect the performance of the engine.

If the indicator spring is removed and replaced with a weaker spring the diagram will show what is happening over the low pressure part of the cycle more quickly. This diagram, drawn at the expense of the higher pressures in the cylinder, will give some indication of the exhaust and scavenge processes and how effectively they are being carried out.

Before 'taking' a set of cards, ensure that the engine has completely warmed through, and that the engine speed and load are stable (i.e. avoid taking the cards in heavy weather).

Blow each cock through before attaching the indicator, because carbon particles entering the mechanism will adversely affect its operation. Ensure that the card is correctly fitted and that the correct spring tensions are set. Allow the indicator to come to temperature; it is not sensible to check one end of the engine with a cold indicator and all the other units with an indicator that is progressively warming up. Lubricate the piston as necessary and take the card by pressing the stylus lightly onto the paper. Draw an atmospheric line first, by closing the cock and rotating the drum under cam actuation (do not pull it by hand). The power card can then be drawn by opening the indicator cock and, again, pressing the stylus lightly onto the card. The atmospheric line is drawn using the cam system so that its length can be measured and checked against the original. Any deviation, as explained earlier, is a result of an indicator fault. The atmospheric line also gives a datum from which the height of the diagram can be measured to determine the firing pressure, or compression pressure as the case may be.

It must be accepted that an indicator is just an 'indication' of what is happening in a cylinder. Indicators do not give accurate measurements but, if used sensibly and with understanding, they can be a diagnostic tool for tracking down discrepancies in engine operations, either across the engine as a whole or between units. Modern technology has developed these systems so that electronic sensors can provide read outs not only of maximum pressures etc., but also of where in the cycle they occur. The pressure readings are given against crank angles so that late or early ignition can be monitored, and adjusted to optimise performance. These electronic systems derive the crank angle relationship from emitters attached to a rotating element (such as the flywheel). Their signals are then integrated with the pressure signal, the latter being generated from sensors fitted in the combustion chamber or from attachments to the indicator cock itself. In other words they are highly refined and more accurate developments of the mechanical indicator.

PISTON RINGS

Piston rings are the engine components which undergo the most arduous of service conditions. They are subjected to great heat during combustion and then substantially cooled as they pass over the scavenge ports. The net effect is quite considerable thermal stressing of the rings. The rings are also subjected to gas pressure. The forces generated by these fluctuating pressures vary in both magnitude and direction. At the top of the stroke the combustion chamber pressure rises to its maximum and forces the rings onto the lower faces of their grooves. In so doing the gas gains access to the back of the ring and pushes it hard against the liner wall. This has greatest effect on the top rings, but each successive ring undergoes the same process with, perhaps, lower magnitudes. Thus the rings are also subjected to mechanical stressing. As the piston descends, the pressure in the cylinder decays and the forces on the ring diminish proportionately, giving rise to variations in the mechanical stressing. The rings themselves act as seals between the combustion chamber and the under piston volume (scavenge spaces on the larger two strokes). Each ring resists gas flow so there is a pressure drop across it to the next, and so on, the accumulated pressure drop being sufficient to contain all gases of combustion above the ring pack.

In Fig 17b it can be seen that the pressures between rings 1 and 2, and 2 and 3 are quite high. These two chambers remain at substantially the same pressure throughout the expansion stroke, so that at the lower part of the power stroke the cylinder pressure will have dropped so much that the top two rings will be pressed up against the upper landing face of the ring groove. This will lead to wear on the upper face as well as that to be expected on all grooves on their lower faces. When the top two rings are in that position, they will also be acting as 'brakes' to the piston's downward movement. Though this may be very slight, its effect, coupled with the reduced gas pressure above the piston, is to reduce the load on the crosshead bearing. At this time, the crosshead bearing undergoes its lowest loading (2-stroke engines only) because the pressure drops to its lowest during the period between the opening of the exhaust and the opening of the scavenge. Any attempt to force lubricate the bearing would be best achieved during this period. (At bdc the piston's inertia works to increase the crosshead bearing loading.)

The adverse effects of both thermal and mechanical stressing are further compounded by the ring friction against the liner. The cylinder liner's properties of self-lubrication (graphite in matrix) are aided by oil lubrication of the ring pack. Many diverse opinions are held about the correct point (during the piston stroke) and time at which to inject oil into the ring pack. The following points are clear.

1. Oil should preferably be injected onto the rings where the ambient temperature is relatively low, for at elevated temperatures the volatile elements in the oil will be driven off leaving behind a sludge, predominately carbon, that will cause abrasive wear and/or gumming up of the rings.

2. To 'hit' the piston ring pack accurately with such a small amount of oil is difficult, especially when the piston is moving quickly. This suggests that attempting injection during the middle of the stroke would lead to problems as the piston would then be moving at its fastest.

It seems reasonable to suggest that immediately

a)

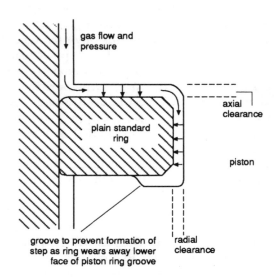

b)

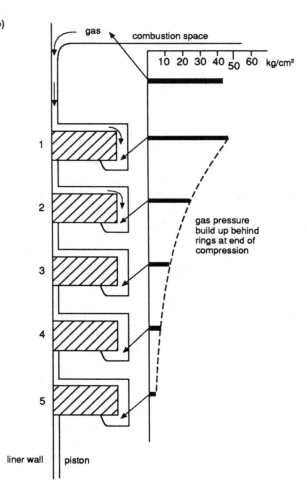

Figure 17 a) Typical plain standard ring with the gas pressures working on it; b) labyrinth sealing effect of a pack of rings between combustion pressure and scavenge pressure (under piston ring pack).

after the closing of the scavenge ports on the upward stroke of the piston would be a suitable point for injection. At this location and time the piston will be cool and travelling slowly. Other considerations such as accessibility, cost/complexity of accurate timing devices or the undesirable penetration of jacket cooling spaces to fit lubricating oil quills, may dictate some other point or timing of injection.

One of the major problems faced by the designer of a piston ring is the need to seal with a surface that may well be irregular and not always concentric. (Liners may be considered as wearing more or less oval over the top section of the piston stroke.) The ring therefore needs to 'conform' with these irregularities whilst still being able to match up with the less worn and probably concentric lower parts of the liner. This conformability of the ring is in-built in the material and is one of the factors governing the 'radial' thickness of the ring, because a ring which is too thick radially would not be able to 'distort' and conform to the variations in liner shape.

The material of the ring should therefore be such that it has an in-built capability to flex during operation, and should also resist wear. These somewhat conflicting requirements are usually met by using a high quality cast iron; to give the ring some form of self-lubrication for the times when the oil lubrication is reduced and metal to metal contact occurs (ring to liner). The self-lubricating properties of both ring and liner help to overcome this condition, although some degree of microseizure (mz) may occur. Microseizure is the fusion between the tiny peaks of both ring and liner which occurs due to pressure between the two surfaces (generating localised high temperatures) and lack of lubrication. The result is that small particles are initially fused together and then torn apart as the ring is moved on by the piston. The running surfaces are roughened and particle detachment occurs. In severe cases the wear rates can be alarming and every attempt should be made to avoid the onset of mz. This may be easier said than done, but some protective steps can be taken.

1. Ensure that rings are the correct ones for the job and that they are correctly fitted.

2. Ensure that the cylinder lubrication is maintained at optimum level at all times.

3. Avoid overloading the engine, collectively and as individual units.

4. Avoid high peak pressures.

5. Ensure that combustion is as clean and crisp as possible (including correct fuel treatment).

6. Monitor ring condition regularly (via scavenge ports).

Much of the rings' good performance is achieved by this 'good housekeeping', but the correct design and manufacture of a ring is critical to its long and useful life. The 'cam' turned method of ring manufacture has evolved to produce a ring that displays the correct operational conditions under all modes. Various methods of ring manufacture are adopted to produce rings for certain services, but the cam turned technique is frequently used for the larger engines because of its superb qualities. They are produced by casting rings with a slight ovality over one part of the circumference. Positive or outward ovality is used on 4-stroke engines (non-ported): negative or inward ovality is used on 2-stroke engines (ported).

The ring shape is then machined to size, still maintaining the 'ovality', which is equally disposed about the but gap. This method ensures that all the characteristics of the casting are retained in the ring. Since no artificial tension is given to the ring, the amount of internal tension is low, giving the ring a high thermal stability and long life. This technique also produces a ring with a very uniform wall pressure (0.5 to 1.5 bar), unlike some of the more conventional methods of manufacture.

The but gap, usually in the region of 8% of the bore, can be used to roughly assess the quality of the ring material. The ring should have an inherent 'springiness' within its normal operating range. If opened up beyond this range the material will go beyond its elastic limit and enter the plastic range, and if further extension is applied it will fracture. To test the quality, the free gap should be measured and the ring carefully opened out until it just fits over the relevant piston. If, when removed, the free gap has increased, it indicates that the ring has gone into the plastic range (permanent deformation has taken place). Such a ring will be unsatisfactory in service as it has lost its elasticity, or never had any. The same test should be applied when removing a piston for routine overhaul. For commercial reaons, some companies re-use as many rings as possible, but from an engineering point of view such practice is questionable. If the free gap is measured before the ring is removed from the piston and then again after removal, the 'springiness', or lack of it, will be indicated by a change in the free gap. Such a change or loss of spring will occur as a result of the constant flexing and exposure to temperature fluctuations in the engine during service.

The wear of the ring will be the main criteria for renewal. If the radial width has reduced by 15% of the original then the ring should be considered to have reached the end of its useful life. (It will have to come so far out of the groove to maintain the seal that it will no longer be adequately supported by the groove, the effect being that it will twist in the groove and eventually fail by fatigue breakage.)

Another quite prevalent form of ring failure is that of 'ring collapse', which occurs when the gas pressure on the outer face of the ring is able to rapidly force the ring back into the groove. Such a process is possible when the gas pocket behind the ring has not been able to form or cannot be maintained. Lack of pressure behind the ring can occur for one or more of several reasons:

a) ring groove so gummed up that gas cannot get behind the ring;

b) lumps of dirt on lower landing face lifting the ring up and venting the back of the ring;

c) distorted landing face ring cannot seal on lower face so the gas pocket cannot be maintained;

d) distorted ring; etc.

Blow past can be another source of premature failure. A new ring, not 'bedded' in to a liner, may suffer localised blow past that overheats part of the ring so that the ring is weakened in that area. The overall spring of the ring will be reduced, or possibly lost altogether.

To overcome the above difficulties, and to help in general with running in, long life and other desirable properties, rings have been designed to provide specific properties for certain service duties. Some of the many rings available are shown in Fig 18.

There is a multitude of ring designs for use in medium speed and high speed engines, and even air compressors. The 'thinking' engineer should examine each type he uses, and attempt to work out the reasons for its design and application.

GOVERNORS

Considered by many merely as a means of speed regulation, the governor is, in fact, a very refined component, which in its most developed form is able to load limit, load share, load sense, regulate rates of acceleration. Not all these features, however, are available or even required in any one unit. A governor is usually made to suit the service demands on the engine to which it is to be fitted. It may provide single speed running conditions irrespective of load changes (isochronous), or be able to respond to increases in load so that acceleration is regulated to a level compatible with the effective and safe running of the engine.

The early forms of 'inertia' type governors were, in essence, overspeed trips, and were not able to increase fuel to suit increases in load. Although these governors are now largely obsolete, the principle behind them is still used in 'overspeed trips'. These trips shut down an engine in the event of an excessive and rapid increase in speed, such as may occur if the propeller shaft were to fracture. These units commonly have a 'fly' or 'bob' weight restrained by a spring. When the engine exceeds a predetermined speed, the weight moves out to strike some form of fuel cut off. The important thing about this action is that as soon as the weight begins to move, its centre of gravity moves radially outward from the centre of the shaft, increasing the centrifugal force so that the weight moves outward with increasing force. This process is therefore very positive in action and no hunting or hesitation occurs. Once the pre-set speed is reached, the overspeed cut out operates, very rapidly. (N.B. Hunting of any component across a small band leads to local wear, which may lead to slackness and the formation of shoulders, which can present problems when a greater movement than the norm is required.)

Centrifugal (CF) governors, unlike the above units, are able to both increase and decrease the fuel setting as loads either rise or fall. However, it is not possible to make a centrifugal governor truly isochronous (constant speed). When an increase in load is experi-

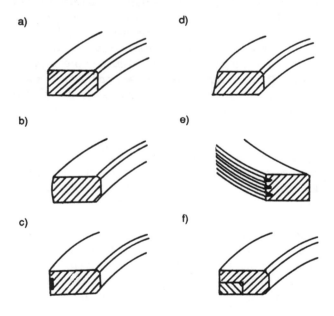

Figure 18   Types of piston rings: a) plain standard; b) barrel faced; c) inlaid; d) taper faced; e) grooved inlaid; f) double seal.

enced by an engine it will tend to slow down. This causes the fly weights of the CF governor to move inwards (with respect to the centre of their drive shaft) under spring force. This, in turn, causes the fuel racks to be pulled out to increase fuel, but if the racks are in a new position then the slide of the governor will also be in a new position, and so the balance between the flyweights and spring will be achieved at some new running speed. This change in final, steady running speed is known as the 'permanent variation', whereas the fall or rise in speed which occurs as loads change is called 'temporary variation'. The temporary variation fluctuates above and below the desired speed value as the governor attempts to settle down to a steady running speed again. This period of hunting that occurs across the desired value is a function of the size of weights; the smaller the weights, and therefore the more sensitive, the longer the period of fluctuations in speed. Large weights settle to a final steady speed more quickly than small weights, but the magnitude of their temporary variation is greater. Thus it can be seen that CF governors are not suitable for regulating engines which drive alternators, where frequency stability is important, but are adequate for dc generation and the control of any other prime mover where strict adherence to a set running speed is not important. One of the major drawbacks of a CF governor is its limited 'governor effort', i.e. the power it develops to operate the fuel racks of the engine. Although large powers can be developed, fairly large fly weights are required; the governor then becomes less sensitive and large changes in running speeds will occur before a

steady condition is reached. Although the governor effort can be increased by gearing up the rotational speed of the flyweights, usually to a maximum and optimum of 1500 rev/min, there is still a limit to the power output (Fig 19).

Where routine maintenance is concerned, the governor should be checked regularly for adequate lubrication. The operating range is usually quite small, giving a tendency for them to wear over limited areas. Then a sudden and larger change in speed than normal may carry the governor onto a ridge of debris or gummy oil deposit so that it may stick at that point. To restrict this problem as far as possible, the governor pivots, slide, etc. should be cleaned and well lubricated whenever possible. It should be borne in mind that the governor structure is such that, were the spring to fracture in any way, the fly weights would be able to move outwards and shut the engine down. The connections from the governor to the fuel racks should be designed in such a way that the governor can both increase and decrease the fuel within the bounds of some hand setting; i.e. the governor can adjust the fuel settings but cannot release more fuel to the engine than is dictated by some predetermined value set by the engine operator.

To overcome the above limitations of the CF governor, 'servo governors' have been developed. These use the power of hydraulics to pump the heavier fuel rack systems associated with the larger engines into the desired position. This 'powered' operation is rapidly and accurately achieved, and the hydraulic flow can be either electrically or mechanically controlled. The speed sensing can be done by a tachom-

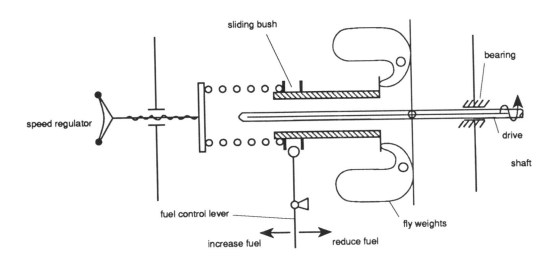

Figure 19 Centrifugal governor.

eter arrangement that can be set to the desired speed, and on sensing any variation a solenoid operated flow valve allows pressurised hydraulic flow into a servo system of pistons/plungers which resets the rack positions. Although this system is quite effective, more mechanically controlled governors are fitted to larger engines. These use the principle of the CF governor, ie. fly weights acting against spring pressure, but instead of the slide working directly onto the fuel racks it simply regulates the flow of hydraulic fluid to the servo pistons controlling the rack positions. This system therefore has the proven reliability and sensitivity of the small CF governor and yet develops quite a large governor effort through the hydraulic fluid.

The spring is usually of the 'trumpet shape' meaning that the weaker coils are compressed out as the spring is loaded so that the spring can follow the curve of the 'square law', rather than the linear reaction associated with a parallel spring. The square law relates to the increment of centrifugal force developed as speed increases, $(CF = mv^2/r)$. Instead of the spring strength and CF force only matching at one point over the operating range, the trumpet shaped spring allows a more balanced relationship to occur over the whole of the speed range (Fig 20).

By a simple lever arrangement the spring tension can be varied with load changes. Then the change in load, causing a change in fuel setting, does not set up a protracted period of temporary variations in speed. As the engine speed approaches the desired value, the spring tension is automatically adjusted so that its original demand for change is moderated. The amount by which this reaction works can be regulated by the governor.

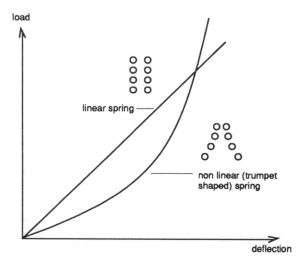

Figure 20   Load-deflection curves for linear and non linear springs.

The fall in speed which occurs as the load on the engine is increased is called 'droop'. With the original CF governor this was inevitable, but with some clever linkages inside the modern hydraulic governor this fall off in speed, or 'droop', can be avoided. The governor is said to be 'isochronous' if there is no change between no load and full load speed. Where there is a small reduction in speed as load increases the governor is said to have 'fine droop', and 'coarse droop' occurs when the final running speed drops well below the desired value as loads are imposed onto the engine. These are usually quoted as a percentage of the no load running speed, so

$$droop = \frac{100 \times (\text{no load speed} - \text{full load speed})}{\text{full load speed}}.$$

The zero droop option means that the governor changes the fuel setting continuously and substantially, whereas coarse droop allows a smaller and less protracted adjustment of the rack setting. The modern governor is a refined, precision instrument and should not be tampered with unnecessarily. Even the oil within it has 'drag' characteristics that are allowed for in the design, so that deterioration of the oil will adversely affect its operation. (Use of the wrong type of oil will dramatically affect the behaviour of these units.) Figure 21 shows the relationships between zero droop, fine droop and coarse droop.

It may be desirable to have zero droop for an alternator (to maintain frequency), but such a refined governor may not be essential on a main propulsion unit. Problems could also arise when engines are run in parallel, so that two governors set to too fine a droop may react with each other. One possible solution may be to set one to a fine droop so that the desired speed can be maintained, and the other to a coarser droop, so that it is able to take care of the load variations that occur during operation. In fact load sharing is a difficult concept and should only be undertaken with advice from the manufacturers of the governors concerned, since specific models of governor may be available to suit the particular problem in hand.

Load sharing should not be confused with 'load limiting'. Many governors, reacting to changes in speed, and in particular to a fall in speed, will attempt to increase the flow of fuel to recover the loss of speed. However, the fall in speed may be due to the engine reaching its power capability and any further release of fuel may only lead to damage to the engine and a loss of efficiency. To protect against this most governors have in-built, load limiting devices, which are usually set (possibly during engine trials) to an upper

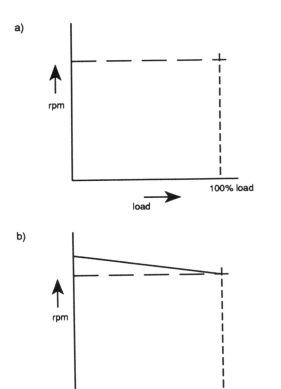

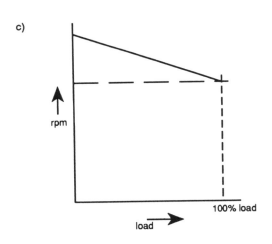

lease of further fuel. The result is that the maximum thermally acceptable load on the engine is not exceeded.

Another refinement for governors regulating alternators is a load 'sensing' process, achieved electrically from the main switchboard (Fig 22). Sensors, reacting to changes in both load and frequency, send an integrated signal back to the governor which preempts the changes in speed of the prime mover to such an extent that the governor is adjusted to accept the change in conditions before the mechanical effects of slowing down/speeding up occur through the system. The net result is a much steadier running speed and a more stable frequency; important for many of the instruments on the vessel, in particular the gyroscope (compass). The signal is applied through a small servo motor on top of the governor. The motor regulates the load on the governor spring, thereby regulating the flow of hydraulic fluid to the servo piston controlling the position of the fuel pump racks. The alternative to this would be to allow the speed changes incurred by load changes to work their way back down the system, through the rotor of the alternator, crankshaft and governor drive. The governor would then begin to react to correct for the change in speed, but the change in speed would have also affected the fuel rack setting, in turn causing a change in the amount of exhaust gas generated, affecting the speed of the turbocharger, which changes the through put of air, which affects the combustion process and running temperatures of the engine. Whereas small changes in load may be absorbed without too much difficulty, a process like this would suffer greatly were there to be a large change such as stopping and starting of a mooring winch or air compressor. It is important that the load sensing equipment operates fully and effectively. The same

Figure 21 Variations in droop: a) zero droop, i.e. speed remains constant over whole load range; b) fine droop, i.e. small change in speed between zero and full load; c) coarse droop, i.e. large change in speed between zero and full load.

limit of engine operating temperatures, exhaust, jacket, etc., so that the engine, on reaching this predetermined loading, is not fed with any more fuel. Some governors have an external adjuster that allows fine trimming of the load limiter, which is simply a 'stop' up to which the governor can call for more fuel but at which even decreasing speed cannot cause the re-

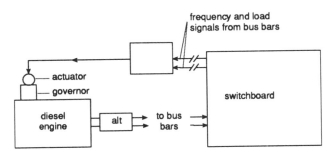

Figure 22 Load sensing arrangement. An integrated signal responding to fluctuations in either or both frequency or load is passed to the actuator. The actuator pre-sets the governor to respond to the changes before the effects feed back via the alternator and diesel engine themselves. Thus the correction is rapidly achieved without great fluctuations in speed of the prime mover.

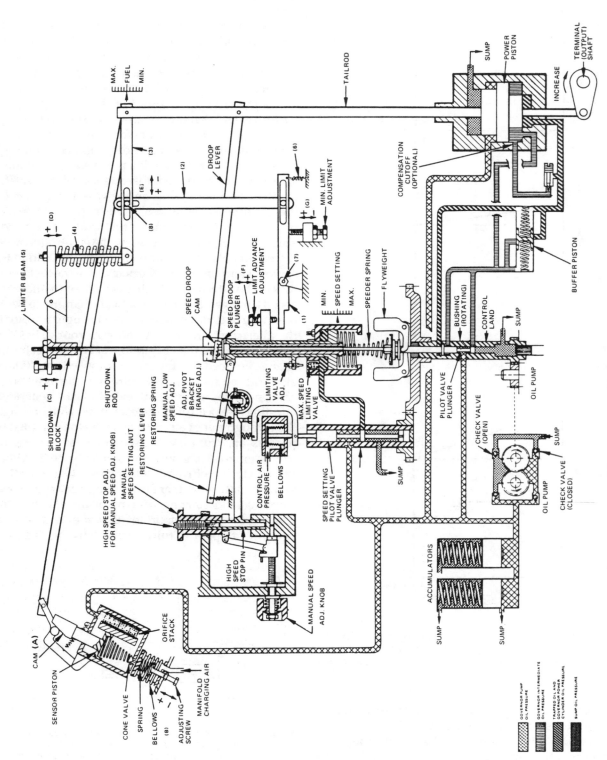

Figure 23   Schematic diagram of PGA governor with manifold pressure fuel limiter.

servo motor is used to regulate the speed of an incoming alternator whilst paralleling it to the existing switchboard frequency. Once coupled, the engine is locked to the frequency (by the synchronising torque) of the system and the governor becomes a regulator adjusting the fuel flow to match the load fluctuations.

With controllable pitch propellers, speed sensing equipment may be used to increase the propeller pitch as the speed rises, so the propeller absorbs more torque and increases the load on the prime mover. As the load torque then exceeds supply torque the speed will fall until the set value is reached again.

Governing prime movers, particularly diesel engines, requires careful consideration. The cyclic variations of a diesel cycle can be passed into the governor drive if it is too 'stiff'. That is, the cyclic vibrations will be imposed on the internal gearing etc. inside the governor housing. To prevent this, some form of damper should be used on the drive into the governor. The mounting point for the governor should be rigid; a vibrating mounting would soon downgrade even the best of governors. Chain or belt drives should be avoided as far as possible, as slapping of the belt or chain produces speed variations causing malfunction of the governor. Similarly the drive from the end of the cam shaft is subjected to torsional vibrations, and governors should not be located at that point. They should be located as close as is practicable to the fuel pumps, thereby limiting the mass/inertia of operating linkage. In all cases, the governor should be matched to the engine requirements in terms of droop, load limiting, response time etc. On large engines there is an inertial resistance to acceleration within the masses of reciprocating and rotating elements of the engine, so that during acceleration fuel could be released to the cylinders at a faster rate than efficient combustion can burn it. In an attempt to compensate for this, and to maintain acceptable combustion during acceleration, a tapping from the scavenge space may be taken and the pressure used to regulate the rate of fuel release to the engine. This process is incorporated into the governor operating system so that the governor releases a quantity of fuel commensurate with the increase in air pressure in the scavenge space (Fig 23). (During deceleration the problem is not so great, as excess air can be tolerated far more easily than can the incomplete combustion associated with insufficient air.)

Figure 23 also shows how other controllers are integrated into the governor. These include droop control, load limiting and speed setting. From the complexity and inter-reaction between these it should be understood that these units, once calibrated and set, should not be casually adjusted. Even the viscosity of the oil is important. An oil that is too thick would slow down the reaction of the governor and would completely alter the flow through the needle valve(s). Whenever a problem is experienced with these refined and reliable governors it is advisable to call in an expert.

CROSSHEADS

Crosshead bearings are very difficult to lubricate and they run under the most arduous of conditions.

Throughout the full cycle, 2-stroke crossheads are subjected to a vertical downward loading that is never reversed, whereas in the 4-stroke engine, the induction stroke reverses the loading on the gudgeon pin. The magnitude of the load varies throughout the stroke, being a maximum around tdc and gradually reducing as the cylinder pressures drop during the expansion stroke. The lowest loading on the crosshead (see *Piston rings*, page 133) occurs around the opening of the exhaust ports when the cylinder pressure drops to below scavenge pressure. (Were it not to do so for whatever reason, blow back into the scavenge space would occur and there would be inadequate scavenging of the cylinder, in addition to the increased potential for a scavenge fire.) It is at this point that the high pressure lubricating oil has the best chance of lifting the pin and forming a film under it in preparation for the next cycle.

The crosshead bearing oscillates about the pin, so that it is difficult, if not impossible, to generate the hydrodynamic 'wedge' of oil much more readily achieved in bottom end and main bearings, or indeed in any bearing/shaft system in which continuous rotation occurs. Even so, a film of oil set up whilst the con rod is swinging at its fastest across the pin (bdc and tdc) provides, to a large extent, hydrodynamic lubrication. At the extremities of the swing of the con rod, as it passes over mid stroke, the movement of the bearing must slow down, stop and reverse in direction. Fortunately the loading at this point is much reduced, so any boundary lubrication conditions that occur are more easily accepted.

One of the greatest problems associated with crossheads is the need for them to absorb very high and almost instantaneous loading just after tdc. At this point the piston rod, connecting rod and crankshaft webs are in virtual alignment so that the full force of the piston load is directed into the crosshead bearing. To accept this the crosshead needs to have extensive bearing surface, and either great stiffness to resist bending or a way of accommodating bending

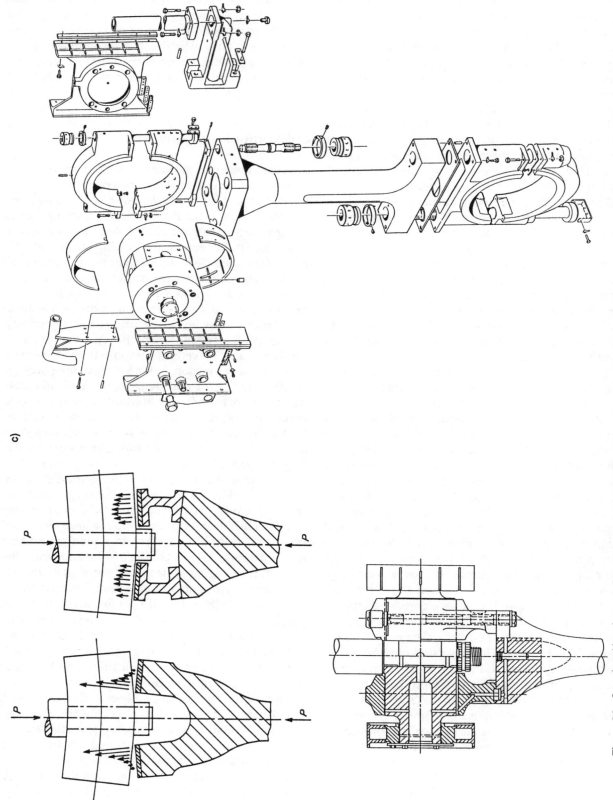

Figure 24 Crosshead bearings: a) diagrammatic view of flexible mounted lower halves; b) section through actual crosshead showing bearing support; c) large dia to length ratio preventing bonding even during peak pressures.

a)

b)

c)

of the pin without causing localised (point) loading of the white metalled surfaces. Examples of both types are shown in Fig 24.

Figure 24c shows a crosshead with great stiffness, i.e. such a large diameter to length ratio that bending under expected loads is unlikely. Its greater weight and size, producing a loss in power, is acceptable in return for reliability of operation.

Figure 24a shows a lighter structure in which the firing forces may cause the pin to deflect (by fractions of a mm). However as the flexible bearing (bottom) halves move with the pin, uniform distribution of loading is still maintained.

In both of the above cases the pins are machined to a very fine tolerance, probably in the region of 0.1mm, with the shell type bearings accurately machined to provide matching surfaces. The old, traditional method of scraping in the white metal should not be applied to these modern units. Hand scraping would lose the concentricity so carefully machined into both surfaces. Many modern crossheads are of the shell type bearing with a steel backing for strength, faced with copper-lead coatings and finished with a lead based white metal. These composite (tri-metal) bearings offer great resistance to corrosion, have high load carrying ability and a resistance to scoring, and are machined to very close tolerances.

Because of the ever increasing mep, and the difficult circumstances in which a crosshead bearing works, lubrication is now taken to it directly. The oil feed, usually from some supply higher in pressure than is required for main bearings, is supplied via 'swinging' links or through 'telescopics'. The residue of this supply is taken 'down' the connecting rod to supply the bottom end bearing. (This has the advantage of supplying the highest loaded bearing crosshead first and at the same time eliminating the need for drillings through the crankshaft, from which fatigue cracks may develop in the highly stressed shaft.) Some of the crosshead oil supply is taken on to lubricate the guide shoes.

There are many forms of crosshead. One employs jacking pumps to increase the oil feed pressure (using the arc of the connecting rod to develop a pumping motion). Another has bearing pins which are divided into two slightly eccentric sheaves, so that the oil film developed as the rod swings over them is extended beyond that formed on a simple single pin. Each of these, as well as the above methods, has been designed to maximise the effective lubrication of the crosshead so that it will operate successfully for long periods.

In all cases attention should be paid to the correct adjustment of the working clearances. Large clearances should be avoided, as the oil will be squeezed out more readily. A rough indication of the state of a bearing can be obtained by checking the oil flow from the bearing, particularly when the oil is hot (thin); after the engine has been running, for example. Any unduly large flows from the crosshead will become obvious as the engine is turned over. It would be sensible to compare the flows between each crosshead so that a pattern can be provided against which the suspect bearing can be compared.

It should be noted that oscillatory bearings (crossheads included) are the only ones in which 'axial' oil distribution grooves are acceptable. (In rotating shaft/bearing systems axial grooves in the loaded area would disrupt the formation of the oil wedge.) Even so, the contouring of these grooves should be carefully regulated so that adequate radii are given to their edges to encourage oil flow and prevent them from becoming oil scrapers.

GUIDES

The firing (and compression) forces are transmitted through the crosshead into the connecting rod so that, apart from tdc and bdc, a turning moment is developed at the crankshaft level. There will be a transverse reaction to these forces at the crosshead level, and this is taken by the guide shoes (slippers) onto the guides. A simple triangle of forces shows this reaction for one point alone in the cycle, for as the cylinder pressure changes so too does the loading on the piston. In other words, the load on the crosshead, and hence the guides, will vary throughout the stroke with variations in crank angle and cylinder pressure. Not only does the magnitude of the loading vary, but its direction of application alters too. During the expansion stroke the forces will be acting on one set of guides (sometimes referred to as the ahead guides) then during the completion of the revolution the thrust is transferred to the other set of guides (the astern guides). From this it should be appreciated that 'both' sets of guides (ahead and astern) are used every revolution, and not only the ahead guides when the engine is running ahead and the astern guides when the engine is running astern. Both sets of guides are used whether running ahead or astern. There will be a greater loading on them during the relevant power stroke than that experienced during the compression stroke.

Wear, under normal circumstances, occurs along the top third of the guide ways and it will generally be slight compared to the wear on the slipper itself. This, being white metal faced and provided with grooved oil reservoirs, is supplied with oil bled from the crosshead feed, as mentioned above.

Clearances should be checked using feeler gauges, at the top, center and bottom of the stroke, with a total clearance (ahead and astern) being taken, as the guide shoe may be resting on either of the two surfaces.

Adjustment of the guides to compensate for wear should be undertaken with great care and any adjustment made should be in order to recover the smallest wear measured and not the largest (otherwise guide clearance may be lost on the least worn areas).

Alignment of the guides should be such that they control/constrain the crosshead, and therefore the extremity of the piston rod, to a path parallel to the movement of the piston. This runs according to the alignment of the cylinder liner so the guides should be parallel to the cylinder liner. Any deviation from this will, apart from producing a knocking sound, give accelerated wear to the cylinder liner, piston rod and possibly the guide shoe and ways.

Adjustment of the guide ways and accurate measurement of the alignment is not usually undertaken by the ship's staff. However an impression of the alignment can be obtained, should some fault be suspected and all other possibilities eliminated, by adopting the following procedure. With the cylinder cover removed and the piston suspended (crane) at the lowest part of the liner, centralise it within the unworn part of the liner by driving in wooden wedges (circumferentially and from both top and bottom of piston). This aligns the piston with the cylinder liner and in so doing makes the rod (freed from crosshead constraints) parallel to the liner. Measurements can then be taken from rod to guides to check for any deviation. More accurate methods, using piano wire centralised to cylinder bore, or laser beams, are available, but the above procedure will indicate any major misalignment.

There are two major forms of guide/guide way; the two-faced guides and the four-faced guides shown in Fig 25, a and b.

When adjusting these to compensate for wear, the effects of any adjustment on the alignment of the piston rod should be considered. The crosshead may be displaced transversely thereby pulling the piston rod end to one side of the engine. The two faced guides are most likely to give problems in this way unless correctly adjusted.

The guides, absorbing the resultant transverse thrust from the crosshead, apply a corresponding turning moment to the engine in the transverse plane about the base. The forces so applied tend to 'rock' the engine (transversely) about its foundation. This in-

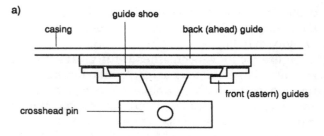

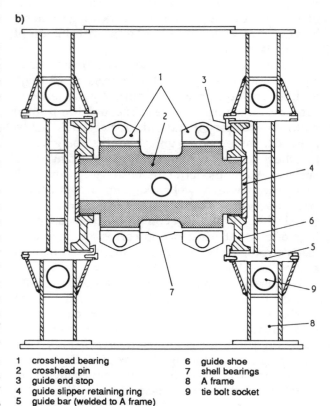

1	crosshead bearing	6	guide shoe
2	crosshead pin	7	shell bearings
3	guide end stop	8	A frame
4	guide slipper retaining ring	9	tie bolt socket
5	guide bar (welded to A frame)		

Figure 25 a) Horizontal section through two-faced crosshead guide; b) horizontal section through A frames, crosshead and guides of the four-faced type.

creases the compressive loading on the chocks of the relevant unit on one side of the engine, whilst simultaneously increasing the tensile stress in the holding down bolts at the other side of the engine. The compression stroke reverses these forces, but not by the same magnitude. Compared to the firing forces and vertical forces in general these transverse, rocking moments are small. Nevertheless, their effects at holding down bolt level should not be disregarded. The combination of otherwise acceptable individual loadings may cause failure. For example, consider the effects of a higher than normal firing pressure and slack or broken chocks on the rocking forces mentioned above.

MEDIUM SPEED ENGINES

This chapter describes the principles behind the large slow speed engines (cathedral type engines) and it is difficult to include anything other than an overview of medium speed and high speed engines. There are multitudes of builders, each with their own design characteristics, and it would be impossible to cover every aspect of medium speed engines within this chapter. A simplistic comparison is made between them and slow speed engines, and the areas where there are major differences are highlighted below.

Crankshafts

Crankshafts may be underslung to protect the bedplates from firing stresses. The crankshaft is supported underneath the crankcase framework by bearing housings bolted up into the frame. There is therefore no real need for a bedplate, and frequently a simple sheet metal sump is sufficient. This means that the frame provides the required longitudinal and transverse stiffness of the engine and the omission of the bedplate reduces the overall weight of the engine. There are some models that have bedplates, usually cast structures, similar to the general layout of a slow speed engine. The other major difference is that the crankshaft is normally a solid unit, forged, or even cast on smaller engines. Forged shafts have to be carefully constructed to provide a reasonable grain flow along the length of the shaft. In many cases these shafts are 'stiff' enough to span worn down bearings without showing up on the deflection or bridge gauge readings. Care should be taken when recording deflections to see that such spanning is checked for.

Main bearings

Main bearings are usually of the shell type; white metal lined (copper lead or aluminium tin) with a flashing of lead indium or lead tin approx 0.0005 inch thick for running in. This flashing may be slightly thicker for a fuller life. The steel backing shells are held in place and shape by the bore of the housing and will be designed to provide 'nip', i.e. sufficient interference fit to provide adequate grip on the bearing shell, preventing it from turning in the housing. The nip provided is not great enough to cause distortion which would adversely affect the running clearances. Axial location of the shaft may be required if the coupling does not incorporate a thrust housing. This is achieved by forming (white metal) rings on the sides of one main bearing shell that allows the shaft to run with a small axial clearance between

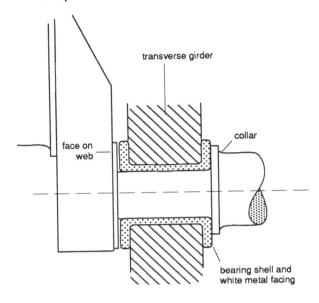

Figure 26 Thick wall bearing with flanges. Locates shaft but does not absorb prop thrust.

running faces on the two adjacent webs (Fig 26). In some cases a small collar may be provided at one side of the bearing.

It is important to appreciate that only one such 'locating' bearing should be fitted to any one shaft. Otherwise the differing thermal expansion of frame and crankshaft may cause problems.

Connecting rods

Connecting rods in medium speed engines are usually of the 'marine type'. The bottom end is separate from the palm of the connecting rod, thereby allowing the fitting of compression plates. (These in turn control the compression ratio and compression pressure.) This connecting rod palm may be of reduced width to allow its withdrawal through the cylinder as the piston is lifted. The removal of a piston is a problem with medium speed engines or trunk engines (trunk engines being those in which there is no crosshead, the piston being directly connected to the connecting rod), as the connecting rod can not be detached from the piston whilst the piston is in the cylinder. The bottom of the connecting rod is often larger than the bore of the cylinder, mainly because it has to carry the bottom end bearing which runs on a shaft which is as large as the cylinder bore in diameter, or even larger. Thus the bottom end must be constructed either to be removable, as in the type shown in Fig 27, or possibly obliquely cut. These are also known as 'fixed' centre connecting rods as it is not possible to fit various thicknesses of compression shim.

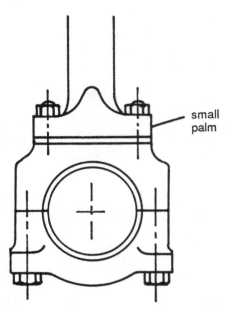

Figure 27   Marine type connecting rod.

Vee type engines provide another problem. If the cylinder centres are transversely in line then the bottom end will also be in line which leads to two bearings wanting to run on the same section of crankshaft. This may be overcome by adopting the fork and blade method, or using articulated connecting rods (Fig 28). In either case, problems arise when overhaul is required, and spare gear levels are increased as the variety of bearing increases. Where vee engines don't have their cylinder centres transversely in line, the connecting rods can run side by side on the same throw of a crank, the crank pin having to be extended to accommodate the two bottom ends. This leads to a heavier crankshaft as well as a slightly longer engine, but it simplifies both access and overhaul.

The lubrication of the top end (gudgeon pin) is usually achieved by oil being fed from the main bearing supply along drillings in the crankshaft to the bottom end, and then up through borings in the connecting rod to the top end. Most medium speed engines are of the 4-stroke type which naturally provides an alleviation of the downward load on the gudgeon pin during the induction stroke, which helps lubrication of the top end bearing. In 2-stroke medium speed engines, this reversal of load does not occur and it is therefore prudent to increase the load carrying area of the gudgeon pin and at the same time maximise the lubrication flow to that area. The reversal of thrust in the 4-stroke causes greater cyclic fatigue problems with the bottom end bearing bolts. For safety's sake, therefore, the running hours given by the manufacturers for their bottom end bolts should be strictly adhered to. Failure of one of these bolts could lead to total engine failure; expensive, undesirable and usually avoidable if bolt tensions, firing pressures and quoted running hours are conformed with.

Pistons

Pistons may be cast iron or, on higher speed engines, aluminium alloy. The use of alloy pistons reduces weight and therefore bearing loading, and the loading on the cylinder walls. Allowance must be made for the larger expansion ratio of the aluminium alloys, and so large piston to cylinder clearances (cold) are adopted. As the engine warms up and expansion of piston occurs this clearance reduces. For this reason, care should be taken to avoid overheating such a piston. Aluminium also suffers from carbon build up with possible burn out when heated above 300°C. Cooling of these pistons may be achieved by spray-

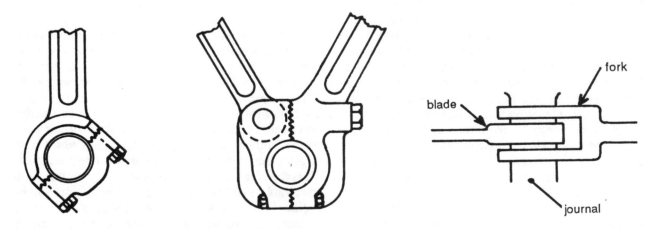

Figure 28   a) Obliquely split connecting rod; b) articulated connecting rods for vee engine; c) fork blade assembly for vee engines.

ing oil onto the under side of the crown. This spray is taken from the lubricating oil fed to the top end. However, if bearing wear occurs, the oil leakage there reduces the flow so that the piston cooling supply also suffers. Improved and more easily regulated cooling can be achieved through coils cast into the piston crown. These may be fed from the oil supply to the gudgeon pin or may be individually supplied via telescopic pipes. A further problem associated with aluminium type pistons is that of rapid ring groove wear, which can be overcome by casting in 'ring inserts' of a harder wearing material and which, if correctly shaped and cared for, last the life of the piston. The crown of the piston may be shaped to accept the open valves as the piston passes over tdc on the exhaust stroke. The shaping may be further arranged to 'squeeze' the air into the centre of the combustion chamber as the piston reaches tdc on the firing stroke. This provides a compressed volume of rapidly moving air into which the fuel can be injected. The air movement ensures adequate mixing between fuel and air so that complete combustion is more easily achieved.

Piston rings

Piston rings will be similar to those in slow speed practice; cast iron alloyed with various proportions of one or more of manganese, molybdenum, or chromium. The top rings may have inserts of chromium for extended life, or possibly bronze inserts to facilitate running in. Running in may also be enhanced by using taper faced rings (1°). This limits the contact surface during the first hours of running so that a seal is more quickly established, the ring gradually bedding in to provide the full running face as a seal. On one type of engine the rings are pegged to the piston so that they rotate with it. The piston is made to rotate by an ingenious rack and pinion mechanism, incorporated at gudgeon pin level, being activated by the swing of the con rod as it completes a cycle. Instead of a gudgeon pin, as such, a spherical end to the connecting rod allows complete and continuous rotation of the piston. The effect of the rotation of the piston is to distribute oil around the cylinder wall much more evenly and accurately than can be achieved with the normally accepted procedures.

Valves

Exhaust valves come in for a great deal of abuse as the engine is running, particularly if there are traces of vanadium or sulphur in the fuel. Many exotic, corrosive-resistant materials have been developed and employed on valve seats to combat this problem (nimonics and stellite). Rotation of the valves has also proved to be a successful method of prolonging valve life, by maintaining the valve seating area at a more uniform temperature. A valve which is not rotated tends to heat up in one area more than another due to the directional flow of exhaust gas and air during the gas exchange period. This non-uniform heating is further accentuated by the heat release from the burning fuel. This localised heating may carry parts of the valve to temperatures beyond the tolerance of the material so that any corrosive products of combustion can more readily attack the metal. The effect is that the valve suffers localised wastage (burning) and holes form through the seat. Another effect of uneven temperature across a valve head is the slight variance in expansion so that effective valve closure may not be achieved. This leads to further heating of the valve, as well as the loss of efficiency, fuel economy and power associated with blow past. Thus overheating not only weakens the material but also promotes attack from the corrosive products of combustion. Valve cooling should therefore be achieved and maintained as carefully and accurately as possible. Rotation is simply an adjunct to accurate cooling of the seat.

The exhaust valves will be slightly smaller in diameter than the inlet valves, reducing the force required to open them against a given cylinder pressure. The power to open them, coming from the rocker arms and pushrods, is from the engine itself. Although this is a power loss, were larger valves used greater scantlings of running gear would be needed and the power loss would be magnified. Similarly, were the exhaust valve dimensions increased, the loading on the actuating cam face would increase, leading to more problems. Even though the valves are smaller than the inlet valves the gas escape is barely retarded as the cylinder pressure itself plays a great part in expanding the gas from the cylinder. The larger air valves are needed so that they do not offer resistance to flow and unnecessary back pressure on the turbocharger.

Springs for the valves may be in series, one above the other, or in parallel, one inside the other. Springs in series are usually associated with slow speed engines where great lift is required. The fitting of a diaphragm plate half way down the springs prevents them whipping as they operate; this lateral oscillation could lead to premature spring failure or even a form of valve bounce. Springs in parallel allow springs of slightly thinner wire section to be used. This prevents them from becoming coil bound, for a given lift, and if the individual coils are of different section they will have different vibration characteristics so the incidence of resonance is reduced. Also, if one spring fails the other will continue to operate the valve and prevent it dropping into the cylinder.

There are situations where the choice of engine depends only on engine room size; small vessels require medium speed engines. However, on large vessels there may be a choice between a large slow speed engine or a multiple medium speed engine installation. Much of the decision is based on installation costs and expected maintenance costs. In general, slow speed engines can consume lower, and therefore cheaper, grades of fuel. Some reasons for the adoption of medium speed engines are outlined below.

1. Ship's reliability increases with more than one engine because failure of one engine does not mean the ship is held up.

2. One or more engines can be shut down when the vessel is running in ballast or lightly laden. This allows the running engines to operate at their optimum power and fuel efficiency, which is impossible with a single slow speed engine under the same conditions.

3. Maintenance is easier because of the smaller size of component. (In the author's experience this is often offset by the sheer inaccessibility of some of the engine components.)

4. Any engines shut down at sea can be overhauled, within limits. This should save time in port.

5. Where vessels of different size are concerned, engines of a common type may be fitted, the differing power requirements being met by varying the number of cylinders or even the number of engines. This provides a fleet of vessels with a common engine type so that replacement is simplified, spare gear costs are lower, and the ship board engineers, becoming familiar with the engines, can move around the fleet without detriment to maintenance.

STARTING AIR

There are several methods of starting a diesel engine, including manual, electrical and mechanical devices. The techniques used on a particular engine depend largely on its size, design and service requirements. Small diesels, such as those employed in lifeboats etc., may well be hand, or perhaps electrically, started. In main propulsion engines, or even diesel generators,

such methods are unable to supply the substantial torque required to overcome the inertia of the large masses involved. These engines usually employ a system using the energy stored in compressed air.

Where the main engine is of the direct drive reversible type, it is essential that it is capable of starting in either direction from any position of rest. To achieve this, it is necessary for each cylinder to be fitted with a starting air valve, the opening of which is dictated by a 'distributor'. This distributor ensures that air is introduced into the relevant cylinder at the correct time to achieve starting in the desired direction from any position of rest. There will be an overlap period during which two cylinders, at the extremities of their air injection periods, will both receive air. This ensures positive starting in the correct direction. (The starting sequence is the same as the firing order for the engine.) The amount of overlap is dependent upon the number of cylinders, the timing of the exhaust opening and so on. (The greater the number of cylinders, the less overlap required.)

Modern practice is to introduce air into the cylinder slightly before tdc. (The alignment of piston rod with con rod at this point is such that little, if any, turning moment is developed.) This allows the air to accumulate in the clearance volume ready to force down the piston once it is over tdc. At the same time, another cylinder will be receiving air (because of the overlap). This unit will be one in which the crank is well past tdc so that it generates an adequate turning moment to carry the above unit over tdc. The first unit, already pressurised, will be able to accelerate the engine up to the 'fuel initiation' speed. The useful expansion of the starting air will cease at the opening of the exhaust. To continue air injection any further would be wasteful and futile. This limit is normal to 3-cylinder engines but is unnecessarily long in engines with more than three units.

A starting air pressure well below the compression pressure of an engine will be able to turn the engine over against the compression because the compression pressure is only reached towards the end of the stroke, whereas starting air is introduced for a much longer period of the stroke. The starting air 'indicator' diagram, Fig 29, shows that there is a far greater energy release below the starting air curve than that required to achieve the compression. Areas below the curves represent, to scale, the energy involved in the relevant operation.

The momentum built up in the rotating elements of the crankshaft will help in smooth starting once the initial inertia has been overcome.

Reversibility can be achieved by introducing air into a cylinder where the piston is approaching tdc, in

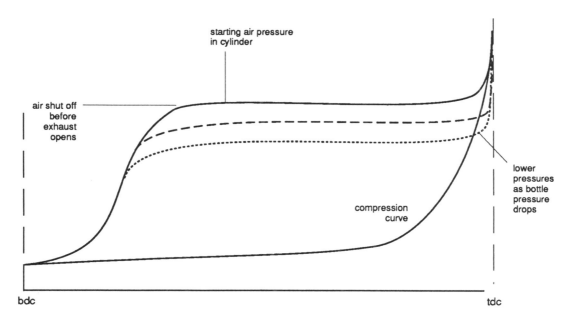

starting air pressure
in cylinder

air shut off
before
exhaust
opens

lower
pressures
as bottle
pressure
drops

compression
curve

bdc

tdc

Figure 29   Starting air diagram.

the direction of rotation in which it was stopped. Exactly the same concepts as discussed above then apply, but in the reverse firing order. Control can be achieved through the distributor or by varying the position of the starting air cams (sliding cam shaft, usually independent of the fuel pump cam shaft). Lost motion clutches had some bearing on the distributor on some engines but the advent of constant pressure turbocharging has led to radical simplification in the design of lost motion clutches.

Where the starting air system is concerned, the following features are usually considered desirable.

1. Between the engine and the starting air receiver there should be a robust and effective non-return valve. This valve should be situated as close to the engine manifold as is practically possible, so that any explosion in the starting air manifold is contained in as small a length of piping as possible, and should be prevented from getting back to the air bottles. Locating the valve close to the engine limits the distance travelled and hence the build up in speed of the explosive wave that would otherwise occur as the wave front travels down the pipe line seeking out oxygen and fuel. This high velocity wave front has been responsible in the past for destroying pipelines and valves. It must therefore be contained to as small a range as possible.

2. Between the above non-return valve and the cylinder valves some form of relief should be fitted (to

vent the forces of an explosion as quickly as possible). These devices may take the form of:

a) an ordinary spring loaded relief valve(s).
These are open to mal-treatment and mis-adjustment so they may not operate adequately enough when needed.

b) bursting discs or caps.
These are relatively tamper proof provided that the correct materials and replacement caps are used. They do vent the manifold completely and, unlike the above relief valve, which resets once the pressure has dropped, require some form of blanking off if the engine is to be started again. For this reason, it is usual for several caps to be fitted to the engine (one per unit), unlike the relief valve where one or two valves are the norm.

c) quick closing valves (air operated).
These are not very common, but are built in such a way that they are rapid in action and virtually tamper proof. They operate on the differential area principle. One side of a piston-like assembly sits against the air manifold; the other end, slightly larger in diameter, is pressurised directly from the air receivers. Should the manifold pressure rise, the 'valve' is blown open and the manifold vented, once the pressure drops the pilot air from the receiver closes the valve again by working on the bigger area. Such an arrangement allows pressure release and then immediate recovery of the air starting system.

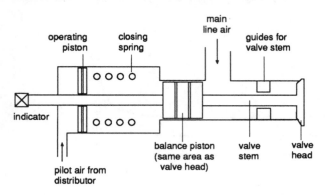

Figure 30 Schematic view of starting air valve.

3. For each unit there is a cylinder valve, a simplistic design of which is shown in Fig 30. Note the following in Fig 30.

a) the 'mushroom' head and balance piston, of the same nominal diameter, so that the main line air simultaneously acting on both faces holds the valve in balance rather than forcing the valve open.

b) the guide on the stem, which ensures correct alignment and reseating as the valve closes.

c) the spring incorporated to close and hold closed the valve.

d) the power piston, of such dimensions that, on the introduction of pilot air, the valve is rapidly opened against spring pressure (and cylinder pressure).

e) spindle, whcih indicates the position of the valve and may be turned to help close a 'sticky' valve.

To ensure that the cylinder valves open in the correct sequence, a distributor is required. The distributor provides the air start timing with correct overlap whether going ahead or astern. Distributors may be cylindrical or circular discs both suitably ported, or radially distributed spool type valves around a central cam, or perhaps similar spool type valves aligned above a laterally sliding independent cam shaft. A schematic of a starting air system is shown in Fig 31.

CRANKCASE EXPLOSIONS

Crankcase explosions can cause serious damage to engine room equipment, but more important is the hazard to the engine room personnel. It is necessary therefore for the engineer to completely understand the process leading to the propagation of conditions favourable to an explosion. The engineer can then maintain his engine so that those conditions should not occur.

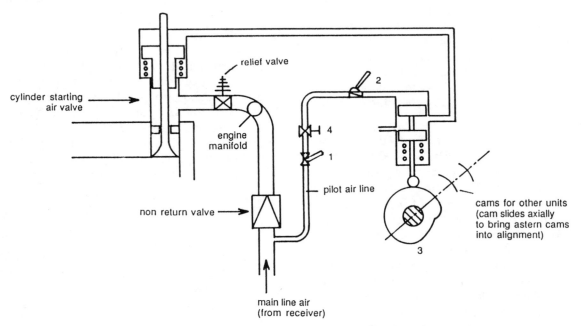

1 Turning gear interlock—prevents engine from being started when turning gear is engaged.
2 Starting lever/valve—may be activated remotely (from bridge) or locally.
3 Camshaft—individual to starting air—carries AHD and ASTN cams for every unit and together with piston valves for each unit acts as time distributor for the pilot air to the cylinder valves. Negative cam provides opening period for cylinder valve.
4 Valve to allow testing of main cylinder valves with distributor isolated such that the engine should not turn over.

Figure 31 Starting air system.

It must first be understood that an explosion can take place in any enclosed mechanism such as a chain case, gear case, crankcase of a diesel engine or air compressor where oil is present. The magnitude of the explosion is governed mainly by the available volume of explosive vapour, and it is this that would make large, slow speed main engine explosions potentially devastating, were they not adequately protected.

It has been proved that engine size does not affect the incidence of explosions (which are as likely in lifeboat engines as they are in large main propulsion engines), and that any moving part within the enclosed space can be responsible for the explosion, eg. piston rods, piston skirts, chains, gears, bearings and so on.

The sequence of events leading up to explosive conditions is as follows. The natural atmosphere in a crankcase consists of large globules of oil (100–300 mm in diameter) dispersed through the air. These globules are relatively so large that they will not ignite explosively, though they may burn under the correct conditions. A 'hot spot' (minimum temperature approx 360°C) can vaporise these globules. The vapour, rising to cooler parts of the crankcase, is then condensed into an oil mist. This oil mist consists of small globules of oil of approx 2–10 mm in diameter. When ignited, an accumulation of this oil mist can cause a heavy explosion. The initial vapour created by the hot spot may cause an explosion, though in most cases there would not be sufficient to cause a heavy explosion.

The oil mist may be ignited by coming in contact with a hot spot or spark at a temperature of 270°C. It may also be ignited if heated above 370°C (self-ignition temperature).

The amount of oil mist generated before ignition regulates the severity of the explosion. A small amount will create a fire; a large amount an explosion. The sooner the generation of oil mist is discovered, the smaller is the chance of an explosion, provided that the correct procedures are then followed.

The ratio of oil mist to air also governs the severity of the explosion. A weak mixture (2% or 3% by volume) will give a mild explosion causing little, if any, damage. A mixture in the middle of the range (5 to 7% oil fuel vapour in air) will, if ignited, cause a heavy explosion, probably blowing off crankcase doors, causing external damage and engine room fires. A rich mixture (9–10% oil fuel vapour to air by volume) may cause a mild explosion. It should be appreciated that, following the explosion, a partial vacuum is created in the crankcase, and the engine room atmosphere flows back into it (Fig 32).

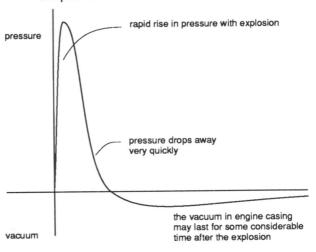

Figure 32 Pressure time relationship of a crankcase explosion.

In the case of the rich mixture, the explosion will be followed by a period when air flowing back into the crankcase dilutes the rich mixture into the middle of the explosive range. A secondary explosion at this condition could be devastating. In past cases the vacuum has been responsible for drawing off the crankcase doors of adjacent engines, laying their atmospheres open for combustion. It is to avoid this 'chain reaction' that crankcase explosion doors are designed to close as rapidly as possible after relieving an explosion, the closing being a way of preventing air ingress to the crankcase. For similar reasons, there should be no cross connecting pipes between the crankcases of engines. Oil return pipes to a common sump should be taken to below the surface of the oil so that an explosion in one engine cannot find its way into the second engine.

Extraction fans exhausting to atmosphere up the funnel are sometimes fitted to keep the engine clean. The fans cause a small pressure depression in the crankcase that prevents oil leakage, as air is drawn in through any small aperture that would otherwise weep oil. The fans must be shut off if conditions that could lead to a crankcase explosion are suspected. If left running, they could dilute a rich mixture to the middle of the explosive range.

Oil mist detectors are fitted to many engines today and are a particular requirement for unattended machinery space vessels. They continuously monitor the atmosphere inside the crankcase, taking samples in turn from both low and high levels along the length of the engine. The samples are compared to a reference so that a change in conditions at any one point is detected quickly. The alarm point is set very much below the lower explosive limit so that a very early warning is provided. The monitor will indicate the location of the detector head providing the alarm reading, and the engineer can check on conditions himself. It should be appreciated that these units are very sensitive and may give alarm conditions because of slight fouling of the lens inside the detector. Regular checking and cleaning of these will reduce the incidence of false alarms. The units should never usually be switched off. It is better to respond to a few false alarms than to ignore a warning preceding an explosion.

An alert watchkeeper can detect rising oil temperatures quickly and respond to the dangers before conditions get too severe. Stopping the engine is by far the best thing to do but this can only be done with agreement from the bridge. Only when there are no hazards in a navigational sense should the engineer slow the engine down and stop it. Permission from the bridge watchkeeper should always be sought before slowing or stopping the engine; which may cause a collision/grounding that would otherwise have been easily avoidable. After checking with the bridge, slow, or preferably stop, the engine, and, if possible, increase the flow of lubricating oil. Never open the crankcase until adequate time for cooling has elapsed. 'Adequate' time is not easy to define but in most cases at least 30 min should elapse, preferably much more. In the crankcase, the hot spot will still have enough heat left in it for it to be located. Carbon dioxide flooding would inert the crankcase, approx 30% by volume being sufficient, but not many engines are fitted with such facilities. Permanent inerting is not practicable, as not only could the gas leak into the engine room atmosphere, but routine maintenance would be inhibited. Inevitably, cost would also preclude the use of permanent crankcase flooding.

Crankcase explosion doors are fitted in order to reduce the effects of an internal explosion. They have to be able to withstand the force of the explosion and the passage of high temperature gases without distortion. Equally, they must close and seal quickly to stop the ingress of air that would otherwise occur during the period of vacuum. They should be fitted along the length of the engine and positioned at high and low level to give maximum protection. Note that the further an explosive wave travels the greater its momentum, so on large engines, doors should be numerous so that the distance travelled by the wave, before its release, is as short as possible. Medium speed engines with cylinder bore less than 12 inches only need explosion doors at the ends. Smaller engines with cylinders of less than 6 inches are not required to have explosion doors at all. Areas of doors are set down by the various governing bodies, as are the lifting pressures (nominally 0.5 bar).

Above all, good and regular attention to the maintenance of the engine, avoidance of overloading and the provision of adequate lubricating oil should mean that explosions never occur, but to protect against the unpredictable oil mist detectors and crankcase explosion doors should always be checked and maintained in satisfactory condition.

Scavenge fires

For a scavenge fire to occur there must be the three sides of the fire triangle; air, fuel and a source of ignition. The removal of any one of these would not only extinguish a fire but prevent it occurring in the first place. It is impossible to prevent air flow through the scavenge spaces as scavenging implies air flow. However, fuel should never be present in the scavenge spaces so a clean scavenge space can never ignite. Ignition itself could occur were there to be any blow past the piston or were the piston to begin to seize in the liner. It may even be possible for the piston rod gland to overheat to the point where it could cause ignition.

The easiest way to avoid scavenge fires is to ensure that the scavenge spaces are maintained clean and free from oily deposits. The ease of this depends, to some extent, upon the engine design, with respect to its breathing, and in particular depends on the pressure of exhaust gases still in the cylinder at the opening of the scavenge ports. However, the engineer can limit fouling of the scavenge spaces by ensuring that combustion is being carried out as cleanly and crisply as possible; there is good fuel timing, atomisation, penetration, air fuel ratio and so on. Similarly, the lubrication of the ring pack needs to be controlled to prevent a build up of lubricating oil in the scavenge spaces. There is a possibility that oil may pass over with the scavenge air from the turbocharger, particularly if the air filters are fouling up. Dust brought in with the air may also be a source of fuel within the scavenge spaces. The liner/ring interface should be well maintained. Use good quality rings and renew them and the liner in good time.

A scavenge fire will manifest itself as a drop in power. There will also be a rise in the exhaust and jacket temperatures local to the fire area, the turbochargers may begin to surge and a smell of smoke/hot paint will be apparent. Automatic alarm systems are available, many of which are wires, the resistance of which alter with changes in temperature, the corresponding change in current flow activating an alarm. Scavenge fires are capable of generating conditions favourable to a crankcase explosion because they put heat into the top plate of the crankcase. That is one reason why the fire should be extinguished as soon as is reasonably possible.

When a fire occurs, the watchkeeper should, apart from raising the alarm, reduce speed (checking with the bridge first), shut the fuel off the affected unit, and slightly increase the cylinder lubricating oil to the affected unit to prevent, if possible, seizure and wear. If the fire does not burn itself out quickly then stop the engine (bridge), put in the turning gear and commence turning the engine. Without turning it is possible that the localised overheating of a piston or piston rod may lead to distortion and subsequent problems. The tie bolts are generally shielded by tubes from the extreme temperatures. Otherwise they may 'stretch' and relax their grip on the structure. In any case it is prudent to check the tension of these bolts after a large scavenge fire.

As with crankcase explosions, the doors should not be removed until the fire has subsided and temperatures have dropped. The early ingress of air may allow an explosion to occur. Air flow through the engine will occur naturally, even when it is stopped. This is due to the convection currents generated by the heat in the uptakes. Wrapping canvas around the turbocharger filters can limit this. The injection of carbon dioxide will rapidly extinguish the fire, but time must be allowed to pass before opening the doors, for a hot spot could cause re-ignition. Carbon dioxide could cause thermal cracking of the hot components within the engine. The use of dry powder would add to the cleaning up required once the emergency is over. Steam is ideal in this situation, provided the line is adequately drained first and the valves have not seized with corrosion. However good it is as a fire fighting agent, steam is not recommended because of the problems associated with corrosion, water slugs preceding the steam and the need to generate it in the first place. See Chapter 11, *Minimising the Fire Hazard.*

AIR COMPRESSORS AND RECEIVERS

Air compressors, for starting air systems, are invariably of the reciprocating type. Although of slightly less volume through-put than rotary, the reciprocating unit is more easily capable of developing the pressures required for starting air systems. Compression should, for maximum efficiency, follow the isothermal law, but in practice it is more closely aligned to the adiabatic curve, with the result that the delivery temperature is somewhat higher than is really desirable. This high temperature has several undesirable side effects, not the least of which is to cause the temperature of the delivery valves to rise and encouraging their fouling up as the oil and dust bake out on the high temperature zones. Air at a high temperature is also less dense, so for a given volume there is a reduction in mass. To limit these problems, as far as is practicable, stage compression is often resorted to. The benefit of this is that each stage is subjected to a low compression ratio so that terminal temperatures are limited and work input is also reduced. Stage compression also allows intercooling to take place between the stages so that the compression can be made to follow the isothermal curve more closely. This too limits the work input required so that either the compressor drive motor can be reduced or compression is quicker. Interstage cooling also causes condensation to occur so that some of the moisture may be drained out after the cooler, the net effect being that drier air is delivered to the receiver. The clearance volume is very important in the efficient operation of a compressor. Too large a clearance and the air trapped there at the end of a compression and delivery stroke will expand back to suction conditions before a fresh charge can be drawn in. This can dramatically reduce the volumetric efficiency of the compressor;

$$\frac{\text{volumetric}}{\text{efficiency}} = \frac{\text{actual volume drawn in}}{\text{swept volume}}.$$

The clearance volume should be kept as small as is safely possible; too small and collision between the piston top and the cylinder cover may result. This problem may occur when bearing wear down takes place in the crankshaft system. The slack so generated may allow the piston to 'throw' itself up and collide with the cover. This dangerous condition is particularly apparent when the compressor is running unloaded (compression is not taking place and there is little or no resistance to piston movement). During compressor overhaul, the engineer should always check bearing clearances as well as bumping clearances (i.e. distance between piston top and cylinder cover at tdc).

The stage compression (and the relatively low compression ratios thereby available) also reduces the amount of air trapped in the clearance volume and hence again improves the volumetric efficiency over single stage compression. Compression in a single stage would, for a given clearance volume, result in a large mass of air being trapped due to the high pressure (pv = mRT) with its consequent expansion greatly reducing the effective suction.

The valves used in both the suction and delivery sides of a compressor are of the plate type. These offer low inertia coupled with large area for flow for only a small lift. The result is rapid opening with minimum resistance to flow. (In a compressor running at 600 rev/min, the operating time for a delivery valve is in the region of 0.025s).

The plates are subjected to shock loading both on opening and closing. To reduce this as much as possible the opening is cushioned, either by shaped pockets that reduce the impact of full opening or by 'cushion' plates that take the brunt of the impact and in so doing offer some protection to the valve plate itself. The impact on closing cannot be avoided and may in time lead to crazing of the sealing surfaces with cracking eventually taking place. For this reason, plates that have worn after subsequent lapping in should not be reversed; otherwise the rate of failure would be very rapid. The lapping in itself should be to obtain as smooth a surface as possible. A mirror-like finish will offer less drag to the air flow, improving efficiency and keeping the temperature of the air down.

The pipes from the compressor to the receiver should also be smooth and have as few restrictions as possible, allowing the air to flow freely to the receiver and entrain with it any solids, liquids etc. These can be separated out in the bottle relatively easily and should not be allowed to accumulate in the pipes where they would cause an obstruction (and possibly corrosion). For similar reasons, the portings in the valve bodies should be as contoured as possible, permitting the air to flow easily through the valve. Ports that are not adequately radiussed will cause turbulence within the air flow, acting not only as a restriction to flow but also tending to heat up the air and consequently the valve and plates.

The gum like deposits that appear on the valves is a combination of lubricating oil from the compressor, oil, and dust from the atmosphere. To limit this build up, piston lubrication should be kept to the minimum necessary to prevent wear (and sufficient to resist air leakage). Similarly, the suction filter should always be kept clean and, depending upon the type, slightly moist with oil.

Leaky valves will cause the compressor to run for longer periods before fully charging the receivers, as well as raising the temperature of the discharge air. Faulty valves are usually indicated by the above and by a change in interstage pressures relevant to the discharge pressure. The sooner they are rectified the better, as unfavourable conditions may occur if the compressor is run at length.

Amongst other things, leaky valves can result in the recycling of compressed air so that the temperature of the air continues to rise, and may develop to a point where any oil fuel vapour present is carried to its self-ignition temperature and detonation occurs. It is best to prevent this arising by regular inspection of running pressures and temperatures coupled with regular maintenance of the valves.

Lubrication of the piston has always been a problem. The use of self-lubricating materials (PTFE coatings etc.) is of great benefit. Where oil has to be used then the minimum commensurate with safety should be applied. If specific lubricating boxes are used for the piston then the choice of oil can be made to match as closely as possible the working conditions in the cylinder. If, however, some form of splash lubrication from the crankshaft system is adopted then a compromise will have to be made. The oil should be able to spread around the cylinder as well as possible to ensure maximum lubrication from minimum oil. The oil should also resist being washed off by the incoming wet air (second stage). An extension of this is that the oil should be able to protect the cylinder, rings etc. from corrosion during idle periods. finally, the oil should have a low coking tendency so that gumming up of the valve plates does not readily occur. This latter requirement contradicts the view that the oil should have a high flash point. High flash point oils have, by nature, a high carbon content, which not only adversely affects valve carbonisation but also implies that the oil is viscous and may not spread easily around the rings and cylinder.

Air cooling is achieved in multi tube heat exchangers circulated with water. The straight tubes are easier to keep clean and offer small resistance to air flow. Should one perforate however, the pressure of the air would immediately be imposed upon the whole of the coolant passages (water being incompressible). This would put such a strain upon the relatively weak casings that rupture would almost certainly result were it not for the large area relief devices fitted to the water casing. These may take the form of spring loaded valves or bursting discs. In either case they offer, on lifting, a rapid release of volume and would drop the pressure quickly enough to protect the casing from damage. Nevertheless always check during overhaul that these devices are still operational.

Air receivers (welded or riveted structures) and air bottles (solid drawn units)

The term 'bottle' is often used to cover both types of structure. Both have to be manufactured to specific requirements. On board maintenance amounts to regular surveys of the inside and mountings. The latter will include, at least, relief valve(s), pressure gauge connection, inlet and outlet valves, manhole, or inspection doors and drains. The drain should be situated at the lowest point of the bottle in such a way that accumulations of oil, water and solids can be blown out. The water forms as the hot, compressed air cools down to below the relevant dew point. The ambient conditions of humidity and temperature will affect the amount of condensate so formed. In any case, the area around the drain should be inspected whenever possible to check on any corrosion that is taking place in that area. Sonic testing can be used to determine the residual thickness if corrosion has occurred. Cleaning and revarnishing (non-spirit based) of the affected areas is essential if further corrosion is to be avoided. The usual inspection of the other mountings should also be carried out during the survey period. Remember to treat the receivers as an enclosed space whenever entry is required and take the relevant precautions, particularly if cleansing fluids are being used or painting is being carried out.

Fusible plugs are fitted if the receiver is isolable from a relief valve. There will always be a relief valve on the high pressure side of the compressor so that when the compressor is being used the bottle is protected. However, this means that the receiver is only protected when the compressor is running. A fusible plug therefore offers protection against pressure development in the event of an engine room fire. The plug (lead, bismuth and antimony) softens as its temperature rises and extrudes from its fir tree type socket. The release of such large quantities of air would impair the effectiveness of any CO_2 fire fighting gas unless extra gas is provided in compensation or the air is piped out of the engine room, say to the fidley.

COOLING SYSTEMS

To keep the materials of the engine within the limits of their thermal and mechanical strengths it is necessary to regulate the heat build up in them. This is achieved by circulating coolants at the correct rate around and through the various components within the engine. Most of these systems can readily be traced out by the ship's engineer, although the bore cooling passage ways may only become apparent when the engine is overhauled.

Water is used as the coolant, although it must be of the correct quality and treated in such a way that it does not encourage corrosion. Hard waters, those that carry a high salt/lime content, should be avoided as they will only lead to scale deposition in the higher temperature zones with the consequent reduction in heat transfer.

It is usual to employ distilled water or some such equivalent. In any case the calcium oxide level should be very low as should the chloride content. To inhibit corrosion an additive such as soluble oil, chromate or nitrate borate can be used. Each of these have their own peculiar advantages and disadvantages. Soluble oil, for example, is safe to handle, reduces cavitation damage and is approved for use with fresh water generators. It is however prone to separation if the system is not clean or if water quality is incorrect, susceptible to foaming and may layer out on high temperature zones forming insulating layers. Its self-lubricating properties favour its use with telescopics used to supply piston cooling. On shut down, any oil based coolant must be circulated longer than water as there is a tendency for the oil to 'bake' out on hot spots, forming insulating layers that promote, when the engine is running, the burning away of piston material on the high temperature combustion side.

For many years chromate has been used as a very effective inhibitor, particularly as concentration levels are almost self-evident from its colour. Chromate too can be used in conjunction with zinc coatings etc. However it is harmful to the skin and must not be handled, and because it is poisonous cannot be used with fresh water generating systems run off the engine coolants. (Be aware of restricted areas when dumping!)

Nitrate borate is probably the most universally used compound as it is an effective inhibitor, the level of which is easily determined aboard. It is also safe to handle and is approved for use with fresh water generator systems run off the engine cooling system. It does attack soft solders and cannot prevent corrosion of zinc.

The ship's engineer generally has no choice but to use whatever inhibitor the engine builder recommends. To that end it is his responsibility to ensure that the coolant system is maintained clean and clear. He should also maintain regular checks upon concentrate level and avoid overdosing as a 'safety margin' as, for example, too much soluble oil causes deposition in high temperature zones. The engine operator should maintain the inhibitor, whatever the type, between the prescribed levels and take the usual precautions when handling the raw material.

It is worth bearing in mind that the return temperature of the circulated coolants is a 'mean' value of the coolant. There will be areas inside the cooling system where the local surface temperatures are very much higher than those indicated at the return. It is obviously very dangerous to run the returns at levels higher than those normally recommended.

Although the circulatory systems of large bore engines are generally considered to be coolants, these same fluids act as heating agents during the warming through period. As discussed in an earlier section, it is necessary to warm through the larger engines, not merely to limit thermal shocking that occurs during starting but also to impart as much heat into the first compressions as possible. This helps to provide adequate temperature at the end of compression so that the fuel absorbing heat from the air will readily rise to its self-ignition temperature and combustion will be ensured. Once the engine has warmed up, the clearances will be taken up (piston to cylinder) and a more positive compression together with heat absorbed from the cylinder cover etc will provide adequate air temperatures for crisp ignition. The heating for the coolant can then be turned off and the normal cooling system reverted to.

VIBRATION

The vibrations set up in a diesel engine are most complex, as both the magnitude and direction of the forces creating the vibration vary throughout one revolution. A mathematical approach is required, but the results of vibration can easily be understood by the watchkeeping engineer and he should always be aware of the potential problems that continued vibration can bring. There are not only different magnitudes of vibration in terms of the force causing the vibration, but also great variations in the frequency of the vibration. The firing forces in a slow running engine create large, low frequency (relatively speaking) vibrations, whereas one could imagine that the blades in the turbocharger rotating at several thousand rev/min are being subjected to a very high frequency of vibration albeit of fairly low magnitude. Each in their turn can lead to component failure, although the design engineer will have done his best to provide scantlings and materials that should, with proper maintenance, provide long service without failure. The failure that results from vibration is almost universally 'fatigue failure', which accounts for the greatest proportion of material failures in engineering (normally accepted as being in excess of 65% of all failures).

Vibrations can nominally be separated into one of two forms. One is natural vibration which is a function of the material itself and its resistance, or lack of it, to movement. The classic example of this is a tuning fork where the legs of the instrument vibrate, once struck, quite freely and for some time until the internal resistance of the metal gradually dampens down the movement. All components will have, to a greater or lesser extent, a natural frequency of vibra-

tion, and the greater the mass involved the greater the natural resistance to vibration and the slower the vibrational frequency. The other form of vibration is forced vibration which is a result of the frequency with which the applied force occurs. For example, a 4-cylinder engine rotating at 100 rev/min will have a forcing frequency of $4 \times 100 = 400$ Hz.

The main problem arises when the natural and forced vibrational frequency coincide. Resonance is then said to occur. The forcing frequency, acting at the same time and in the same direction, tends to magnify the natural frequency substantially to such an extent that the strength of the material may no longer be able to withstand the stressing. Ultimately, fatigue failure occurs with the cracks passing through the material until insufficient area is left to carry the load and complete failure takes place.

Most large bore engines have a 'critical speed' which is one at which resonance occurs. The particular range of revolutions will be marked on a plate adjacent to the controls and the engine should always be taken through the range as quickly as possible. Bridge controlled engines have an automatic block over the range to prevent inadvertent operation at that speed. The so called critical speed is that at which the torsional forces created by the firing impulses and the reactions from the propeller synchronise with the natural frequency of the shafting system. Balance weights may be fitted to change the natural frequency of the shaft as well as to counter some of the rotational, out of balance forces generated by the crank throw. Detuners, usually in the form of a floating mass in the shaft system, are particularly useful in dampening down the vibrations generated at critical speeds. This is achieved by changing the natural frequency of the shaft as the floating mass puts drive back into the shaft as it hesitates over a critical speed. Figure 33 shows how the magnitude of the vibration at the critical speed is modified when the detuner comes into action.

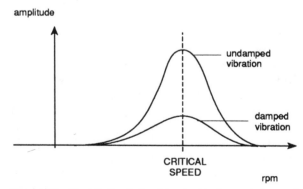

Figure 33 Magnitude of vibration at critical speed, damped and undapmed.

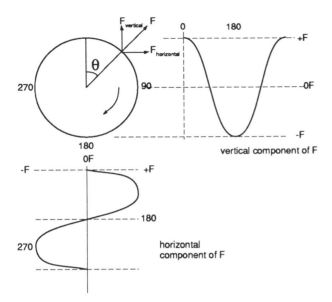

Figure 34   Horizontal and vertical components of force of a rotating mass.

The complexity of the vibration can be understood by considering the piston and crosshead as a reciprocating mass. (It is also normal to include the top two-thirds of the connecting rod in the reciprocating masses, the lower third being considered as a rotating element.) The reciprocating masses are forced down the cylinder during the expansion stroke by the expanding pressures of the combustion gases. The shape of the power card shows the pattern of pressure distribution above the piston and gives some idea of the change in applied force over the expansion stroke. Needless to say, the momentum of the piston over bdc creates another quirk in the vertical loading. Then, on two strokes, the compression stroke resists the upward movement of the piston giving, yet again, a variance in the vertical forces being generated. It will once again be necessary to consider the momentum of the piston, this time as it passes over tdc. Complicated as this seems, it is simple compared to the distribution of the angular forces generated by the rotating elements within the engine. Just as each cylinder produces a disturbing force acting along the axis of each cylinder due to the acceleration of the reciprocating masses, so too does the rotating element produce out of balance forces, for even at constant speed the direction and magnitude will vary as indicated in Fig 34. It should be noted that the crankshaft generates not only vertical forces but also horizontal ones. Because of these it is necessary to tie the engine down securely with the holding down arrangement and at the same time provide the seating with some side chocks to help resist transverse move-

ment. The engineer should be aware of these forces, and ensure that the engine is maintained so that it can withstand them. Figure 35 shows a schematic view of some of the forces and loading generated at one point in the cycle. A quick look at the diagram will show the following.

1. The compressive force built up in the piston rod never changes in direction (in a 2-stroke) but does vary in magnitude.

2. The forces on the guides will vary in both magnitude and direction. One guide takes the forces generated by the firing forces and the other those generated during compression. These will change in magnitude and direction as the engine goes astern.

   These forces attempt to rock the engine about its foundations, alternately increasing and decreasing the tensile loading in the holding down bolts. To a lesser extent the juncture between the A-frame and bedplate are subjected to the same rocking motion. It is important to keep a prudent eye on the integrity of both sets of bolts.

3. The force in the connecting rod, like the piston rod, will vary in magnitude but not in direction.

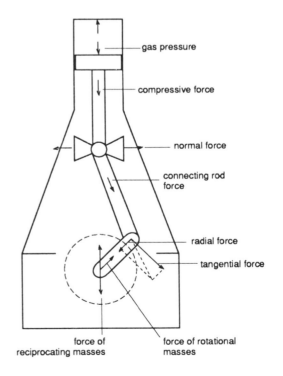

Figure 35   The direction of forces at one point in the cycle of a two stroke engine. All forces change in magnitude as the engine completes its cycle, and some change in direction.

4. The result of the thrust from the connecting rod will generate both radial and tangential forces at the bottom end. It is the tangential force that turns the crankshaft and develops power whilst the radial force either tries to compress the webs or extend them as the cycle is completed.

5. There will be a force generated by the masses as they rotate about the shaft axis. This centrifugal force acts against the radial force at one part of the cycle and with it at another. The centrifugal forces, taken in the horizontal plane are responsible for 'couples' that try to turn the engine in the horizontal plane as each couple is formed. This causes a snake-like movement to be attempted in the bedplate. Once again holding down and side chocks protect against this, as does the in-built stiffness of the bedplate structure.

To dampen out some of the rotational forces many modern engines use specially driven wheels to which are attached balance weights. The rotation of these weights is timed to act against the out of balance forces mentioned above. Any good text book on the theory of machines will explain the principle of the Lanchester balancing concept.

CONCLUSIONS

Engineering is changing and expanding continually, so that new developments are always being investigated. By the time this volume has been printed there will be new developments and procedures that will supplement the above information, such as the possibility of using steel for cylinder liners. Steel, much tougher than cast iron in its resistance to cyclic stressing, does not have the inherent self-lubricating properties, but may be accepted in engines of the near future. Similarly, exhaust valves are being subjected to extensive investigation. Nimonic facings or Inconel coatings are being checked, together with the possibility of stellite inserts on the mating surfaces, all being attempts to reduce the damage caused by acid and heat attack which occurs as ever worsening grades of fuel are being burned. Novel ideas to reduce ring/guide friction losses may come forward as the search to improve engine performance continues. Further waste heat recovery from turbochargers may be fed back into the engine output shaft, improving the already high thermal efficiency of the modern marine diesel. The material in this chapter is a foundation on which an engineer can build and extend his knowledge of engines and engineering concepts, but to be competent and well informed the possibilities for the future should also be considered.

Chapter 4
Marine Fuel Oil

R F Thomas

INTRODUCTION

In 1870 the *Constantine* sailed the Caspian sea using oil in her boilers to produce steam for propulsive purposes. A further twenty-four years elapsed until the first Atlantic crossing by the *Baku Standard* was made in the same manner. At the beginning of the nineteenth century over 22% of the world's merchant fleet was still made up of sailing vessels and the remainder, with few exceptions, obtained their energy for propulsion from coal. In the intervening period up to the outbreak of the First World War, marine fuel oil started to be increasingly used in merchant fleets. While the pioneers had utilised the oil in a boiler, it was during this period that the marine diesel engine evolved in an ocean going vessel. The first ocean-going motor ship was the *Selandia*, which sailed on her maiden voyage from Copenhagen to Bangkok in February 1912.

By 1914, 2.62% of the total merchant gross tonnage used fuel oil for boilers, 0.47% used oil in internal combustion engines, 89% used coal, and the remainder were sailing ships. In 1921, the respective percentages were 20.65%, 2.0%, and 72%. Figure 1 shows the adoption of oil for the world merchant fleet from wind and coal.

In 1921, practically every motor ship afloat ran on a distillate grade known as diesel oil, whilst oil fired steamers operated on a residual grade known as fuel oil or boiler oil. The difference between the two grades is considerable.

By the mid 1920s, at least one motor ship had been designed to burn boiler oil in both her main engines and auxiliaries. One can conclude, however, that overall the commercial incentive to burn residual fuel did not exist because of the low cost differential of diesel and residual fuel and the increased maintenance cost as a result of using the latter. In the depression of the 1930s, boiler oil was used by some owners as a short-term cost saving measure.

As the cost differential increased, the economic incentive existed to prove technically the feasibility of burning residual fuel in motor ships. A full account of one successful endeavour was presented to The Institute of Marine Engineers in 1947[1], and was followed by others in the next few years.[2,3] Ship owners were anxious to convert existing vessels capable of burning such fuels. The fuel generally available, with the possible exception of that from the Americas, was of a fairly consistent quality and gave few problems. In the early part of the twentieth century, practically all marine fuel oil was produced by straight distillation of crude oil, but to meet the increased demand for various products such as gasoline and middle distillates beyond those proportions that could be produced by the process known as straight distillation, secondary refining processes were introduced.

In 1936 a secondary refining process, generally referred to as catalytic cracking, was developed to increase the gasoline yield. This was introduced on a commercial basis in the United States in the early 1940s and by the early 1950s plants had been installed in many refineries, in various geographical areas. In

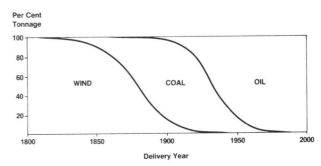

Figure 1 Adoption of oil for the world merchant fleet from wind and coal.

the 1930s, processes for increasing the yield of middle distillate from residue were developed, and commercial adoption of these processes, of which the common one is thermal cracking, an example of which is visbreaking, took place on a limited scale in the 1950s. By the 1970s, this technique was being increasingly adopted, so from one barrel of oil an increased yield of middle distillate and a smaller yield of residue was obtained. Hence the characteristics of the residuum contained in marine fuel oil today are very different to those of the oil used by the early pioneers a century ago.

The present situation is complicated by the wide variations in product demand in individual countries. These wide variations cannot be accommodated by crude oil selection alone because of demand volume requirements. Further, within any single geographical area several crude sources are used and numerous refinery process configurations are employed. The result of this is that fuel for the marine market on a world-wide basis is subject to considerable variation in its properties. Whilst this has basically always been the case, the variations today are more pronounced than they have been in the past. Marine fuel oil only accounts for 4%–6% of the barrel, yet provides the main energy to transport the trade of the world by sea, and more tonne-miles are covered in this manner than by all other means of trade transportation combined.

SPECIFICATION

For the majority of ship owners, bunkers account for a significant part of the vessel's operating costs. The exact proportion depends upon the type and size of vessel, and the trade in which it is employed. For the marine market, with the exception of the distillates, fuel oil is often ordered by viscosity. Whilst viscosity is an important characteristic it does not give any indication of the other characteristics of the fuel. With viscosity as the sole criterion for the ordering of marine fuels, ship owners remain unaware of these other characteristics. Similarly, the designers of the machinery and fuel systems are not always suitably informed of the fuel characteristics to which they should be designing.

During the late 1970s and 1980s a considerable amount of work was carried out within the marine industry on the development of national and international standards. The first national specification was the British Standard BS MA 100: 1982, which was revised in 1989 to make it identical with the international standard. An extract of the International

Table 1   Requirements for marine distillate fuels.

Characteristic	Limit	Designation ISO–F–			
		DMX	DMA	DMB	DMC
Density at 15°C, kg/m³ [a]	max	[b]	890.0	900.0	920.0
Kinematic viscosity at 40°C, cSt [c]	min	1.40	1.50	—	—
	max	5.50	6.00	11.0	14.0
Flash point, °C	min	43	60	60	60
Pour point (upper), °C [d] winter quality	max	—	–6	0	0
summer quality	max	—	0	6	6
Cloud point, °C	max	–16 [e]	—	—	—
Carbon residue, Ramsbottom % (m/m) on 10% residue	max	0.20	0.20	—	—
Carbon residue, Ramsbottom % (m/m)	max	—	—	0.25	2.50
Ash, % (m/m)	max	0.01	0.01	0.01	0.05
Sediment by extraction, % (m/m)	max	—	—	0.07	—
Water, % (V/V)	max	—	—	0.30	0.30
Cetane number	min	45	40	35	—
Visual inspection	—	[f]	[f]	—	—
Sulphur, % (m/m)	max	1.0	1.5	2.0	2.0
Vanadium, mg/kg	max	—	—	—	100

[a] Density in kilograms per litre at 15°C should be multiplied by 1000 before comparison with these values.
[b] In some countries there will be a maximum limit.
[c] 1 cSt = 1 mm²/s.
[d] Purchasers should ensure that this pour point is suitable for the equipment on board, especially if the vessel is operating in both the Northern and Southern hemispheres.
[e] This fuel is suitable for use at ambient temperatures down to –15°C without heating the fuel.
[f] Clear and bright.

Standard ISO 8217 (First edition 1987-04-15) 'Petroleum products—fuels (class F)—specifications of marine fuels' is given in Tables 1 and 2.

CIMAC (International Council on Combustion Engines) has issued a document entitled 'Recommendations regarding fuel requirements for diesel engines'.[4] These recommendations are based on ISO 8217, and include a number of additional characteristics. It is envisaged that these additional characteristics will be incorporated in a revision of ISO 8217.

MARINE FUEL OIL CHARACTERISTICS

Terminology

Within the marine industry both distillate and residual fuels are used, and at present the various grades of fuel are referred to by different names depending on the terminology of the supplier.

Table 2 Requirements for marine residual fuels.

Characteristics	Limit	Designation ISO–F–													
		RMA 10	RMB 10	RMC 10	RMD 15	RME 25	RMF 25	RMG 35	RMH 35	RMK 35	RML 35	RMH 45	RMK 45	RML 45	RMH 55	RML 55
Density at 15°C, kg/m³ [a]	max	975.0	991.0		991.0	991.0		991.0		—		991.0		—		391.0	—
Kinematic viscosity at 100°C, cSt [b]	max	10.0			15.0	25.0		35.0				45.0			55.0	
Flash point, °C	min	60			60	60		60				60			60	
Pour point [c] (upper), °C winter quality summer quality	max max	0 6	24 24		30 30	30 30		30 30				30 30			30 30	
Carbon residue, Conradson, % (m/m)	max	10		14	14	15	20	18	22		—	22		—	22	—
Ash, % (m/m)	max	0.10			0.10	0.10	0.15	0.15	0.20			0.20			0.20	
Water, % (V/V)	max	0.50			0.80	1.0		1.0				1.0			1.0	
Sulphur, % (m/m)	max	3.5			4.0	5.0		5.0				5.0			5.0	
Vanadium, mg/kg	max	150		300	350	200	500	300	600			600			600	

[a] Density in kilograms per litre at 15°C should be multiplied by 1000 before comparison with these values.
[b] 1 cSt = 1 mm²/s.
[c] Purchasers should ensure that this pour point is suitable for the equipment on board, especially if the vessel is operating in both the Northern and Southern hemispheres.

In some smaller vessels, and in the auxiliary engines of some larger vessels, gas oil is used. This grade of fuel is marketed under various names including bunker gas oil, and marine gas oil. Such a fuel is a light distillate with a clear and bright appearance, and is a clean fuel in that it does not contain any residual fuel. On the other hand, diesel fuel may contain a small amount of residual fuel and be dark or black in colour, and is known as marine diesel oil or marine diesel fuel.

Various names are used by suppliers for residual fuels, including the terms bunker C fuel, heavy fuel oil, bunker fuel oil and marine fuel oil. These fuels are the highest viscosity and thus the cheapest residual fuel available at a port. Often a range of intermediate fuels are available which have a lower viscosity than the cheapest fuel available at that port, and are supplied to a stated viscosity. Such products are given different designations depending on the supplier, and include such terms as light marine fuel, intermediate fuels, thin fuel oils, and interfuels. The maximum viscosity at 50°C in centistokes is often suffixed to the designation. For example, IF 180 would be an interfuel with a maximum viscosity of 180cSt at 50°C.

Density

Density is the absolute relationship between mass and volume at a stated temperature and the SI unit is kg/m³. This gives values of 800–1010kg/m³ for marine fuels. An alternative unit is kg/l, which gives values lower by a factor of 1000. Knowledge of the density of a fuel is needed for quantity calculations;

also its value needs to be known in order to select the optimum size of gravity disc for purification. Densities are measured over a range of temperatures, usually, for convenience, at the temperature at which the fuel is stored. The value is then corrected back by the use of standard tables to a reference temperature, which is usually 15°C.

The reason that some grades in Table 2 have a density restriction of 991 kg/m³, is that this is the accepted limit for fuel centrifugal purification. Density gives an indication of other fuel characteristics, including specific energy and ignition quality.

Viscosity

Viscosity is a measure of the resistance of a liquid to shear or flow, and is measured in centistokes (cSt) with a quoted reference temperature. The methods of reporting in Redwood, Saybolt, and Engler units are now obsolete. For distillate fuels the reference temperature is 40°C. In recent years 50°C has been used as the reference temperature for residual fuels, and this temperature has been associated with the classification of the fuels as discussed in the section on terminology. In the specification shown in Table 2 a reference temperature of 100°C is used.

Each fuel has its own temperature/viscosity relationship, and although oil suppliers publish temperature/viscosity charts, it should be appreciated that these charts are based on average data of a large number of representative fuels. As the relationship for any particular fuel depends on its crude oil source and the refinery processes employed, estimations made from the charts cannot be regarded as precise. In general, for the lower viscosity fuels the difference is small, but it becomes wider as the viscosity of the fuel increases. A knowledge of the viscosity is necessary for the determination of the heating required for a fuel for transfer purposes, and the temperature range required for satisfactory injection and combustion at the fuel atomiser.

When all residual marine fuel was manufactured by straight run distillation, viscosity was a broad and generally accepted indicator of fuel quality. Today, due to the world-wide adoption of secondary refining processes, viscosity is no longer any indicator of fuel quality.

Flash point

The flash point of a fuel is the lowest temperature at which sufficient vapour is given off to produce a flash on application of a flame under specified test conditions. The flash point may be measured as a closed or open cup figure and for marine fuels the closed cup figure is used. The test method uses the Pensky-Marten apparatus. The minimum flash point for fuel in the machinery space of a merchant ship is governed by international legislation and the value is 60°C. For fuels used for emergency purposes, external to the machinery space, for example the lifeboats, the flash point must be greater than 43°C. The purpose of defining a minimum flash point is to minimise fire risk during normal storage and handling.

Cloud point

The cloud point of a distillate fuel is the temperature at which wax starts to crystallise out, and this is seen when the clear fuel becomes opaque. For marine fuels as specified in ISO 8217, this characteristic is only applicable to grade DMX as shown in Table 1.

Pour point

The pour point is the lowest temperature at which a marine fuel oil can be handled without excessive amounts of wax crystals forming out of solution. At a lower temperature the fuel will gel, thereby preventing flow. Although marine diesel oil is sometimes received on a vessel as a clear product, and is generally considered as a distillate, for the purpose of wax indication it is considered 'black'. This is because not all marine diesel oil is clear, and it can be delivered through the same transfer lines as residual fuels. For fuels that are 'black', i.e. those containing residual components, the influence of wax is indicated by pour point. For vessels using fuels of a low viscosity, storage heating may be necessary to prevent wax formation rather than pumping limitations, but with the more viscous fuels the temperature needed to reduce the viscosity to pumpable levels is sufficient to avoid all pour point problems.

Carbon residue

The carbon residue of a fuel is the tendency to form carbon deposits under high temperature conditions in an inert atmosphere, and may be expressed as either Ramsbottom carbon residue, Conradson carbon residue (CCR) or micro carbon residue (MCR). This parameter is considered by some to give an approximate indication of the combustibility/deposit forming tendencies of the fuel. The values in fuels which result from secondary refining processes, such as visbreaking, are higher than those from other refinery processes.

Water

Normally the level of water in the fuel is very low, since effort is made by the supplier to deliver the fuel as dry as possible and 0.1%–0.2% by volume is typical. The ingress of water can come from a number of sources, which include tank condensation and tank leakage. Where steam is used for tank heating purposes, heating coil leakage is another potential source of water. Water is normally removed by gravitational separation in the fuel tanks and by the centrifugal purification system.

Ash

The ash value is related to the inorganic material in the fuel oil. The actual value depends upon three factors, firstly the inorganic material naturally present in the crude oil, secondly the refinery processes employed, and thirdly, upon possible subsequent contamination due to sand dirt and rust scale. For distillate fuels the ash level, which is defined as the residue remaining after all the combustible components of the oil have been burned is negligible. The ash constituents from the crude oil are concentrated in residual fuels. Vanadium, and other materials such as silicon, aluminium, nickel, sodium and iron, are the usual main contributing components.

Vanadium

Vanadium is a metal that is present in all crude oils in an oil soluble form, and the levels found in residual fuels depend mainly on the crude oil source, with those from Venezuela and Mexico having the highest levels. The actual level is also related to the concentrating effect of the refinery processes used in the production of the residual fuel. There is no economic process for removing vanadium from either the crude oil or residue.

Sediment and stability

Sediment by extraction is a measure of the content of what are mostly inorganic materials in the fuel, and as such is of limited relevance. These materials are insoluble contaminants such as sand, dirt, and rust scale, and are not derived from the fuel. What is of greater importance is the total sediment content of the fuel, which can include hydrocarbon material which relates to stability. A stable fuel may be defined as one which does not precipitate asphaltenic sludge. The extent of precipitation of such sludge is determined by the total sediment test, which is a filtration method.

Sulphur

Sulphur is a naturally occurring element in crude oil which is concentrated in the residual component. Hence the amount of sulphur in the fuel oil depends mainly on the source of the crude oil and to a lesser extent on the refining process. Typically for residual fuel on a world-wide basis the value is in the order of 1.5%–4% wt. The level of sulphur in the fuel has a marginal effect on the specific energy as shown by the empirical equation in a later section. In the combustion process in a diesel engine potentially the presence of sulphur in the fuel can give rise to corrosive wear. This can be minimised by suitable operating conditions, and suitable lubrication of the cylinder liner with alkaline lubricant.

In the future the sulphur content of marine fuel oil may be limited so as to reduce atmospheric pollution, in the form of sulphur dioxide, from international shipping.

Asphaltenes

Some organisations have suggested that asphaltenes provide an alternative indicator of combustion behaviour. From trials it would appear that there is no simple relationship between asphaltenes and combustion performance. It should be noted that the term asphaltene used in the generic sense covers a wide range of the heavier hydrocarbon structures. Used in the normal analytical sense, the term only defines a certain group of asphaltenes.

Silicon and aluminium

Silicon may be present in the fuel in the form of sand, and aluminium may also be present in very small quantities, having been picked up by the crude oil in sub-surface rocks. It is generally accepted that an indication of aluminium represents the potential presence of catalytic fines. These catalytic fines are particles arising from the catalytic cracking process in the refinery and are in the form of complex alumino-silicates. Depending upon which catalyst is used this particulate matter varies in both size and hardness. It should be appreciated that this is an expensive material for the oil refiner and stringent measures are taken for its retention. During the 1980s the generally accepted parameter for limiting the amount of catalytic fines in marine fuel was by specifying a limit for aluminium of 30 mg/kg. The composition of this catalyst is variable and now the concept of limiting the amount of catalyst present by limiting the combination of silicon and aluminium to 80 mg/kg is gaining acceptance.

Operational experience has shown that excessive catalytic fines can lead to high piston ring and liner wear. The level of catalytic fines in delivered fuel can be significantly reduced by efficient centrifugal purification prior to combustion in the engine.

Ignition quality

Cetane index is an empirical measure of ignition quality for distillate grades of marine fuel (DMX, DMA, DMB; see Table 1). This index is calculated from the mid boiling point and density, i.e. from parameters which relate indirectly to the chemical composition of the fuel. Research work in the 1980s developed two empirical measures of ignition quality for residual fuel. In both equations, use is made of the density and viscosity parameters of the fuel. The calculated ignition index (CII) equation gives values for residual fuel in the same order as the cetane index for distillate fuels, while the calculated carbon aromaticity index (CCAI) gives numbers in the range 760–870. It should be noted that in both equations density is the dominant characteristic. Figure 2 is a nomogram which incorporates both CII and CCAI.

It is not possible to make general recommendations on the minimum CII or maximum CCAI value for a particular engine, as the original design, the present mechanical state and operating conditions will affect the ignition quality requirements. Some engine manufacturers limit the ignition quality of the fuel for their engines by limiting the density of the fuel.

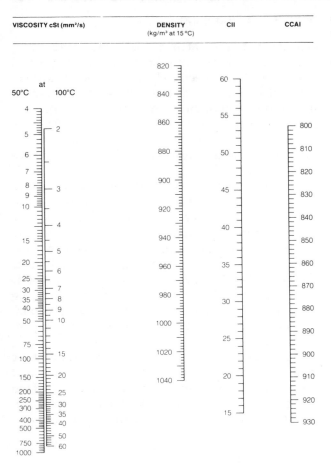

Figure 2 Nomogram for deriving CCAI and CII.

of the fuel and the application of corrections for any sulphur, water and ash that are present.

Gross specific energy (MJ/kg) =

$$\left(52.19 - 8.802\rho^2 10^{-6}\right) \times \left[1 - 0.01(x + y + s)\right] + 9.42(0.01s)$$

Net specific energy (MJ/kg) =

$$\left(46.704 - 8.802\rho^2 10^{-6} + 3.167\rho 10^{-3}\right) \times \left[1 - 0.01(x + y + s)\right]$$
$$+ 0.01(9.42s - 2.449x)$$

where:
  ρ is the density at 15°C kg/m³;
  x is the water content, expressed as a percentage by mass;
  y is the ash content, expressed as a percentage by mass;
  s is the sulphur content, expressed as a percentage by mass.

On a world-wide basis the specific energy does vary slightly, depending mainly on the density and sulphur content of the fuel. Figure 3 shows the net specific energy (MJ/kg) taking account of variations in density of sulphur and water, and is illustrated with a density of 987 kg/m³, 2.5% sulphur and 0.02% water, to give a net specific energy of 40.37 MJ/kg. If required, the slight effect of ash may be taken into account by subtraction of 0.02 MJ/kg for each 0.05% wt ash. Typically the ash value is in the order of 0.03–0.1% wt.

Specific energy

Since marine fuel is purchased by the ship owner to produce heat for conversion into work, one might expect this characteristic to be quoted in a specification. The specific energy is not controllable in the manufacture of marine fuel oil, except in a secondary manner by the specification of other properties. Specific energy can be calculated with a degree of accuracy sufficient for normal purposes from the density

Sodium

In general, fuels leaving the refinery have a sodium level below 50 mg/kg. However should the fuel contain some salt water the sodium level will increase. A 1% sea water contamination represents a potential 100 mg/kg increase. Normally sea water can be removed from the fuel by gravitational separation in the settling tank and centrifugal purification. It is well known that there are low melting temperatures of sodium/vanadium complexes of certain critical ratios. The most critical sodium to vanadium ratio is about 1 to 3.

Compatibility

Whilst every fuel is manufactured to be stable within itself, in that it does not have the tendency to produce asphaltenic sludge, it does not necessarily follow that two stable fuels are compatible when blended or mixed together. Compatibility may be defined as the

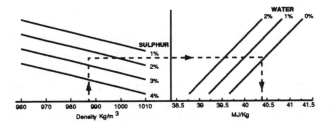

Figure 3 Nomogram to determine net specific energy.

lack of asphaltenic sludge formation following mixing. In order to avoid the potential problems of two fuels being incompatible, the general recommendation is that mixing and blending of fuel from different sources on board ship should be avoided as far as is practicable.

HEALTH, SAFETY AND ENVIRONMENT

When properly used, with safe handling procedures and high standards of personal and industrial hygiene, marine fuels are unlikely to present risks to health and safety. However if good standards are not maintained, hazards can arise.

General precautions when using marine fuels

The most common means of exposure to marine fuel is probably through skin contact. It is therefore important that good hygiene practices are followed if the possibility of adverse health effects from skin contact is to be avoided. Good working practices should minimise potential for skin contact and only disposable 'wipes' should be used. Oily rags or tools should never be put into pockets. Cotton or polyester/cotton overalls normally provide adequate protection where only intermittent or occasional contact is likely. Where a higher degree of contact is possible additional protective clothing, such as gloves, aprons and oil resistant footwear should be worn as appropriate. Clothes should be changed regularly, immediately if they are impregnated with oil, and laundered before re-use. Oil saturated clothing should not be allowed to chafe against the skin.

Fuels such as kerosene or gas oil, or solvents like white spirit, should never be used to wash the skin as they themselves may cause dermatitis, or even skin cancer if used repeatedly. Petroleum products should be washed off the skin with soap or proprietary skin cleansers and warm water. Barrier creams may help to prevent grime becoming ingrained into the skin but offer little or no protection against harmful substances. Skin cleansers and moisturising creams should be used regularly as they prevent defatting and help replace natural oils.

High standards of equipment maintenance and machinery space cleanliness should be followed to minimise exposure. Adequate ventilation of the spaces is essential. Precautions must be taken to eliminate or minimise exposure to oil mists which may be emitted into the working environment during certain operations, e.g. the testing of fuel injection equipment. The concentrations of such mists should be as low as possible and should not exceed 5 mg/m³. Although specialised equipment is required to measure oil mist concentrations, the presence of a visible mist, when viewed against background light, indicates that unsafe levels may be present.

Special procedures and precautions should be adopted for anyone entering a fuel tank, in order to avoid asphyxiation or other hazards arising from the build-up of toxic or flammable gas from fuel or sludge. An appropriate safety code should be consulted for detailed advice.

Whenever protective equipment is required, its use should be fully understood, and facilities must be available for cleaning, inspection, maintenance and storage of the equipment.

To reduce the risk of accidental swallowing (ingestion), marine fuels should never be stored in unlabelled or incorrectly labelled containers. Accidental ingestion of the lighter marine fuels may cause vomiting followed by aspiration of liquid into the lungs which can cause serious damage. For this reason vomiting must not be induced as a first aid measure.

Ash from fuel oil combustion, whether from a boiler or a diesel engine can contain irritant and toxic substances. It is therefore important that suitable personal protective equipment, including approved respirators, is used when removing ash deposits.

Flammability

Even when residual fuels are at a temperature below their measured flash point, they are capable of producing light hydrocarbons in the tank headspace, such that the vapour composition may be near to or within the flammable range. Hence all residual fuel oil headspaces should be considered to be potentially flammable.

Traditionally, gas detectors such as explosion meters have been used to check that enclosed spaces are 'gas free'. They have also been used to measure the 'flammability' of headspaces as a percentage of the lower flammable limit (LFL). Such detectors rely on a calibration carried out normally on a single hydrocarbon (e.g. methane), which may have LFL characteristics that are far removed from the hydrocarbons actually present in the headspace. When using an explosimeter to assess the degree of hazard in residual oil tank headspaces, it is recommended that the instrument is calibrated with a pentane/air or hexane/air mixture. This will result in a more conservative estimate of the flammability, but the readings should not be regarded as providing a precise measurement of the vapour space condition. When taking measurements, the manufacturer's operating instructions should be closely followed. It is also important that the calibration of the instrument should be checked frequently. This is necessary as the oxidation catalyst detectors are likely to be suscepti- ble to poisoning, when exposed to residual oil va- pours.

In view of the problems associated with obtaining accurate measurements of the flammability of re- sidual fuel tank headspaces using readily available portable equipment, the measured percentage of the LFL only broadly ranks fuels in terms of relative hazard. Care should therefore be exercised in inter- pretation of the figures generated by such gas detec- tors. Measure levels in excess of 50% LFL are gener- ally considered to indicate that precautionary meas- ures are required.

At all times the temperatures in the fuel oil system should conform with recognised codes of practice and excessive local temperatures should be avoided. Particular care should be taken to ensure that any flame screens/traps are in good condition on the various fuel oil tank vent pipes, and that there are no ignition sources in the area immediately surround- ing the venting system. The reason for this is that when tanks are being filled, the tank headspace gas will be displaced through the vent pipes. When fill- ing empty or near empty tanks, it should be ensured that the heating coils are shut down and cool. Fuel oil contacting hot exposed heating coils could lead to a flammable atmosphere being rapidly generated. All residual fuel oil tank headspaces should be classified as 'hazardous' and all electrical equipment within the space must meet the appropriate safety standard.

All operations, such as ullaging and sampling, should be carried out to avoid any hazards associated with static electrical charges. These precautions would, for example, include ensuring that metallic sampling equipment and ullaging equipment is properly earthed or bonded to the tank structure. When tanks are opened, it is important not to stand downwind of the tank and to ensure that there are no sources of ignition within the vicinity of the tank hatch.

The flammability of the headspace of residual fuel oil tanks should be monitored regularly. Should a measured value in excess of the recommended level be detected, action should be taken to reduce the vapour concentration by purging the headspace with low pressure air. (IMO resolution A.565 (14) states 50% LFL as the recommended value.) Gases should be vented to a safe area with no ignition sources in the vicinity of the outlet. When venting has been com- pleted, gas concentrations within the tank should continue to be monitored and, if necessary, further venting should be undertaken. Once the tank has been purged with air, consideration may be given to inerting the headspace should it be practical to do so.

Environment

Unrestricted disposal of oil-contaminated mixtures, such as sludge from fuel treatment, into the sea is forbidden by international law, except under well defined conditions laid down in MARPOL, the inter- national convention for the prevention of pollution from ships 1973, and its 1978 Protocol, Annex 1. In practical terms there are two ways of disposing of fuel oil sludge; by on board incineration, or by stor- age on board for eventual discharge ashore. Some vessels have an incinerator which, besides being designed to burn sludge, can also deal with other ship generated waste. On other vessels there may be arrangements by which the sludge can be burnt in an auxiliary boiler.

In some ports and local geographical areas there are environmental regulations which apply to the emissions arising from the burning of marine fuel oil. The great majority of current regulations apply to the sulphur level of the fuel burnt, which determines the sulphur dioxide (SO_2) on combustion. In order to meet these requirements it is often necessary for vessels trading to such areas to have an additional fuel oil storage tank with a fuel of the defined maxi- mum level of sulphur.

Another environmental aspect relating to emis- sions resulting from the combustion of fuel oil is the nitrogen oxides (NO_x) level of the exhaust gas. The level of NO_x formed depends mainly on the combus- tion process, and for a diesel engine can be as high as 1500 ppm. This level can be reduced slightly, either by adjustment of the engine, usually with a slight rise in specific fuel consumption, or by burning a fuel oil emulsion (a mixture of fuel finely dispersed with water). These methods alone, or in combination, are capable of giving the levels of reduction which are being discussed for future regulations. However, at present a few ports have local regulations which require much higher reductions; to meet these the exhaust gas has to be treated chemically. The plant required for this is large and expensive.

FUEL SYSTEMS

Each fuel system on a vessel can be conveniently sub- divided into two parts, storage and treatment, before the fuel is finally delivered to the boiler or diesel engine.

Bunkering

When bunkering, every effort should be made to segregate bunkers from different sources in different tanks. The reason for this is that whilst reputable suppliers manufacture fuels which are in themselves stable products, it may be that they are incompatible with fuels already on board. In such a case an unstable blend may occur in the ship's tanks, which could result in precipitation of asphaltenic deposits as sludge in the tanks, pipes, filters and centrifuges.

It is the responsibility of the ship's staff to obtain from the fuel supplier a sealed, labelled, and representative fuel sample at each bunkering operation. This should be retained for at least 90 days and should be available for use in the event of any dispute with the fuel supplier. The bunker delivery is accompanied by a bunker delivery receipt note, and the amount of information given in this document on a world wide basis is variable. The quantity delivered will be indicated by either tank dips or flow meter readings, and these readings should be witnessed. To calculate the quantity in tonnes, the density of the fuel and the delivery temperature must be known.

Fuel testing

Analysis of particular characteristics of the fuel delivered may be carried out by some independent shore based laboratory, or by tests carried out onboard. Various organisations offer the shipowner comprehensive fuel analysis and advice on how the fuel should be handled or treated. The two most widely used are Lloyd's Register's 'Fuel Oil Bunker Analysis and Advisory Service' (FOBAS), and 'DNV Petroleum Services'. From the number of samples analysed from all over the world, both organisations have built up extensive databases.

Testing of fuel on board ship may range from one or two tests to fully automated online monitors. Whatever tests are used it is essential that there is a reasonable degree of confidence for the values determined. Shipboard manual tests which give such confidence are available for density, viscosity, water content and flash point. It is interesting to note that it is a requirement that United Kingdom passenger ships carry a Pensky-Marten closed cup flash point testing apparatus, so that the flash point of all the fuels bunkered for use in the machinery space can be tested to show that they have a flash point greater than 60°C.

In the case of fully automated on line monitors there is a direct read out for viscosity, density and elemental analysis (e.g. sulphur, silicon, vanadium), as well as derived parameters such as 'ignition index', expressed as either CCAI or CII. Whilst onboard testing provides effectively immediate results, it is not possible to replicate the total analysis carried out in the laboratory ashore.

Storage and transfer

The bunker tank configuration depends on the ship design, but a feature of all arrangements is a transfer pump and, for residual fuel, some heating system. For most vessels using residual fuel, tank heating is carried out by low pressure steam, but on some vessels thermal fluid heating is used. The temperature of the fuel should be maintained above the pour point, otherwise there is the possibility of wax formation. In the case of fuels with a high wax content if left to cool, it may be difficult to reheat the fuel to a temperature above the pour point. A temperature of 5°C above the pour point is usually sufficient to keep any wax in solution, but since the pour point is not usually advised at the time of bunkering it is preferable to maintain the fuel in the bunker tanks at a temperature of 35°C.

Figure 4 shows a simplified tank arrangement. It should be noted that all storage tanks are fitted with a sounding arrangement, temperature sensing point if heated, and a vent. The outlet of this vent is always external to the machinery space and the end fitted with a wire gauze diaphragm serving as a flame trap. When the storage tank is in the machinery space the outlet valve is of such a design that it can be closed remotely in the event of fire. A section of such a valve is shown in Fig 5.

The pumps for fuel transfer are of the positive displacement type and are usually of screw or gear

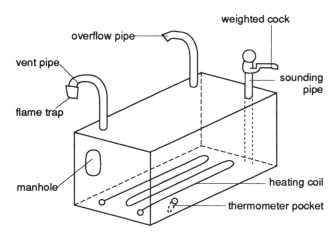

Figure 4   Simplified tank arrangement.

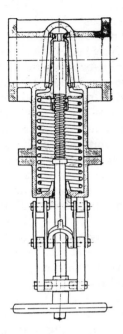

Figure 5   Section of quick closing sluice valve.

design. With such designs the pump output is regulated by means of a by-pass arrangement. It is generally accepted that the maximum viscosity for pumpability is 1000 cSt. Figure 6 shows the approximate temperature/viscosity relationship for the grades shown in Table 2. Clearly high viscosity grades will require to be heated to 45°C to reduce the viscosity to a pumpable level.

Shipboard treatment of marine fuel

Once a vessel has bunkered fuel, and before the fuel is burnt in either a diesel engine or a boiler, shipboard treatment takes place. In the case of vessels burning distillate fuel, the treatment probably only consists of a filter, which may be of a coalescer type in order to trap any water that is present. For vessels burning residual fuels the shipboard treatment will be more extensive. The arrangements vary, and depend on whether the vessel is a steamship or motorship. For a steamship, in addition to settling tanks, cold and hot filters are installed in the system prior to the boiler. In the case of the motorship, which accounts for over

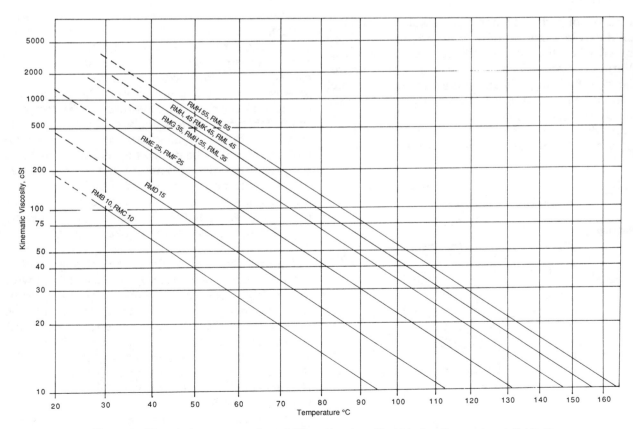

Figure 6   Viscosity/temperature chart of different grades of fuel (designation as given inTable 2).

97% of the world's merchant fleet in terms of number of vessels, the shipboard treatment is more complex. In addition to settling tanks and filters, centrifuges are installed in the great majority of such vessels for the shipboard treatment of the fuel. The reason the fuel treatment plant is more complex is because it is necessary to clean the fuel to take account of the fine clearances which exist in the fuel system of the diesel engine.

FILTERS

The term 'filters' when applied to the fuel oil system can mean various arrangements. Usually all systems have a transfer pump and this is protected on the suction side by a filter to prevent large solid material from damaging the pump internals. In distillate fuel systems a coalescer filter is often included. For residual fuel systems 'hot filters' are also fitted. Examples of some of each are described below.

Suction filters

These can be coarse mesh filters, which have to be manually cleaned, or an 'Auto-klean' type as shown in Fig 7. The 'Auto-klean' filter consists of a stack of thin steel annular discs, mounted on a central spindle. A number of guide rods pass through each disc and the rods carry thin steel washers which separate the discs by a small clearance. Over the bottom disc there is a blank circular plate and the arrangement is

mounted so that the oil flow is through the spaces between the discs. Thin steel cleaning blades project into the space between each pair of discs and these are fixed close to the stack by means of a square sectioned spindle. The plate stack is rotated past the cleaning blades and these are shaped so that whichever way the stack is rotated, the dirt lodged between the plates is pushed out and falls to the bottom of the chamber. Sometimes magnetic elements are incorporated in suction filters to trap any loose ferrous particles.

Coalescer filter

A coalescer is a filtering device for use with distillate fuels for the removal of water and solid impurities.

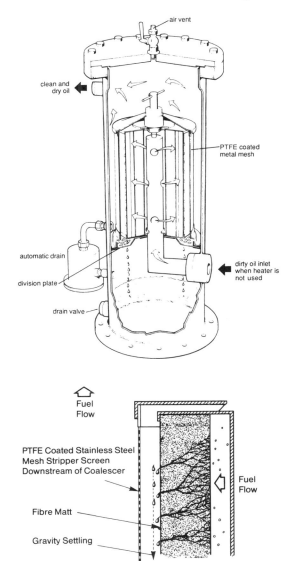

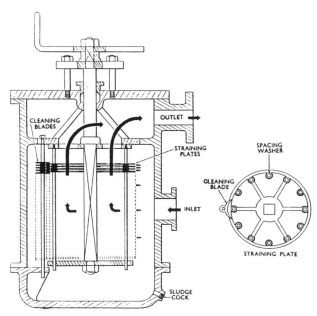

Figure 7   Auto klean filter.

Figure 8   Coalescer with detail of element.

As it is a static device it requires little attention. However, if large amounts of water are present, the cost of renewal of the filter cartridge becomes excessive.

Figure 8 shows a typical combined filter coalescer unit. A two stage process takes place in the filter coalescer cartridge, which is a single replaceable assembly. The fuel to be treated flows radially outwards through the cartridge, firstly through a pleated inner element and secondly through the outer coalescer stage. The inner element which is made from synthetic fibre is pleated with folds separated by spacers. This inner element removes particulate matter down to 5 μm from the fuel, so protecting the outer coalescer element from excessive quantities of contaminant. In the outer coalescer element, which is made from inorganic fibres suitably pressed to a predetermined density and depth, any fine water droplets are agglomerated to such a size that they fall by gravity to the sump. To further assist in the removal of water from the fuel, there is a PTFE coated outer steel mesh. Water from the sump may be drained either manually or automatically.

Hot filters

A typical automatic full flow hot filter for residual fuel is shown diagrammatically in Fig 9. The design of the filter is such that there are two separate filter chambers and a distributor driven by a hydraulic motor. One of the filter chambers is for full flow filtration, whilst the other is a diversion chamber. The actual filtration takes place through disc type elements, and within each chamber the elements are divided by ribs into eight sections. When assembled, the ribbed elements form eight independent filtering columns. The hydraulic motor 'H' rotates the distributor 'C' in steps and the profile of the distributor is such that each part of every column is back-flushed once per rotation. Complete rotation of the distributor takes place every one to three minutes. This continual back-flushing ensures a low and constant pressure drop across the filter.

Referring to phase 1 in Fig 9, the unfiltered fuel enters at 'A' and flows into chamber 'B'. This is the space between the distributor 'C' and the inner perimeter of the sleeve on which the filter elements 'D' are fitted. From chamber 'B' the oil is distributed into and through seven of the eight filtering columns formed by the elements. Here the solid material is trapped on the inner side. The filtered oil is led into chamber 'E', and passes to the filter outlet 'F'. While 'full flow' filtering is taking place in seven columns, solids are being removed from the elements in one

Phase 1

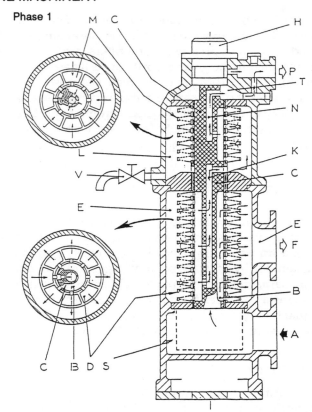

Phase 2

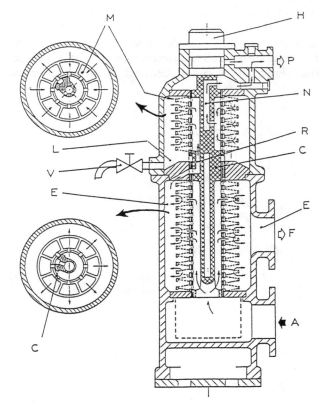

Figure 9   Moatti type filter.

column by back-flushing using part of the filtered oil from chamber 'E'. This back-flushed oil passes through 'K' to the diversion chamber 'L'. It then passes radially inwards through six columns of the diversion filter elements 'M'. The filtered oil passes through passage 'N' in the distributor 'C' and is returned to the suction side of the circulating pump through outlet 'P'.

In phase 2 of Fig 9 it will be seen that the distributor, driven by the hydraulic motor has rotated ¹⁄₁₆ of a revolution in relation to phase 1. Filtration is only carried out in six of the eight columns of the full flow chamber and no back-flushing takes place. Part of the filtered oil in chamber 'E' passes through channel 'R' and through the diversion filter elements 'M' in one column (radially outwards), so removing the trapped solids from the outer side of the elements. The heavy particles settle to the bottom of chamber 'L'. Back-flushed oil now passes radially inwards through the other seven columns, where any remaining solids are trapped on the outer surface. Finally the filtered oil passes through passage 'N', before discharge to the suction side of the circulating pump. The solids trapped in the diversion chamber 'L' are periodically drained through the valve 'V' to the sludge tank.

Another type of hot filter is shown in Fig 10. The feature of this is the notch wire element, which is wound in the shape of a cage. The filter consists of an upper (clean side) and a lower duty chamber, which is separated by a central dividing plate. In the base plate there are holes around the circumference which provide locating positions for the filter elements and a path for the oil flow from the dirty to the clean side of the filter. Under normal operating conditions the back-flush outlet is closed by a solenoid valve and hence the full flow of oil passes through the filter elements.

The filter has a pneumatically operated hydraulic back-flushing system, which uses the system pressure and the reverse flow of the clean oil through the filter elements. Back-flushing is initiated either by a pre-set differential pressure across the filter unit or at pre-set time intervals. The back-flush cycle is usually 2–3 minutes, during which time each element is back-flushed at least twice. If one complete cycle is insufficient, the differential pressure switches will activate a repeat cycle. The filter can be back-flushed at any time by means of a manual override. To ensure that efficient back-flushing is achieved, an orifice plate is fitted in the back-flush outlet. This is sized so that the loss of oil during the back-flush cycle is less than 10% of the system flow.

It is frequently the practice to have a final filter adjacent to the diesel engine before the fuel enters the

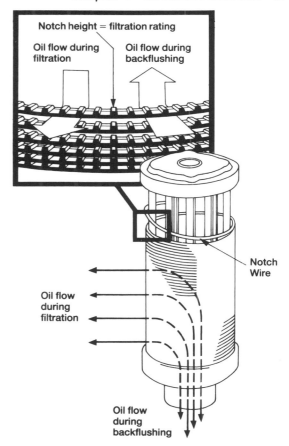

Figure 10   Notch type hot filter.

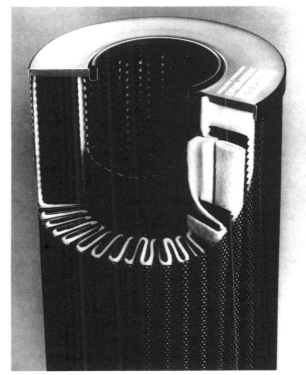

Figure 11   Depth filter.

engine. The purpose of this filter, which is often fitted in duplex, is to provide further particulate control of the fuel. These can be of various types and one such type, a depth filter, is shown in Fig 11. This filter is disposable, and by its pleated design combined with the filtering medium is capable of retaining a large amount of particulate matter. The filtering medium is a synthetic felt, with a nominal filtration rating of about 5 μm. Operationally, the condition of the filter can be assessed by observing the differential pressure across the element.

Settling tank

The settling tank makes use of gravity to separate particles which have a greater density than that of the fuel oil. These particles can be free water which may be dispersed in the fuel, or solid particulate matter such as sand, rust, scale or catalytic fines. For a particular installation the effectiveness of the settling tank depends on a number of factors. These include the residence time for separation, which is determined at the design stage with respect to the number of settling tanks fitted, the tank capacity in relation to the fuel demand, and shape of the tank. The only factor which can be controlled on board is the temperature of the tank, as heating of the fuel reduces the density, as shown in Fig 12. This increases the difference in density between the oil and the free water and solid particulate matter. From Stokes' Law it may be shown that this increase in density difference and reduction in viscosity assists in the rate of separation. For those installations where only one settling tank is fitted, it is preferable to keep this tank periodically topped up to obtain the maximum settling time.

The particulate matter and water is periodically drawn off by means of a manually operated spring loaded drain valve. This valve is spring loaded so that it cannot be accidently left open. It should be noted that over a period of time there is likely to be a build up of sludge in the settling tank so it is good practice to periodically clean these tanks of accumulated sludge. There are usually two suction valves on the settling tank; high and low suction. Both these valves are of similar design to that shown in Fig 5; they can be closed remotely.

In situations where two settling tanks are installed, the treatment of the fuel can be described as a batch process, whilst for those plants where there is only one settling tank the treatment is a continuous process.

Centrifuge

Instead of making use of gravity to cause separation the centrifuge uses centrifugal force, which is much greater. The ratio of the centrifugal force to the gravitational force is often referred to as the 'G value', which depends on the rotational speed and design of the centrifuge and is in the order of 7000–9000.

Marine centrifuges can usually be set up to operate in two modes; as a clarifier or as a purifier. When operating as a clarifier there is only one outlet, which is for fuel oil, but when operating as a purifier there is an additional outlet for the discharge of water.

Principle of operation of the centrifuge

A simple centrifuge can be developed by rotation of the settling tank (Fig 13a) through 90 deg, and adding a second as shown in Fig 13b. When the bowl is rotated, centrifugal force will throw any item with

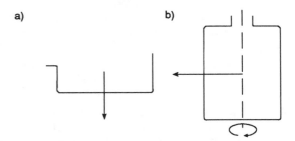

Figure 13   Development of a simple centrifuge.

a density greater than the fuel oil density (the solid matter and free water) to the periphery of the bowl. To form a clarifier, Fig 13b can be developed by the addition of inlet and outlet connections and the inclusion of a number of discs, as shown in Fig 14. It may be shown that the efficiency of the centrifuge is increased by the inclusion of a number of discs, which have the effect of increasing the surface area to aid separation. These discs are separated a distance of

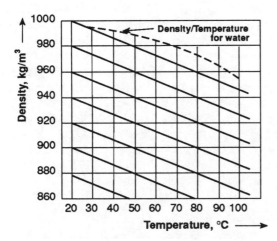

Figure 12   Variation of density of oils with temperature.

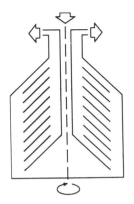

Figure 14 Centrifuge as clarifier.

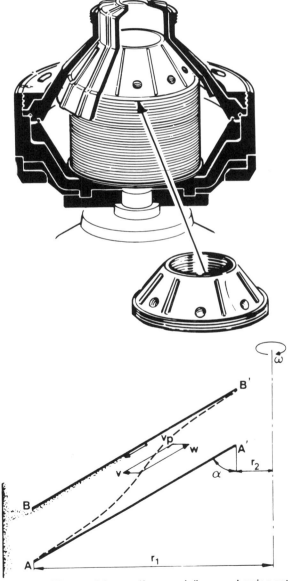

Figure 15 Disc stack in centrifuge, and diagram showing path of limit particle through separation channel.

0.5–0.6mm by a series of caulks fixed to the upper side of the disc, as shown in Fig 15.

After passing down the central passage, the untreated oil is carried by centrifugal force towards the periphery of the bowl and then passes up through the disc stack. It is here that the actual separation takes place, in the channel formed between two discs. In this channel the velocity of the oil is greatest at the centre and zero at the disc surface. Each particle, solid or liquid, is acted upon by two forces. On the one hand, the particle is being forced upwards with the oil stream towards the centre (**w**), whilst on the other, centrifugal force is directing it to the periphery (**v**). It is the resultant of these two forces which determines the path of the particle between the discs (**vp**). In order to be separated out, the particle must be deposited on the upper disc (B–B$_1$ in Fig 15), that is at a radius greater than or equal to r_2. The particle is considered to have separated out on reaching the disc stack surface, and as the liquid velocity is negligible close to this surface, the particle moves outwards by centrifugal force towards the periphery of the bowl. For the worst case, the particle starts from the most difficult position, namely A in Fig 15, and moves along the dotted line as shown, so that it is barely separated out at point B$_1$. In this case all larger particles will become separated out. If the particle enters the disc stack at some intermediate position between AB, the particle size removed will be smaller, when compared to a particle of the same density entering the disc stack at A.

Figure 16 shows the two modes of operation of the centrifuge; clarifier and purifier. In both cases when the machine is in service particulate matter will be collected on the wall of the bowl and, if no corrective action is taken, will continue to build up to such an extent that it is at radius r_1, the outer radius of the disc (see Fig 15), and obstruct flow through the centrifuge. With the centrifuge set as a clarifier the particulate matter may be a combination of both water and solid material, but if the centrifuge is set as a purifier, the particulate matter will only be solid material, as the free water will have been continuously discharged (described in a later section). In older machines it was necessary to stop the centrifuge and manually clean the bowl and disc stack, but with the majority of machines today it is possible to discharge the bowl contents whilst the centrifuge is still running. The actual method of discharge, which may be total or partial, depends on the model, and reference should be made to the manufacturer's handbook for the exact mode of operation.

Centrifugal purifier

When the centrifuge is set as a purifier, there is a

a)　　　　　　　　　　　　　　　　　　　　　　b)

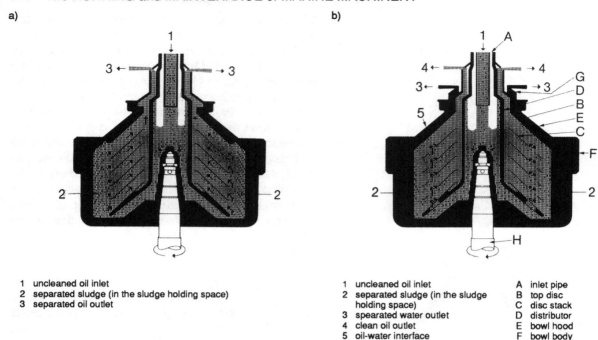

1　uncleaned oil inlet
2　separated sludge (in the sludge holding space)
3　separated oil outlet

1　uncleaned oil inlet
2　separated sludge (in the sludge holding space)
3　spearated water outlet
4　clean oil outlet
5　oil-water interface

A　inlet pipe
B　top disc
C　disc stack
D　distributor
E　bowl hood
F　bowl body
G　gravity disc
H　spindle

Figure 16　The centrifuge as a) clarifier; b) purifier.

second outlet pipe for the discharge of water (shown in Fig 16b). For the fuel oil purifier, the untreated oil is a mixture of oil, solids and water which the centrifuge separates into three layers. Whilst in operation a quantity of water remains in the bowl to form a complete seal around the underside of the top disc and, because of the density difference, confines the oil within the outside diameter of the top disc. As marine fuel oil normally only contains a small quantity of water, it is necessary to prime the bowl each time it is run; otherwise all the oil will pass over the water outlet side to waste. The water outlet is at a greater radius than that of the fuel, and within the water outlet there is a gravity disc, sometimes referred to as a dam ring, which controls the radial position of the fuel/water interface. A set of gravity discs is supplied with each machine and the optimum size to be fitted depends on the density of the untreated oil. If the internal diameter of the gravity disc is too small the separating efficiency will be reduced as the interface will be formed within the disc pack. If the internal diameter is too large, the interface will form at a diameter greater than the top disc, and oil will pass to waste through the water outlet. In addition to the density ratio between the oil and the water, there are other factors which can influence the position of the interface. These are viscosity, flow rate and variation in density. A decrease in viscosity, due to an increase in temperature, a decrease in flow rate, a decrease in

back pressure or a decrease in density will result in the interface moving inwards. Conversely, an increase in viscosity due to a decrease in temperature, an increase in flow rate, or an increase in density, will move the interface outwards, ultimately resulting in a loss of the liquid seal. The optimum position of the interface is between the edge of the disc stack and the outer diameter of the top disc as shown in Fig 16.

Some centrifuges are fitted with a manually operated interface control device in order to reduce the frequency of changing gravity discs as a result of changes in density from different bunkerings. This device is available for centrifuges with a paring disc discharge pump for the treated oil, and consists of a pressure balanced valve, fitted into the discharge line. By applying a counter pressure to the discharge line the interface can be moved outside the disc stack without changing the gravity disc. This feature, however, does not replace the requirement for effective control of throughput and temperature.

Arrangement of centrifuges

For a vessel operating on residual fuel, the generally recommended practice is to operate two machines in series. The first machine should be set as a purifier, and the other as a clarifier. This arrangement improves overall separation efficiency, and the clarifier provides a safety margin if the purifier is not set for optimum performance. This safety margin is beneficial in the treatment of high density fuels, when the purifier is operating near to the limit of its performance.

Limitation of the centrifugal purifier

As the density of the fuel increases it becomes difficult to maintain the correct interface position for optimum results in a purifier. The generally accepted density limit is 991 kg/m³ at 15°C. If the fuel density is greater than this value, the density difference between the fuel oil and fresh water is so small that the hydraulic equilibrium in the bowl becomes unstable. This means that any small changes in oil temperature, viscosity or flow rate will cause the oil/water interface to fluctuate, leading to a potential failure of the water seal and impaired separation efficiency.

Treatment of high density fuels

If the residual fuel has a density greater than 991 kg/m³ at 15°C an alternative arrangement to the traditional purifier is required. One such arrangement is the Alcap system, by which fuels up to a density of 1010 kg/m³ at 15°C can be treated.

The centrifuge basically operates as a clarifier. Clean oil is continuously discharged from the clean oil outlet, and any free water and separated sludge accumulate at the periphery of the bowl. When the sludge space is filled up, the separated water approaches the disc and traces of water start to escape with the clean oil. Increased water content in the clean oil is a sign of reduced separation efficiency. In the Alcap system changes in the water content are sensed in the clean oil outlet by the water transducer, as shown in Fig 17. The electrical signals from the transducer are continuously transmitted to and interpreted by the control unit. When the water content in the clean oil reaches a specific 'trigger' point, the control unit determines, based on the time elapsed since the last sludge sequence, which of two methods it will use to empty the bowl. This can either be through a water drain valve or with the sludge through the sludge ports at the periphery of the bowl.

With this type of installation the treatment process is carried out in a single stage. Hence only two machines, one in service and one on stand by, need to be installed.

Homogenisers

A homogeniser is a device used to create a stable uniform composition from a mixture. When included in a marine fuel oil system, its purpose can be to break down relatively large water particles, or to reconstitute an emulsion that has separated out so as to give some stability to the mixture. The fuel oil homogeniser works by agitating the fuel, either mechanically or acoustically. Mechanical agitation includes such methods as pumping the fuel through very fine orifices, while acoustical agitation includes the use of ultrasonic frequency (greater than 30 kHz). The homogeniser does not remove any contaminants which may be present in the fuel being treated.

Fuel heating

Residual fuels invariably have to be heated to reduce the viscosity to that required for atomisation. In the case of a steam plant this is usually in the range 15–65 cSt, whilst for diesel engines the injection viscosity is usually 8–27 cSt. Fuel heaters may be operated by low pressure saturated steam, a thermal fluid or electrical elements. Whatever medium is used, it is important to ensure that the fuel oil is maintained at the correct viscosity range under all conditions. Local overheating may cause cracking of the fuel, which may lay down deposits on the heating surface, impairing the efficient operation of the heater.

Viscosity controller

A viscosity controller is often installed downstream of the fuel oil heater so that a constant injection viscosity can be maintained either to the boiler or diesel engine. There are various types of these instruments, which work on different principles. Funda-

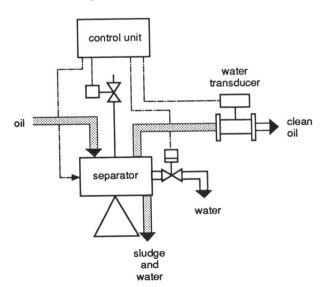

Figure 17 The Alcap system.

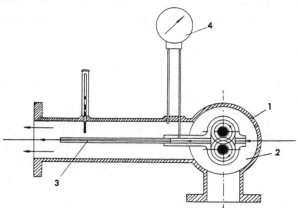

Figure 18 Viscosity controller.

mentally each one measures the viscosity of the fuel, and this value is compared to a set point, generating a signal to control the temperature of the fuel oil heater. Various types of viscosity controllers are available. Some measure shear force, between a fixed and rotating plate, some measure the magnitude of damping caused by the viscosity of the oil on a vibrating rod and others measure the differential pressure resulting from the laminar flow through a capillary tube.

A schematic arrangement of the capillary tube principle of measurement is shown in Fig 18. The stainless steel gear pump '1', is driven by an electric motor, and continuously draws a constant amount of oil from chamber '2', and forces it through the capillary tube '3'. The differential pressure shown at '4', which is directly proportional to the viscosity of the oil, is then used as a signal.

Diagrammatic arrangements

Figure 19 shows the diagrammatic arrangements of the residual fuel system for a motorship. For clarity the storage, transfer and treatment arrangements have been omitted. It should be noted that although many engines are operated from pier to pier on residual fuel, the facility always exists for the fuel lines to be flushed through with diesel oil.

Figure 20 shows the diagrammatic arrangement of the residual fuel system for a steamship. For clarity the storage and transfer arrangements have been omitted. Under normal circumstances diesel oil would only be used to flush the fuel lines prior to an extended shutdown, such as a repair period.

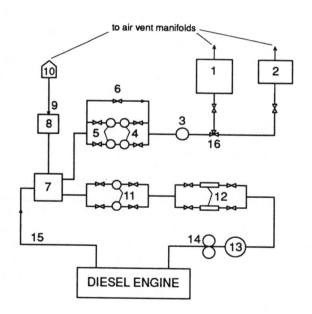

1 Heavy oil daily service tank	9 Automatic float vent valve
2 Diesel oil daily service tank	10 Condenstaion water tap
3 Flow meter	11 High pressure booster pump
4 Suction filter	12 Fuel heater
5 Low pressure oil feed pump	13 Viscosity controller
6 Pressure regulating valve	14 Discharge filter (fine)
7 Buffer tank (mixing tank)	15 Fuel return line
8 Vent unit	16 Valve to diesel

Figure 19 Diagrammatic arrangement of the residual fuel system for a motorship.

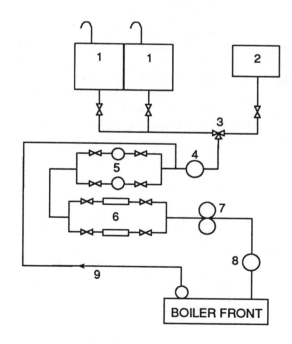

1 Settling tank	6 Heaters
2 Diesel oil service tak	7 Hot filters
3 Three way valve	8 'One turn close' valve
4 Flow meter	9 Fuel return line
5 Fuel pumps	

Figure 20 Diagrammatic arrangement of the residual fuel system for a steamship.

ADDITIVES

Under certain circumstances, following careful assessment of the plant, operating conditions and the fuel quality, the use of additives in marine fuel can be advantageous to the ship owner. In overall terms, the introduction of additives must be cost effective, otherwise the vessel's operating cost is increased unnecessarily. There are two distinct categories of additives, namely those which assist in reducing potential problems in pre-combustion and those which react during the post-combustion phase.

The pre-combustion phase covers the period from receipt of the fuel on board, through storage and shipboard treatment, up to the time it is atomised in a burner or injector. With normal fuel handling procedures, with respect to correct heating, and avoiding mixing of fuels from different bunkerings, no problems should occur. In the event of problems occurring, an effective additive for this phase should be able to make a positive contribution to the following aspects.

1. Dispersion of possible sludge in the fuel tanks.

2. Promotion of the separation of any dispersed water within the fuel.

3. Prevention of sludge formation.

During the post-combustion phase the potential areas of concern depend upon the type of plant installed. In the case of a steamship there is the possibility of corrosion of the superheater tubes, and slag build-up on both the superheater and steam generating tubes, and in the economiser and air heater there is the possibility of low temperature corrosion and carbon. For diesel engines the potential areas of concern are corrosion of exhaust valves, turbo charger fouling, carbon deposition and low-temperature corrosion.

In order to reduce the problems that may occur in the post-combustion phase an additive, which has the effect of an ash modifier, may be beneficial under certain circumstances. The ash is related to the inorganic material in the fuel oil, and when burnt with the oil, the compounds formed due to this material are complex. The type of compound formed and its properties depend upon the operating conditions, and it is also influenced by the presence of unburnt carbon and sulphur gases. Slagging and high temperature corrosion occurs when molten ash adheres to the metal surfaces. Hence, the ash modifier should have the ability to increase the melting point temperature and make the ash more friable. By increasing the melting point temperature a point may be reached where the ash is not in a molten form and hence is less likely to stick to metal surfaces and affect heat transfer.

Numerous ash modifying chemicals which affect the melting process in different ways are available, and the physical nature of the conditioned ash also varies depending upon which compound is used. Situations can arise when, by incorrect application, the effect of the ash modifier can cause further problems in the down stream post-combustion phase.

Some additives are termed 'combustion catalysts'. Their function is to cause the carbon to be more extensively burnt. They influence the reaction and are present in relatively small quantities. Dosage of combustion catalysts is not as critical as with ash modifiers, and to be fully effective the suppliers' instructions must be carefully followed.

REFERENCES

1. Lamb, J. (1948). The burning of boiler fuels in marine diesel engines. *TransIMarE*, **Vol. 60**.
2. Lamb, J. (1950). Further developments in the burning of boiler fuels in marine diesel engines. *TransIMarE*, **Vol. 62**.
3. Arnold, A.G. (1953). The burning of boiler oil in two and four-stroke cycle diesel engines and the development of fuel injection equipment. *TransIMarE*, **Vol. 65**.
4. CIMAC (1990). Recommendations regarding fuel requirements for diesel engines. (3rd edition) **No. 11**.

Chapter 5
Electrical Machines

F Taylor

THREE-PHASE, CAGE ROTOR INDUCTION MOTORS

The three-phase, cage rotor induction motor is the 'first choice' marine motor because of its electrical and mechanical simplicity. The lack of electrical connections to the rotor removes the need for brushes and commutator/sliprings and leads to simple, tough construction, reliable operation and low cost maintenance. The limitation of the simple cage motor is its single available speed. Modern developments, apart from constructional improvements, are mainly towards improving the starting performance and providing some form of speed control.

Construction and operating principle

There are two main components in an induction motor, the rotor and the stator. The stator is the stationary part of the motor. It consists of a frame (yoke) which is fitted with high quality slotted steel laminations forming a magnetic core. Insulated 3-phase windings are located in the slots. The stator winding produces a rotating magnetic field when it is connected to a 3-phase supply. The rotor rotates inside the stator and is a forged steel shaft carrying a laminated steel magnetic core. The aluminium or copper cage winding has conductor bars embedded in the surface of the core and the ends of the bars are shorted together by end rings. The air-gap between the rotor and stator is only 1–2 mm wide. The smaller the air-gap, the smaller the starting surge current and the higher the operating power factor. High precision ball or roller bearings are required; sleeve bearings do not give the required accuracy. Most motors are self-cooling although some large variable speed motors may have air circulated by a fan driven by a small auxiliary motor. This prevents overheating at low speed. On aluminium cages, integral fins are cast onto the end rings to agitate and circulate internal air to improve heat transfer.

Figure 1 shows a stator with part of the winding removed so that the core slots can be seen easily. Air ducts between the core and yoke assist heat transfer to keep the motor cool.

Figure 2 shows a typical rotor with a cast aluminium cage winding. Here the rotor core has been sectioned to show the rotor bars and ventilation holes. Notice the integral fins on the end ring castings.

Enclosures for marine motors range from drip-proof, open ventilated (IP22), for locations where water and dust problems are unlikely, to totally enclosed, fan ventilated (IP54) where a greater degree of protection is required (see Fig 3). Deck motors (IP56) can be completely immersed for short periods. All screws have sealing washers and there is a labyrinth seal between the shafts and the end shields.

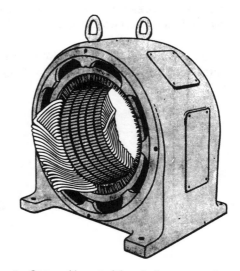

Figure 1   Stator with part of the winding removed.

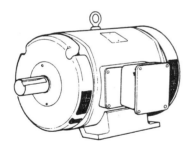

Figure 2 Typical rotor with cast aluminium cage winding.

Special motor enclosures are required if the motor is located in a hazardous area where flammable atmospheres are expected, e.g. pump rooms, paint stores, battery lockers, etc. Flameproof (Exd) and increased safety (Exe) motors are used in these hazardous locations and they need maintenance and inspection procedures according to hazardous area codes of practice.

All electrical equipment enclosures have ingress protection specified by a two or three digit code. Table 1 shows how this code operates.

The third digit for mechanical protection is often omitted for metal enclosures and is used to indicate the strength of polycarbonate enclosures.

IP22

IP54

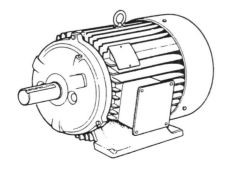

Figure 3 Enclosures.

MOTOR RATED CURRENT (I_e OR I_n)

When a motor is idling, the rotor speed is only slightly lower than the speed of the rotating magnetic field. The input stator current is low since there is little power demand. As load is applied, the motor slows down and draws extra current to supply the power demanded by the load. When the current increases with load, it raises the temperature of the stator winding insulation. The motor current must not be allowed to reach an excessive value which would overheat the stator winding insulation causing it to break down.

The ageing of insulation is a chemical process which is rapidly accelerated by prolonged operation at excessive temperature. To avoid reducing the service life of a motor it must not be run above its rated current for long periods. Short duration overloads will not have an appreciable effect on the insulation. As a rough guide, for every 10°C above the maximum recommended temperature the service life of the insulation will be halved.

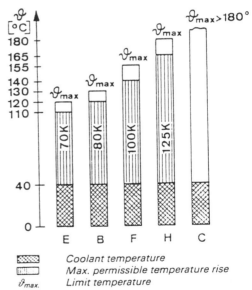

	Coolant temperature
	Max. permissible temperature rise
$\vartheta_{max.}$	Limit temperature

Figure 4 Insulating material classes according to IEC 34.

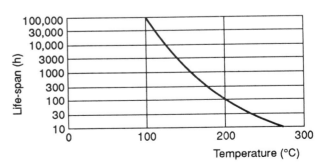

Figure 5 Variation in motor lifespan with temperature.

Table I Operation of Ingress protection code.

1st figure: protection against solid bodies			2nd figure: protection against liquids			3rd figure: mechanical protection		
IP	tests		IP	tests		IP	tests	
0	No protection		0	No protection		0	No protection	
1	Protected against solid bodies larger than 50mm (e.g. finger of the hand)	⌀52.5 mm	1	Protected against vertically falling drops of water (condensation)		1	Impact energy	150g / 15cm
2	Protected against solid bodies larger than 12mm (e.g. finger of the hand)	⌀12.5 mm	2	Protected against drops of water falling at up to 15° from the vertical		2	Impact energy	250g / 15cm
3	Protected against solid bodies larger than 2.5mm (e.g. tools, wires)	2.5mm	3	Protected against drops of rain water at up to 60° from the vertical		3	Impact energy	250g / 20cm
4	Protected against solid bodies larger than 1mm (fine tools and small wires)	1mm	4	Protected against projections of water from all directions		5	Impact energy	500g / 40cm
5	Protected against dust (no harmful deposits)		5	Protected against jets of water from hose nozzle from all directions		7	Impact energy	1.5kg / 40cm
6	Completely protected against dust		6	Protected against jets of water of similar force to heavy seas.		9	Impact energy	5kg / 40cm
			7	Protected against the effects of immersion				

Insulating materials are divided into different classes according to how well they can withstand temperature. Figure 4 shows temperature limits for different classes of insulating material. Figure 5 shows the deterioration of Class E insulation as operating temperature is increased.

MOTOR STATOR WINDING CONNECTIONS

Many modern motors are designed for dual voltage operation. To understand what this means, consider a motor designed for delta operation on a 380V supply with a rated current of 100A (see Fig 6).

Each of the windings is designed to carry a maximum current of $100A/\sqrt{3} = 58A$. The phase windings are insulated to withstand 380V. The same motor can be star connected as in Fig 7, but it must be on a $380V \times \sqrt{3} = 660V$ supply so that the current will be $100A/\sqrt{3} = 58A$ to keep the power input the same. The phase windings still operate at 380V, 58A.

A problem arises if the motor is connected in star to the same 380V supply, as in Fig 8. Because the motor speed is determined by supply frequency the motor output power and input power are the same

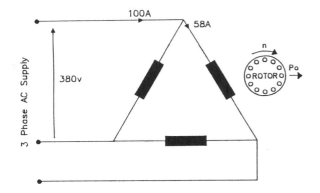

Figure 6   Delta connected motor.

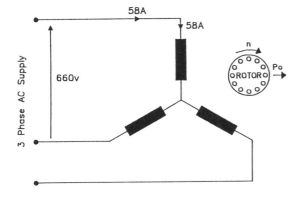

Figure 7   Star connected motor.

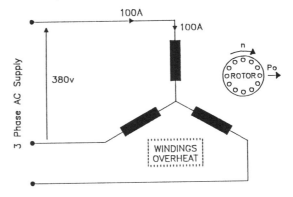

Figure 8   Motor connected in star to the same 380V supply.

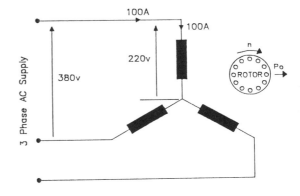

Figure 9   Star connected motor.

for star and delta connections, i.e. line current is 100A in both cases. This causes a severe overload in the star-connected phase windings which, if allowed to continue, will result in burnout of the motor.

A motor designed for delta operation on mains voltage must never be run in star at that voltage.

Many marine motors are designed for star operation at mains voltage, star motors being preferred because they are more durable under certain fault conditions and easier to protect. If a motor is designed for star connection to, say, a 380V supply and has a rated current of 100A, the cross-sectional area of copper in the phase winding is greater than for a similarly rated delta motor so it does not overheat (see Figs 9 and 10).

If this motor is inadvertently connected in delta to the same supply, there does not appear to be a problem. Once again the output speed and power are virtually unaffected. The input current is 100A which makes the phase current 58A.

There is a problem, however, and it is with the winding voltage. The star motor winding insulation is only capable of withstanding just over 220 V and 380 V is now being applied. Situations have been

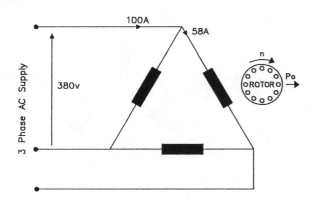

Figure 10   Delta connected motor.

reported of engineers being concerned about star motors seeming to run too hot. They reconnect the motor delta and the problem seems to be solved until, some weeks later, the motor burns out. The insulation withstood the excess voltage until, possibly, a combination of voltage surge, high humidity and ambient temperature causes the insulation to break down. The excess voltage causes increased iron losses leading to overheating which contributes to the breakdown.

The motor nameplate must always be checked and the motor connected correctly for the mains voltage.

MOTOR STARTERS

When the stator windings of an induction motor are switched directly on to a three phase supply a surge current is taken by the motor which dies away as the motor accelerates up to speed. This starting surge current can be up to eight times the motor rated current and occurs because there is no generated emf in the

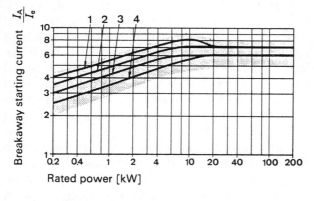

1   Standard value for 2-pole motors
2   Standard value for 4-pole motors
3   Standard value for 6-pole motors
4   Standard value for 8-pole motors

Figure 11   Breakaway starting current range of standard motors as multiple of rated operational current.

windings to control the current at standstill. The graphs of Fig 11 show starting currents for standard motors.

Starting a motor by simply connecting it to the supply is called direct-on-line starting and is the simplest, most economical method of starting. Most marine motors are direct-on-line started. Special reduced voltage starters (star/delta and autotransformer) are used when excessively large starting currents may cause severe voltage 'dip' on the supply which could affect the operation of other loads. Large motors, and smaller motors intended for connection to the emergency generator, use reduced voltage starters.

Starting current does not significantly decrease from standstill to half speed and only reduces to a reasonable level at 80% speed. Figure 12 shows how motor current varies during the run-up period for a 3 kW motor and a 90 kW motor.

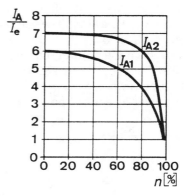

I_{A1} 3kW motor
I_{A2} 90kW motor

Figure 12   Typical starting current curve (as multiple of rated operational current) as a factor of rotational speed of squirrel-cage motors.

It is important that motors accelerate quickly up to speed to prevent excessively long run-up times causing overtemperature in the stator winding insulation and long duration voltage dips on the supply. Run-up time depends on the starting torque developed by the motor which, in turn, is proportional to the square of the supply voltage ($T \propto V^2$). Obviously, the load on the motor will also have an effect on the run-up time. It is worth noting here that the size of the starting current is not increased when the motor is started against load. The starting current is only determined by the value of the supply voltage and the standstill impedance of the stator windings.

Figure 13 shows that unloaded motors reach their idling speed very quickly, and even when started against load most run-up times should not cause problems. Some drives, such as centrifuges and large fans, may require special high torque motors if ac-

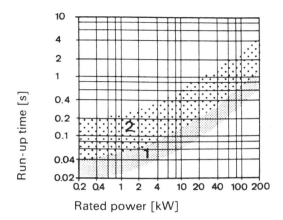

1 Idling (motor + clutch etc.)
2 Starting under load (without large rotational masses)

Figure 13   Standard values for run-up times of standard motors as a function of rated power.

ceptable run-up times are to be achieved. Modern standard motors are designed for high efficiency and minimal manufacturing costs. They usually have large starting currents and poor thermal capacity. When run-up times are expected to be over 10 seconds, a larger standard motor or special high-torque motor is used.

Direct-on-line starter

Local control (Fig 14)

Start — Manual push button

Stop — Manual push button

    automatic when thermal overcurrent relay trips or supply voltage failure occurs

Reset — Manual after tripping of thermal overcurrent relay.

Protection

Protection is by three-pole thermal overcurrent relay against small prolonged overloads, phase unbalance and phase failure.

  Opening of enclosure door is only possible when the isolator is in the off position. Short-circuit protection must be provided by fuses or circuit breaker on the supply side of the starter.

Operation

Push ☐ (17–18)

  —contactor coil KM1 (A_1–A_2) is energised;

  —KM1 power contacts (1–2, 3–4, 5–6) close and motor starts;

  — auxiliary contacts (13–14) close so that start button Push ☐ (17–18) can be released.

Power circuit

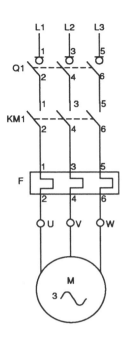

Control circuit

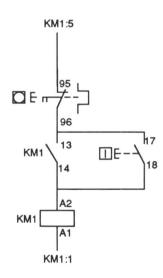

Figure 14   Local control.

If supply voltage fails, KM1 de-energises and opens contactor. When supply is restored motor can only restart when the start button is operated.

To stop, push button ⬜. On overload, phase unbalance, or phase failure, overcurrent relay F will open the stop contacts (95–96).

Remote control (Fig 15)

The addition of a remote control station with parallel start and series stop buttons gives duplicate control.

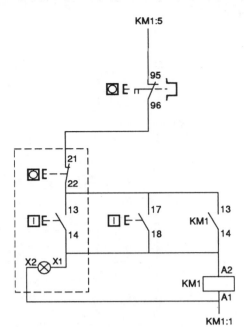

Figure 15   Remote control.

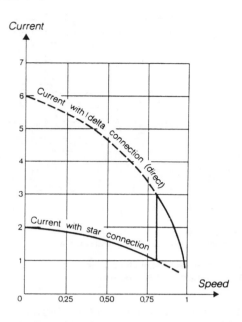

Figure 17   Variation of current with speed in star connected and delta connected stator windings.

Star-delta starter (Fig 16)

This starter is used to reduce the starting current in 6-terminal motors designed for delta operation. It is the most cost-effective method of reduced voltage starting. The motor is direct-on-line started with the stator windings star connected. The starting current and torque are about 30% of the values obtained by direct-on-line delta starting (Figs 17 and 18). Starting high inertia loads may be a problem, in which case a motor with a high starting torque must be used at extra cost.

When the start button is pressed KM1 and KM2 close together which connects the motor windings U_1–U_2, V_1–V_2, W_1–W_2 in star to the supply. A time delay is set to allow the motor to run up to about 80%

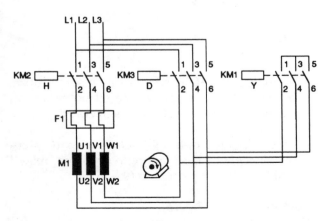

Figure 16   Normal star-delta starting.

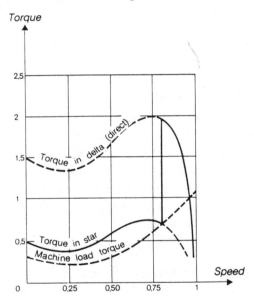

Figure 18   Variation of torque with speed in star connected and delta connected stator windings.

speed at which point the relay opens KM1 and closes KM3 so that the motor is converted from a star connection to a delta connection.

The switch over between star and delta is usually automatic, using a time delay relay or delayed auxiliary contacts on the contactors. In addition a time delay must be inserted between switching off the star contactor and switching on the delta contactor to ensure that the switching arc in the star contactor has been quenched before the delta contactor is closed. If the switch over is too fast a short circuit is applied to the supply as shown in Fig 19.

Conversely, if the switch over time delay is too long, the motor speed will fall so that the delta closing current becomes excessively high. Figure 20 shows how this makes the star-delta arrangement ineffective. Once time delays have been set in the starter it is important that they are not altered if 'open transition surge' problems are to be avoided.

A further problem can occur due to switch over if the motor delta connection is not as shown in Fig 21.

When switching from star to delta, the stator current stops flowing when the star contactor opens, but the rotor currents flow in a closed circuit and they decay gradually from their instantaneous values at the moment of switch-off. These decaying rotor currents are dc and produce a flux which is stationary with respect to the rotor conductors. This flux rotates with the rotor, cuts the stator windings and induces an emf just like an alternator. The frequency of the

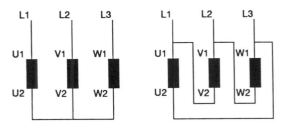

Figure 21   Correct wiring of motor phases for clockwise rotation.

emf in the stator falls as the rotor decelerates.

If the supply is reconnected when this emf is out of phase with the supply voltage (as with faulty synchronising of an alternator) then heavy surge currents can lead to severe momentary torques up to 10 or 15 times full-load torque. This can cause mechanical damage to shafts and keyways and even the driven machine. Insulation failure due to movement of the end windings can occur.

This synchronising effect will be aggravated if the motor is incorrectly connected in delta.

Although the delta connection in Fig 22 will still give clockwise rotation it could result in damaging surge currents and torques. Always ensure that star/delta connections are as shown in Fig 21 for clockwise rotation and Fig 23 for counter-clockwise rotation.

These connections are shown on the Telemechanique starter system in Fig 24.

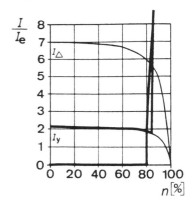

Figure 19   Switch-over pause too short—short circuit across the arc—fuse is tripped and system is turned off.

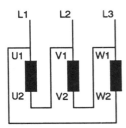

Figure 22   Incorrect wiring of motor phases also causes clockwise rotation.

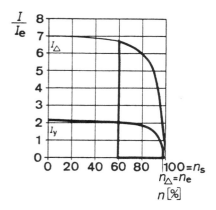

Figure 20   Switch-over pause too long—shaft speed drops off—direct on-line start in delta arrangement.

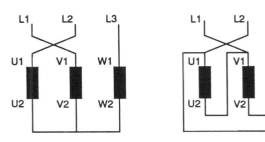

Figure 23   Correct wiring of motor phases for counter clockwise rotation.

Star-delta starter with fusible isolator (Fig 24)

(With time delay contact block on contactor KM2)

Power circuit operation

Manual closing of Q1

Closing of KM1: star connection

Closing of KM2: motor supply

Opening of KM1: star connection opens

Closing of KM3: delta connection

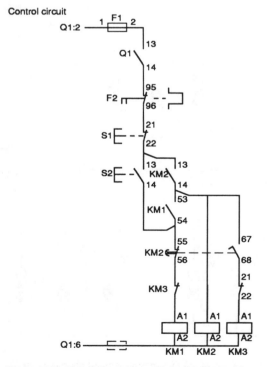

Figure 24 Star delta starter with fusible isolator.

Features

The voltage permissible across the motor windings, connected in delta must correspond to the main supply voltage.

Q1 : rated for motor I_N

F2 : rated for motor $I_N/\sqrt{3}$

KM1: rated for motor $I_N/\sqrt{3}$

KM2–KM3: rated for motor $I_N/\sqrt{3}$

Control circuit operation

Operate S2—   closing of KM1

Closing of KM2 by KM1 (52–54)

Hold-in of KM1–KM2 by KM2 (13–14)

Opening of KM1 by KM2 (55–56)

Closing of KM3 by KM1 (21–22) and KM2 (67–68)

Stop by operating S1

Features

Electrical interlock between KM1 and KM3.

The time delay contact block LA2-D has a switching time of 40 ms between the opening of the N/C contact and the closing of the N/O contact. This eliminates risk of short-circuit on change-over from star to delta.

Many star-delta starters are fitted with mechanical interlocks between contactors KM1 and KM3 which prevents them both being closed at the same time. If they are closed simultaneously the supply will be short-circuited. The time delays in the system will prevent this in normal operation but an engineer may attempt to press both contactors shut when fault-finding to check circuit operation. Never try to manually press contactors shut on a live circuit. If there is no mechanical interlock use extreme caution and never remove electrical safety interlocks from any equipment.

To summarise:

Star-delta starters can only operate effectively when the time delay between star open and delta close has been correctly set. If the change over is too fast two problems may arise.

1. Short-circuit current will flow if the star contactor has not quenched the arc.

2. If the arc is quenched but the rotor flux has not had enough time to decay then 'synchronising' type currents and torques can cause mechanical damage when the delta contactor closes.

If the change-over time is too long then the rotor decelerates and delta starting current is taken on reconnection.

This type of starter is used for motors designed for delta operation and where the load torque is low enough to avoid unacceptable run-up times.

Autotransformer starter

Technically, this is the best way to optimise the start up of an induction motor. It best resolves a conflict involved in reduced voltage starting. The conflict is between reducing the surge current taken at start and causing the run-up time to be excessive. The transformer provides a number of secondary tappings, typically 50%, 65% or 80% tapping. The starter can be wired to the appropriate tapping point which gives an acceptable reduction of surge current without undue increase in run-up time. A major advantage of this type of starter over the star-delta is that the simple Korndorffer connection and sequence allows the motor to be run-up to speed without disconnecting from a driving voltage. This avoids the open transition current surge problems associated with the star-delta starter. Generally, this starter tends to be used for larger drives (above 60 kW) but may be seen in smaller drives where star connected motors have been adopted for ease of protection. Delta connected motors are more difficult to completely protect against single-phasing conditions than star connected motors.

The operating principle of this starter is that a step-down transformer is used to provide reduced voltage to the motor at start. The motor is allowed to run up to speed and then full voltage is applied. The transformer will require protection against overtemp-

Power circuit

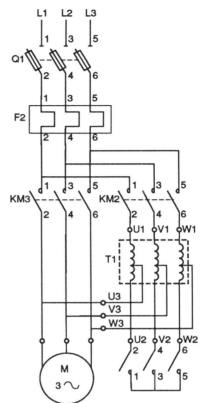

Control circuit

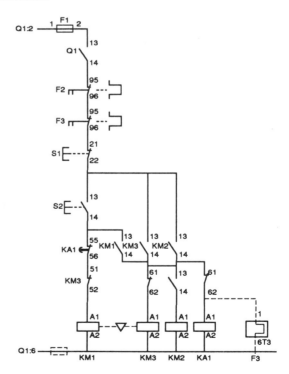

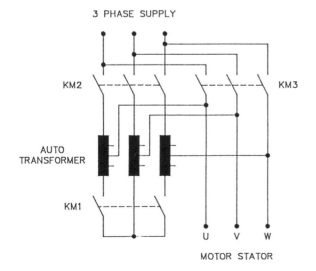

Figure 25 Arrangement of autotransformer starter in Korndorffer connection.

Figure 26 Power and control circuits of a Telemechanique starter.

erature due to too frequent starting, since the motor overcurrent relay is not designed for this function.

Fig 25 shows the arrangement of an autotransformer starter in a Korndorffer connection. When the 'start' button is pressed contactors KM1 and KM2 close together which applies a reduced voltage to the motor windings, U, V, W, via the autotransformer. After a pre-set time delay which allows the motor to run up, contactor KM1 opens. This ends the autotransformer action and the motor is connected to the main supply through part of the autotransformer windings which merely act as series choke coils. Now KM3 closes and full voltage is applied to the motor. KM2 opens and disconnects the transformer from the supply.

So the sequence is

KM1 and KM2 close

time delay

KM1 opens

KM3 closes

KM2 opens.

The motor is never disconnected from the driving voltage which avoids current surges. The power and control circuits in Fig 26 show how a Telemechanique starter achieves the Korndorffer sequence and provides frequent-start protection for the transformer.

SPECIAL HIGH TORQUE INDUCTION MOTORS

Standard induction motors started direct-on-line are capable of driving most loads quickly up to speed without excessive voltage dip on the supply. For some large, high inertia loads the heavy surge current and long run-up time may result in unacceptable voltage dip. Reduced voltage starting cannot be used because the loss of starting torque will prevent the motor from starting the high inertia load. The problem is further compounded if alternator capacity is limited. Special high torque, low current motors are available; the double-cage induction motor and the slipring induction motor. Both motors work on the principle of having high resistance in the rotor winding when starting and low resistance when running. High rotor resistance produces high starting torque and low surge current but results in poor performance i.e. low efficiency and high speed regulation. High rotor resistance is used for starting and low resistance for running.

The double-cage motor achieves this by having a high resistance outer cage and a low resistance inner cage. The outer cage dominates during start-up and the inner cage takes over when running.

The slipring motor connects an external starting resistance to the rotor windings to produce high resistance at start. As the motor accelerates the resistance is reduced. Maximum driving torque can be developed throughout the run-up if the resistance is cut out correctly. The slipring motor also gives limited speed control if required. The advantages of the simple cage rotor are lost because brushes and commutator are necessary. Figure 27 shows the power circuit of a slipring motor with rotor resistance starter.

MOTOR PROTECTION

Motor protection sets out to achieve three objectives:

1. to protect the motor against rapid destruction when stalled or during run-up;

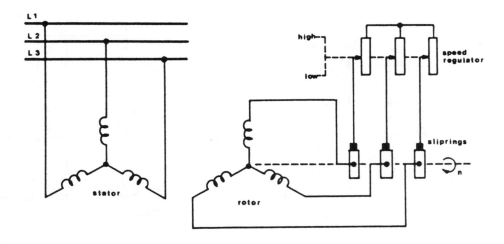

Figure 27   Power circuit of slipring motor with rotor resistance starter.

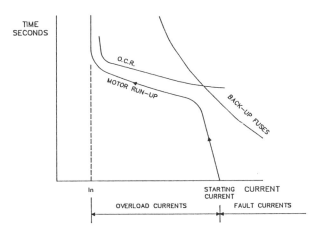

Figure 28 Tripping characteristic of fuses crosses OCR characterstic at motor starting current.

2. while running, to prevent unacceptable reduction in the life of the insulated winding due to overtemperature;

3. to prevent unnecessary disconnections when the motor is not at risk.

Most marine motors are protected by a thermally operated overcurrent relay which monitors the motor load current. The overcurrent relay trips the motor contactor when the motor exceeds its rated current I_N. Fuses cannot provide the close overload protection required by modern maximum continuous rated (mcr) motors which have no overload capability; they would be blown by the motor starting current. The tripping characteristic of the overcurrent relay will give the necessary close overload protection but will not be tripped by the motor starting current. Motor contactors are capable of breaking excess currents up to the stalled (starting) current of the motor, that is, currents up to $8\,I_N$. If a short circuit occurs the overcurrent relay is too slow for fast short circuit tripping.

Fuses provide the necessary breaking capacity and fast action on short circuit. Figure 28 shows that the overcurrent relay will trip the contactor on overloads up to stalled current and the fuses blow short circuit currents before the contactor has a chance to operate. Motors used in the operation of electro-hydraulic steering gears are not fitted with an overload trip. The overcurrent relay sets off an overload alarm but does not trip the motor. Fuses provide short circuit and stalled rotor protection.

Co-ordination

Although fuses will clear a short circuit fault quickly to prevent damage to the cables and other healthy equipment feeding the fault, it may not prevent damage to the starter itself. Publication BS 4941 refers to the co-ordination between fuses, contactor and overcurrent relay in direct-on-line starters in the event of a short circuit current. Three co-ordination types are specified:

Type 'a'— Destruction and necessary replacement of the complete starter provided that its enclosure remains intact

Type 'b'— No damage to the contactor apart from possible contact burning and welding. But there may be a permanent alteration to the operating characteristic of the overcurrent relay.

Type 'c'— No damage permissible apart from possible contact welding.

After a short circuit in a motor system the starter must be inspected and any damage rectified. It is unlikely that engineers are aware of the type of co-ordination used and any alteration to the overcurrent relay characteristic is not generally discernable by a visual inspection. This means that the motor may not

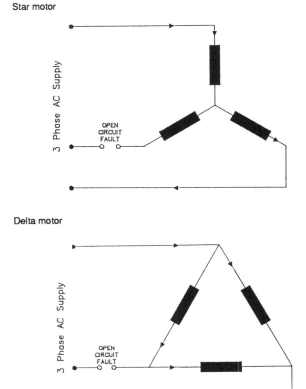

Figure 29 Disconnection of supply line to motor.

be adequately protected against overload, risking future motor burn-out. Further concern arises if the cable sizes have been selected according to motor full-load current and cable overload protection is provided by the relay.

After short circuit, if the overcurrent relay is apparently undamaged but the type of co-ordination cannot be ascertained, the relay must be replaced or recalibrated to BS4941.

Single-phasing

This condition occurs when one of the supply lines to the motor stator becomes disconnected due to an open circuit such as a blown fuse or bad contact (Fig 29). Three-phase operation is lost and the motor runs on the remaining 'single phase'. Instead of producing a rotating magnetic field the stator produces a pulsating magnetic field which results in magnetic noise and vibration.

If the motor is running when this occurs it keeps on running at a slightly reduced speed. The mechanical power output is maintained and the current on the two remaining lines increases to maintain the electrical power input. If the motor is running on full-load then the current on the remaining lines is about twice full-load current, which will operate the overcurrent relay. The tripping characteristics of three pole relays are based on the condition that all three bimetal strips are similarly loaded. If only two bimetal strips are heated then the trip time will be extended. A protection relay which operates on differential current in addition to overcurrent may be required for delta connected motors. If a delta connected motor is running on about half full load when single phasing occurs the current in the two remaining lines goes up to about full load value. Inside the motor one phase could reach 30% above its rated current.

Figure 30 shows a motor rated at 100A line current. Each phase has a rated current of $100A/\sqrt{3} = 58$ A.

Figure 31 shows the motor on half load and one line disconnected. The line current reaches 100 A which would not cause an overload trip. One phase is heavily overloaded, carrying 67A instead of the rated 58A, and this will burn out the phase.

Star connected motors are not at risk in this way because phase current is the same as line current.

For delta connected motors, particularly those above 10kW, it is advisable to use an overcurrent relay which incorporates phase-failure protection.

When single-phasing occurs when a motor is running, it generally keeps on running if on light load. If the motor is stopped it will not restart. A 3-phase motor produces zero starting torque when single-phased. Repeated attempts to start a stalled motor could result in thermal damage. After each start attempt the overcurrent relay cools and resets faster than the motor can cool. Each attempt pushes the motor temperature up. If the motor has not started after two attempts, investigate the cause.

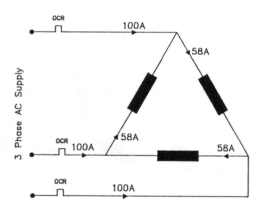

Figure 30 Full-load healthy 3-phase condition.

Overcurrent relays

The tripping characteristic of the overcurrent relay (overcurrent relay) protecting the motor against overloads, must be delayed to allow the starting current to flow for the run-up time, yet still provide close overload protection. Three general types are used: thermal, magnetic and electronic. Most marine motors are protected with thermal relays with some large motors having electronic protection.

Figures 32 and 33 show the operation of a thermal overcurrent relay on both overload and differential single-phase conditions.

Thermal overcurrent relay's contain three bimetal elements (typically Invar and ferronickel). Each ele-

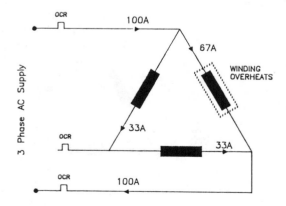

Figure 31 Half-load single phase condition.

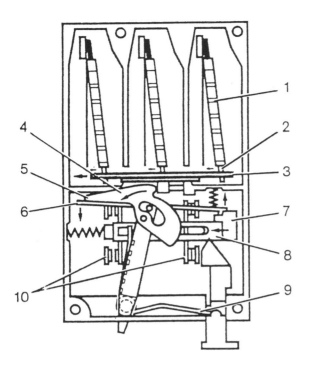

When a high current flows through the heater windings (1), the bimetal elements (2) bend and the differential bars are drawn along in the direction of the arrow. Cam (4) is also drawn and rotates on its shaft. The leading edge of this cam (5) rotates the bimetal compensation (6), the holding stop (7) is released, freeing the moving part which is attracted by a spring (9). Contacts (10) change position. In this drawing the relay is in the set position, ready to be tripped.

Figure 32 Principle of operation of thermal OCR on overload.

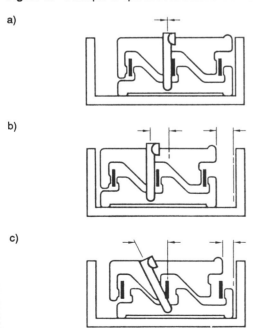

Figure 33 Differential device for thermal OCR: a) cold position; b) hot position, balanced operating; c) hot position, unbalanced operating.

ment is fitted with a heater coil connected in each phase or line of the motor. When heated, the element bends. When a motor overcurrent occurs, the heater temperature increases and bends the bimetal elements causing the overcurrent relay to trip the motor. Most thermal relays have ambient temperature compensation to prevent changes to the tripping characteristic. Mounted opposite the bimetal elements, the compensation element balances the bending of the main elements.

The relay cannot be reset until the main elements have cooled sufficiently.

The differential device causes the relay to trip when the currents flowing through the three elements are not identical (unbalanced mains or single phase fault).

Setting a thermal overcurrent relay

Relays are fitted with an adjustable knob or lever which allows the tripping characteristic to be adjusted over a limited range. The range is calibrated in motor current (I_N).

Most relays are type 1, where the correct characteristic is obtained by setting the relay current to equal the motor full-load current. Occasionally a type 2 relay may be encountered, where the setting must be 120% of the motor rated current.

When setting the relay check, for delta motors, which current, phase or line, is being monitored by the relay. Correct setting of either type of relay is very important to avoid damage when overcurrent occurs. Many motors run below rated current and good protection can be provided if the overcurrent relay is set for the actual running current rather than the higher rated current.

Relays are calibrated to the requirements of BS 4941. This calls for an ambient temperature compensated relay to take 105% of motor rated current for two hours without tripping. The current is then increased to 120% and tripping should occur within the next two hours. On these figures it seems that a motor could run for two hours on 120% rated current. This is highly unlikely in practice because modern relays perform well within the requirements of BS 4941. A tripping time of ten minutes or even less is typical on the 120% load test.

The use of more sophisticated protection relays which obtain their characteristic from electronic circuits provide much closer overload protection and a wide range of protection options. At the present time these expensive relays are usually used for large, probably high voltage, continuously running motors protected by circuit breakers rather than contactor/

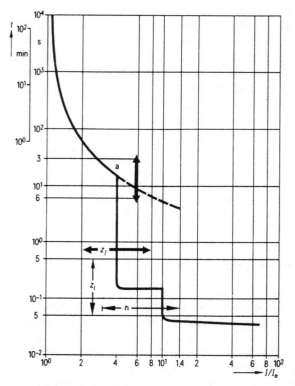

a   long delay overcurrent release
n   instantaneous overcurrent release
z   short delay overcurrent release
z_I setting current range
z_t time setting range

Figure 34 Tripping characterstics of the electronic overcurrent release for a circuit-breaker.

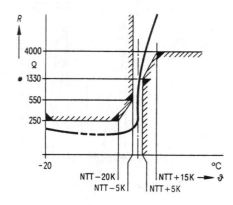

θ   temperature
NTT   nominal trip temperature

Figure 35 Typical resistance values of a PTC thermistor with characteristic curve according to DIN 44081/June 1980 (resistance rise to several powers of base 10 in response range).

fuse. The relay has the usual delayed overload characteristic. An instantaneous trip can be set at just above the stalled rotor current to trip the circuit breaker quickly on short circuit (Fig 34).

A relay of this kind would be used for 6.6 kV air conditioning motors on large cruise ships.

Thermistor protection

In contrast to overcurrent relays which are operated by current and protect the motor when an excessive current flows for a given time, thermistor protection operates on the actual winding temperature. This gives overtemperature protection, whatever the cause.

Thermistors are resistors which change resistance suddenly at a designed temperature. Positive temperature coefficient (PTC) thermistors exhibit an increase of resistance at the nominal trip temperature (NTT) (Fig 35).

The thermistors must be installed by the motor manufacturer in the stator windings as near as possible to the most critical location in terms of tempera-

ture rise. The NTT of the thermistor used will be determined by the class of stator insulation. In the case of standard cage rotors up to about 15 kW the stator winding heats up faster than the rotor when stalled. The thermistors trip the supply and the stator transfers heat to the cooler rotor. This ensures no thermal damage to either stator or rotor. Larger motors are usually 'rotor critical'. When stalled the rotor heats up faster than the stator. When the stator reaches NTT the rotor far exceeds this temperature. After tripping, the rotor heats the stator so that the insulation may suffer excessive temperatures. For 'rotor critical' motors an additional current operated overcurrent relay is required to prevent rotor or stator damage during a stall.

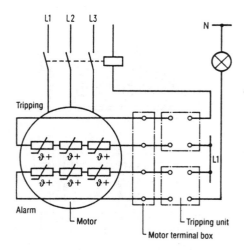

Figure 36 Typical circuit diagram of thermistor motor protection for alarm and shut down.

If a temperature alarm is required before a motor is tripped then an additional set of three thermistors with a lower NTT can be installed by the motor manufacturer (Fig 36).

On large, specially designed motors, thermal characteristics may not be so well understood as with mass produced motors. Negative temperature coefficient (NTC) linear thermistors are sometimes used which allows individual calibration and trip setting.

Electromagnetic overcurrent relays

The motor current is passed through a coil producing flux in a steel core. When the current is excessive it pulls the core up to operate a trip bar. Time delay is achieved by oil dashpot and piston. These relays are generally considered to lack the required accuracy for mcr motor protection but are frequently found protecting older machines.

Before the mid 1950s motors could usually withstand at least 20% excess current for quite prolonged periods without suffering damage. They were oversized, well ventilated and had considerable thermal inertia. Over the next twenty years fierce competition between manufacturers saw power/weight ratios almost doubled. This has led to the evolution of the modern maximum continuous rated (mcr) motor which has virtually no overload capacity.

If an old motor is replaced by a modern motor of the same rating then the overcurrent relay should be checked to ensure that the required accuracy of protection is achieved. Electromagnetic relays may have to be replaced with thermal or electronic types.

CONTACTORS

At the heart of every motor starter is an electrically operated switch called a contactor (Fig 37). It consists of a fixed magnetic core, a moving magnetic armature carrying the contacts and a coil. When the coil is energised it magnetises the core and pulls in the armature against a spring. This closes the main contacts. When the coil is de-energised the core is demagnetised and the armature is forced back by the charged spring. This opens the main contacts. Considerable changes in contactor design and construction have taken place over the last thirty years. Previously, contactors were large, and used blow-out coils and long arc-extinction principles. Although oversized, contact life was short compared to modern equipment. This short life was mainly due to prolonged arc durations, and the use of copper contacts with rolling or wiping action causing a loss of contact material.

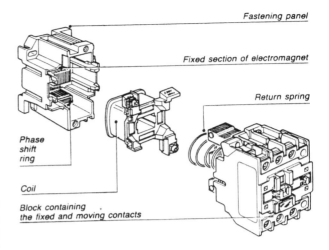

Figure 37 Contactor.

The old practice of filing contacts to keep them smooth did not help matters. The need for more compact and economic control equipment has led to the evolution of ac switchgear with very high electrical service life. It is based on a philosophy of keeping arc lengths short to minimise arc power and obtaining current-zero extinction.

Main contacts are usually silver cadmium oxide which has a very long life. Engineers often misjudge the condition of these contacts. Blackening and pitting are usual and do not adversely affect contact performance. Contacts should not be filed or scraped. Only replace contacts when the bulk of the contact material has been eroded. Some larger contactors (> 80A) have wear indicators as shown in Fig 38.

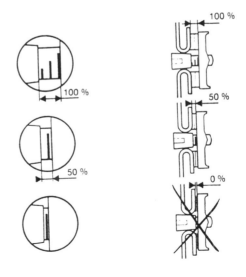

Figure 38 Contact wear indicator.

Many contactors still have the older style copper or silvered copper contacts. Copper contacts can be filed when they become seriously pitted or burnished if they form an oxide film. The black silver oxide on silver plated contacts is almost as good a conductor as silver and should not be removed.

A problem that can occur with the electromagnetic core is 'chattering'. This is vibration set up by foreign matter lodged between the moving and fixed part of the core. The core surfaces should be kept clean but never scraped, filed or painted. If they are particularly dirty, clean them with cleaning fluid. Incomplete closure of the core in this way reduces the impedance of the contactor coil causing excess current and overheating. Another result is insufficient pressure on the main contacts which overheat and may even weld together with motor starting current. Similar effects are produced if the contactor coil is connected to incorrect voltage or frequency. High voltage or low frequency cause overcurrents in the coil and overheating. Low voltage or high frequency can cause 'chattering' and contact damage. Contactors are designed for 50Hz and 60Hz operation provided the volts/hertz ratio is kept more or less constant. This means that a given contactor can operate on 60Hz if the voltage is about 1.2 times the 50Hz voltage. The optimal ratio of these two control voltages alters with magnet size. For simplicity a manufacturer will usually recommend a single ratio for all sizes. 1.15 is typically used because this produces several frequently encountered pairs, e.g. 42V 50Hz /48V 60Hz; 380V 50Hz /440V 60Hz.

SPEED CONTROL

The operating speed of an induction motor is determined by the speed of the rotating magnetic field (n_S). This, in turn, is determined by the stator supply frequency (f) and the number of pole pairs (p) in the flux pattern of the rotating magnetic field; $n_S = f/p$.

Supply voltage variations have no appreciable effect on motor speed apart from some difference created by the associated change of driving torque.

Marine systems use dual wound or pole-change machines for multi-speed applications and Ward-Leonard or inverter-fed motors for variable speed operation.

Multi-speed motors

A speed ratio of 2:1 is achieved using a six-terminal pole-changing winding first developed by Dahlander in 1897. Each phase winding is in two sections and the

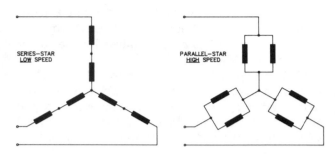

Figure 39   Star and double star connections providing variable torque.

ends brought out to the terminal block. Connection of the windings in series and then parallel changes the number of poles and the speed by a factor of two. Multispeed operation of fans, rotary compressors, pump drives and windlass/warping capstans require different torques at the two speeds.

The star/double-star connection in Fig 39 provides this variable torque. Series-star gives the low speed and parallel-star the high speed.

In practice 2:1 speed change is not in the greatest demand. The close speed ratios (4:6, 6:8, 8:10, 10:12 poles) are more useful. The dual-wound motor has traditionally been used to provide these ratios. Two separate windings are used on the stator with consequent loss of power/weight ratio at increased cost. In 1957 Professor G H Rawcliffe of the University of Bristol invented and patented a method of arranging the internal connections of stator windings so that it was possible to produce any speed ratio, still using six terminals and the same switching sequence for a Dahlander motor. These are called pole amplitude modulated (PAM) motors, the close-ratio windings giving particularly good performance.

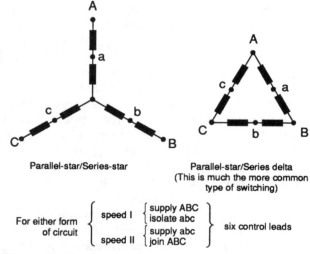

Figure 40   Simple connections for a PAM motor.

Figure 40 shows the simple connections for a PAM motor.

Every item of performance of a PAM motor is considerably better than the equivalent dual-wound machine at only 75% of the cost. This evidence makes it difficult to justify the use of dual-wound motors for close ratio multi-speed applications.

Three speed motors are available which use one Dahlander/PAM winding and a separate single speed winding. Four speeds are obtained using two separate Dahlander/PAM windings.

Variable speed systems

The development of electronic thyristor frequency converters has given speed control of induction motors over a 10:1 speed range. The thyristor is a solid state controlled rectifier. It will block current when reverse biased and will only conduct when forward biased after a gate signal is applied. The forward current must fall below a threshold value before conduction will cease. Thyristor bridges are used for controlled rectification to control dc motor speed or as frequency converters for induction motor control.

The object of a converter is simply to convert fixed frequency three-phase mains into variable frequency to drive an induction motor at variable speed. A complication is introduced by the necessity for motors to have constant air-gap flux at all frequencies. This provides constant torque at all speeds and ensures optimum use of magnetic core material. To obtain constant flux the supply voltage must be made to vary in proportion to the frequency. In other words the volts/hertz ratio must be kept constant. If this is done the speed/torque characteristics will be as shown in Fig 41.

Most motor controllers use a dc link converter arrangement. The incoming 3-phase supply is rectified to dc which is then inverted to variable frequency

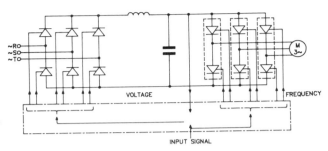

Figure 42 Variable dc obtained through thyristor controlled rectifier.

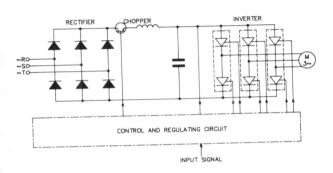

Figure 43 Variable dc obtained through a diode rectifier combined with a chopper.

3-phase. To obtain variable voltage either a thyristor controlled rectifier can be used to give variable dc or a diode rectifier is combined with a chopper to give variable voltage to the inverter. The two systems are shown in Figs 42 and 43.

When load is applied at a set speed, the ac electrical power input must increase. The control circuits can be arranged to produce two different forms of load response. A voltage-source converter responds like a normal electrical supply. As load is increased voltage is kept constant and the current increases. In a current-source converter the control circuits hold the current constant and the voltage is varied. The main advantage of the current-source arrangement is that no further components are required for regeneration. The system is also virtually short-circuit proof due to the constant current.

An alternative system which can also use current- or voltage-source response is the pulse-width-modulated (PWM) converter. High frequency voltage pulses generated inside the inverter are put together to make up the output voltage wave form.

Figure 44 shows the power components of a PWM frequency converter. In this system both voltage and frequency are changed in the inverter section. The

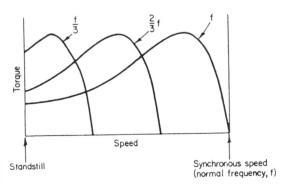

Figure 41 Speed/torque characteristics at different frequencies.

a)

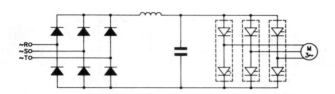

b)

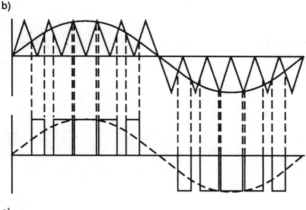

c)

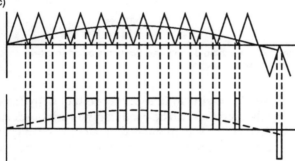

Figure 44 PWM frequency converter and its power components: a) PWM frequency converter; b) maximum voltage and maximum frequency for PWM; c) half voltage and half frequency for PWM.

waveforms show the width of the pulses is varied to determine voltage amplitude and frequency.

Thyristor control systems should provide good reliability. Clean, dry operating conditions are absolutely essential for the successful operation of power electronics systems. Air filters on thyristor blowers should be regularly washed in a mild detergent solution and thoroughly dried before replacement. Monthly cleaning is usually recommended, but if the system is operating in a dust laden or oil contaminated atmosphere, the filters should be cleaned more frequently. The inside of cubicles should be thoroughly cleaned as often as possible. The thyristor system manufacturer will provide typical healthy waveforms taken at various points in the circuit. An oscilloscope must be used to check that the wave-

forms conform to specification during fault-finding and routine checking. For example, a monthly check of thyristor bridge output current and voltage and firing pulses should be made. If a breakdown occurs, fuses and thyristors should be checked first. Then an examination of the cables and connections in the power system should carried out. Any loose connections must be tightened. If the control and pulse triggering circuits are faulty, follow manufacturers procedure to locate a faulty printed circuit board (PCB). The PCB or its edge connectors may need cleaning. Always use vacuum cleaning and be careful not to cause electrostatic damage to the PCB components. To clean edge connectors, spray a cotton bud with a suitable cleaner (RS 554-838, Super Solv, Flurosolv), other sprays may decompose polycarbonate board/socket material. Gently wipe the cotton bud across the gold contact of the edge connector. Do not attempt to mechanically clean the sockets. Lightly spray with cleaning fluid. If the PCB is faulty, replace with a spare. Spare PCBs should be kept well wrapped and packed in cardboard boxes. Boards carrying MOS (metal oxide semiconductors) devices which are susceptible to electrostatic damage must be wrapped in conductive plastic envelopes. Printed circuit boards carrying electrolytic capacitors will have a limited shelf life of about one year.

DC MOTORS

The advantages of the dc motor are simple speed control and a wide range of speed-torque characteristics. Cargo handling is the main application using thyristor controlled rectifier units or the Ward-Leonard system for speed control. In both cases the three phase mains provides the power input. An induction motor driving a dc generator provides the necessary rectification for the Ward-Leonard system. The system often incorporates a closed loop control system to keep the set speed when the load varies.

Figure 45 shows a thyristor controlled motor and Fig 46 shows a Ward-Leonard system. In both cases the motor speed is set by adjusting the voltage applied to its armature. A tachogenerator is used to provide a feedback speed signal.

DC machines require more frequent inspection and maintenance than induction motors because of the commutator and brushes. During normal operation, commutators and sliprings acquire a shiny protective surface gloss which reduces wear and lengthens service life. This film is a combination of copper oxide and graphite and should form on the surface of a raw copper commutator after several days or weeks

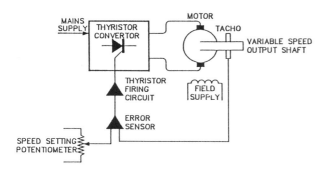

Figure 45 Thyristor controlled motor.

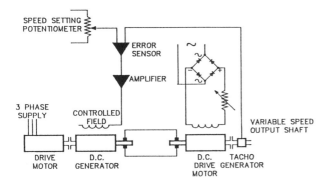

Figure 46 Ward-Leonard system.

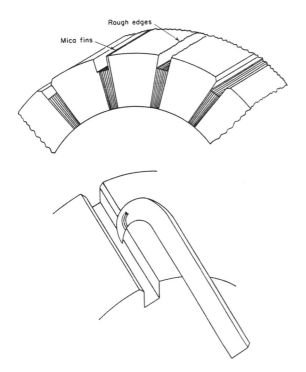

Figure 47 Rough edges and mica fins that must be removed by side cutting.

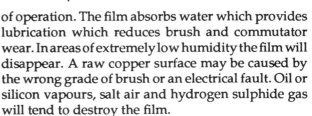

of operation. The film absorbs water which provides lubrication which reduces brush and commutator wear. In areas of extremely low humidity the film will disappear. A raw copper surface may be caused by the wrong grade of brush or an electrical fault. Oil or silicon vapours, salt air and hydrogen sulphide gas will tend to destroy the film.

Mica undercutting is essential to good commutation and should not be neglected. Mica is harder than copper and will form ridges as the copper wears down. This will cause sparking and chipping of brushes. Mica should be undercut to a depth equal to its thickness. A hacksaw blade, with the sides ground down to remove protruding teeth, can be used for undercutting. The undercutting process can produce thin slivers of mica or copper at the segments edges. These are removed by cutting a light chamfer on the segment with a sharp knife. If they are not removed these slivers flake off, become embedded in the brushes and score the commutator.

Figure 47 shows how this should be done. Brushes come in a variety of grades. Very soft brushes tend to deposit graphite on the commutator and wear down quickly. Hard brushes scour the commutator. The softer brushes are preferred for machines operating on light load and the harder grades for operation on heavy loads or in oily atmospheres. Brushes of different grades should never be mixed and replacement brushes should be to the machine manufacturers specification. New brushes should be seated to the commutator or slipring curvature to ensure good brush performance. Before fitting new brushes, check the pigtails for fraying and loose connections. To seat the brush place sandpaper, not emery, between the brush and the commutator surface. Pull the sandpaper back and forth under the brush with the sand side against the brush. Remove all carbon dust with a vacuum cleaner. Run the machine on light or no load to allow the brush to achieve the exact curvature of the commutator or slipring. The pressure of the brush on the commutator surface is important. Insufficient pressure causes chattering and arcing which wears the brush. Too much pressure gives good electrical contact but the excessive friction also gives rapid brush wear. The correct pressure depends on the brush grade, softer brushes requiring less pressure; 0.138 bar is a typical pressure for electrographitic brushes.

The force on the brush can be measured using a spring balance and paper strip as shown in Fig 48. The leather loop is placed under the spring finger where the finger presses on the brush. The scale is read when the strip of paper can be removed with very little effort. The force necessary to provide the

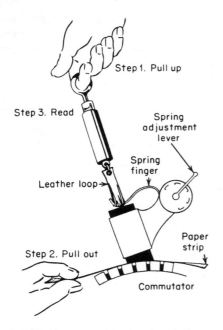

Figure 48   Measurement of the force on the brush.

correct spring pressure is obtained by multiplying the recommended brush pressure by the cross-sectional area of the brush face. For large, horizontal machines, the weight of the brush may have to be taken into account.

Frequent visual inspection of commutator surfaces can give early warning of abnormal operating conditions. Copper-drag, an abnormal build up of copper material, forms most often at the trailing edge of the bar. This condition is rare but can cause flashover if not checked.

Pitch bar-marking produces low or burned spots on the commutator surface. The number of these markings equals half or all the number of poles on the motor. Slot bar-marking can involve etching of the trailing edges of the commutator bar. Streaking on the commutator surface shows the beginning of serious metal transfer to the carbon brush. Threading of

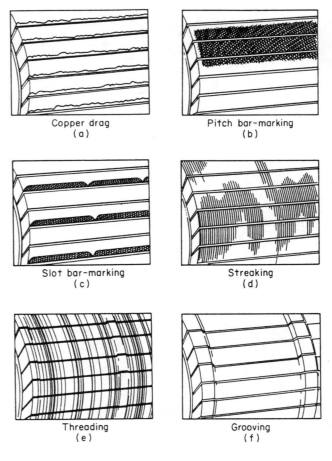

Figure 49   Indications of unsatisfactory brush and commutator performance.

the commutator with fine lines results from excessive metal transfer. Resurfacing of the commutator will be required. Grooving is produced by abrasive material in the brush or atmosphere. These commutator surfaces are illustrated in Fig 49.

Table 2 indicates the corrective action necessary when these undesirable conditions occur.

Table II   Commutator check chart.

	Electrical adjustment	Electrical overload	Light electrical load	Armature connection	Unbalanced shunt field	Brush pressure (light)	Vibration	Type of brush in use		Contamination	
								Abrasive brush	Porous brush	Gas	Abrasive dust
Streaking			•			•		•	•	•	•
Threading			•			•			•	•	
Grooving								•			•
Copper drag				•	•	•			•		
Pitch bar-marking				•	•	•	•	•			
Slot bar-marking	•	•								•	

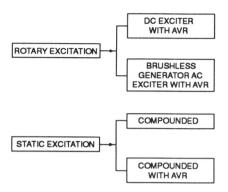

Figure 50   Categorisation of excitation configurations.

THREE-PHASE AC SYNCHRONOUS GENERATORS

In many marine electrical power systems the ac generators and automatic voltage regulators (AVRs) are required to meet very onerous duties, particularly with regard to switching performance. The generating equipment should be a composite design to obtain optimum performance from generator and AVR prime mover governor in relation to the electrical load requirements. In particular, the system should provide an economic solution which meets the specified performance in systems of limited capacity where the starting of large motors is carried out direct-on-line. Over the years generator manufacturers have developed a multitude of excitation configurations to meet these requirements. These configurations can be roughly categorised as shown in Fig 50, but many systems will use a combination of different types of excitation and voltage control.

Rotary excitation

The dc exciter system shown in Fig 51 is rarely specified for new buildings and is now non-standard for marine generators.

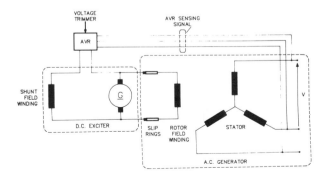

Figure 51   Dc exciter system.

Voltage build-up is initiated by residual magnetic flux in the poles of the dc exciter causing it to self-excite. Voltage adjustment is achieved by adjusting the current in the shunt field winding using the trimmer control on the AVR. Similarly, the AVR automatically adjusts the excitation voltage and current to maintain the generator output voltage constant.

The brushless generator has the advantage of eliminating the brushes, commutator, sliprings and the associated maintenance. Figure 52 shows a schematic diagram of a brushless generator and Fig 53 shows the rotor of a typical machine.

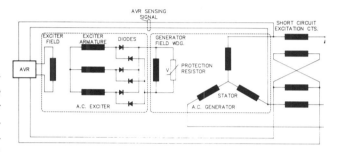

Figure 52   Scheme of brushless generator.

Figure 53   Motor for a type AG, 1750kW, 440V, 1500 rev/min brushless ac generator.

The exciter is a rotating armature ac generator with a stationary salient-pole dc excitation winding. When the set is run up residual magnetism in the exciter pole cores generates ac in the star connected exciter armature. The diodes rectify the ac to dc which is then fed to the generator rotor field winding. This generates a small output voltage in the generator stator which is rectified by the AVR and fed back to the exciter field winding. The output voltage builds up to the set value of the AVR.

Under short circuit fault conditions the generator is required to provide up to 3 times its rated current for 2 or 3 seconds to ensure circuit breakers trip selectively. Compounding CTs in the generator output are used to provide the necessary excitation when the system voltage has collapsed on short circuit. An alternative on high speed machines is to use a permanent magnet pilot exciter.

Under certain types of load change or during out-of-phase synchronising there is a possibility that the generator excitation current may try to reverse. This will be blocked by the diodes causing a large reverse voltage which can damage the diodes. A voltage dependent resistor is connected across the field winding to provide a path for the reverse current. Modern diodes are very reliable but when they do fail it is usually a short circuit breakdown. This puts a short circuit across the exciter armature. The generator excitation current and the output voltage fall, the AVR will increase the exciter field current and that increases the exciter armature short circuit current. To protect the exciter armature and maintain generator voltage fuses are connected in series with each diode. Figure 54 shows the rectifier assembly.

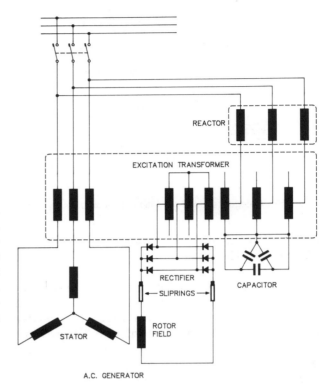

Figure 55   Constant voltage generator.

Generator current is not sensed with CTs but connected directly to the excitation transformer.

Under short circuit fault the capacitor creates a resonant condition in the excitation transformer to maintain generator output for circuit breaker tripping. In some systems an AVR is included to provide a voltage trimming facility.

Generally, the most severe dips of supply voltage occur when starting and changing speed of large motors. Lloyd's requirements specify that the voltage regulation should not exceed +15% when 35% load at a power factor between 0 and 0.4 lagging. The output voltage must be restored to within 3% of rated voltage in 1.5 seconds. The advantage of the static excitation system is fast speed of response due to the lack of a rotary exciter. This makes the static system preferable when large cargo handling motors are switched direct-on-line.

Figure 54   Rectifier assembly.

Static excitation

A rotating exciter is not used. The excitation is supplied by the generator itself through a static excitation unit. This is basically a three-phase, step-down transformer and rectifier bridge which feeds dc excitation current to the rotor through sliprings. Voltage build-up relies on residual magnetism in the generator rotor pole cores and a permanent magnet exciter may be required to assist the process. Voltage control is achieved by compounding. As the load current changes, the output from the excitation CT's adjust the generator field current to maintain the output voltage constant. Figure 55 shows the arrangement of a Siemens constant voltage generator.

GENERATOR MAINTENANCE

Generators with rotary exciters require routine maintenance of sliprings, commutators and brushes of the type outlined earlier in this chapter for motors. For all generators, routine inspection and cleaning of ventilation passages and air filters is essential. Insulation in generators is usually not subject to a severely detrimental environment as is often the case with motors. Regular blowing out of dust and dirt with dry compressed air as the machine is running down should be all that is required to maintain the quality of the insulation. Bearing lubrication and replacement must be carried out according to the manufacturers recommendations.

Chapter 6
Marine Electrical Power Systems

F Taylor

Most ships generate 3-phase alternating current at 440 V or 380 V. The 60 Hz American standard frequency is preferred to the European standard 50 Hz.

The electrical power demand in newbuildings continues to increase and high voltage systems using 3.3 kV and 6.6 kV are becoming necessary. High voltage systems generally have an earthed neutral whereas medium voltage practice is to leave the neutral insulated. Earth faults are less likely to cause tripping when the neutral is insulated. A single earth fault on the insulated system produces line voltage to earth on the unfaulted lines as shown in Fig 1.

Figure 1 Voltage to earth produced after single earth fault on insulated sysetm.

Also a second earth fault on an opposite pole would cause a fault current and trip services. Earth lamps are required as shown in Fig 2.

If an earth fault occurs on L_3, lamps H_1 and H_2 will go bright and H_3 dark. Earth faults must be located and removed at the earliest opportunity. The use of an insulated neutral precludes the use of a 4-wire system to provide single phase supplies for lighting and sockets. Delta-delta transformers are used to step down the voltage for lighting, galley and socket supplies (Fig 3).

An advantage of this is that circuits which are prone to earth faults, such as galley and deck lighting,

cannot interconnect with faults on the main supply. For the same reason, the secondary side of every lighting transformer requires its own set of earth lamps. A better prediction of insulation problems is obtained using earth leakage monitors.

Figure 4 shows an earth fault monitor which passes dc current through the insulation. Reduced insulation resistance or an earth fault will result in an

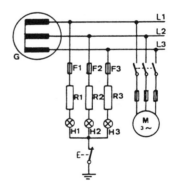

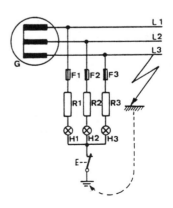

Figure 2 Arrangement of earth lamps to indicate earth faults.

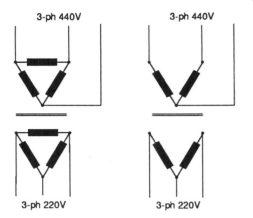

Figure 3 Delta-delta transformers.

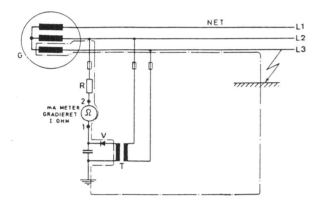

Figure 4 Earth fault monitor.

increased dc current in the milli-ammeter which will initiate an alarm. Similar monitors are used to indicate the condition of insulation resistance of disconnected equipment. These off-line monitors are usually used to check the condition of motors. This prevents a motor with low insulation resistance be-

Figure 5 Single channel on-line monitor and meter.

ing switched on until the insulation resistance has been brought up to an acceptable value. Most off-line monitors are individual units mounted in the motor starters, feeding a lamp or MΩ meter on the panel. The unit and meter are shown in Fig 5.

More comprehensive monitoring systems are now becoming available. These systems use scanning techniques to ascertain the insulation status of both on-line and off-line equipment. They are particularly useful when ships are mothballed because radio or telemetry links can be used. This avoids the need for maintenance crews to carry out routine testing. Automatic real time fault reporting can be obtained in hard copy.

High voltage systems (above 1 kV) usually have the neutral earthed through a neutral earthing resistor. This resistor is included to limit fault currents to about $2 \times I_N$ for the ac generator. Insulation resistance can be monitored by directly measuring the ac leakage current at the neutral as in Fig 6.

When ac generators with earthed neutrals are run in parallel the neutral of only one machine is earthed. This avoids the circulation of harmonic currents between the generators via the neutral earths.

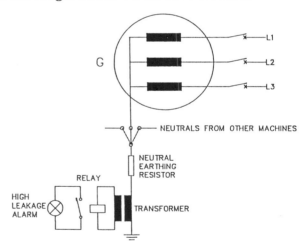

Figure 6 Direct measurement of ac leakage current at the neutral.

LOW VOLTAGE SUPPLIES

The delta-delta transformers used for low voltage single phase supplies are often three separate single-phase transformer units rather than a single core 3-phase transformer. If one unit develops a fault, a fourth stand-by transformer can be connected by the appropriate connection of copper links within the main switchboard.

A single fault in the 3-phase single core transformer would put the complete unit out of commis-

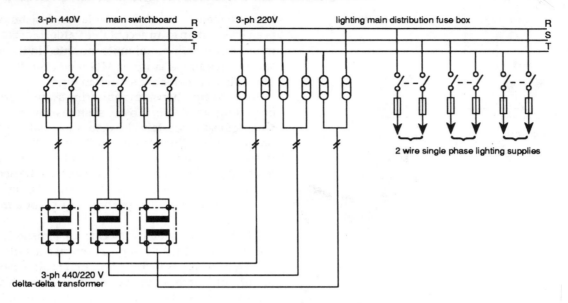

Figure 7   Use of delta-delta connection to provide security of supply.

sion. The use of a delta-delta connection provides security of supply. As shown in Fig 7, all circuits will still be maintained if an open circuit fault occurs on a phase but the transformer cannot be operated at full-load. Transformers rarely develop serious problems if they are kept clean, dry and well ventilated. Transformers should be regularly disconnected and top covers removed. Dirt and dust should be brushed out and vacuumed. Blowing out with compressed air is not recommended because it tends to force deposits into the insulation. Insulation resistance between phase windings and to earth should be measured and the values logged. Any fall of resistance should be rectified. Cleaning and heating may be necessary to remove dirt and moisture. The condition of winding inter-turn insulation can be determined by continuity tests. A low value can indicate short-circuited turns in the winding. Most marine transformers rely on natural air circulation for cooling. Protective grids and screens should be thoroughly cleaned and nothing should be allowed to compromise the cooling of the unit. Overheating can be caused if the area around the transformer is used for storing boxes of spares etc. Check that all terminations are tightened down and make a visual inspection for signs of burning or damage. Replace all covers and screens.

SWITCHBOARDS AND SWITCHGEAR

The main switchboard provides a location for marshalling electrical power from the main generators and distributing the power for utilisation throughout the vessel. Switchboards are sectionalised by bus-bar isolators, shown in Fig 8, to allow safe routine maintenance.

Bus bars are air insulated, hard drawn, high conductivity, electrolytic copper. These are mounted on Permali type insulators which are firmly secured to the inside of the cubicle. The bus bars are rigidly mounted to maintain clearances under short-circuit conditions. All copper joints are bolted and the jointing surfaces tinned.

Modern switchboards are invariably of the 'dead front' type where all switchgear and equipment are enclosed in sheet steel compartments. Operating handles and push buttons are mounted on hinged doors at the front of the switchboard. Most front panels and back doors are hinged to facilitate operation, inspection and cleaning. Steel walls are fitted between switchboard sections to prevent arcs and molten metal due to short circuits from entering neighbouring sections. Generally, switchboards are arranged symmetrically with the generator panels in the middle and the most important circuits equally distributed on either side as shown in Fig 9.

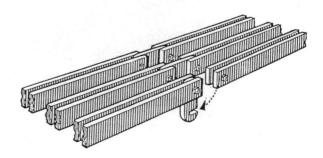

Figure 8   Isolating switch for the main bus bar.

Figure 9 Arrangement of the switchboard.

Figure 10 Isolating and tilting the circuit breaker.

Switchgear is of the 'draw-out' type to facilitate inspection and maintenance. Either the complete front panel and switchgear unit can be totally removed or, the panel is hinged and the circuit breaker racked out on rails and tilted as in Fig 10.

Circuit breakers control and protect generators and incoming feeders, the bus bars and outgoing feeders. If prospective fault currents are very high then bus-bar splitting circuit breakers may be used. These breakers split the board when a fault occurs to limit the fault current that has to be tripped by the outgoing circuit breakers. An alternative is to connect the two bus-bar sections through a reactor which will limit the flow of fault current from one side of the switchboard to the other.

Circuit breakers

The majority of marine circuit breakers are air-break rather than oil-immersed or vacuum-break.

Figure 11 shows a typical circuit breaker construction. It comprises fixed and moving main and arcing contacts, arranged so that the arcing contacts make before and break after the main contacts. The main contacts are usually silver faced copper, copper with silver inserts or silver cadmium oxide, and the arcing contacts are usually silver tungsten or silver cadmium oxide. These combine to provide minimum contact resistance for current carrying with reduced arc erosion. If severe burning or pitting occurs on the main contacts they may require filing. The manufac-

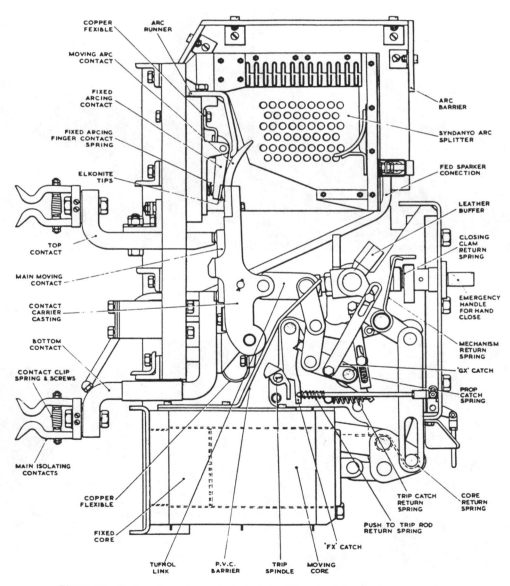

Figure 11   Section through arc chute and circuit breaker (electrically operated).

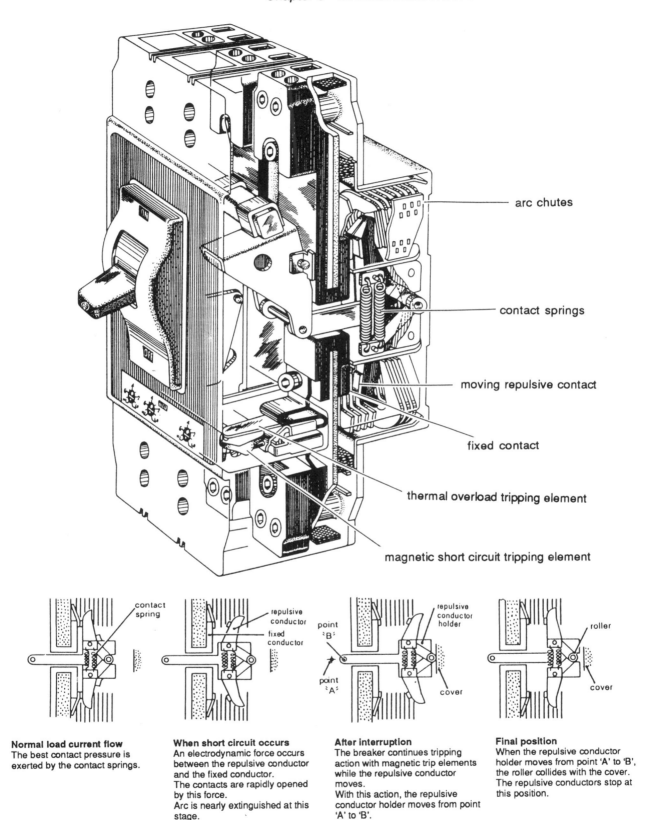

arc chutes

contact springs

moving repulsive contact

fixed contact

thermal overload tripping element

magnetic short circuit tripping element

Normal load current flow
The best contact pressure is
exerted by the contact springs.

When short circuit occurs
An electrodynamic force occurs
between the repulsive conductor
and the fixed conductor.
The contacts are rapidly opened
by this force.
Arc is nearly extinguished at this
stage.

After interruption
The breaker continues tripping
action with magnetic trip elements
while the repulsive conductor
moves.
With this action, the repulsive
conductor holder moves from point
'A' to 'B'.

Final position
When the repulsive conductor
holder moves from point 'A' to 'B',
the roller collides with the cover.
The repulsive conductors stop at
this position.

Figure 12   Terasake no-fuse moulded case circuit breaker.

turer's handbook will give instructions to rectify this condition. It is often caused by misalignment of the contacts. The arcing contacts are normally subject to burning and can be dressed with a smooth file, but not emery cloth. Circuit breakers are capable of breaking very large short circuit currents. This is achieved by providing fast break with long travel to hinder arc formation. Arc extinction occurs as the arc rises into the splitter (arc chute). Never allow a circuit breaker to operate with the arc chutes removed.

Here is a general guide to circuit breaker maintenance:

1 *Monthly*—operate circuit breaker

2 *Annually*—check:
   tightness of all electrical connections;
   condition of arc chutes and arcing contacts, clean or replace as necessary;
   condition of main contacts;
   operation of breaker-opening, closing and charging;
   cleanliness—clean as necessary;
   lubrication—lubricate as necessary; do not over lubricate.

3 *After a fault trip*—check main and arcing contacts and arc chutes.

This is the minimum maintenance required. Manufacturers' recommended procedures should be followed.

There is a limit to the number of switching operations a circuit breaker can perform. It is designed to be closed continuously and is primarily intended for protection purposes. The circuit breaker trip can be initiated by a wide range of fault conditions, particularly generator circuit breakers. Short circuit, undervoltage, overload, phase imbalance, low frequency and prime-mover overspeed are possible trip conditions. To obtain a fast break, circuit breakers are fitted with powerful spring mechanisms which can be very dangerous. Handling and maintenance should always be carried out with the springs discharged. The closing/tripping mechanism is complicated, as shown in Fig 11.

Carefully follow manufacturers' instructions for maintenance and lubrication.

Circuit breaker closing is achieved either manually or electrically by solenoid or motor. A mechanical latch holds the circuit breaker in the closed position. The circuit breaker is tripped by releasing the hold-on latch.

Feeder circuits are often protected by moulded-case circuit breakers (MCCB) which have current ratings in the range 30–1500A. These are generally manually operated and have a magnetic short circuit and thermal overload trips incorporated. Back-up fuses are sometimes necessary because the MCCB does not have the short circuit capacity of an air-break circuit breaker.

Figure 12 shows the construction of a Terasaki no-fuse MCCB with a fast acting repulsive mechanism which does not require back-up fuses.

Smaller sizes are fully encapsulated and contact cleaning is achieved by periodically closing and tripping a few times. This should also be done with breakers that are closed for long periods in order to free the mechanism, clean the contacts and check for contact welding. After isolation, tighten all terminals on the breaker. The larger sizes are accessible and maintenance is similar to the air-break type. After a short-circuit trip the breaker should be inspected for possible damage to contacts and the close/trip mechanism operated and checked. Insulation readings between poles and each pole to earth should be taken. A minimum of 5 MΩ is usually specified by the manufacturer.

Many distribution boards are now fitted with miniature circuit breakers (MCB) instead of fuses for sub-circuit protection. Current range is 5–100A and thermal overload and magnetic short circuit trip facilities are provided.

POWER SYSTEM OPERATION

To obtain satisfactory parallel operation between ac generators certain requirements concerning the prime mover speed governor and the automatic voltage regulator (AVR) must be met. It is also necessary for the operating personnel to have a clear understanding of the terms active power and reactive power.

Active power is more often called kilowatts (kW) and reactive power called kilovars (kVAr).

kW (Active power)

This type of power flow is best illustrated by considering a simple resistor connected to a single phase ac supply of V volts. The resistor will take a current I and will take electrical energy from the supply and convert it into heat. The waveforms of voltage and current are in phase, $i = v/R$. The power waveform is obtained by multiplying the voltage and current together. You will see that when v and i are both negative the power waveform will be positive; in fact the power flow is always positive. Positive power flow means that power is taken from the supply and converted by the resistor into a power output. This

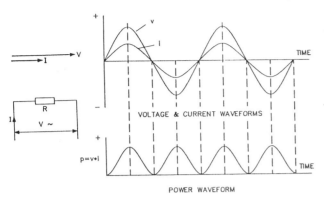

Figure 13   Waveforms of voltage, current and power for active power flow.

type of power flow is called active power (symbol, P). Active power flow occurs when V and I are in phase, as in Fig 13.

kVAR (Reactive power)

Figure 14 shows a reactive device. It is a coil which has zero resistance, wound around a steel core. The device is connected to an ac supply of V volts and will take an ac current I amps.

Consider the current waveform. At instant A the current is zero, as the current starts to increase it will create a magnetic field Φ in the steel core. The strength of this field increases as the current builds up.

During the quarter cycle between A and B the electric current transfers energy from the supply and stores it in the magnetic field. In the next quarter cycle, B to C, the current falls to zero and the magnetic field, along with its stored energy, disappears.

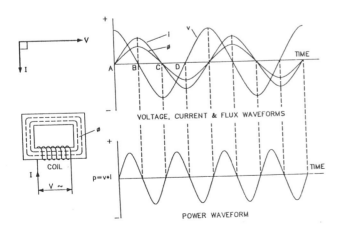

Figure 14   Waveforms of voltage, current and power for reactive power flow.

Since there is no power output, the only place it can go is back into the supply, so the device now feeds power back into the supply. In the next quarter cycle, C to D, the current builds up again and power flow is supply → device and the process repeats itself. Power is alternately positive and negative as energy is stored and discharged. So the power waveform is first positive and then negative.

To create this power flow the current lags behind the voltage by 90 deg.

This to-and-fro flow of electrical power is called reactive and is caused by power devices which can store energy in magnetic fields (motors, fluorescent lamps etc.).

Reactive power, $Q = V \times I$.

When V and I are at 90° to each other the reactive power reverses every quarter cycle.

Units of reactive power
If V is in volts, and I is in amps, Q is in VAr
(1000 VAr = 1 kVAr; 1,000,000 VAr = 1MVAr)

Marine electrical services
The main electrical services comprising a typical ship's load would be electric motors, lighting, and heating.

All these loads will draw kW from the supply because they all provide power outputs, but motors and fluorescent lighting have coils and steel cores so they also require kVAr. A typical load will require both kW and kVAr simultaneously from the generator. To do this the load draws a current which lags the voltage at an angle ϕ, where ϕ is somewhere between 0 deg and 90 deg.

You will recall that
$$P = \text{volts} \times \text{amps in phase,}$$
and $$Q = \text{volts} \times \text{amps at 90 deg,}$$

so $$P = V.I \cos\phi \, / 1000 \quad \text{kW,}$$
and $$Q = V.I \sin\phi \, / 1000 \quad \text{kVAr (Fig 15).}$$

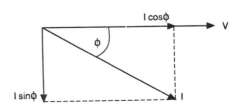

Figure 15   Phasor diagram.

Apparent power

You will notice from the phasor diagram that there are 3 volt-amp products.

a) $V \times I \cos\phi$ the active power (P);

b) $V \times I \sin\phi$ the reactive power (Q);

c) $V \times I$ the volts times the actual current, a power but not a new type. It is just the combination of P and Q and is called the apparent power (S);

Apparent power = volts × circuit amps.

Units of apparent power

If V is in volts, and I is in amps, S is in VA.
   (1000 VA = 1 kVA; 1,000,000 VA = 1 MVA)

Power factor

If you know the kVA in a system you may need to know how much of it consists of kW. This is indicated by the power factor of the system.

$$\text{Power factor} = \frac{\text{kW}}{\text{kVA}} = \frac{VI\cos\phi}{VI} = \cos\phi.$$

Power in 3-phase systems

In 3-phase systems, the formulæ for P, Q and S are the same as for single phase systems except that each formula is multiplied by $\sqrt{3}$, i.e.:

single phase	3-phase
$P = VI\cos\phi$	$P = \sqrt{3}VI\cos\phi$
$Q = VI\sin\phi$	$Q = \sqrt{3}VI\sin\phi$
$S = VI$	$S = \sqrt{3}VI$
power factor = $\cos\phi$	power factor = $\cos\phi$

GOVERNOR AND AUTOMATIC VOLTAGE REGULATOR

The two factors essential for the production of generated voltage in an ac generator are rotational speed and magnetic flux. Field windings on the rotor create strong magnetic field 'poles' when direct current is passed through them.

The rotor is driven at constant speed by the prime mover (diesel, turbine or main shaft). This produces voltage at the generator stator terminals of the correct frequency (60 Hz or 50 Hz). The dc current (called the excitation) in the rotor is adjusted until the generator produces the correct voltage (typically 440V).

Both the frequency and voltage are affected by changes of electrical load on the generator.

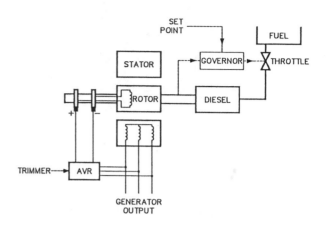

Figure 16   Schematic diagram of diesel/alternator system.

To keep the frequency constant when the load changes a speed governor is fitted to the prime mover.

To keep the voltage constant when the load changes an automatic voltage regulator (AVR) is fitted to the generator (Fig 16).

The governor and AVR also play an important part in the successful parallel operation of ac generators.

Effect of kW loading

When the generator is on no-load the governor set-point is manually adjusted until the frequency is correct. The AVR trimmer (if fitted) is adjusted until system voltage is correct. The prime mover does not require much fuel to run the generator on no load so the governor has only opened the fuel throttle valve a small amount. If a kW load such as heating is switched on to the generator, then energy is drawn from the generator and converted into heat. This energy must be provided by increasing the rate of fuel supply to the prime mover. This happens automatically in the following way:

1. When kW load is applied the load draws current from the stator windings.

2. This current flowing in the stator windings produces a rotating magnetic field. This field rotates at the same speed as the rotor.

3. The stator field lies across the rotor field and exerts a magnetic 'pull' or 'torque' on the rotor which tries to pull the rotor backwards as in Fig 17.

4. The magnetic torque exerted on the rotor causes the rotor to slow down. This reduction of speed is detected by the governor.

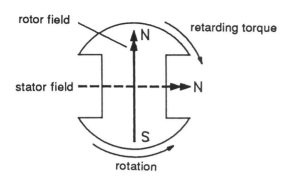

Figure 17 Exertion of torque on rotor due to stator field.

5. The governor opens up the throttle valve to increase the fuel supply.

6. The throttle valve is opened until the frequency is back to normal (in fact slightly less). Now the prime mover is developing enough power to drive the alternator at the correct speed and meet the kW load demand.

The governor responds to changes of kW load to keep the system frequency constant.

Governor characteristic (Fig 18)

When kW load is applied the governor tries to keep the frequency constant. The graph of frequency against kW for the governor shows how closely it maintains constant frequency.

For perfect accuracy the characteristic should be horizontal. This means the system frequency is exactly constant at every kW load. This is called isochronous. In practice most marine governors exhibit a 'droop' of up to 5%. This is so that the generator can be run in parallel with other generators.

Some modern electronic governors may provide a selector switch where isochronous operation is selected when the generator is running alone and droop inject for running in parallel.

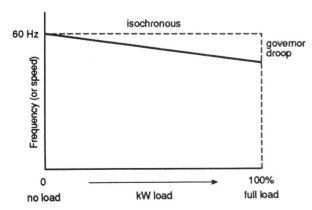

Figure 18 Governor characteristic.

Effect of kVAr loading

When a kVAr load is applied to an ac generator there is no power demand on the prime mover. This is because the energy flow with kVAr loading is backwards and forwards between the generator and the load, the prime mover is not involved. The stator current again produces a rotating magnetic field, but unlike the kW loading it does not exert a magnetic torque on the rotor. This time the stator field is in line with the rotor field so no torque is produced.

It can be seen from Fig 19 that the stator field is acting in the opposite direction to the rotor field which results in a large reduction of flux in the machine, and reduced flux means reduced output voltage. The AVR responds to the fall of output voltage and boosts up the excitation current to the rotor to increase the flux. The excitation is increased until the voltage is back to normal (in practice slightly less than normal).

The AVR responds to changes of kVAr load to keep the system voltage constant.

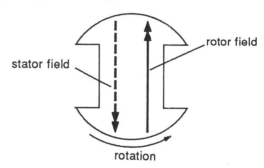

Figure 19 Opposition of stator field and rotor field resulting in reduction of flux and decreased voltage.

AVR characteristic

This is a graph of volts/kVAr and like the governor, exhibits a 'droop' which is required for stable parallel operation.

PARALLEL OPERATION OF AC GENERATORS

Parallel operation of ac generators requires both synchronising and load sharing procedures. In many large systems these operations are completely automatic, being carried out by a computer-based power management system. Generator sets are automatically run-up, synchronised and loaded or disconnected and stopped as the load demand varies. A more common system requires engineers to respond to changes in load demand but the processes of synchronising and load sharing are automatic after initiation by the engineer.

Synchronising

Figure 20 shows the arrangement of an automatic synchronising unit. Before the incoming generator can be connected to the live system three conditions must be met to ensure 'synchronisation'.

1. The frequency of the incoming generator and the bus bars must be within acceptable limits.

2. The incomer and bus bar voltages must be within acceptable limits

3. The phase difference between the incomer voltage and the bus bar voltage must be within acceptable limits.

When the incoming generator circuit breaker is closed a surge of current and power circulates to lock the machines at the same frequency, voltage and phase angle. To avoid generator damage due to excessive surge torque during synchronising it is important that the synchronising unit is correctly commissioned and periodically checked. The types of damage due to incorrect synchronising reported to Lloyd's Register of Shipping include deformation of stator windings, movement between stator core and frame, failure of rotor diodes on brushless machines, twisted rotor shafts, localised crushing of shaft end keyway and broken couplings.

Figure 21 shows synchronising damage.

For manual synchronising, the operator should ensure that the incoming voltage is within 5% of the busbar voltage. Ideally, the incoming machine frequency should be within 0.2% of the bus bar frequency, which is indicated by one revolution of the synchroscope every ten seconds. In practice this may be impossible to achieve if the bus bar frequency is fluctuating with load changes. It is usual to synchronize with the incoming machine slightly fast so that the synchronising surge does not operate the reverse power trip.

Closing the incoming machine circuit breaker when the two voltages are out of phase will result in severe mechanical torques exerted on the rotors to bring them into synchronism. It is essential that the circuit breaker is closed at the instant the incoming machine voltage is in phase with the bus bar voltage to limit these synchronising torques. This condition is indicated by the '12 o'clock' position on the synchroscope. The circuit breaker is operated slightly before this position to take into account the circuit breaker closing time. To avoid eventual damage to generators synchronising should also be carried out with incoming machine voltage, frequency and phase angle as close as possible to the bus bar conditions. Check synchroniser units are usually fitted to prevent faulty manual synchronising. This unit prevents the incoming circuit breaker from closing unless the voltage, frequency and phase angle differences are within preset limits. Check synchronisers are often provided with an override switch for use in an emergency, this can lead to problems if the override is left activated after the emergency.

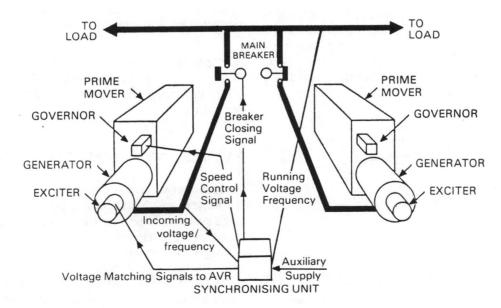

Figure 20   Automatic synchronising unit.

a)

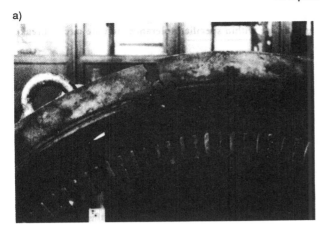

b)

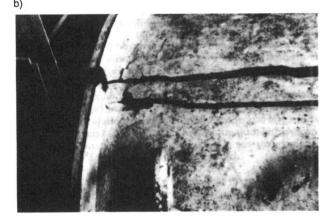

Figure 21   Broken stator housing on 556kVA, 440V generator caused by rotation of stator lamination pack. a) End view showing key still in lamination key slot, jammed below the next inner stiffener of the frame; b) external view of damage resulting from shell being pushed outwards.

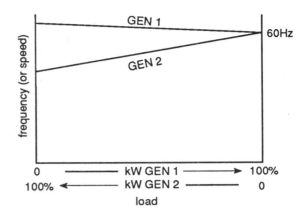

Figure 22   After synchronising GEN2.

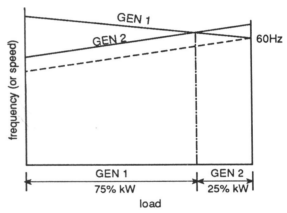

Figure 23   After increasing governor setting of GEN2.

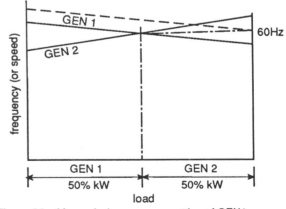

Figure 24   After reducing governor setting of GEN1.

Load sharing

After the incoming generator has been synchronised it is now ready to take up load. It will be recalled that the generator will have to provide two types of ac power, kW and kVAR.

The governor settings of the generators are adjusted to achieve kW load sharing and the excitation is adjusted to achieve kVAr load sharing.

kW Load sharing

After synchronising, GEN1 is still supplying all the load kW while GEN2 supplies zero kW. The governors of both machines are producing 60 Hz. This situation can be depicted graphically as in Fig 22.

The kW of GEN1 are measured left to right and the kW of GEN2 are measured right to left. It can be seen in Fig 22 that both machines are producing 60 Hz, GEN1 is supplying 100% of the load kW and GEN2 is supplying 0 kW.

GEN2 can be made to supply kW by adjusting its speed trimmer to increase the set point of the governor as shown in Fig 23. This has the effect of 'lifting' the whole characteristic which results in GEN2 taking load and GEN1 losing load. A problem is that the system frequency increases.

Now the speed trimmer of GEN1 is adjusted to reduce the set point of the governor (Fig 24). This

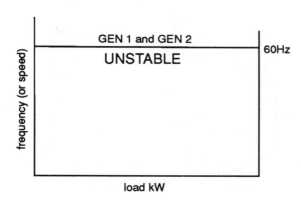

Figure 25 Generators with flat governor characteristics are unstable in parallel.

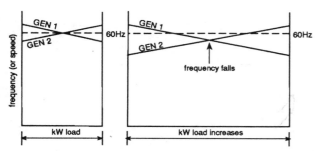

Figure 26 When droop is large frequency changes with kW load but generators are stable in parallel.

lowers the characteristic of GEN1 allowing GEN2 to take up more of the load and brings the frequency back to 60 Hz. This load balancing is monitored on the kW meters of each machine.

Stability

If two generators are to share load their governor characteristics must have a definite 'crossing point' that is why governor 'droop' is necessary.

If the characteristics are flat (isochronous) as shown in Fig 25 then system accuracy is good because frequency stays constant as kW load changes, but machines cannot be run in parallel. With flat characteristics the load swings repeatedly from one machine to the other because the characteristics have no definite crossing point.

The amount of governor droop is a compromise between accuracy and stability. If the governor droop is large then the system is stable but the frequency will change slightly as kW load changes as shown in Fig 26.

kVAr Load sharing

This is achieved automatically by the AVR units which adjust the excitation after synchronising so that each machine shares kVAr and generates the correct voltage.

As with the governor, the AVR requires a 'droop' for stable parallel operation. As kVAr load changes the AVR responds to keep the system voltage constant.

A simplified diagram of a typical 'direct feed' thyristor AVR is shown in Fig 27. The generator voltage is stepped down by a transformer and rectifier and then applied to the reference circuit. Any difference between the generator voltage and the desired voltage produces an error voltage. The error voltage is amplified and fed to a blocking oscillator which controls the firing angle of the thyristor. The magnitude of the excitation current depends on the time during each cycle for which the thyristor is conducting. If the generator voltage falls the conduction time is increased by the increased error voltage. This results in increased excitation current and rotor flux which brings the generator back to the desired value. Short circuit excitation current transformers (CTs) are used to prevent complete collapse of the generator excitation under short-circuit conditions. These CTs provide all the excitation under short circuit conditions and enable a sufficiently large generator current to be maintained to ensure circuit-breaker tripping.

For parallel operation the AVR must have 'droop'

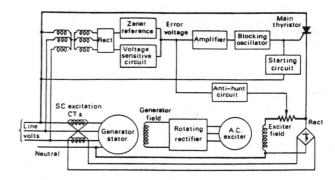

Figure 27 Typical direct feed thyristor AVR.

and a quadrature current compensation (QCC) circuit consisting of a CT and resistor is used. The CT detects lagging load current and causes the AVR to reduce the output voltage. This is shown in the static excitation AVR circuit in Fig 28.

SHAFT GENERATORS

There are many different configurations of shaft generator systems available. Essentially, they can be classified into what may be called the conventional type and the constant frequency type as shown in Fig 29.

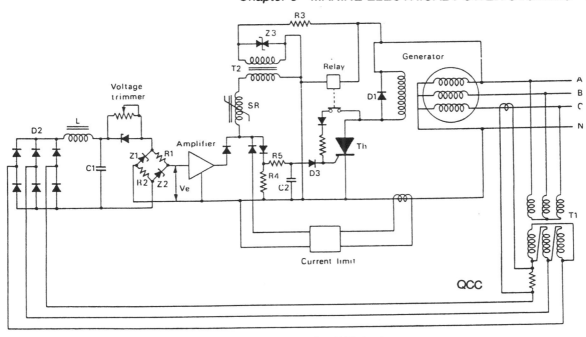

Figure 28 Static excitation AVR circuit.

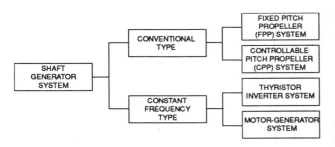

Figure 29 Classification of shaft generator system configurations.

Conventional type

In this system the output from the shaft generator is directly connected to the main bus bars which means that the output frequency is directly influenced by main engine speed. For controllable-pitch propellers (CPP) the main engine speed and output frequency are almost constant. Typically, the design frequency range would be 59 Hz to 61 Hz with a rough sea tolerance of ±2 Hz. This frequency range is wider for the fixed pitch propeller; from about 55 Hz to 61 Hz. The frequency variation prevents parallel operation with auxiliary generators and blackout changeover is necessary. The range of engine speeds within which the shaft generator can be operated is generally from 90% to 100% of normal.

Figure 30 shows the arrangement of a conventional type shaft generator system.

The gearing for conventional type systems is usually designed so that a high speed generator with lower size, weight and cost can be used. A 4-pole machine running at 1800 rev/min and producing 440 V at 60 Hz has become a standard for this application.

Constant frequency system

If the frequency variation in the conventional system is unacceptable then a constant frequency output can be achieved with a thyristor frequency converter. The generator field poles may be mounted directly onto the main shaft with the stator windings, core and frame surrounding them and separated by a 5–7 mm air-gap. The generator can be placed in the main propeller shafting or located in front of the main engine as shown in Fig 31.

In both cases the generator speed is that of the main engine, about 100 rev/min and the output

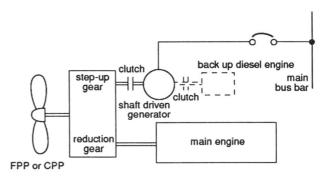

Figure 30 Conventional type shaft generator system.

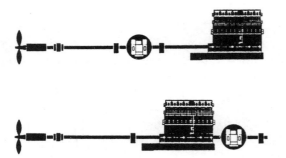

Figure 31 Generator positioned in the main propeller shafting or in front of the main engine.

frequency between about 10 Hz and 15 Hz. The low speed operation means that the generator is large for the power output but the overall arrangement takes relatively little space.

In Fig 32 the generator is connected to the propeller shaft or crankshaft by step-up gearing. The more conventional operating speed results in a more compact generator.

Figure 33 shows a constant frequency shaft generator system. The variable frequency ac output is converted to dc by the thyristor rectifier. The thyristor inverter then converts the dc to fixed frequency 3-phase ac. Changes in frequency and voltage caused by changes of propeller shaft speed or by electrical load variations are met by adjustment of the shaft generator excitation by the control system. The rectifier/inverter unit cannot supply reactive power (kVAr) for the ship's system. This is provided by the synchronous condenser, which is a large, dedicated, synchronous motor or an auxiliary generator, de-clutched from its diesel, running as a motor. The synchronous condenser is run on no-load at a leading power factor and operates essentially as a power factor correction capacitor. The shaft generator provides the system kilowatts at unity power factor and the synchronous condenser provides the kilovars. If the synchronous condenser is a dedicated motor it

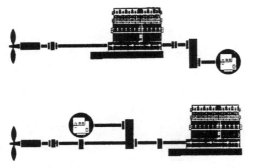

Figure 32 Generator connected to the propeller shaft or crank shaft by step up gearing.

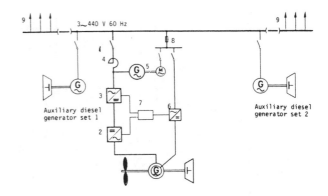

1	shaft generator	6	excitation converter
2	thyristor rectifier (main circuit)	7	control system
3	thyristor inverter (main circuit)	8	power supply 3 x 440V, 60Hz
4	system reactor	9	loads
5	synchronous condenser with run-up motor		

Figure 33 Constant frequency shaft generator system.

requires a run-up motor to bring it up to speed for synchronising.

The system reactor connected between the thyristor inverter and the bus bars improves the voltage wave-form by smoothing out dips caused by commutation of the thyristors. It will also limit short circuit current delivered by the shaft generator system.

Most systems can provide full power output down to 75% or 80% of rated speed and reduced power down to approximately 50% rated speed as shown in Fig 34.

Further improvements in efficiency can be obtained by combining the shaft generator mechanically or electrically with an exhaust gas turbogenerator.

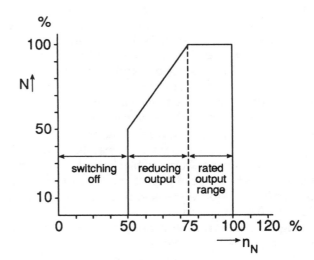

Figure 34 Load diagram.

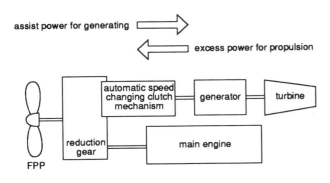

Figure 35 Exhaust gas turbogenerator coupled to the main engine.

Figure 35 shows an exhaust gas turbogenerator mechanically coupled to the main engine. When the turbine power output exceeds the electric power demand in the ship the excess power is applied to the main engine to assist propulsion. When the electrical load increases and exceeds the power output from the turbine the shortfall is taken from the main engine.

An electrically coupled system is shown in Fig 36. When the electrical power demand is low, power from the turbo generator drives the shaft generator as a synchronous motor and provides propulsion. As the electrical load increases the shaft generator takes power from the main engine to assist the turbogenerator. In the event of main engine failure the shaft generator can be used as an emergency 'takehome' motor supplied by the diesel generator.

The last system to be considered is the motor-generator type. This is used for small power systems below about 400 kW. The output from the shaft generator is rectified and fed to a dc motor. The speed of the dc motor is held constant by a regulator and it drives an ac generator.

BATTERIES

The ability of a battery to deliver electrical power instantly, together with its convenience, has enabled the battery to become widely used as an emergency power source and to power portable equipment.

The basic single unit in a battery is referred to as a 'cell'. Cells are connected in a series arrangement to form the battery. The emf of a cell is quite small, typically 1–3V. The series connection of cells in a battery enables larger and more useful voltages to be made available.

A cell produces electrical current by chemical reaction. It consists of two electrodes (anode and cathode) of different materials which are connected by an electrolyte; a chemical which reacts suitably with both electrodes.

An electrochemical series shows the relative positions of possible electrode materials.

Potassium	*Anodic:*
Sodium	*More corrosive end of table*
Lithium	
Magnesium	
Zinc	
Lead	
Hydrogen	
Copper	
Mercury	
Silver	
Carbon	
Sulphur	*Cathodic:*
Oxygen	*More noble end of table*

Any two substances in the list will form a couple in conjunction with a suitable electrolyte. The further apart the couple is in the list, the greater the emf developed.

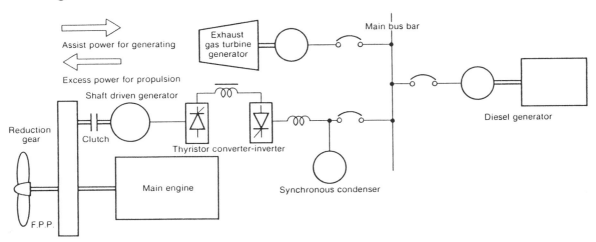

Figure 36 Electrically coupled system.

In 1800, Professor Volta produced the first battery using a zinc-silver couple with a brine electrolyte which developed an emf of 1.4 V.

The electrochemical series shown is by no means a complete list of possible substances but the series would seem to indicate the possibility of an enormous number of cell couples.

In reality, the difficulty of combining suitable electrode materials with an electrolyte that will give stable chemical action with stable operating voltage and long life limits the number of practical cells that are possible.

Primary cells

When the chemicals within a primary cell have been used up, the cell must be discarded and replaced.

The Leclanché cell of 1868 used a zinc carbon couple with an acidic ammonium chloride electrolyte. This was the first cell to be used extensively commercially for A.G. Bell's early telephone installations in the 1880s. The same zinc carbon cell is still in widespread use today but in its dry cell form as the tried and tested torch battery. The zinc carbon cell develops an emf of 1.5 V.

Alkaline cells
Alkaline cells, such as the mercury cell and the manganese cell, are familiar to in their use in cameras and personal cassette recorders. These cells are also widely used in commercial portable equipment, being superior to the zinc carbon cell in terms of operational life and range of operating temperatures.

Developments in the electronics industry have stimulated the need for newer forms of cell. As electronic components have become smaller and smaller, so there has arisen a need for cells with much higher power to weight ratio, much longer shelf life and even wider range of operating temperature. The small zinc carbon button battery has one of the highest power to weight ratios. A range of lithium cells appeared in the 1980s. Lithium cells have a shelf life of 10 years compared with one or two years for zinc carbon and develop an emf of over 3 V. Lithium has a very low relative density and lithium cells have an energy to weight ratio of over five times that of the zinc carbon cell. Lithium cells are used in various specialised electronic equipment where their long life allows a fit and forget policy to be used, or where their low weight and small size is of particular advantage. Applications include such equipment as distress beacons, portable electronic devices such as measuring instruments, as battery back-up of the volatile memory units in computers, smoke detectors, emergency lighting etc. Although lithium cells for general consumer use are safe, the components not being particularly toxic, some lithium cells do present a potential hazard to safety. The lithium/sulphur dioxide cell (Li/SDX) contains liquid sulphur dioxide gas under pressure. Abuse, such as a short circuit or incineration, produces sufficiently high temperatures to cause the case to tend to explode and then to release its toxic sulphur dioxide gas. The Li/SDX cell and other lithium cells with similar hazardous characteristics usually have a blow off vent in the case to give relief to pressure build up and prevent explosion. As would be expected such cells are not generally available for consumer use, but are restricted to industrial use.

Care must be taken with such cells not to tamper with associated circuit protection components, not to short-circuit the cells, and not to dispose of these cells, or any other cells, by incineration. Replacement of such cells and repair of circuit protective components should be by qualified personnel and not by untrained third parties.

The low power demand of electronic circuits and some portable appliances makes the small and compact primary cell a most suitable power source. However, the large power demand made on engine starting batteries and ships' emergency lighting batteries normally requires that larger rechargeable batteries be used.

Secondary cells

Secondary batteries are rechargeable. That is, when the chemicals have been used up, they can be re-formed to their original state and the battery recharged with electrical energy, by passing a charging current through the battery in the reverse direction.

The need for battery charging equipment to be included in the battery installation is a matter of considerable expense and some inconvenience, but the cost of continual replacement of an equivalent primary battery would be totally unacceptable for a large-power installation.

Batteries on board ship intended to power emergency services, such as emergency generator starting and emergency lighting, are generally operated in a stand-by mode, being called upon to supply power when the main supply fails.

Services such as radio equipment, telephones, alarm circuits, etc. are commonly battery operated, being supplied from two batteries operated in a regular charge/discharge mode.

Two types of secondary battery are in common use, the lead acid and the nickel cadmium alkaline.

The lead acid battery develops a nominal 2V per

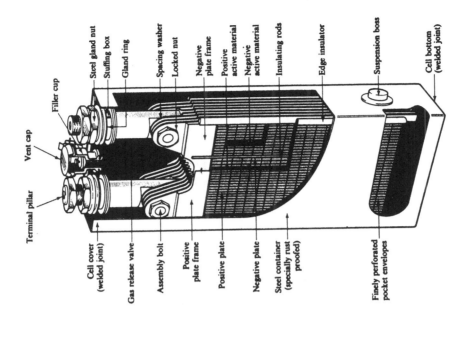

b)

Filler cup
Vent cap
Terminal pillar

Steel gland nut
Stuffing box
Gland ring
Spacing washer
Locked nut
Negative plate frame
Positive active material
Negative active material
Insulating rods
Edge insulator
Suspension boss
Cell bottom (welded joint)

Cell cover (welded joint)
Gas release valve
Assembly bolt
Positive plate frame
Positive plate
Negative plate
Steel container (specially rust proofed)
Finely perforated pocket envelopes

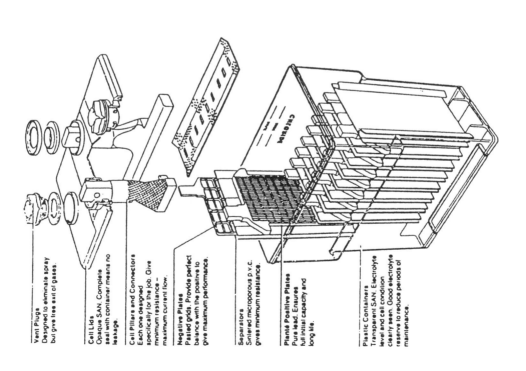

a)

Vent Plugs
Designed to eliminate spray but give free exit of gases.

Cell Lids
Opaque SAN. Complete seal with container means no leakage.

Cell Pillars and Connectors
Each one designed specifically for the job. Give minimum resistance – maximum current flow.

Negative Plates
Pasted grids. Provide perfect balance with the positive to give maximum performance.

Separators
Sintered microporous p.v.c. gives minimum resistance.

Planté Positive Plates
Pure lead. Ensures full initial capacity and long life.

Plastic Containers
Transparent SAN. Electrolyte level and cell condition clearly seen. Good electrolyte reserve to reduce periods of maintenance.

Figure 37 Cell structures: a) lead acid cell; b) alkaline cell.

cell demanding a 12 cell battery for the normal 24V low voltage supply. In comparison the alkaline battery develops 1.2V per cell demanding a 20 cell battery for the same 24V supply.

The lead acid battery is less expensive in initial cost and is more efficient, but the alkaline battery has the longer life of up to 20 years compared with 5 to 10 years, depending upon the construction, of the lead acid battery.

Traditionally, the alkaline battery was preferred for emergency power supplies being more suited to long periods of idle operation on stand-by. It was also regarded as being more reliable. The lead acid battery was preferred for the regular recycling duty of essential power supplies operated in the charge/discharge mode.

However, many current installations have lead acid batteries specifically designed for the stand-by duty of emergency power loads and emergency generator starting.

The electrolyte of the lead acid cell is a dilute solution of sulphuric acid; that of the alkaline cell a solution of potassium hydroxide, both aqueous solutions.

Both types of cell 'gas' when on charge, the alkaline cell more or less continuously and the lead acid cell when nearing the top of the charge. Hydrogen and oxygen gases are evolved due to the chemical breakdown of the water content of the electrolyte. The cells are vented to allow gases to escape and prevent internal pressure build up. Gassing presents several problems. Hydrogen is a highly dangerous explosive gas and the evolved gases carry with them a mist of corrosive acid or alkaline electrolyte.

Large batteries (above 2 kW) must be installed in specially prepared rooms or lockers, well ventilated to remove the explosive hydrogen gas, illuminated by suitable explosion protected luminaires and steelwork painted to resist corrosion. In addition personnel must exercise care not to cause sparks or produce naked flames when inspecting batteries. Notices to this effect must be displayed.

The evolution of gas, together with evaporation causes a significant water loss from the electrolyte and this must be made good by topping up with distilled water as necessary.

Acid batteries and alkaline batteries must not be located in the same room, to prevent danger of battery damage caused by contamination of the alkaline battery by acid.

Battery maintenance

Battery maintenance is substantially the same for both types of battery. Cell tops must be kept clean and dry, vents clear and free of deposits, terminal connections tight, free of corrosion and coated with petroleum jelly to prevent corrosion. Electrolyte levels should be checked and topped up with distilled water to cover the plates.

Safety precautions necessary during these procedures include wearing suitable protective clothing (rubber apron, rubber gloves and eye goggles), ensuring no sources of naked light are taken into the battery room and using insulated spanners and none metallic jugs and other utensils to prevent sparks and short circuits.

In addition suitable first aid treatments should be available. Sulphuric acid splashes on the skin should be washed off with fresh water and treated with a saline solution (one tablespoon of salt to half a litre of water). Potassium hydroxide splashes should again be washed off with fresh water but treated with boracic powder or a boracic acid solution (one teaspoonful of boracic powder to half a litre of water). Splashes in the eye are particularly dangerous. Liberal splashing of water in the eye, followed by washing in the aforementioned neutralising solutions is the immediate treatment. Rapid action and large quantities of water are essential, followed by seeking qualified medical attention.

The state of charge of a cell can be checked by measuring its terminal voltage while supplying load current; the terminal voltage of an idle cell is likely to be high giving a false indication of a fully charged cell.

The terminal voltage of a fully charged alkaline cell is about 1.2V, falling to 1.09V when fully discharged.

The terminal voltage of a fully charged acid cell is about 2.0V falling to 1.75V when fully discharged.

If voltage readings are taken while the battery is on charge the end of charge is indicated when the terminal voltage of an alkaline cell levels out at about 1.7V. For acid cells, the end of charge is indicated at about 2.6V, measured while on charge.

Maintenance procedures include measuring the relative density (or specific gravity) of the electrolyte. In the case of lead acid batteries, the relative density is a valuable indication of the state of charge of a cell, varying from 1.275–1.285 (specific gravity 1275–1285) for a fully charged cell, to about 1.1 (specific gravity 1100) when fully discharged. The relative density readings vary with temperature and temperature corrections must be made to arrive at a meaningful value. The above values are quoted for an ideal electrolyte temperature of 15°C. Actual readings should be corrected by adding 0.007 for each 10°C above 15°C and subtracting 0.007 for each 10°C below 15°C.

In the case of alkaline batteries, the relative density does not change and gives no indication of the state of charge of the cell. Nevertheless, the relative density should be measured regularly. As the cell ages, the relative density gradually falls. A new cell will have a relative density of about 1.190. When this falls to about 1.145, indicating that chemical deterioration has occurred, the electrolyte should be renewed or the battery replaced. This may be necessary only after 5 to 10 years depending upon the duty cycle for which the battery is employed. Manufacturers recommendations should be followed for renewing electrolyte.

The relative density of the electrolyte of a cell is measured using a hydrometer of the syringe type (Fig 38).

Batteries should be charged from suitable charging equipment according to manufacturers' instructions. The battery capacity is rated in terms of its discharge current at the 10 hour rate. A 250Ahr battery can supply 25A for 10 hours. Charging current can also be based upon the 10 hour rate but frequently is based upon shorter time rates such as 7 hours or 6 hours.

Lead acid cells should be charged until gassing freely, and charging should then continue for a further period until the charging voltage per cell levels out at about 2.6V. Overcharging causes overheating, distortion of cell plates and consequent dislodging of plate active materials.

Lead acid cells suffer self discharge; if the battery is left idle an internal discharge would slowly dissipate the charged energy. A fully charged lead acid cell must be maintained on a trickle charge, a low rate charge, to make up the loss due to 'self discharge'.

Alkaline cells should be charged at the recommended rate until gassing freely and the charging voltage per cell rises to about 1.7V. Charging should continue for a further two or three hours. Alkaline cells are able to retain their full charge for a considerable period and do not suffer self discharge except at high temperatures. Periodically, alkaline batteries should be given a short (two to three hours) refresher charge. Alkaline cells are well suited to the float charge mode of operation of stand-by power batteries. Here the battery is connected across the load supply and is charged up to the supply voltage after which the battery merely floats on the supply, neither supplying nor taking electrical energy.

The maximum recommended operating temperature of both types of battery is 50°C.

The minimum operating temperature is the freezing point of the electrolyte.

Alkaline batteries can operate down to –40°C but lead acid batteries can operate down to –32°C, fully charged, but only –9°C, fully discharged.

Lead acid batteries must be maintained in a fully charged condition, especially at low ambient temperatures, otherwise freezing can cause cracked cases and the subsequent leakage of electrolyte and corrosion of surrounding steel structures.

Sealed batteries or sealed gas recombination cells

Sealed batteries, or sealed gas recombination cells as they are more properly called, are commonly located within items of equipment. Vented cells, with their emission of explosive gases and corrosive mists, must be located in a 'safe' central battery room. Vented cells contain free liquid (and spillable) corrosive electrolyte. Water loss occurs demanding topping up.

Sealed cells, both acid and alkaline types, are specially designed and manufactured so that gassing does not occur in normal regular service. The cells can thus be sealed without danger of pressure build-up, require no topping up, demand very little maintenance and are safe for installation at sites out of bounds to the vented cells, such as within office equipment and electronic equipment. Many items of equipment such as navigation lights, fire detection and alarm systems, engine room control consoles, etc. now have their own emergency battery located within their own cabinet and are self contained, rather then having to rely upon a remote centralised emergency power supply unit. In case of fault and abuse, the cells have a 'blow-off' vent to relieve any pressure build up caused by possible gassing.

An emergency battery is installed to give protec-

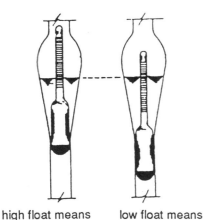

high float means   low float means
high specific gravity   low specific gravity

Figure 38 Hydrometer and float readings.

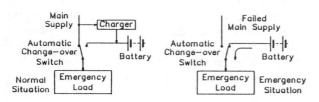

Figure 39 Standby power supply system.

tion against power supply failure. A typical installation would incorporate a contactor to reconnect the load from the main supply to the emergency supply if a mains failure occurred.

This arrangement (Fig 39), referred to as a standby power supply system, is satisfactory for most loads such as emergency generator starting and emergency lighting. However, the computer and allied office equipment cannot tolerate the loss of supply experienced during the period of contactor changeover; even a 20 ms delay may be unacceptable.

Computers are used on board ship for a wide variety of purposes and to ensure their uninterrupted operation during a mains power supply failure, they should be supplied via an uninterruptible power supply (UPS) system.

A typical UPS system incorporates a battery maintained on float charge. In the event of a failure of the main power supply, the battery is immediately available to supply the load.

The system (Fig 40) also incorporates circuits to filter out mains disturbances such as transients and spikes which can corrupt computer operation.

Units rated up to 300 kVA are available but a typical shipboard unit would be rated about 1.5 kVA.

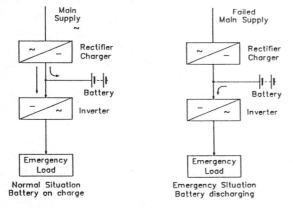

Figure 40 Uninterruptible power supply system.

MAINTENANCE

Maintenance is applied to equipment in an attempt to extend its useful life; to ensure that it re-

mains in a safe and serviceable condition. To many people, maintenance is regarded as being merely repairs or replacement of equipment that has suffered breakdown, indeed, such an approach is still widely applied today.

In 1969–1970 the costs and dangers involved with breakdown led to in-depth studies of the practices used. These studies were government sponsored and the results were published by HMSO. The report suggested that maintenance in general was in urgent need of planning and control to improve utilisation of labour, to improve care of valuable physical assets and to reduce the national financial loss resulting from plant down time and loss of services.

The demand for improvements in maintenance was made under the name of terotechnology.

In general, maintenance philosophy can be classified under the three headings, breakdown or failure maintenance, periodic maintenance and condition maintenance.

Breakdown or failure maintenance

This is applied because of breakdown of equipment or its inability to meet its operational requirements. The equipment is left untouched until failure occurs. At this time the equipment must be repaired or replaced and any other procedures carried out. On board ship, if failure occurs, the defect is brought to the attention of the chief engineer, who then decides on the course of action to be taken.

There are disadvantages with failure maintenance.

1. A serious breakdown of equipment may cause sufficient down time to put the ship out of commission until it is repaired.

2. If several breakdowns occur at about the same time, the available manpower on board may not be able to cope adequately, resulting in delays.

3. Some items of equipment may need the specialist services of the manufacturer to carry out repairs and this may cause further delays.

Despite these disadvantages, it is believed that failure maintenance is still widely applied, the responsibility for implementing maintenance being given to ship's staff, who see failure maintenance as a simple and logical practice.

Planned maintenance

A degree of planning is required in the operation of failure maintenance in organisation and for stocking spare parts and tools. However, the term planned maintenance is only applied to maintenance schemes where the application of maintenance and the practices involved are pre-planned and rigorously applied.

The object of planned maintenance is to prevent failure and breakdown of equipment and so avoid the consequent disadvantages that are incurred. However, breakdown and failure can still occur and emergency failure maintenance may still have to be applied.

Two systems of planned maintenance are in common use; periodic maintenance and planned maintenance.

Periodic maintenance

Periodic maintenance is the application of specified routine maintenance after a predetermined calendar period has elapsed, or after a number of running hours for the equipment have been recorded. A special case arises for equipment in which no inspection or repair is possible. For such equipment life maintenance is applied. Life maintenance means that no maintenance is carried out during the units predetermined useful life. At the end of this period, the unit is replaced (unless, of course, breakdown occurs and emergency unscheduled replacement maintenance applied).

There are specific advantages of periodic maintenance.

1. There are fewer breakdowns and the consequent reduced down time produce much higher levels of operating efficiency.

2. Maintenance is carried out at times most favourable to the operation of plant.

3. There is more effective utilisation of labour because maintenance is carried out at times favourable to the ship's staff.

4. Replacement equipment can be ordered in advance at opportune times.

5. Equipment is maintained in a safe condition and with reduced possible dangers.

6. When the specialist services of the manufacturer are required, they can be arranged for opportune times.

7. Life maintenance of short life components is arranged at scheduled times.

The operation of a periodic maintenance system requires the setting up of specially designed wall charts and documentation and is controlled, usually, by the chief engineer. Regular planning meetings (weekly) where decisions on the work to be done are a feature of the system.

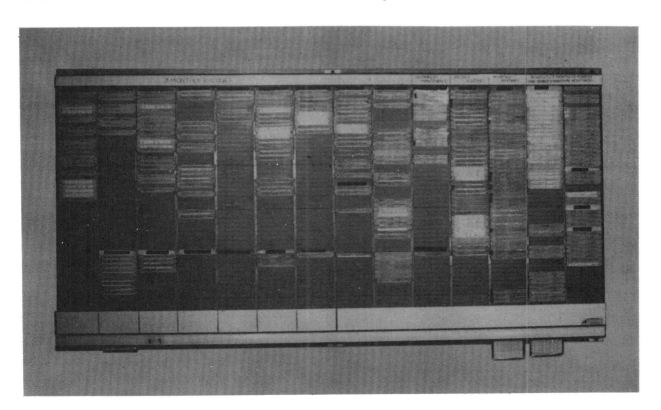

Figure 41   Main planning board (periodic maintenance).

The wall charts consist of:

a) A main planning board—this being the 'main control panel' for the whole system (Fig 41).
A typical display would include all planning documents for:
three months of calendar maintenance routines;
monthly and weekly maintenance routines;
hours-run maintenance routines;
unscheduled and defect notes;
work not completed in the period;
work to be carried out in port.

b) Planning documents for each item of equipment (Fig 42) which detail:
the item of equipment;
the work to be carried out;
the tools and spare parts required;
the necessary safety precautions;
a record that the work has been carried out;
notes for future reference.

c) A work allocation board—where the names of all operating staff are displayed.
Work is allocated by transferring the planning documents from the main planning board to the work allocation board against the names of the individual staff members. The names of shore contractors and manufacturers can also be displayed for work allocated to them.

d) Defect documents
When defects are discovered on equipment which are outside the scope of the work scheduled in the planning documents, they are recorded and displayed on the main planning board for future attention.

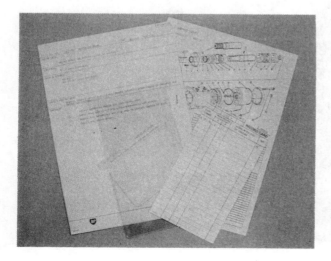

Figure 42 Documentation cards.

The chief engineer will be in charge of operating the system. Weekly meetings with all staff and daily inspection of the main planning board will bring agreement as to the work to be carried out, when and by whom.

The operation of the system usually follows a flow chart. Although systems, at first sight, appear complex, they usually operate very well and do produce significant end results.

One defect of periodic maintenance is that maintenance work is carried out on equipment whether it needs maintenance or not. It has been said that periodic maintenance is an expensive way of opening up equipment and finding it did not need to be opened up at all. It must be said that this comment is not altogether true as the results of experience have shown. Nevertheless, it is this point that has promoted the development of the third system of maintenance.

Condition maintenance

The concept of condition maintenance is altogether different from the two categories of maintenance already described. Condition maintenance has been developed to avoid routine interference with equipment that is performing perfectly satisfactorily. The system is designed to detect trends in the operating characteristics of equipment that indicate that deterioration is developing and therefore that maintenance is required. The techniques involved in monitoring the condition of the equipment are based upon periodic measurement of:

a) vibration and shock pulse to detect bearing deterioration;

b) insulation testing to detect electrical insulation deterioration;

c) performance checks to detect general deterioration by measurement of current, speed, temperature, pressure, or other prescribed quantities;

d) visual checks to detect wear, leakage, corrosion, security of mountings and the like.

Experience has shown that most failures in electrical machines are not due to electrical faults, but, rather due to mechanical faults, the commonest of all being bearing failure. It is obviously difficult to quote general figures for the proportion of electrical motor breakdowns which are directly attributable to bearing failure but a figure of 50% seems conservative—some operators put the figure as high as 90%. The cause of bearing failure depends to a large degree upon the size of the motor and its load application and this accounts for this wide range of figures.

Vibration measurement

All machinery installations have characteristic vibrations when in operation. Recordings of these vibration characteristics, taken when the machinery is in good condition and operating satisfactorily, provide a standard against which to judge the future condition of the machinery, to diagnose faults and to decide on the maintenance required.

The vibration measuring equipment comprises a probe to be applied to the machinery. The probe is connected to an electronic indication unit as shown in Fig 43.

An equipment history card details how the probe is to be applied and the readings obtained are recorded on the card.

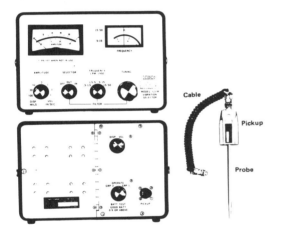

Figure 43 Probe and electronic indication unit for vibration measurement.

Although the operator must be skilled in the use of the equipment, a motor can be monitored in only a short time.

The machinery is regularly monitored. When measurements fall outside predetermined limits, the vibration characteristics are analysed to identify the cause and enable appropriate maintenance to be applied.

Shock pulse measurement

The rolling bearings of machinery, when in operation, generate shock pulse waves. These shock pulses are due to imperfections or damage to the bearing surfaces. Even new bearings have slight imperfections and generate shock pulses. Figure 44 shows typical shock pulse measuring equipment.

A typical development of bearing shock pulse measurement is shown in Fig 45. The fluctuations in the curve are caused by variations in the extent of the damage and the bearing rolling out of regions of existing damage. The normal and the maximum shock pulse limits can be calculated for every bearing. A bearing's normal limit may not be reached for months or years. When the normal limit is passed the shock pulse increases rapidly to approach the maximum allowed before breakdown becomes likely.

As the maximum is approached, readings should be taken more frequently so that maintenance can be carried out in good time before failure can occur.

The shock pulse method was developed by SPM Instruments of Sweden and has gained particular favour with users. Equipment comprises a portable indicating unit, a transducer applied to the machinery and earphones or stethoscope. A machinery history card details how the probe should be applied and allows records of readings to be made.

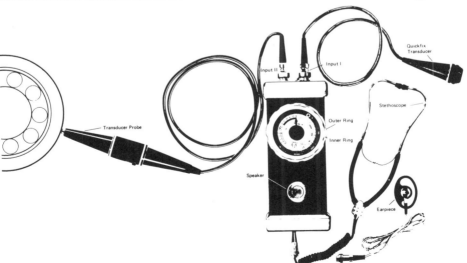

Figure 44 Typical shock pulse measuring equipment.

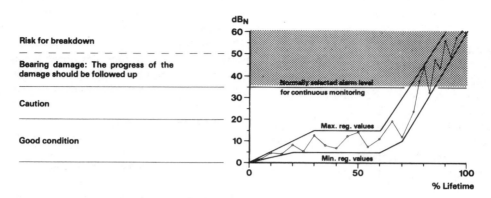

Figure 45   Development of bearing shock pulse measurement.

Again the user must be skilled in the use of the equipment but a motor can be monitored in less than a minute.

Insulation testing

The electrical insulation of electrical machines and cables is regularly measured using a standard 'Megger' type insulation tester. Readings are recorded on a history card together with other relevant data such as ambient temperature and humidity, and insulation temperature (Fig 46).

Insulation is made of organic substances and so gradually deteriorates with age. Although a figure of at least 1 MΩ is generally regarded as a minimum, in fact an acceptable value depends upon the size of the machine and its age.

When tests indicate that insulation resistance is approaching a predetermined dangerous value then a decision regarding the need for maintenance must be made.

Temperature, load, visual checks

Standard checks of temperature, load current and a visual check of cleanliness, security, general damage, corrosion and the like can be quickly carried out and give valuable indications of impending trouble and the need for action.

Attempting to measure temperature with the bare hand on equipment is most unreliable. A thermometer should be used, the bulb covered with wadding and attached in contact with the equipment with a suitable compound such as Plasticine. Many portable electronic thermometers are now available with suitable probes for such application. The readings should be compared with the temperature rating of the equipment and also used to estimate the temperature rise of the equipment above ambient temperature. A method of temperature measurement using simple

CIRCUIT: No. 1. COMPRESSOR		
DATE	IR (MΩ)	COMMENTS
5-1-82	17	Engine room cold (in dry dock)
2-10-82	12	Warm
8-5-82	5	Hot and humid
15-3-83	2	Warm—motor cleaned and dried
16-3-83	25	Repeat test after cleaning

Figure 46   Example of history card.

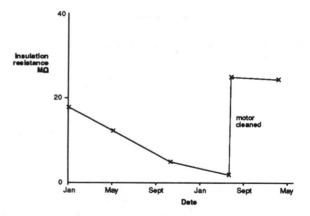

Figure 47   Change of motor insulation resistance after cleaning.

stick on tape devices has gained favour in some quarters. The tape changes colour as temperature changes—a danger signal being given when the tape changes to black.

High temperatures can be caused by poor ventilation, surface dirt which acts as an insulant, overload, high cooling air temperatures, or faults within the equipment.

Readings of load current of motors and other equipment can be measured using a clamp-on ammeter. The readings should be compared with the rated current as indicated on the equipment rating plate. High load current will cause overheating of equipment and the consequent danger of electrical insulation failure.

The cause must be investigated—it may be due to overload, supply voltage and frequency departing from their rated values, or other faults. Whatever the cause, the condition must be rectified before damage arises.

A correctly operated maintenance scheme will incorporate and integrate all the types and aspects of maintenance mentioned. Despite all correctly applied maintenance procedures, unscheduled equipment failure will inevitably occur and emergency action will have to be taken. The maintenance scheme must be flexible enough to handle such emergency situations.

The mechanics of operating a maintenance system may well be perfectly understood and carried out by the maintenance team. However, the continuing benefits of the system depend entirely upon the good offices of the team and their outlook on their tasks. The system must be looked on as a continually developing unit and improvements made as and when required.

Management of the system involves continual review and analysis of the system and practices employed to improve the way jobs are carried out, to improve maintenance control so that the ship's performance is also improved. Frequent staff meetings should include discussions to determine whether or not jobs can be carried out in reduced time, whether jobs can be done less often or methods improved, whether additional aids and tools should be provided, and whether planning could be improved so that more work would be carried out at sea so reducing the work load and costs when carried forward to docking repair periods. The system should also be updated when new equipment is fitted, better methods are devised, frequency at which jobs are done or the time to do jobs is changed.

At least one large British shipping company in the business of transporting petroleum products successfully operates a maintenance system in this manner. The use of computers in storing data and records has eased the management of the maintenance scheme. The computer has particular advantages in that it can handle large quantities of feed back data and provide management information from analysis of costs, spares, usage, downtime, etc. The computer can be interrogated at any time for management information.

Terotechnology is the total approach to maintenance which combines management, financial and other functions in the maintenance of equipment and physical assets at economic life-cycle cost. The ship board maintenance team is the vital element.

SAFETY AND ELECTRIC SHOCK

Most people have suffered electric shock of various degrees of severity. In many cases it has proved fatal. The actual effects of electric shock depend upon various factors including age, sex, health and size of the person concerned. Many people suppose that dc is more dangerous than ac, but in fact this is not so; dc is known to be at least twice as safe as ac, especially at power frequencies of 50–60Hz commonly in use.

Regulations currently in force state that voltage levels up to 50V ac and 250V dc are regarded as safe and unlikely to cause fatality.

However, data produced by the IEC suggests that even these levels may be too high as shown in the table of safe voltages, Table 1.

When it is considered that voltages commonly in use on board ship range up to 10 kV then the danger of electric shock is obviously very real.

At all times, and especially when carrying out maintenance on electrical equipment, great care must be exercised in following recommended safety procedures.

Prior to any work on electrical equipment, it is important that the circuits are 'dead' and switched off by means of the main switch or isolating switch. It is important that this is done personally; do not rely on other people. The fuses should be removed and taken away. The main switch or isolator should be locked off. Warning notice cards should be displayed at the fuse box and the main switch.

The circuit should not now be assumed to be dead. The circuit should be checked with a suitable voltage indicator. The voltage indicator device itself should be checked prior to use to confirm that it is operating correctly.

Table 1   Safe voltages.

Frequency	Population	
	95% safe	100% safe
dc	120V	50V
50Hz ac	50V	25V
1000Hz ac	120V	50V

These simple steps are vital to ensure safety. When accidents do occur, they frequently follow some rash unthinking action that the person concerned would normally never contemplate.

In the case of high voltage systems (above 1000 V) then procedures for working on such equipment should follow a 'permit to work' system.

The 'permit to work' is a document that details the set safety procedures to render the equipment safe to be worked on, the work to be done, when the work will be done and by whom, and finally to recommission the equipment. A designated trained person (chief engineer) is responsible for isolating and proving the equipment safe to be worked upon and for recommissioning the equipment. As each set of the specified procedures and work is carried out, the document is signed. When all work has been carried out, the 'permit' is cancelled and the equipment recommissioned.

SHIPS' SURVEY REQUIREMENTS

An overview of relevant rules and regulations appertaining to safety on board ship helps place the importance and relevance of surveys.

Ships for registration within Great Britain must comply with the following rules and regulations:

a) The Merchant Shipping Rules and Regulations—Department of Transport;

b) The Regulations for the Electrical and Electronic Equipment of Ships of The Institution of Electrical Engineers—which incorporate:

The Regulations of the International Convention for the Safety of Life at Sea (SOLAS)—International Maritime Organisation;

The British Standards Institution;

The International Electrotechnical Commission (SI Standards).

These regulations must be satisfied when the vessel is designed, constructed and commissioned.

The vessel must also comply with the rules and regulations of the appropriate classification society.

Classification societies include: American Bureau of Shipping (New York); Det Norske Veritas (Oslo); Germanischer Lloyd (Hamburg); Lloyd's Register of Shipping (London); Nippon Kaize Kyokai (Tokyo); Registro Italiano Navale (Genoa); USSR Register of Shipping, (Moscow).

When the vessel has been commissioned, the shipowner and his staff must thereafter maintain the vessel and its electrical equipment to the requirements of the classification society throughout the lifetime of the ship.

The rules and regulations of the classification society require that a survey of the ship be carried out at regular intervals. Every four years a complete engine survey is carried out and at this time the electrical equipment aboard ship is inspected and tested.

The purpose of the electrical survey is to verify that the electrical installation is correctly and adequately maintained according to the rules of the classification society and that the ship is in a safe and serviceable condition.

All classification societies have their own rules and regulations which although similar, do differ in detail. The general guide notes that follow concerning the electrical survey are based upon the requirements of Lloyd's Register of Shipping.

The following items in general are included in the survey of all ships: generators and their governors; circuit breakers, switchboards and fittings; cables; insulation resistance; motors and their starters; emergency power equipment; steering gear; navigation lights and indicators; UMS systems; and tankers.

For tankers, gas carriers and ships transporting flammable cargo, an additional survey of all the electrical equipment installed in hazardous areas is carried out at each docking survey and each annual survey. In effect, electrical equipment installed in hazardous areas is surveyed every year.

Prior to the full inspection by an electrical surveyor from a classification society, it is recommended that the following points be checked out. It is emphasised that these are guide notes and are not necessarily the limit of the surveyors requirements.

Generators

Generators should be clean and windings free of oil and moisture. Insulation should be healthy with no damage or cracking. Insulation resistance should be measured with the machine still hot after just being shut down. Insulation resistance should ideally be at least 1 MW between windings and between windings and earth.

Slip rings and commutator surfaces should be smooth and display no eccentricity. Brushes should be of the correct type and length and make contact with the slip rings/commutator over the full contact area. Springs should be set correctly and carbon dust should be absent.

The generators should respond to adjustments of controls correctly and operate at rated values of voltage and frequency. When operating in parallel generators should demonstrate their ability to maintain stable load kW and kVAr sharing and to respond correctly to sudden load changes.

Circuit breakers

Circuit breakers should be checked visually for cleanliness and all contacts checked for burning and overheating, wear and erosion and misalignment. Arc chutes and barriers should be clean, free of blackening and arc debris. All the auxiliary wiring should be sound. All connections and fixings should be checked for tightness. Linkages and other mechanical parts should be checked for wear, together with springs, clips and the like.

Tests on the racking gear should demonstrate smooth correct operation with shutters and indicators operating correctly. Closing and tripping operations should be demonstrated.

The settings of overcurrent protection devices should be checked. The operation of protective devices may have to be demonstrated to the surveyor but this usually requires the use of 'injection equipment' operated by shore specialist operators.

Switchboards

Switchboards should be clean (inside and out). All connections and fixings should be checked for tightness. All bus bars should be checked for overheating and corrosion at joints and connections and bus bar insulation checked for deterioration and tracking. All auxiliary wiring should be checked for soundness. Incoming cables should be checked for soundness and their glands inspected.

The security of bonding of the main earth should be checked together with all auxiliary earth bonds on panel doors, instrument cases and the cases of other equipment, instrument transformers and earth indication devices.

Switches and isolators should be checked for correct operation, wear and overheating. Fuses also should be checked for overheating

Protection relays

Settings should be correct and relay operation confirmed where possible during generator operation tests.

Cables

Cables should be subject to visual examination, particularly cables installed in locations subject to arduous conditions such as on the open deck. Points to be checked are signs of damage to the outer sheath and the armour particularly at glands and expansion loops and stopper boxes.

Cable support brackets and clips should be sound. Deterioration of cables due to oil or oil vapour should be looked for especially at cable ends.

Flexible cables of portable appliances are especially prone to abrasion damage and cuts and require particular inspection.

Insulation resistance

Insulation resistance records for all ships' equipment and circuits should be checked for regular entries and acceptable values.

Motors and starters

Motors and starters should be checked for cleanliness. All connections and fixings should be checked for security. Slip rings and commutators should be inspected for smoothness and even wear, and brushes for correct type, adequate length, good contact with rotating surfaces and correct spring tension.

Starter contacts condition should be checked and all auxiliary wiring should be sound.

Motors should be run, and checked for vibration and smooth running. All start and stop controls, local and remote should be checked and all indicating lamps should operate correctly.

Any other points identified in the regular maintenance schedules should also be checked.

Emergency power supply equipment

Emergency power supply equipment, including the generators, switchboards and circuit breakers, should be inspected and checked as previously detailed. In addition, the emergency generator must be proved to be able to start, either manually if so arranged, or automatically by simulating a mains power failure, the starting equipment being observed for correct operation. Also the 'automatic start' relays must be checked and their operation tested. The emergency load, comprising emergency services, must be proved to operate correctly and to be supplied at rated voltage, frequency and current. Any interlocks fitted in the system must be checked.

The emergency battery installation should be checked to ensure that safety requirements are met and that correct battery maintenance has been regularly carried out.

Safety requirements include the display of safety notices, availability of safety clothing and ensuring ventilation arrangements function correctly. Maintenance requirements include ensuring that the battery is clean and dry, all electrolyte levels are correct, electrolyte specific density is correct and all connections are tight and free from corrosion. The 'charger' equipment should be inspected for cleanliness, tight connections and other evidence of general good maintenance.

Steering gear

Most steering gear systems on board ship are electro-hydraulic; electric motors drive hydraulic pumps which power the rudder actuators.

Control from the bridge is by hydraulic telemotor, by electric controller, or a combination of both.

Steering gear 'running' indicators and overload alarms are installed in all control stations and rudder position indicators are installed on the bridge and the steering flat.

Electric motors, their starters and any changeover switches must be checked as already described for 'motors'.

The steering gear must be tested using all available forms of bridge control, including auto-pilot. Such tests require the rudder be swung from hard a'port to hard a'starboard within the regulatory 28 seconds. Main and emergency supplies must be proved.

During operational tests the running indicators and rudder position indicators should be checked. The operation of the overload alarms should be proved by simulating an overload condition.

Navigation lights

Navigation lights must be proved to operate and the navigation light indicators and failure alarms must also be proved to operate correctly. Both main and emergency power supplies must be proved. Additionally all wiring and cables, especially on the open deck, should be checked for soundness.

Unattended machinery space (UMS) ships

These are fitted with remote control of engines equipment, various back-ups and interlocks to ensure fail safe operation, alarms and fire detection and alarm equipment.

All electrical equipment should be checked for cleanliness, tight connections and fixings, acceptable insulation resistance and equipment confirmed to be in overall sound condition.

Effective control of the main engine from all control stations must be proved. The associated electrical control equipment will be proved at this time.

Correct operation of the electrical generator control equipment must be proved by demonstrating that in the event of failure of the service generator, the back-up generator will automatically start up and connect to the bus bars within the required 45 seconds. In addition the sequential start equipment should then restart the designated essential auxiliaries. Similarly, in the event of complete failure of the main generators, it must be shown that the emer-

gency generator will automatically start up and connect to the bus bars.

For those essential services where duplicate equipment is provided, it must be shown that failure of the service unit will result in automatic start up and operation of the back up unit.

The alarm system must be proved to operate correctly. The main alarm display unit, repeater display units and the accommodation alarm call units should be checked, together with the main and standby power supplies.

All alarms fitted to the main engine, to their essential service equipment and to the auxiliary generators must be proved to operate by simulating a fault condition. Where automatic shut-down of equipment must occur under fault conditions, this also must be confirmed by simulating a fault condition. (Correct operation of alarm sensors by a real fault condition may need the use of specialist equipment not normally available on board ship).

The fire detection system should be inspected and tested, all sensors should be checked and all control station and accommodation alarms proved to operate.

Tankers

On tankers, electrical equipment located in hazardous areas must be checked to confirm that it is of the correct type according to BS 5345 and Lloyd's Register requirements, and in a safe condition. In general, and where applicable, electrical equipment should be checked for cleanliness, security of mounting, corrosion, tight connections and adequate insulation resistance.

Flameproof equipment (Exd)

Flame path flanges should be clean, undamaged and free from corrosion. Weatherproof gaskets and seals should be intact, all bolts should be present, of the correct type and tight. Paint should not obstruct flamepaths nor obscure name plates.

Pressurised equipment (Exp)

It should be checked that correct purging and pressurising cycles occur and that, in the event of loss of internal air pressure, automatic electric shut down occurs.

Intrinsically safe equipment (Exi)

This should be checked for soundness. Portable measuring instruments and communication equipment be checked to confirm that they are intrinsically safe and that uncertified none-safe (not IS) equipment is not taken into hazardous areas.

Chapter 7
Automation and Control

R Beams and A W Finney

INTRODUCTION

The field of automation and control is immense. There are many different ways of achieving the effects required by the operator of marine systems. It is impossible to cover all aspects of the subject in the space available here, but this chapter endeavours to give an overview of automation and control in a marine environment which will provide a good starting point for study.

TERMINOLOGY

There is a terminology peculiar to the subject of automation and control, and it can be very confusing for the beginner and for some experienced engineers. Before studying control systems in any depth, the reader should become familiar with the terminology associated with automation and control by reference to British Standards BS1523[1]. Some of the more important terms and definitions are given in this chapter.

THE CONTROL SYSTEM

Definition of control

A control system is an arrangement of elements, or devices, such as sensors, amplifiers, converters, actuators, human operators, and so on. These devices are interconnected and interact in such a way as to maintain or to affect in a prescribed manner, some condition of a body, process or machine which forms part of a system.

An automatic control system is one which does not include a human operator. If a human operator is included, the system is a manual control system.

When the control system is used to control some physical quantity or condition of a process, it is known as a process control system. Typical examples of process control systems are temperature control of a fluid, such as diesel engine cooling water, by diverting the fluid past or through a cooler, or boiler water level control.

Reasons for automatic control

There are many factors which have influenced the development of automatic control in the marine environment, but all are connected with either economy or human factors.

The cost of wages—reduced manning
Before automation and control engineering became a reality in the marine environment, instruments giving an indication of the conditions in a plant were under the continual surveillance and control of an engineer. In the 1950s and 1960s, it was not uncommon for an average vessel to carry seven engineers and, perhaps, two electricians. A modern automated vessel may now only carry three engineers.

Wages are not the only staff costs to be considered by an employer. Hidden overheads such as food and provisions, hotel services, taxes and so on, can double the cost of an employee to a company. Over the last decade the trend has been for the employer to reduce manning levels. If the expensive human element could be replaced by machinery, one would reduce the running costs of a vessel.

The human element
The task of monitoring and controlling parameters such as temperatures and pressures by manual methods can be very repetitive and boring, but accuracy depends on the intelligence and experience of the

operator. It has been shown statistically that repetitive work and boredom can lead to 'human error', claimed to be the cause of most accidents.

Relieving the human operator of tasks that are boring, unpleasant and strenuous by the use of machinery can reduce the risk of accidents and release the operator for more useful and interesting work. Long periods of intense concentration can result in mental and physical strain and, more importantly, general deterioration in performance. An automatic system will detect changes in a plant more quickly and accurately than a human operator and, if properly designed and applied, will make corrections to maintain or recover the desirable condition of operation more efficiently.

Cost of fuel and operation efficiency

The cost of fuel oil for a ship has influenced the introduction of automation and control. The current cost of fuel oil can be affected by international and national politics, finance and territorial disputes. As a consequence the financial outlay for fuel can be very high and the ship owner must achieve maximum efficiency using the fuel to maintain an acceptable operating profit.

Today's marine fuels require extensive treatment, usually with centrifugal separators, before they can be used. The introduction of automatic cleaning separators relieved the engine room staff of a time-consuming, laborious task. Having treated the fuel ready for burning in the engine, the use of combustion monitoring equipment is essential to keep the engine tuned and maintain maximum efficiency.

Advances in technology

In the early 1980s the design and implementation of complex electronic systems were revolutionised by the use of the microprocessor. Prior to its introduction, electronic digital control systems were designed using logic gates and bi-stable devices (flip-flops). These were initially engineered from discrete components but integrated circuits subsequently became available for these functions.

The microprocessor forms the heart of the microcomputer and is also used in programmable logic controllers (page 244).

What do we want to control ?

Within the environment of a marine plant there are many parameters which need to be controlled or monitored including: temperature; pressure; level; viscosity; flow; speed; torque; voltage; current; machinery status (on/off); and equipment status (open/closed).

Where do we control ?

Historically it was the role of the watchkeeping engineers to monitor and control the machinery plant. This was achieved by periodic tours of the engine room and manual inspection—basic watchkeeping. Often the engineer was totally dependent on his natural senses, frequently supported by only the minimum of widely distributed simple monitoring devices.

The demand to reduce manning levels led to the development of automated control arrangements for the engine room plant which enabled unattended operation of machinery spaces. Vessels capable of safe operation for any period of time in this mode qualify for assignment of the class notation 'UMS' (unattended machinery space). Although not essential for such installations, the control and monitoring facilities were usually grouped together in a centralized control room. The option of operation from a centralized control station under continuous supervision qualifies a vessel for assignment of the class notation 'CCS'.

Initially the control room was in the vicinity of the engine room, with extended monitoring and alarm systems on the bridge and in the accommodation areas during UMS periods. Some vessels were built with the engine control room adjacent to the bridge.

The modern trend is towards a centralised control room, using a totally integrated system for all aspects of ship operation, including engineering, cargo, navigation and general administration.

Whatever the system, most controlled elements can have one or more of the following points of operation:

a) local manual control;

b) remote manual control;

c) automatic control.

Local control implies that the point of control is in the immediate area of the device, whereas for remote control the point of control is some distance away from the device, such as in a control room.

The operation of a bilge suction valve in the engine room by its handwheel is an example of local manual control. If the valve was fitted with an extended spindle through to the deck above and was operated from that point, it would be remote manual control. In both these cases the valve would be operated by a human operator. If the bilge valve was fitted with a hydraulic motor to operate the valve, and the valve opened and closed according to the position of a float controller in the bilge well, this would be an automatic control system. The human element is removed.

How do we control ?

There are many different media for control, and the most common on ships are :

a) mechanical—using shafts, gears and wires;

b) hydraulic—using special hydraulic oils;

c) pneumatic—using low pressure compressed air;

d) electrical—using electric motors and relays;

e) electronic—using computers and logic devices.

The equipment used in control, alarm and safety systems should be suitable for its working environment and intended purpose and, where practicable, be selected from a list of type approved equipment issued by the relevant national government department or national classification society. To gain type approval the equipment is subjected to a series of tests to ensure its suitability for its intended purpose.

Control systems may either use one of the above media, or a combination of two or more. When combined media are used, it is often necessary to convert a signal from one medium to another, especially for transmission over a long distance. The process of signal transmission over long distance is generally called telemetry and the devices used are called transducers.

A transducer used to be defined as a device which produced an electrical signal proportional to a physical stimulus such as a pneumatic signal. Nowadays the definition of a transducer is widened to a device which converts a signal in one medium to a signal in another, such as pneumatic to electrical or pneumatic to hydraulic.

ELEMENTS AND MEASUREMENTS OF A CONTROL SYSTEM

The basic elements

Control systems consist of the following common essential elements, or components.

1. A measuring device which reacts to the machinery or process parameter to be controlled, such as temperature, pressure or rotational speed.

   In its simplest form, where only a single measurement value is required, this could be a temperature, pressure or centrifugal switch. For measurement throughout a whole range of values a transducer would be employed having all or some of the following components:

   a) A sensing element which possesses some property which varies with changes in the parameter to be measured. For instance, increasing temperature causes mechanical bending of a bi-metallic strip, increase in the electrical resistance of a coil of platinum wire and increase or decrease in the electrical resistance of a thermistor, depending on its type.

   b) A conversion device to produce an output signal in a form that the control system can use. There are standardised ranges of output signal so, in the above examples, a pneumatic signal in the pressure range 0.2–1.0 bar could be produced by the movement of the bi-metallic strip against a nozzle, or the resistance values could be converted to 4–20 mA current signals, or voltages in the 0–10 V range. Many systems, however, accept the direct connection of resistance or thermocouple devices.

   Conversion devices usually involve some degree of amplification of the signal from the sensor and produce output signals which can be transmitted for some distance without loss of accuracy. For long distance transmission the signal must be converted to a form which does not lose accuracy even though the signal strength is diminished. This could be a frequency modulated (FM) voltage signal or a serial digital transmission.

   c) Compensation arrangements to protect the output signal from variation due to changes in parameters other than the one being measured. For instance, pressure transducers which employ strain gauges on diaphragms or tubes are provided with dummy gauges to compensate for changes in ambient temperature.

2. A controller, which evaluates the deviation, i.e. the difference between the measured value and the desired value of the controlled condition (the set point value) and determines the output control signal, i.e. the setting of the actuator at any given time. Types and actions of controllers are discussed below.

3. An actuator or other similar final controlling element, which performs the necessary correcting action, such as an electric motor to open or close a valve.

Classification of systems

Control systems are classified in several ways, but the most common classifications are as either an open-loop control system (also known as an unmonitored

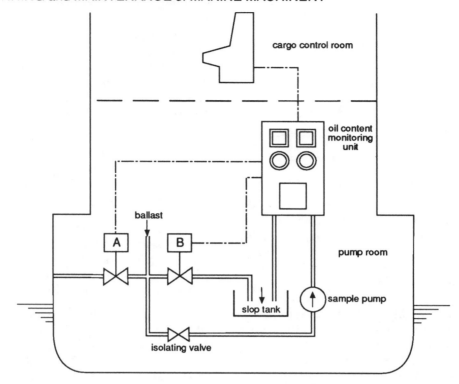

Figure 1   Open-loop control system; system required to prevent pollution by discharge.

control system), or a closed-loop control system (also known as a monitored control system).

An open-loop control system is one without monitoring feedback of the value of the controlled parameter.

A closed-loop control system possesses monitoring feedback, the deviation signal formed as a result of this feedback being used to control the action of the final control element in such a way as to reduce the deviation to zero.

To illustrate the above classification and significant terms in describing control systems two examples are given.

Operation of an open-loop circuit (Fig 1)
The system shown is that required to prevent pollution by discharge from a tanker. The oil content of the ballast water being pumped is constantly measured by taking samples through the monitoring unit, which also includes the control function.

When the oil content is below the limiting value the controller operates actuator A to open the overboard discharge valve. If the sampled oil content exceeds the permitted limit the controller causes actuator A to close the overboard discharge valve and actuator B to open the valve that passes the contaminated water to the slop tank. All the compo-

nents of a control system are present, i.e. measuring device, control functions and actuators, but there is no arrangement for signals to be sent back to the controller confirming that the flow is overboard or to the slop tank.

Operation of a closed-loop circuit (Fig 2)
The temperature of the lubricating oil for a main diesel engine has to be controlled to prevent it rising to a level at which the oil viscosity becomes too low for effective lubrication.

In order to achieve this the oil is cooled by passing it through a water-cooled heat exchanger. Low oil temperature and the resulting high viscosity could prevent adequate flow of oil to the engine so the control system has to regulate the temperature of the oil entering the engine to an approximately constant value.

For an electrical/electronic system to control oil temperature the measuring device could be a platinum resistance coil feeding its signal directly into a proprietary electronic controller (such as that shown in Fig 3) with an electric output signal to a motor which positions the three-way valve determining the proportion of oil flow to pass through the cooler. With the system in a steady state the three-way valve will be positioned so that the cooler dissipates heat from the oil at exactly the same rate as that at which

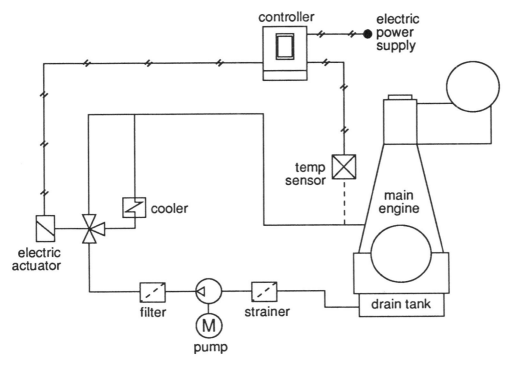

Figure 2 Closed-loop circuit; main engine lubricating oil temperature control.

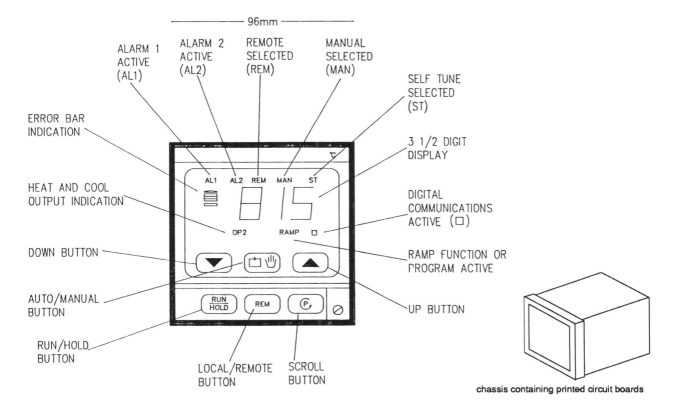

Figure 3 Electronic three term (PID) controller (see page 238).

the engine is heating the oil. If the engine conditions, speed or load change, or the water temperature or flow rate in the cooler vary, the valve will have to adopt a different position to restore the balance of heat flow and maintain the required oil inlet temperature at the engine.

In the terms set out in BS 1523, the 'controlled condition' is the lubricating oil temperature as it enters the engine. The operator wishes the control system to maintain this at the 'desired value' so sets the 'command signal' as an input to the 'controller'. The command signal to a process control system is known as the 'set value' or 'set point' and may differ from the desired value if the operator is aware that the system operates with an 'offset'. The temperature sensor provides a 'monitoring feedback' signal indicating the current value of the controlled condition to the controller. It is the provision of this monitoring feedback signal which defines the arrangement as a 'closed-loop control system'.

THE CONTROLLER

Elements of a controller

If we take as an example an analogue controller using integrated circuit amplifiers operating with voltage signals in the range –10V to +10 V, then for the engine temperature control system already described the command signal or set point might be a temperature in the range 50°C to 120°C. This would be converted to a voltage signal by the operator setting a potentiometer or, possibly, some thumb-wheel switches. The device used for such input signal conversion is termed the 'input element'.

Not every controller will require this element. For instance, the command signal might already be a voltage from an engine warm-up programme control system. In such a case, called a 'cascade control system', the signal passing between the two controllers must match for scaling (same volts/°C) and zero (0V represents the same temperature for both systems). Another example of cascade control would be a boiler combustion control system where the output signal of the master controller becomes the input signal for the fuel oil valve controller and the air supply controller.

In a similar manner the transducer signal indicating the current value of the controlled condition almost always requires conversion to the type of signal used within the controller. As this signal represents a measurement the element responsible for its conversion is, rather misleadingly, termed the 'measuring element'.

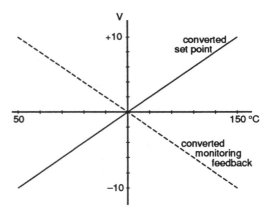

Figure 4　Input signals to the comparing element in a temperature control system.

Needless to say, the scaling and zero of the converted command signal and monitoring feedback signal must be the same but they are often of opposite polarities. For example, with a scaling of 0.2V/°C, and 0 V representing 100°C, the set point would be –10V for 150°C and +10V for 50°C. This is illustrated in Fig 4.

The element essential to every controller is the 'comparing element' which produces an output signal representing the difference between the measured value of the controlled condition and the command signal. This difference is termed the 'deviation' or error signal. In our example if the command signal is 120°C and the measured oil temperature is 110°C, the deviation is 10°C.

The actual voltage signal represents the difference within the controller, known as the 'converted deviation' and in this case would be 2.0V as the set point signal would be +4.0V and the converted feedback signal would be –2.0V. As the signals are of opposite polarity the difference is obtained by adding them together.

Depending on the 'action' of the controller, explained below, there may be a 'signal processing element' to modify the deviation signal in order to enhance accuracy or speed of response. Signal processing and the output signal to the final controlling element usually require more power than is available from the input and measuring device so an 'amplifying element' is necessary in order to boost the power. The power source is usually external but in some cases power is drawn from the process which is being controlled.

The elements of a controller are not necessarily distinct pieces of hardware. The different functions may be combined together in one amplifier circuit. In a digital controller, where the signals are processed as binary numbers, the comparing and signal processing elements would be activities controlled by sections of the software.

TYPES OF CONTROL ACTION

The relationship between the input and output signal of a control element is termed the 'control action' of that element. The simpler types of action are 'discontinuous', for instance the 'on-off' action of the valve controller in Fig 1 which will change the valve immediately from one position to the other as soon as the deviation signal changes sign. For 'two-step' action the output signal value changes between any two defined values when the input signal changes polarity. On-off action is thus a particular example of two-step action, where one of the two possible values of output signal is zero.

With 'continuous action' the output signal of a control element or system is a continuous function of the input signal, but the form of that function can vary. Figure 5a shows the relationship between the output signal and the input converted deviation signal for a control element with 'proportional action'.

Expressed mathematically, the relationship is

$$V = -K_1\theta,$$

where K_1 is the 'proportional action factor'. Considering, for the moment, only slowly changing signals, K_1 is also the 'gain' of the control element. Two possible values of gain are shown on Fig 5a; unit gain and a gain of 5.

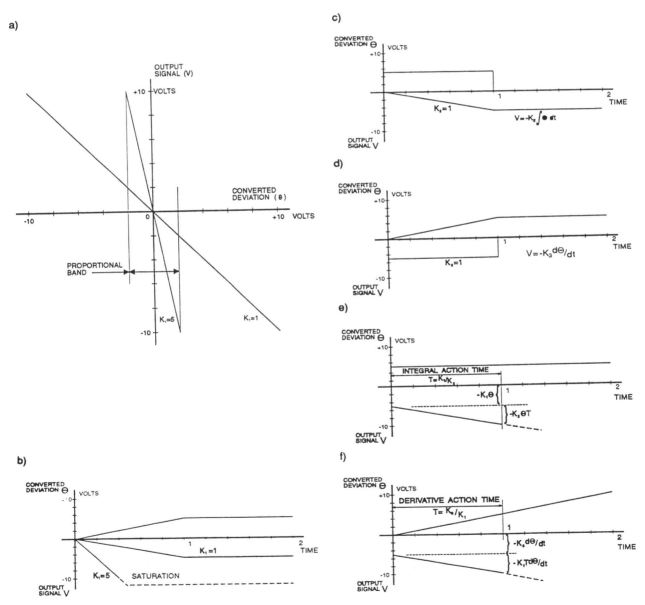

Figure 5   a) Proportional control action; b) proportional control action; c) integral control action; d) derivative control action; e) proportional + integral action; f) proportional + derivative action.

With the higher value of gain it can be seen that the full range of output signal is produced by a limited range of the input deviation signal. This range of values is known as the 'proportional band' and may be expressed as a percentage of the input signal range, in this case 20%, i.e.

$$\text{proportional band} = \frac{100}{\text{gain}}\%$$

The output signal cannot exceed 10V by much because the amplifier output is limited, so for input signal values outside the proportional band the output of the element is 'saturated' and the input–output relationship is no longer linear.

Another way of illustrating proportional action is shown in Fig 5b where the output signal resulting from an input deviation signal which varies with time is plotted.

'Integral action' is shown in Fig 5c. The output signal is proportional to the integral of the input deviation signal, i.e.

$$V = -K_2 \int \theta \, dt$$

where K_2 is the 'integral action factor'.

Put another way,

$$\frac{dV}{dt} = -K_2 \theta,$$

so the rate of change of the output signal is proportional to the input deviation or error signal.

'Derivative action' is shown in Fig 5d. The output signal is proportional to the rate of change of the input deviation signal, i.e.

$$V = -K_3 \frac{d\theta}{dt}$$

where K_3 is the 'derivative action factor'.

In a 'two-term controller', proportional action is combined with integral action (a PI controller) or with derivative action (a PD controller). The relative effectiveness of the proportional and other action is expressed by the time taken for the effects of the two actions to be equal. This is shown in Fig 5e for a PI controller where the 'integral action time' is the ratio K_1/K_2 and in Fig 5f for a PD controller, where the 'derivative action time' is the ratio K_3/K_1.

A 'three-term controller' combines all three actions, proportional, integral and derivative, giving rise to its other title, a PID controller (Fig 3).

Effects of control actions

The diagrams in Fig 5 show the relationship between the deviation, or error signal, and the output of a controller in isolation from any other system elements. Since the error signal depends on the controlled condition and the controlled condition is directly affected by the output of the controller, as soon as the controller output signal in a closed-loop system starts to change, the error signal will also start to be modified. The result of this interrelationship is that while the error and output signals retain the mathematical relationship to each other shown in Fig 5, their variation with time will no longer be the simple straight line relationships shown.

The time-dependence of a control system's response to change is one of the most important design considerations. There are two tests which can be applied experimentally to a system or mathematically, or experimentally to a computer model of the system. The first test looks at the system's response to a step change of load on the system (e.g. sudden demand for steam from a boiler) or of set-point value (e.g. positional control of steering gear). The response of the controlled condition will vary greatly due to factors such as thermal or mechanical inertia but is likely to be in the form shown in Fig 6. The controlled condition is shown overshooting then oscillating about its final value. The oscillations may be reduced or eliminated by damping (cf. automobile suspension systems).

With proportional action alone the final value of the controlled condition will always have an offset from its desired value because this error signal is required to give the change in controller output necessary to accomodate the change in load applied. The offset may be reduced by increasing the gain of the controller but too high a value of gain can lead to instability as explained below. The addition of integral action will eliminate any static offset since the existence of even a minimal error signal would integrate up in time to produce a large correction. The further addition of derivative action has the effect of reducing the time taken for the controlled condition to settle at the set-point. This is achieved by two means. Firstly, as the derivative of the step change in demand is infinite, the initial corrective impulse to the system will be the maximum possible. Secondly, as the controller output has negative proportionality to the rate of change of error signal, the derivative control term tends to resist change in the controlled condition value and will therefore reduce the number and severity of the oscillations.

The second test involves calculating or measuring the response of a system to a sinusoidal cyclic input usually superimposed on the command signal to the controller. The amplitude of the input signal is kept constant while its frequency is varied over a range

a)

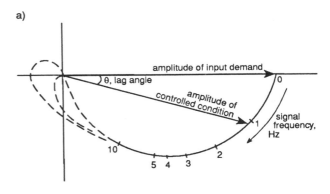

b)

appropriate to the system—high frequencies for light mechanical positioning servos and low frequencies for process control systems. The effect of increasing the freqency of the input signal to a mechanical system with proportional action can be visualised as follows.

At very low frequencies the controlled condition will follow the input signal without any lag, and the amplitude of the output will change very little as the frequency starts to be increased. Every system has some degree of inertia and mechanical drive systems are subject to some resilience, or springiness due to compression or twist of components. As the input frequency is increased the acceleration required in order to follow the sine waveform increases. The forces required to achieve the acceleration compress or twist the system components with the result that the output controlled condition begins to lag behind the input. As the difference in phase between the input and output increases, the amplitude of the output is reduced because the input signal changes its polarity before the output peaks. The results of this test are recorded as a 'harmonic response diagram'

Figure 6 Typical action response curves: a) applied load on process; b) proportional action; c) integral action (mean); d) proportional + integral action; e) proportional + integral + derivative action; f) hunting.

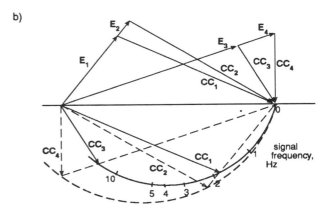

Figure 7 a) Harmonic response diagram; b) effect of increasing gain.

(Fig 7) on which each vector length represents the ratio of the output amplitude to the input amplitude at a particular frequency and the angle of the vector to the axis represents the phase difference between the input and output signals. The frequency scale is marked along the locus of the vector ends.

The curve of the harmonic response diagram can take various forms according to the order of the differential equation which defines the complete system. All curves will eventually end at the zero point—no output response when the input signal is infinite frequency. One particular form of the harmonic response curve is significant when it passes through the horizontal axis to the left of the origin. At this point the lag of the controlled condition signal is 180°C. This signal is subtracted from the demand signal to produce the error but the 180° shift of the sinusoidal signal has changed what used to be a negative feedback signal into a positive one. There is now no tendency for the feedback to reduce the error, rather the reverse, so at the frequency at which this occurs the system can sustain oscillatory motion without the need for any input signal. If the oscillation has a constant amplitude the system is said to be 'hunting'. When there is less damping the system will be instable and the oscillations will build up until some physical limit or destruction of the system stops the process.

Figure 7b illustrates how a change in gain can affect the stability of a system. The vector E_1 is the error signal obtained by vector subtraction of the controlled condition signal from the input demand. If the controller gain is increased the effect of the error signal will be increased to E_2 so the output becomes CC_2. The locus of the new values of controlled condition is outside the old locus so is more likely to pass to the left of the origin with resultant instability.

It should be emphasised that the above descriptions are illlustrative only, and control system engineering books should be consulted for a rigorous mathematical treatment of the subject.

Fault finding control systems

When a control system has been set up and adjusted in accordance with the manufacturer's instructions and has operated satisfactorily for some time any subsequent deterioration in performance needs to be investigated very carefully before any actions are taken.

Most failures occur outside the controller, e.g. wire breakage, transducer fault or power failure. The result could be one of the following.

a) Controlled condition goes to one or other extreme of its range. This could be due to a loss of the

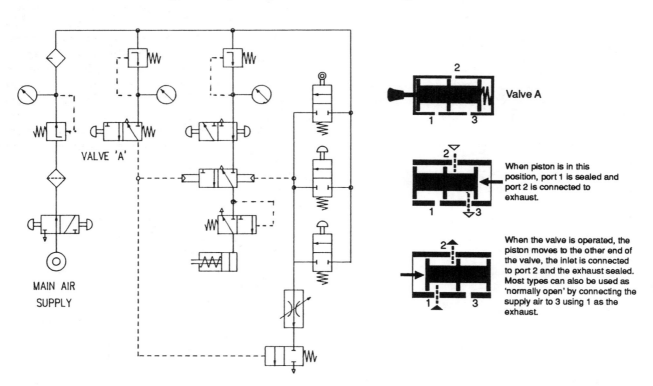

Figure 8   Pneumatic clutch operating system using piston type valves and drawn with standard symbols (see BS 2917 for interpretation).

feedback signal due to transducer failure or associated wire break.

b) Controlled condition stays at zero. This could result from a failure of the output element—valve or actuator, or its connections or power supply.

c) Controlled condition oscillates—hunting. In hydraulic systems this may be due to air in the oil causing springiness of the drive. Positioning systems may exhibit this condition if the position measuring instrument has become loose on its shaft.

All the external components and circuits should be checked and proved sound before any consideration is given to making any adjustments to the controller settings.

Piston (or spool) valve controllers

Piston control valves are very common on ships and have many uses. They are simple in construction, robust and easily maintained. They are used for main engine control and protection systems, clutch control systems, boiler burner withdrawal systems and hydraulic control systems such as winches.

Figure 8 shows a pneumatic clutch operating system using piston type valves.

MICROPROCESSOR SYSTEMS

So far we have considered control systems having on-off components such as spool valves or electrical relays, and controllers in which one physical quantity, such as voltage, is used as an analogy for an external physical quantity such as temperature. This type of controller is an analogue control unit.

Digital systems comprise components which are basically on-off devices so they can be used without much difficulty as substitutes for relay systems. For control or regulation of variables a digital system uses numbers to represent the set point and controlled values. The numbers are in binary form, i.e. each digit may only have one of two states, 0 or 1, and the value of a 1 in each successive digit position increases in powers of 2. 'Binary digit' has been contracted to create the term 'bit'. An 8-bit number is termed a 'byte', and can represent any number up to the decimal value 255.

The basic constituent units of a digital system are shown in Fig 9. The solid-line blocks indicate hardware, usually produced as separate units, although single-chip microcomputers are made. Essential to the operation of the system is the list of instructions, the program, which resides in part of the memory hardware.

To distinguish it from the physical hardware, for instance when considering system costs, the program is referred to as software.

Central processor unit and busses

The microprocessor as such corresponds with the central processor unit (CPU) shown in Fig 9. Some chips also include the system timing clock circuit. The operations performed by the CPU may be arithmetic or logical functions. To carry out these operations the CPU includes a limited amount of memory for working registers and sufficient built-in program to enable it to interpret the instructions of the system program. The transfer of information within the system to and from the memory and the interface units is all under the control of the CPU. The precise timing of these operations is controlled by pulses derived

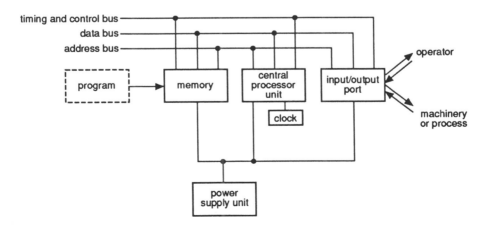

Figure 9 Basic constituent units of a digital system.

from the clock circuit which is usually a crystal controlled oscillator operating at a frequency which could exceed 50MHz.

The path by which information enters and leaves the CPU is the data bus. This consists of a group of conductors connecting all the active components of the system. For an 8-bit microprocessor system there are eight conductors forming the data bus. In control applications 8-bit systems may well be adequate, but 16- and 32-bit systems have become available in the personal computer field.

In a 32-bit microcomputer, the data bus may have 32 conductors or it may have only 16, the data being transferred as two 16-bit signals in succession.

In order that program instructions may be accessed and data stored in and retrieved from memory, every location in the memory, where a single byte of data may be stored, must have a unique address. For 8-bit systems, there are usually 65, 536 addresses, 2^{16}, and so a 16-bit binary number is needed to define each address. In computer terms there are 64K addresses, 1K being 2^{10} (i.e. 1024). The address bus in this case would be a group of 16 conductors connecting all the active components of the system. Where systems require more than 64K of memory to be addressed, additional conductors are required or two successive signals may be passed along the address bus.

The operation of the timing bus and control bus can be illustrated by considering the process by which the CPU writes information into memory and reads information or program from memory.

To write, the CPU performs the following operations:

1. It selects the memory register which is to receive the data and connects its address signal to the address bus.

2. It puts the byte of data that is to be transferred onto the data bus.

3. It sends a signal via the control bus to indicate that a write operation is to be carried out.

4. After a delay period sufficient to allow the memory address decoding circuit to function, the CPU sends a signal via the timing bus to cause the data to be stored at the selected address.

In order to read from memory the CPU controls the following sequence of events:

1. It selects the memory register from which it requires data or program information and connects the appropriate address signal to the address bus.

2. It sends a signal via the control bus to indicate that a read operation is to be carried out. This causes the memory to connect the output of the selected register to the data bus.

3. After a delay period sufficient to allow for signal propagation along the data bus the CPU admits the information on the data bus to the appropriate internal register.

Program information is directed into the instruction register where it is decoded to determine the processor operation required. A large number of various instructions can be used and these are known collectively as the 'instruction set' for a particular type of processor. Most microprocessor instructions are of a very simple form, moving data between the several internal registers or to and from memory or input/output circuits. One particular type of register, the accumulator, may be used to perform addition, subtraction and logical functions using its own data content and that of another specified register or memory address.

The decision-making ability of computers is due to 'conditional jump' instructions. These cause the computer to branch to another part of the program depending on the result of a previous arithmetic or logical operation. The criterion for a jump may be selected from such conditions as the result being positive, negative or zero, or whether the previous operation produced a carry bit.

For example, a digital alarm system would read an alarm set-point value from a memory address into an accumulator, subtract the value of the measured parameter (temperature, pressure, etc.) read in via an input circuit, and when this produces a negative result effect a jump to the section of program which produces the appropriate audible and visual alarm outputs.

Memory

The types of device used to store information in a microprocessor system vary according to the application, the number of similar systems to be produced and the degree of reliability required. A range of memory devices is shown in Fig 10, where they are presented in order of permanence of content, the most transitory being on the left.

The major division of memory types is between devices which lose their stored information when the power supply is removed (termed volatile) and those which do not. Another division exists between those types which connect directly with the system's address and data busses, and those such as magnetic media which require special interfacing circuits.

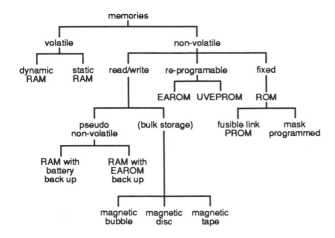

Figure 10 Types of memory.

RAM

A semiconductor memory device which the microprocessor can read information from and write information to is known as a random access memory (RAM). Any location in a RAM may be chosen at random and immediately accessed for storage or retrieval of its contents.

The access time for RAM is a few hundred nanoseconds (10^{-9} seconds), a range of speeds being available to suit particular system needs. The faster devices are more expensive.

In static RAM each binary digit is stored in a latching circuit which may be set to logic level 1 or reset to logic level 0 when addressed, and remains unchanged at all other times while the power supply remains on.

In a dynamic RAM information is stored as minute electrical charges on microscopic capacitors. The charge tends to leak away so that it is necessary every few milliseconds to check which capacitors are charged and restore their charges to the initial level. This process is carried out by a 'refresh' circuit.

Where the volatile nature of RAMs is not acceptable they may be rendered immune to loss of external power supply by connection of a small back-up battery, usually soldered to the printed circuit board on which the RAM is mounted. For dynamic RAMs the refresh circuit must also be provided with back-up power.

ROM

Much of the information used by a microprocessor system will not require alteration in the operational life of the system. This includes data on conversion factors and physical constants and also the operating system. Information of this nature is stored on read only memory (ROM) devices and is known as

'firmware'. The 0s and 1s that constitute each byte of information in a ROM are determined by connections within the microcircuit on the chip.

For applications where many thousand devices will be produced the internal connections are most economically made at the production stage by generating a special mask for printing the microcircuit. For smaller production quantities, a general purpose circuit is produced which can be programmed by the user. This is a programmable read only memory (PROM). As produced a PROM has a zero in every digit position. A digit 1 is produced at each required location by melting a connecting link in the microcircuit by means of a brief pulse of current.

Once programmed, the contents of neither type of ROM can be erased so system modifications necessitate the replacement of the device by another containing the new information.

For system prototyping purposes, when several successive changes of program or data are likely to be required, it is more cost effective to use devices in which the information content can be erased and the device re-programmed. The first such type of device developed for general use employs ultra-violet radiation as the means of erasure and is consequently known as an ultra-violet erasable programmable read only memory (UVEPROM). Erasure of the stored information is effected by 20 to 30 minutes exposure of the chip to the emission of an ultra-violet fluorescent lamp through a transparent window in the top of the package. Individual bytes of stored information cannot be selectively erased.

A UVEPROM is electrically programmed and this is usually carried out by means of a separate piece of equipment from which the UVEPROM is transferred to a socket in the operational system.

A more versatile device has since been developed which is known alternatively as an electrically alterable read only memory (EAROM) or an electrically erasable read only memory (EEROM). This too is programmed electrically, but in this case the process may be performed *in situ*. Erasure is also carried out electrically and either a single byte or the whole content may be erased in a few milliseconds.

Magnetic medium

For the permanent storage of large quantities of data or program information some form of magnetic medium is employed. This may be cassette tape, flexible ('floppy') disk, or magnetic bubble memory. Small hard disks may be used, but they must be environmentally tested. For the marine environment, where high humidity and vibration levels may be encountered, magnetic bubble memories, being completely non-mechanical, would be an obvious design choice but for their high cost.

In marine machinery control and alarm applications magnetic disk and tape storage is unlikely to be employed as on-line memory. Their principal functions are to retain copies of the system program where the working program is held in RAM and to accept logging information for subsequent analysis by another computer.

Input/output (I/O) circuits

Within a microcomputer system, information is transmitted very quickly in parallel form. Each digit of data is present simultaneously on its own individual conductor in the data bus for a fraction of a microsecond. Without special interfacing circuits, data in this form is incompatible with any other equipment except another computer. Interface circuits are connected to the data, address and control busses of the microcomputer system. Inputs are read by the microprocessor in the same way as bytes of data in memory, and output data is written to the circuit's address in a similar manner to storing data in memory.

For mechanical devices such as keyboards and printers, the process is slowed down by latching the data into a parallel output register which holds it long enough for the mechanical parts to respond. The interface circuit is adaptable and may be used as an input or output device according to instructions given to it by the microprocessor from the system program.

These circuits are known variously as programmable peripheral interface (PPI) or peripheral interface adaptor (PIA) devices according to the manufacturer.

For recording data on a single channel tape recorder or for transmission via co-axial, optical or satellite link, the digits must be presented sequentially in time, i.e. serially. A general purpose circuit is used for this function so that transmission speed and data verification methods may be selected via the program.

The recording of data onto disks and the retrieval of such data is controlled by a disk operating system which is a piece of software dedicated to this hardware interface.

For output to a visual display unit (VDU), either red/green/blue video signals or modulated UHF (i.e. television) signals are produced by special purpose chips.

The peripheral equipment above is such as would normally be associated with any microcomputer. For machinery control and alarm applications other ad-

ditional circuits are required. On/off signals to operate solenoid valves will require driver circuits of appropriate power. These signals and inputs from switches (temperature, pressure, level, etc.) will use an I/O device such as the PPI or PIA but, in order to isolate the microcircuits from the higher voltages used on machinery, opto-isolators are interposed. These consist of light emitting diodes (LEDs) and photo transistors encapsulated together so that the only medium of connection is light. They give typically 1.5 kV electrical isolation.

Where the input information is in analogue form, e.g. 0–10 V or 4–20 mA instrumentation signals representing pressure or temperature etc., the analogue signals have to be converted to parallel digital signals by analogue to digital (A to D) convertors before being read into the system via a PPI/PIA circuit. Similarly for an analogue output control signal a digital to analogue (D to A) converter circuit is required. Converter circuits can be shared among a number of signal inputs or outputs by means of signal selection and storage circuits.

Power supplies

The quality of the power supply unit for a microprocessor system needs to be better than would be required for a system employing electro-magnetic relays. The 5.0 V output must be held within ±10% regardless of the mains input voltage and frequency excursions which necessitate special stabilisation of power supplies for shipboard applications.

A further problem with power supplies, particularly on board ship, is due to the susceptibility of micros to electromagnetic interference (EMI). This is due to the fact that the energy content of signals within micro systems is comparable to that of the interference. It is, therefore, necessary for the power supply unit to suppress any mains-borne EMI. Similarly the overall system needs to be protected from radiated EMI.

All programmable electronic systems for marine automation and control applications need to be tested to ensure that they are not susceptible to EMI at the frequencies and strengths found typically in ships.

PROGRAMMABLE LOGIC CONTROLLERS

There are a number of levels of control instructions for digital systems (see above). The most fundamental are those built into the microprocessor which enable it to interpret and act on each command of its instruction set. The next level is the operating system which is a software program in the memory external to the microprocessor. The operating system controls routine microprocessor operations such as updating the VDU display, read/write operations of tape and disk memory, processing input signals from the keyboard and interpreting instructions from a higher level programming language into machine code. An operating system converts a selection of hardware into a general-purpose computer. In order to enable a computer to perform a specific function, such as word processing, an 'application program' is required. Application programs occupy many kilobytes of memory but they enable those who are not computer specialists to make use of computer systems.

A programmable logic controller (PLC) is a microcomputer with an application program which dedicates the system to machinery or process control purposes. The concept was developed in order to enable designers of analogue and relay control systems to use digital technology without having to learn computer programming. By virtue of its application program a PLC is able to perform all the normal control functions—arithmetic, logical, sequencing, proportional, PI and PID.

A working system has to be defined by selecting which functions are performed on particular input signals and where the resultant output signals are directed. This stage of programming is usually carried out with the aid of an external unit like a personal computer connected to the PLC. On completion of system development PROM firmware may be produced and plugged into sockets in the PLC. Logical and sequential operations are usually represented as ladder diagrams (Fig 12) on the VDU screen of the programming unit. Continuous control operations such as comparison and PID functions are usually represented as block diagrams. A permanent record of the completed system can be produced by printing out the appropriate diagram. Because software can be easily modified but is relatively difficult to check, it is most important that a record is kept of each version of software that is produced. Firmware packages should be clearly marked with their version number and so should floppy disks or other program media.

As an example of the various ways in which the operation of a system may be visualised in order to describe its required features, consider part of a main engine alarm system. Figure 11 shows the electrical circuit diagram for the low lubricating oil pressure alarm. The symbols are those of IEC 617–7, equivalent to BS 3939: part 7: 1985. Signal progression is, in general, from left to right and top to bottom. Contacts are drawn unoperated. Contacts outside the control cubicle, such as those of the pressure switch, are sometimes distinguished by a dash-line box around their symbols.

The system is able to store the information that a fleeting fault has occurred so the designer has built in a short (10 sec) delay to prevent spurious alarm operation. As the main lubricating oil supply is pro-

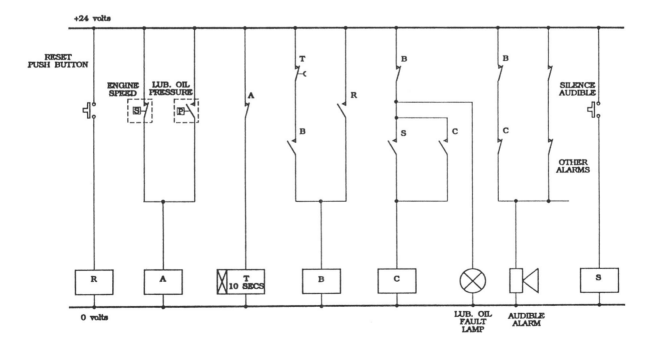

Figure 11 Low lubricating oil pressure alarm—relay circuit diagram.

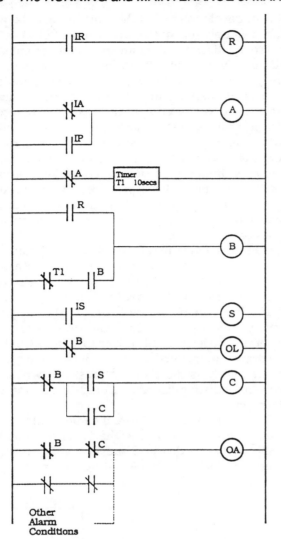

Figure 12   Low lubricating oil pressure alarm—ladder diagram.

vided by an engine-driven pump the signal from the pressure switch is arranged to have no effect until the engine is up to some minimum running speed. The system has two other features to note:

a) the pressure switch contacts open for the alarm state so a wire breakage would also be announced by an alarm;

b) when the lubricating oil alarm has been accepted by silencing the audible alarm the occurrence of any other alarm condition will re-start the sounder.

Figure 12 shows the system in Fig 11 depicted by means of a ladder diagram, commonly used for PLC systems. The symbols here do not differentiate between internal and external functions so they have been identified by prefixes I for input signals and O for output signals. With large systems, where the units are usually identified by numbers, it is essential that inputs and outputs are listed and correlated with their respective systems hardware.

Figure 13 is a logic diagram using the symbols defined in IEC 617-12: 1991, BS 3939: part 12: 1991. The input and output devices are not shown; nor are any necessary interface circuits. The signal is taken to be logic 1 when the descriptive statement is true, e.g. engine running = 1, so that the input is 0 when the engine is stationary. The diagram shows the principles of the system. It is not a circuit diagram although it could be implemented by connecting integrated logic circuit elements together in the same order as the symbols. Each logic function may also be carried out by a programmable system in which case each symbol represents a portion of the software.

Figure 14 is a flow chart to BS 4508: 1987. This is a means of analysing a system's requirements so that

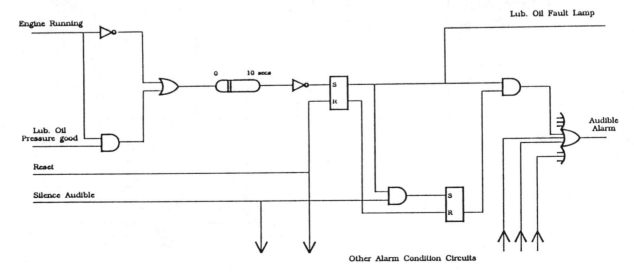

Figure 13   Low lubricating oil pressure alarm—logic diagram.

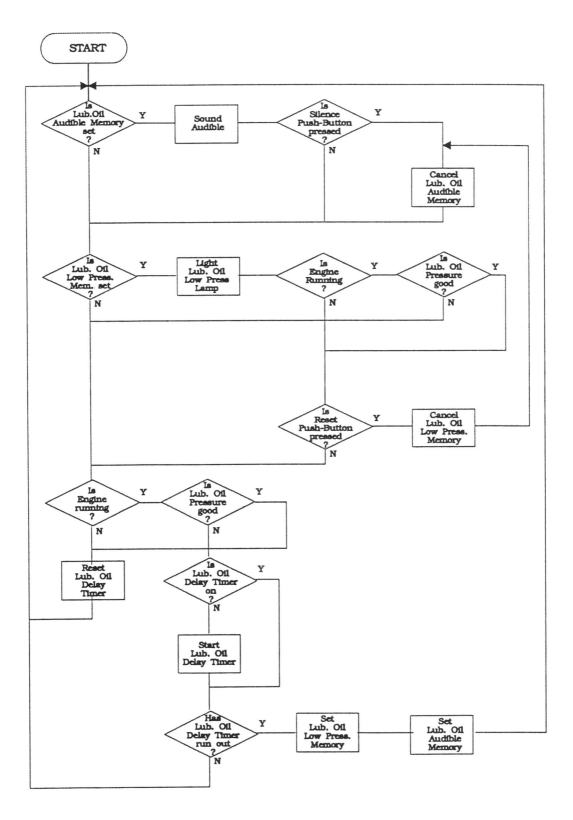

Figure 14   Low lubricating oil pressure alarm—flow chart.

they are broken down into a series of yes/no decisions. The system may then be implemented by any two-state devices, relays, logic elements or programmable systems.

Distributed systems

There are several advantages to be gained by dividing a large control or alarm system into smaller units and siting them close to the equipment to which they relate. Such an arrangement is known as a distributed system because each unit contains a microprocessor and thus the 'intelligence' of the system is not centralized at a single position. A typical arrangement is shown schematically in Fig 15.

The most obvious cost saving is from the purchase and installation of cable since all the sensors and actuators have only to be connected to their local unit. Because of the high speed of operation of microsystems all the sensor data can be transmitted to the rest of the system via a network. The process is known as multiplexing.

In the event of damage to cables between the control station and the machinery space the repair time for a distributed system would be minimal, thus reducing the loss of revenue resulting from the non-availability of the vessel.

By distributing control and alarm functions to several widely separated locations and designing the local units to be autonomous, systems can be protected from total failure due to a single event such as a fire at the control station or in a cable duct leading to it. This eliminates a major hazard of centralized systems while still allowing control and monitoring to be carried out from a single central position. Since there are usually only two data paths connecting the units of a distributed system it is not very costly to provide a second control station at a separate location, thereby further enhancing system integrity. The security of data transfer between the units can be improved by using optical fibres as the transmission medium, since these are immune to electromagnetic interference.

Because a distributed system has a microprocesoor in every unit it can handle much more information than a centralized system could with only one. Local units perform signal pre-conditioning and validity checks in order to reduce the workload of the central unit which can concentrate on functions such as graphical display of the information.

Self-monitoring arrangements

PLC systems require different self-monitoring arrangements from those applicable to conventional control and alarm systems. It is necessary not only to check the external circuit continuity, but also the correct functioning of the microprocessor itself. This is usually carried out by an independent circuit called a watchdog. In its simplest form this consists of a resettable delay timer which gives an alarm unless it is repeatedly reset by signals regularly put out by the microprocessor system. In the event of either a hardware fault or software error causing the system to fail to repeat its cycle of program instructions the watchdog circuit will not receive its signal and so will raise an alarm. The location of a hardware fault should be indicated by means of built-in test facilities. In the absence of such assistance the equipment could be inoperable for long periods of time.

In distributed systems the validity of data transmitted between units should also be verified. The simplest means of checking is by the use of a parity bit. As the bits that constitute the data are serially transmitted the number of digit 1s are counted. For 'even parity' an extra 1 is added, if required, to make the total an even number. Every transmission will then consist of an even number of digit 1s. The receiving unit counts the incoming digits and indicates a fault or requests re-transmission if an uneven number of digit 1s is received. A single parity bit will detect the presence of a single error but more sophisticated methods employing several parity bits are capable of detecting multiple errors in a transmission, and may even locate which bits are at fault.

The economic arguments for and against the use of any computerised system are complex. The capital cost of the computer hardware is low compared with

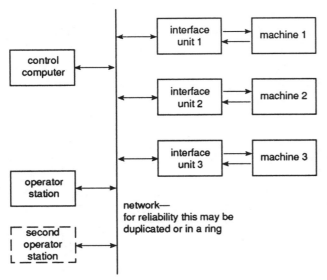

Figure 15   Distributed system.

conventional hardware, but the software programs can be expensive in terms of man-hours to develop and debug.

Irrespective of the equipment fitted in centralised control and monitoring centres, an important consideration is redundancy. Redundancy is the duplication of equipment such that if there is a failure there is no loss of vital services.

Thus if a computer system is used to monitor and control, the computers must be duplicated and always have a manual means of operation of the controlled equipment in the event of a total computer failure. The most important aspect is that safety shut down systems should have no components in common with control systems so that both cannot fail together.

Electronic displays

The microprocessor has revolutionised the format in which data can be displayed. Simple display devices include the LED (light emitting diode) and the LCD (liquid crystal display) which are commonly used for displaying alpha-numeric text.

A major advantage with the microcomputer is that it makes available the facility of the VDU (visual display unit), or CRT (cathode ray tube), which provides a new media for the display in alpha-numeric format, or more importantly graphical format, of system data.

It is not uncommon for control centres to have multiple VDU displays for control, monitoring and alarm systems. Early VDUs were monochrome, which had limited capabilities, but the use of colour VDUs has opened greater opportunities for displays.

Use of colour

There are several problems with the use of colour which have been identified during various research studies.[2] A standard for the use of colours for indicator lights, push buttons and annunciators was introduced only as recently as 1986.[3]

There is still no acceptable standard for the use of colours on VDU displays, the major problem being that as more system information can be collated on the display screen then existing individual colour standards begin to conflict.

People interpret colours differently, mostly from traditional practices. When colours, especially green and red, can represent on/off, open/closed, direction and safe/unsafe at the same time on the same screen, confusion will occur and accidents will happen. Because of this and the possibility that the opera-

tor may be colour-blind, unacknowledged alarms must not be differentiated from acknowledged alarms by colour alone.

The most common form of colour blindness is that of red and green; less common is blue and yellow colour blindness. Navigation officers are subject to a colour eye sight test during examination for certificates, but some engineering disciplines only require a colour matching test, where colours must be matched (e.g. when joining colour coded wires together), and not identified.

CONTROL SYSTEM LOGIC

The mathematics of control system logic is known as Boolean algebra. An understanding of this subject is more essential to the system design engineer than to the system operator.

However for any automatic control system, it is important to understand the logic of that system, especially that of 'logic gates'. Gates are elements of a control circuit, which are in effect 'decision' devices, in that they determine the direction of a signal flow path according to certain conditions. The use of gates is normally associated with electronic systems, but the theory can be applied to both hydraulic and pneumatic systems. Gates appear also in the software

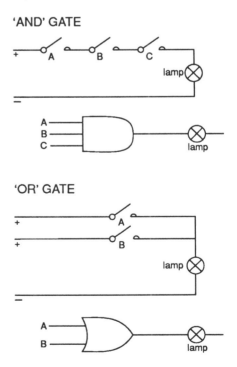

Figure 16 The 'AND' and 'OR' gates, with their electrical analogies.

of computer programs, but there they are normally known as logical operators.

Figure 16 illustrates common gates for electronic and pneumatic systems.

Standard drawing symbols

Equipment manufacturers and shipyards produce control system drawings which use standard symbols for the control devices and instrumentation, e.g. a clutch control circuit (Fig 8). The advantage of these symbols is that, irrespective of the language in which the text on the drawings is written, any user should be able to decipher the operation of the system using the symbols alone. Before studying a control system drawing and being able to interpret its operation, the reader should refer to the relevant standards publications to become familiar with these symbols.[4, 5]

Frequently a manufacturer has a device which does not comply with any standard symbol and one can often find non-standard symbols on manufacturers' drawings.

MONITORING SYSTEMS

To replace the human operator, who would normally carry out the role of monitoring any operation, automatic monitoring systems must be introduced. Monitoring systems vary in both size and complexity, ranging from a simple make-break switch operated by pressure to activate an alarm, to a sophisticated sequential scanning system.

The sophisticated system may have some of the following features:

1. Sequential monitoring of sensors and comparison of readings with a stored data bank of alarm limit settings. Some modern systems can have over 6000 monitoring points around the ship.

2. Data acquisition and storage on computer tapes or disks for later reference. Some ships now will automatically transmit this data by satellite to the company headquarters for statistical analysis.

3. Data logging of monitored processes, with trend analysis computer VDU displays.

4. Assessment of the machinery operating conditions, and automatic adjustment to provide the optimum operating conditions for the prevailing conditions. This particular facility may be used to adjust the speed of a ship in passage to give the greatest fuel economy possible.

5. Machinery condition monitoring. The machinery may be fitted with sensors to monitor the combustion process and general health of the engine to aid efficient running and predictive maintenance schedules.

Generally the monitoring system of a ship would also comprise the following sub-systems.

Alarm systems

Within the rules and regulations are features which must be included into the design of control equipment, in particular the alarm system.[4, 5, 6] Alarm systems are associated with control and safety systems and are normally an integral part of the monitoring system. The design must allow the alarm system to function independently of any control or safety system, where practical, so that the alarm system will still function if there is a fault in these other systems.

Any alarm system must have an automatic change over to a stand-by power supply in the event of a main power supply failure. It must be self-monitoring for faults within the alarm system itself, such as a broken wire or sensor failure. Any internal system fault should cause the alarm system to give an alarm.

The alarm system fitted must advise duty personnel quickly of any fault condition. The presence of any unrectified faults should be indicated at all times. Machinery, safety and control system faults must be indicated at the control stations and alarms should be both visual and audible.

If a vessel is being operated in the UMS mode, then audible and visual indication of machinery alarms must be relayed to the engineers' accommodation so that the engineering staff are aware that a fault has occurred. If any machinery alarm has not been acknowledged in the control room within a predetermined time the engineers' general alarm should sound automatically.

Any indication of a machinery fault should also be relayed to the bridge, so that they are aware of the fault, know that it is being attended to, and when it is cleared.

Visual alarms are colour coded[3] to give an indication of priority level. They can be steady state lamps or flashing lamps, depending on their application. An audible alarm 'silence button' should not extinguish any visual alarm.

Audible alarms for different systems should have different tones or sounds. The telegraph alarm should be different from the general engine room alarm, which in turn should be different from the fire alarm

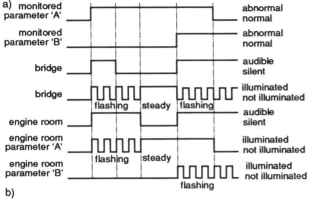

b)

	lamp	siren
normal condition	off	off
fault condition	flashing	on
silence alarm warning	flashing	off
accept (acknowledge) alarm	steady on	off
fault cleared	off	off

Figure 17 Alarm system; a) functional diagram; b)typical method of operation of logic for a machinery alarm system.

bell, so that ship's staff responding to the alarm can both quickly react to the alarm and have some knowledge of the alarm type. A typical method of logic of operation for a machinery alarm system, using a visual lamp and an audible siren, would be as shown in Fig 17.

There are many other different features which may be fitted to alarm systems and these include :

a) automatic reset—where the alarm will automatically reset after normal conditions have been restored (but this would not be acceptable to classification societies unless the alarm has already been accepted or acknowledged);

b) manual reset—where the alarm must be manually reset after normal conditions are restored;

c) lock in on fleeting alarms—where the alarm condition is still displayed even though the fault condition has quickly appeared and then disappeared;

d) time delay to prevent raising of spurious alarm signals;

e) event recorder—which prints out a record of the alarm details and the sequence and time of alarms;

f) 'first up' or 'first out'— enabling identification of the first alarm that operated within a group or 'flood' of alarms.

The industry is currently facing a problem with 'flood' alarms or alarm overloads. With a fully auto-

mated main propulsion plant, if there is a failure of some nature which causes a shutdown of the plant, such as a total electrical 'blackout', then the alarm system may have to cope with hundreds of alarm signals in a very short space of time. If the recording devices are not of suitable speed and quality then it becomes difficult to actually identify the correct order of events and the initial cause of the failure.

Safety systems

Safety is of paramount importance in any control system. A safety system is a system which reduces dangers and risks of injury to personnel and damage to machinery. Any safety system should operate automatically to prevent endangering both personnel and machinery.

Typical safety systems

There are numerous examples which could be used to illustrate safety systems, below are some of the more commonly fitted.

Machinery auto start-up

These systems are provided with a stand-by device which will automatically start in the event of the running device failing through a fault condition. The start-up of the stand-by device must restore the normal operating conditions and give an alarm on failure of the online device.

Main cooling water and lubricating oil circulating pumps are fitted in pairs and arranged so that while one machine is in service, the other is in the stand-by mode, ready to automatically start in the event of failure of the running pump.

Electrical generators can be arranged with automatic start-up, which can be initiated by a failure of the running generator, or by the electrical load on the switchboard exceeding the maximum safe load for one generator. In the latter case the switchboard must also be fitted with automatic synchronising equipment to allow the two generators to run in parallel and load share.

Reduction of power

With this safety system the machinery output power is temporarily reduced to meet the prevailing conditions. There are several situations which may trigger this device, the most common being excessive high temperatures, low pressures or high loads on the machinery.

This device is fitted to a main propulsion diesel engine cooling water temperature monitoring system. If the engine becomes overloaded and the jacket cooling water outlet temperature exceeds a 'high' set point, an alarm will be raised. If that alarm is not responded to and the temperature continues to rise to a 'high-high' set point, then the engine will automatically go into a load reduction, e.g. the engine revolutions will be reduced from 120 revs/min to 45 revs/min in the case of a slow speed diesel engine.

This type of safety system with its alarm is known as a first stage protection device.

Typical systems with power reduction protection on a main propulsion diesel engine are :

a) high scavenge air temperature;

b) high oil mist level in crankcase;

c) low piston cooling pressure or flow;

d) high piston cooling outlet temperature;

e) low cylinder cooling pressure or flow;

f) high cylinder cooling temperature;

g) high exhaust gas temperature on a cylinder, or high exhaust gas temperature deviation from average exhaust temperature.

Machinery shut down

With the shut down safety system the machinery is protected from critical conditions by shutting off the fuel supply or power supply thereby stopping the machinery. In some cases a shut down will follow a reduction of power if the prevailing conditions continue to develop into a critical situation or if no remedial action is taken after a certain time period.

Consider the scenario of the diesel engine with a high-high jacket water temperature. If, after the reduction in power decreases the speed of the engine to 45 revs/min, the temperatures stay high-high, then after 3 minutes an engine shut down will be triggered, stopping the engine.

The electrical power supply to electric motor driven circulating pumps may be isolated if, for example, a shaft bearing fails, which may increase the electric load on the motor. An overload trip will isolate the power.

This type of safety system with its associated alarm is known as a second stage protection device, and it must be independent of the first stage device.

Bilge level detection system

An alarm system must be fitted to provide warning when the contents of the machinery space bilge wells has reached a predetermined level. This level must be low enough for the contents of the bilges not to overflow onto the tank tops.

Bilge water moving over the tank tops is particularly dangerous for several reasons.

1. It can be a fire hazard, especially if there is oil in the bilge water. A local fire could rapidly spread through the machinery space.

2. There is danger of free surface effect on the stability of the vessel.

3. There is a possibility water damage to electrical cables and motors, from splashing.

Accumulation in the bilge wells must be detectable at all angles of heel and trim of the vessel. Ships of 2000 tonnes gross or more must be fitted with two independent detection systems so that each branch bilge is provided with a level detector.

Some ships are fitted with automatic pumping for bilges. Before the bilge level reaches the alarm level a float controller will activate the bilge pump, open the required valves and activate the bilge pump. The system must be designed to avoid causing pollution or masking an actual leak situation.

Fire detection alarm systems

The fire detector indicator and alarm system must be situated in such a position that fire in the machinery spaces will not make it inoperative. Commonly it is sited on the bridge or in a special fire control centre.

The system panel normally gives local audio-visual alarms and indicates the source of the fire alarm. If the local warning alarm is not acknowledged within a certain time it will initiate the main audible fire alarm, which must be capable of being heard on the bridge, in the fire control station, and in the accommodation and the machinery spaces.

Particular fire detector loops or individual detectors are capable of being temporarily isolated, and the status of loops must be indicated on the panel. If a detector is inadvertently left off, the alarm system must reactivate the detector automatically after a certain time period, usually 30 minutes.

The alarm system must be self monitoring and any power or system failures, such as short circuits or broken wires, should raise an alarm but with a different tone to that of the main fire alarm.

Fail safe policies

Any control system should be designed to 'fail safe'. This means that if the control system has a failure, then the controlled equipment must fail to a condition so as not to cause an unsafe situation to arise, such as mechanical or thermal overloads of machinery.

Depending on the particular use of the equipment the failure mode can be different, for example a pneumatically operated valve can be arranged to:

a) 'open on air failure' (OAF);

b) 'close on air failure' (CAF); or to

c) 'fail fixed', i.e. the valve remains in the position it was in at the time of the air failure.

According to the Rules of Lloyd's Register, failure of the actuator power should not permit a valve to move to an unsafe condition.[7]

A good example of fail safe operation is with a controllable pitch propeller system. The response firstly depends on the type of hub fitted, which can be either a spring loaded type or an all hydraulic type. With the spring loaded type the hub is fitted with a spring so that in the event of a hydraulic failure the propeller blades will fail to the ahead position. The vessel will be able to maintain its navigation speed, but reduced to about 75% of maximum, as the water

pressure acting on the propeller blades can overcome the spring pressure above this power level.

With the all hydraulic hub type the response is dependent on the speed of the vessel through the water. Generally speaking, the blades will move to the zero pitch position. To get under way again the blades will have to be jacked, using a manually operated hydraulic pump, and locked in the ahead position. If the main engine is reversible the vessel can operate as if with a conventional fixed pitch propeller.

For any fail safe device it is important to establish what it should do in a failure mode and then test the device to ensure it operates correctly.

CALIBRATION

Nowadays, especially in unattended engine rooms, the monitoring system with its instruments must

Figure 18 Calibration test bench.

measure the variables and, through a control system, automatically alter the operating conditions to the required value in a precise manner. This must be done in a harsh environment under conditions of vibration, changing humidity and temperature, and with an atmosphere containing salt, oil and dust contamination.

Generally, instruments designed specifically for marine use are more reliable than those used in shore installations. Measuring instruments are becoming more sophisticated and the performance of all instruments depends on the following factors.

a) Accuracy, i.e. how close the reading is to the true value;

b) precision, i.e. whether several readings by the same instrument agree;

c) sensitivity, i.e. the smallest change of the measured quantity to which the instrument responds;

d) rangeability, i.e. the range of readings within which any error is acceptable.

Quality, precision or reliability of control equipment and instrumentation is no guarantee of accuracy. If there are any doubts, the equipment must always be recalibrated.

Instruments should be checked regularly since drift over a period of time due to many reasons, such as mechanical wear, may not be noticed by the operator. There is a need to regularly recalibrate the elements of a control system.

Environments such as oil platforms have stringent requirements for calibration and carry their own calibration test benches (Fig 18). Many hours of work can be wasted tuning control process systems with instruments that need recalibrating. If calibration equipment, such as a deadweight tester, is on board a ship it is often in a neglected condition. Periodic calibration of process instrumentation helps to ensure optimum operation of process plant, potentially reducing energy costs and pollution whilst minimising waste and controlling plant down time. Down time is time lost during stoppages for repair or maintenance, when the process plant could possibly be running and earning money.

The resultant improvements in energy efficiency and productivity will be complemented by corresponding quality improvements, which is why implementation of approved calibration procedures are integral to current manufacturing and quality standards, such as British Standards 5750[8], ISO 9000[9] and Allied Quality Assurance Procedures (AQAP)[10]

Primary calibration standards are maintained in the UK by the National Physics Laboratory (the NPL), to which all other calibration instruments should be ultimately traceable. To ensure traceability and quality of calibration, the NPL controls and monitors, by means of regular audits, a number of accredited calibration laboratories, which are listed[11] and under the auspices of the National Measurement Accreditation Service (NAMAS).

RULES AND REGULATIONS

Rules and regulations for the control engineering installation on board ships are issued by various regulatory authorities, At the international level, IMO (International Maritime Organisation) have mandatory regulations for ships operating with periodically unattended machinery spaces and these are contained in the International Convention for the Safety of Life at Sea (SOLAS). Further mandatory regulations may be imposed by the national administration with which the ship is registered and these usually take the form of an interpretation of the SOLAS regulations.

The international classification societies, such as Lloyd's Register of Shipping, Det norske Veritas, American Bureau of Shipping, Bureau Veritas and Germanischer Lloyd, issue detailed rules specifying precisely the minimum controls, alarms and safeguards that need to be fitted for the ship to be assigned a classification notation. The classification societies meet through the forum of IACS (International Association of Classification Societies) to ensure that there is no significant difference between their minimum requirements and that the SOLAS regulations will also be complied with through the classification process.

It is important to appreciate that when a ship is assigned the UMS notation (or equivalent), the flag authority will normally permit some dispensation on the engineering manning level. This dispensation is only permitted while the UMS notation remains valid and accordingly the classification societies periodically survey the controls, alarms and safety systems throughout the ship's service life. If defects are found in the control engineering installation which affect the UMS notation, it would be suspended.

This can have serious consequences because the manning level may no longer be sufficient to comply with the requirements of the flag state and cases have been known where they may detain the ship until either the engineering complement is increased or the UMS notation is made good.

ON BOARD TESTING AND MAINTENANCE

Regular on board testing and maintenance of the control installation and correct calibration of instruments as described previously is vital if the benefits that automation can bring are to be fully realised and the survey requirements are to be met without undue difficulty.

Test and maintenance periods and the way in which these activities are carried out should be determined with regard to the system and component reliability and their performance criteria or criticality of function. There are a number of important considerations to be taken into account when formulating test procedures and a correct balance has to be achieved:

1. Shortening the intervals between testing and maintenance should increase the success of detecting faults, but it also increases the degree of human interference and disturbance to the system. Consequently an increase in testing can mean that the system is more sensitive to human error and faulty test procedures.

2. Test procedures should be completely thorough and constitute a check of all functional aspects of the system. Partial testing may fail to reveal faults which are already in existence, but it is not always expedient or practical to carry out a complete test due to operational restrictions.

3. Test procedures should be fully described and leave no doubt as to the methods to be used and the results to be expected. This however can produce an approach which is inflexible and difficult to modify.

It would be impractical to test all controls, alarms and safety systems at one time and accordingly a schedule of testing is required bearing in mind the three foregoing points. The test schedule should be arranged so that over a given period of time all these functions are tested at least once, but, depending on their criticality, certain functions may be tested more frequently. Having regard to the workload involved, a typical schedule could be based on a twelve to sixteen week period.

Where it is only possible to partially test a particular function provision should be made in the schedule to carry out a realistic test, including a test of the sensor. The test schedule should identify each alarm and safety systems channel and the associated set point, and make provision for appropriate remarks where adjustments etc. are required as a result of the test.

Where it can be demonstrated to attending surveyors from any of the classification societies or national administrations that regular testing is undertaken and is well documented it gives them confidence that the control installation is being maintained in good condition, but not least it gives the ship's engineers confidence that they can operate unattended safely and reliably.

Notes and references

1. British Standards Publication, BS 1523 : 1967, *'Glossary of terms used in automatic controlling and regulating systems'* Part 1. Process and kinetic control.
2. Shipwide Information Distribution and Collection System (SIDACS) Project, *'A UK efficient ship programme study'*, R Beams and S Jordan, MCC 88, Marine Management (Holdings) Ltd., London.
3. British Standards Publication BS 4099: Part 1: 1986; IEC 73: 1984 *'Colours of indicator lights, push-buttons, annunciators and digital read-outs'*.
4. British Standards Publication, BS 2917 : 1977, *'Specification for graphical symbols used on diagrams for fluid power systems and components'*. The same document is published as: International Standards Organisation Publication, ISO 1219–1976, *'Fluid power systems and components—Graphical symbols'*.
5. British Standards Publication, BS 3939 : 1985, *'Guide for graphical symbols for electrical power, telecommunications and electronic diagrams'*.
6. *'SOLAS 74/78 as Amended'*, IMO Publication
7. *'Rules and Regulations for the classification of ships'*, in particular *'Part 6: Chapter 1 : Control Engineering Systems'*, Lloyd's Register of Shipping
8. British Standards Publication, BS 5750
9. International Standards Organisation Publication, ISO 9000
10. *'Allied Quality Assurance Procedures (AQAP)'*, Ministry of Defence Directorate of Standardization (First Avenue House, High Holborn London WC1V 6HE).
11. Accredited laboratories are listed in the NAMAS Executive M3 publication, *'NAMAS Concise Directory'*, National Physics Laboratory, Teddington
12. Department of Trade, *'Survey of passenger ships, instructions for the guidance of surveyors'*, Volumes 1 and 2, HMSO

Bibliography

1. For further reading on the subject of PLCs, the book 'Programmable Logic Controllers and their Engineering Applications' by A J Crispin (McGraw-Hill) is recommended.
2. R Munton, J McNaught, J N MacKenzie, 'Progress in automation', Trans IMarE Vol 75 (1963) and R Munton, J McNaught, 'Automation of highly powered diesel machinery', Trans IMarE Vol 78 (1966).
3. *'Notes on instrumentation and control'*, G J Roy, Stanford Maritime London

Chapter 8
Marine Refrigerating Plant

A C Stera and J Templeton

INTRODUCTION

During the 19th century an international trade in natural ice was developed and ice was harvested in Scandinavian countries and in New England (USA) and exported to the tropics and other parts of the world. The ice was carried in the ships' holds insulated with pine sawdust. Although this use of natural ice served the purpose of short term preservation of produce at chilled temperatures and enabled a trade to flourish between the USA and Europe in fruit and butter, and to some extent chilled beef, it became apparent that the growth of the manufacturing industries in Europe in the middle of the century and the consequent increase in the urban population at the expense of the rural population was giving rise to a situation where indigenous food supplies, particularly meat, were no longer adequate. At the same time, Australia, New Zealand and the Americas were raising sheep and cattle mainly for wool and hide purposes. The meat they were producing could not all be consumed by the local population. There was, therefore, a need for a means to bring the ever increasing surplus of meat in the sheep and cattle raising countries to hungry consumers in the industrial countries of Europe.

Refrigeration was brought into use on land long before it was successfully applied to shipboard transport. As far back as 1824 a patent was taken out by Vallence for an ice making machine and progress was made, although somewhat spasmodically, in refrigeration techniques by such people as Perkins and Kingsford until, in 1861, Thomas Mort established the first freezing works in the world at Sydney Harbour, New South Wales. By this time mechanical refrigeration plant had reached a point where the major step of transporting meat between the continents could be attempted and in 1877 a Frenchman,

Tellier, carried a cargo of beef from the Argentine to France in his steam *Frigorifique*. Although the voyage was not fully successful, a sufficient quantity of meat arrived in an edible condition to show that refrigerated transport was a practical proposition and a few months later another Frenchman, Carre, improved on the above achievement and successfully carried a cargo of frozen meat from Buenos Aires to Marseille in his vessel *Paraguay*. These vessels used ammonia as the refrigerant, but leakage problems were so great that its use, for the time being, was abandoned. Engineers in Great Britain concentrated on air as the refrigerant and in 1879 a Bell-Coleman cold air machine was installed and tested onboard the Anchor Line *Circassia* trading to America.

In 1880 the *Strathleven*, fitted with a Bell-Coleman cold air machine, carried a cargo of frozen meat in perfect condition from Australia to London, thus starting the frozen meat trade between continents. Two years later the Albion Line *Dunedin* started the frozen meat trade from New Zealand to Europe and the revolution in the worldwide carriage of refrigerated produce was firmly established, progressing until it arrived at the various differing modes of carriage which comprise today's seaborne transportation system. At the end of 1991 there were about 1,200 fully refrigerated vessels afloat, with a total capacity of approximately 300M ft^3, and 1,330 container carrying vessels with a carrying capacity of 220M ft^3.

REFRIGERATED CARGO

Marine refrigerated transport is most suitable for carrying perishable cargo under controlled temperature, relative humidity and, recently, under controlled atmospheres (reduced oxygen and increased carbon dioxide levels).

In 1991 it was estimated that over 30M tons of perishable cargo was carried around the world by sea annually under refrigeration; about 70% in partly or fully refrigerated vessels, and the remainder in containers.

A perishable is something that is easily injured or destroyed. Frozen produce, meats, seafood, dairy produce, fresh fruit and vegetables, juices, horticultural produce, such as flowering bulbs and fresh flowers, confectionery, chemicals, pharmaceuticals and photographic material are all perishables. Without careful treatment, the time taken to deteriorate to a condition which will either reduce the value, or render it unsaleable, may become unacceptably short. The object of refrigeration is to prolong the storage life of a perishable food product by lowering its temperature so that metabolic deterioration and decay caused by micro-organisms or enzymes are retarded. The successful carriage of refrigerated cargo depends upon correct preparation for transport, packaging, handling during loading and unloading, correct storage on board, relative humidity and temperature, required fresh air ventilation, sufficient air circulation in holds, and correct levels of O_2 and CO_2 if transported under controlled atmosphere.

Animal products

These products, which may be carried frozen or chilled, do not generate any gases or heat during the sea voyage and are frequently referred to as 'dead' cargo.

Frozen meat

Frozen meat should never be carried at temperatures higher than $-10°C$. Although microbiological activity has ceased at $-8°C$, chemical and physical deterioration continues, although at a diminishing rate, as the temperature decreases. In practice, the carrying temperature depends on the type of meat and its package, length of voyage and destination, and is likely to be within the range $-29°C$ to $-15°C$ with the current trend being towards the lower temperature.

The frozen cargo stack should be well dunnaged, away from any heat transmitting surface, e.g. the ship's side and bulkheads. Provided the cargo is all loaded at or near the carrying temperature, it is more important to maintain a good air flow around the outer perimeter of the stack than through the stack.

Chilled meat

Chilled meat may be carried in vacuum bags packed in cartons. An alternative method is to wrap the quarters of meat in a thin transparent liner material and hang them on chains and hooks in the chamber. The quality of the chilled meat is largely judged in terms of temperature, appearance and smell at the time of off-loading. To ensure the maximum storage life, the chilled meat must not only be prepared in a clean fashion, but also protected from subsequent contamination during loading, the main source of which will come from air borne mould spores.

The mould problem may be particularly acute if fruit has been the previous cargo, so the cleanliness of the chamber and meat handling is of paramount importance. Before loading commences chambers are usually scrubbed with hot water and detergent followed by fumigation by formaldehyde, or similar, for 24 hours with fans running.

Chilled meat is carried at around $-1°C$, with a temperature $-1.8°C$ being more suitable for unpacked cargo. If the temperature falls below this value the meat starts to freeze, resulting in the partial disruption of the tissue and formation of large ice crystals, which is detrimental to the quality of the meat. It is therefore of utmost importance that the chamber temperature is closely controlled. The cargo storage arrangements are to be such that a uniform temperature distribution is achieved.

Horticultural products

Fruit, vegetables and flowers

Such products are frequently referred to as 'live' cargoes, because they remain alive after harvesting, and respire, absorbing oxygen (O_2) from the atmosphere and exhaling carbon dioxide (CO_2). During this process energy is released and a host of volatiles given off. Normally, a higher rate of air circulation is required in the holds than for meat cargoes, together with the introduction of fresh air to maintain CO_2 concentration within acceptable limits.

In order to secure maximum storage life and reduce the load on the cooling system, fruit and vegetables should be brought close to the carrying temperature before they are loaded on the ship. The only exception is a banana cargo, which is usually loaded non-precooled. Uniform temperature and steady relative humidity in the hold are of prime importance and can only be achieved with good ventilation. Warm air pockets may result in the accumulation of carbon dioxide and other metabolic products, and may encourage mould development and general deterioration.

The optimum carrying temperatures for live products vary with variety, producing area, season and duration of transport and, with a few exceptions, will be as close to freezing as possible in order to slow, but not prevent, the ripening process. Some fruits, however, if kept below a certain temperature, which may be well above the freezing point, may sustain damage due to the ripening process being prematurely arrested and the fruit will never attain the full flavour of 'eating ripe' fruit. One such fruit is the banana.

Bananas

Bananas are carried by sea in greater quantitites than any other commodity. They are very sensitive to bruising, temperature fluctuations and the presence of CO_2 and ethylene in excessive quantities, and are regarded as one of the most difficult cargoes. They must be packed in a state of maturity that will allow them, under normal transport conditions, to arrive at their destination before ripening has commenced. Thirty years ago bananas were carried by sea on the stem, wrapped in polythene sheets, but today they are separated into hands, washed and given and antifungal treatment, then placed in 20kg cardboard boxes and transported as bulk or palletized cargo.

The average product temperature will be approximately 30°C when loaded. At this temperature bananas emit, like other 'living' cargoes, large quantities of heat, carbon dioxide and ethylene, whilst their ripening process continues. If the heat and gases are not removed quickly enough there will be a temperature and ethylene concentration increase which may result in premature ripening. The rate of cooling (Fig 1) is limited by the minimum transport temperature of bananas which, depending upon the variety, will be between 13°C and 14°C. If the hold temperature is reduced below this level even for a short time, the biological activity of bananas may decline to such an extent that it will be impossible for them to ripen after unloading.

It is common practice to introduce fresh air to the holds as soon as, or sometimes even before, cooling is completed, to remove even small traces of ethylene, the presence of which promotes ripening of the bananas. Carbon dioxide concentrations below 2% are sometimes tolerated as they assist in retarding the ripening of the bananas by reducing the rate of respiration. In higher concentrations of CO_2 the fruit may suffocate, unless its oxygen level is reduced (controlled atmosphere).

Taint, odour and the remedies

Tainting may be defined as contamination of refrigerated cargoes by odours from other cargoes. The intensity of tainting is a function of the prevailing odour concentration in the storage space and the duration of exposure to the odorous atmosphere. A considerable number of perishable commodities give off volatile odorous substances which may taint susceptible cargo. Oranges, other citrus fruits and apples are particularly problematic although tainting may also be caused by other fresh fruit such as pineapples, pears, peaches and apricots and by potatoes, onions and other vegetables with strong odour. Cheese can also contribute to odour problems.

Adequate caution must be used in allocating the available cargo spaces to different commodities. Needless to say, goods which may taint each other should never be stored in the same space, even if this would be acceptable with regard to temperature requirements, etc. Moreover, loading of odour generating goods in the same hold as susceptible commodities must be avoided unless there is full assurance of the complete gas tight separation between the individual spaces in the hold. There is also considerable risk of tainting during loading and unloading. Ozone is widely used for deodorising holds after unloading. Little is known about what concentration and duration of treatment is required under various conditions, but it is often recommended to supply 3–6 mg of ozone per hour per m^3 of space. Activated carbon filters may also be used for the deodorisation of empty holds.

FUNDAMENTALS OF REFRIGERATION AND THE VAPOUR COMPRESSION SYSTEM

Refrigeration

Refrigeration is a process of cooling by the transfer of heat. Heat is a form of energy and is indestructible so if heat is removed from a space or substance to cool it to a temperature below that of its surroundings, the heat removed must be discarded to some substance

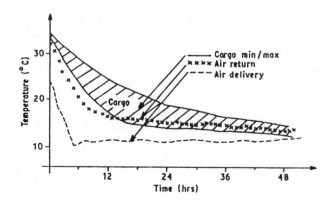

Figure 1　Rate of cooling of bananas.

at a higher temperature where it is of no consequence. Since heat will not flow freely from a body at a low temperature to another at a higher temperature, it is necessary to expend mechanical work, heat, or electrical energy from an external source to achieve it. Refrigeration thus depends on thermodynamics, heat transfer and fluid flow for its practical achievement.

The withdrawal of heat to accomplish the desired degree of refrigeration requires the use of any one of several refrigerating processes. Each of these depends upon the use of a substance called the refrigerant, which can readily be converted from a liquid into a vapour (evaporation), and also from a vapour into a liquid (condensation), within a reasonably narrow range of pressures.

The refrigerant, if first stored as a liquid under pressure, then allowed to flow at reduced pressure through an evaporator coil in the closed system, will withdraw heat from its surroundings during the evaporation stage. The heat so absorbed is removed from the refrigerated area when the vapour returns to that portion of the refrigeration equipment designed to cool down and compress it again to the liquid state for re-use.

The two main refrigeration systems in commercial use are the absorption system and the vapour compression system. Most marine refrigerating plants are of the vapour compression type.

Vapour compression system

The basic principles of the vapour compression system are as follows.

1. A fluid requires and absorbs large quantities of heat when it changes state from a liquid to a vapour. The heat absorbed during this process is called the latent heat of evaporation.

2. The temperature at which a fluid evaporates or condenses depends on the pressure existing at the interface between the vapour and the liquid. This temperature is called the saturation temperature. For example, in a steam boiler operating at 10 bar above atmospheric pressure, water boils at 185°C. Conversely, in a vacuum chamber operating at

pressure 0.5 bar below atmospheric, water boils at 82°C. The pressure–temperature relationship of commonly used refrigerants is shown in Table 1.

3. A vapour or a gas can be liquefied by compression and cooling. This process is called liquefaction. The property which makes the vapour compression system an economic proposition is that any vapour or gas can be liquefied and recycled by suitably compressing it to a sufficiently high pressure and then cooling it. If this were not the case, no refrigerant other than air or water could be used economically, and neither air nor water is ideal for a number of reasons.

Vapour compression cycle

The vapour compression cycle takes place in a closed system, comprising a compressor, a condenser, a liquid receiver, an evaporator, and a flow control or expansion valve, interconnected by discharge, liquid and suction lines (Fig 2).

The liquid refrigerant, e.g. R22, is stored at high pressure in the receiver. The liquid flows from the receiver through the liquid line to the flow control, which regulates the rate of flow to the evaporator to suit the rate of evaporation. As it passes through the flow control, the pressure of the liquid is reduced to the evaporating pressure, so that the saturation temperature of the refrigerant entering the evaporator is below that required in the refrigerated space. Note that as it passes through the flow control, a portion of the liquid evaporates instantly (flash gas) in order to reduce the temperature of the remaining liquid to the evaporating temperature.

The liquid–vapour refrigerant mixture then flows through the evaporator, where it extracts heat from the refrigerated space, and changes to a dry saturated vapour at approximately the same temperature and pressure as that at which it left the flow control.

The evaporating pressure is maintained constant by the action of the compressor, which removes vapour from the evaporator at the same rate as that at which it is formed. In practice, the control system regulating the refrigerant flow is designed to ensure

Table 1 Common refrigerants

Refrigerant	Boiling point at atmospheric pressure °C	Pressure-absolute		Latent heat	
		at -35°C saturation bar	at 30°C saturation bar	at -35°C saturation kJ/kg	at 30°C saturation kJ/kg
Ammonia (R717)	-33.3	0.93	11.68	1374.0	1144.37
R.22	-40.8	1.32	11.92	230.15	172.51
R.12	-29.8	0.81	7.45	167.48	131.89

that the vapour leaving the evaporator is slightly superheated, thus ensuring that only dry vapour is handled by the compressor.

In the compressor, the temperature and pressure of the vapour are raised by compression. The compressed vapour flows through the 'hot gas' discharge line from the compressor into the condenser, using water or air as the cooling medium. The vapour in the condenser first gives up its superheat as it is cooled from the discharge temperature to the saturation temperature corresponding to the condensing pressure, and then gives up its latent heat as it condenses back to a liquid. The liquid then flows from the bottom of the condenser into the receiver, thereby completing the cycle. When its temperature is below the condensing temperature, it is said to be subcooled.

The cycle described above, and shown in Fig 2, can more easily be depicted on a pressure–enthalpy (P–H) or Mollier diagram, Fig 3.

Line A to B represents the change from high to low pressure, or expansion process (from 11.92 bar to 1.32 bar).

Line B to B^1 represents the amount of liquid 'flashed-off' in the expansion valve cooling the remaining liquid.

Line B to C represents the evaporation process at constant saturation temperature and pressure in the evaporator (–35°C and 1.32 bar). At point C the refrigerant is a dry saturated vapour.

Line C to C^1 represents the superheat absorbed by the dry saturated vapour (from –35°C to –25°C).

Line C^1 to D represents the compression process.

Line D to E represents the superheat given up by the vapour in the condenser (from 90°C to 30°C). At point E the refrigerant is a dry saturated vapour.

Line E to F represents the condensation process at constant saturation temperature and pressure (30°C and 11.92 bar). At point F the refrigerant is a saturated liquid.

Line F to A represents the sub cooling of the condensed liquid (from 30°C to 20°C).

Refrigerating effect

The amount of heat absorbed by each unit mass of refrigerant as it flows through an evaporator is known as the refrigerating effect, and is equal to the difference between the enthalpy of the vapour leaving the evaporator and the enthalpy of the liquid at the flow control.

Thus, for the system shown in Fig 3, refrigerating effect,

$$q_E = h_{C^1} - h_A = 398.3 - 230.3 \text{ kJ/kg}$$
$$= 168.0 \text{ kJ/kg}.$$

Refrigerating capacity

The rate at which a system will absorb heat from the refrigerated space or substance is known as the refrigerating capacity, and is expressed as,

refrigerating capacity, $Q_E = m \times q_E$ kJ/s

where m = mass flow of refrigerant through the evaporator (kg/s).

For the system shown in Fig 3 to achieve a specified refrigerating capacity of 150kW, say, the required masow rate is

$$m = \frac{Q_E}{q_E} = \frac{150 \text{ kJ/s}}{160 \text{ kJ/kg}}$$
$$= 0.94 \text{ kg/s}.$$

Compressor capacity

The capacity of a compressor must be such that it removes the vapour from the evaporator at the same rate as that at which it is formed. If the capacity is too small the excess vapour will accumulate in the evaporator, causing the pressure and saturation temperature to rise. Conversely, if too large, it will remove the vapour from the evaporator too rapidly, causing the pressure and saturation temperature to fall. To maintain a specified operating condition, a compressor must have a swept volume equal to the volume of vapour formed in the evaporator per unit time (m³/h).

For the system shown in Fig 3 to maintain constant operating conditions and produce the required refrigeration duty would require a compressor with a swept volume:

$$V = m \times v \text{ m}^3$$

where v = specific volume of the vapour at the compressor suction inlet, m³/kg, and v at –25°C and 1.32 bar = 0.18m³/kg.

I.e. V = 0.94 × 0.18 × 3600 = 609 m³/h.

Heat of compression

The energy input from the compressor motor to raise the pressure of the vapour to the required condensing temperature is known as the heat of compression, and is equal to the difference between the enthalpy of the vapour at the compressor outlet and inlet.

Thus for the example shown in Fig 3, heat of compression,

$$W_C = h_D - h_{C^1} = 470 - 398.3 \text{ kJ/kg}$$
$$= 71.7 \text{ kJ/kg}$$

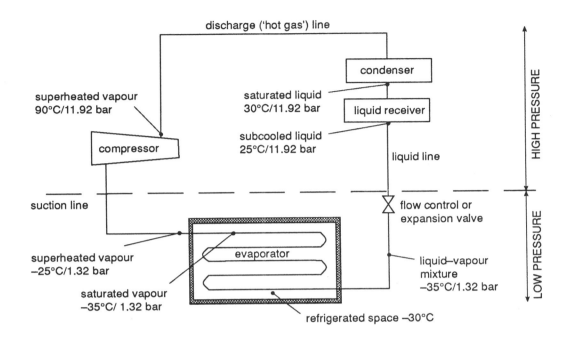

Figure 2   Flow diagram of a simplified vapour compression system using R22 refrigerant.

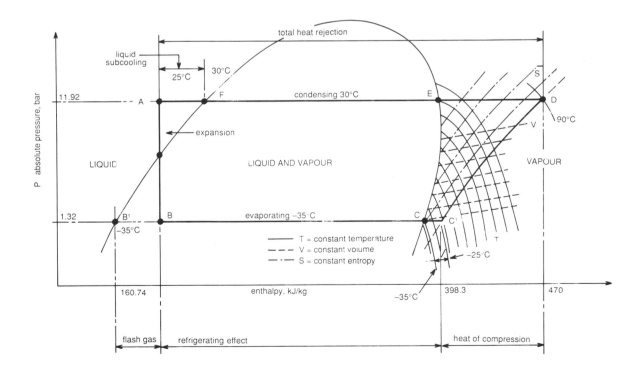

Figure 3   P–H diagram of a simplified vapour compression system.

Condenser duty

The rate of heat transfer from the refrigerant in the condenser to the cooling medium is known as the condenser duty, and is expressed as,

$$Q_C = m \times q_C \text{ kJ/s (kW)}$$

where q_C, the total heat of rejection, is equal to the refrigerating effect plus the heat of compression. Thus for the system shown in Fig 3,

$$Q_C = m(q_E + W_C) = 0.94(470 - 230.3) \text{ kW}$$
$$= 225.3 \text{ kW}$$

Coefficient of performance

The ratio of refrigerating effect to the heat of compression is known as the coefficient of performance (*CoP*).

Thus for the system shown in Fig 3,

$$CoP = \frac{h_C - h_A}{h_D - h_{C^1}} = \frac{168.0}{71.7} = 2.34.$$

REFRIGERANTS

Primary refrigerants

Primary refrigerants are the working fluids used in vapour compression systems. It is desirable for a primary refrigerant to:

a) be non-flammable, non-explosive, and non-toxic, and it should not contaminate foods or damage the environment in the event of a leak.

b) be non-corrosive, and it should not react unfavourably with lubricants, moisture, and materials used in plant construction.

c) have moderate working pressures. The condensing pressure should be as low as possible in order to keep down the mechanical strength required in the compressor and high pressure side of the system. The evaporating pressure should be as high as possible because pressures below atmospheric result in air and moisture being drawn into the system in the event of a leak.

d) have a high co-efficient of performance (CoP) value, i.e. low compressor per input power unit of refrigerating capacity.

e) have a moderate temperature after compression. A low discharge temperature reduces the risk of oil decomposition and overheating of the compressor.

f) be low in cost and readily available.

Marine refrigerants

The refrigerants currently used in marine refrigeration plants, and some of their properties, are listed in Table 2.

The uses of the refrigerants in ships are as follows:

R11 is used in marine air conditioning, especially for cruise ships, and for cleaning out marine refrigeration machinery.

R12 is used for marine air conditioning and food stores in ships, and has universal use in refrigerated containers.

R22 is used in marine air conditioning and food stores in newer ships, and in most central cargo refrigeration plant, fishing boat refrigerated storage and freezing plant, and liquid gas tanker re-liquefaction plant.

R502 has very occasional use for low temperature refrigeration.

Table 2   Properties of marine refrigerants.

	Ammonia (R717)	R11	R12	R22	R502
Chemical formula	NH_3	CCl_3F	CCl_2F_2	$CHClF$	$CHClF_2$ CF_3CClF_2
Evaporating temperature at atmospheric pressure (°C)	33.3	23.8	−29.8	−40.8	−45.6
Absolute evaporator pressure at −15°C (Bar)	2.3	0.2	1.8	3.0	3.5
Absolute condensing pressure at 30°C (Bar)	11.6	0.9	7.4	12.0	13.0
Latent heat at −15°C (kJ/kg)	1314	194	159	217	156
Coefficient of performance at −15°C evaporator, 30°C condensing	4.77	5.03	4.71	4.67	4.37

Notes:
1. Refrigerants, because of their complex chemical formulae, are identified by an international numerical code, which is prefixed by 'R'.
2. R11, R12 and R502 are fully halogenated chlorofluorocarbons (CFC) refrigerants, and R22 is a hydrofluorocarbon (HCFC) refrigerant. They are also known by their various trade names, 'Freon', 'Arcton', etc.

Ammonia (R717) is used for large freezing and low temperature storage installations on board fish factory vessels, and has very occasional use in central cargo refrigeration plant.

Chemical properties

The hazards associated with primary refrigerants, and the necessary safety precautions, are described in *Safety*, page 283.

CFC and HCFC refrigerants
Rll, Rl2, R22 and R502 do not react with steel, copper, aluminium and brass, but attack lead, tin, zinc and magnesium and their alloys. They also attack natural rubber, some elastomers and polytetrafluoroethane (PTFE), so it is important to ensure that the correct materials are used for gaskets, seals, jointing and packing.

Ammonia
Ammonia reacts with copper, zinc and their alloys, so steel only should be used in ammonia plants. It also attacks natural rubber and some elastomers, so it is important to ensure that the correct materials are used for gaskets, seals, jointing and packing. Ammonia gas is extremely toxic, with a long term threshold limit of 35 parts per million (ppm), and may be lethal at concentrations of 2500ppm and above. It has a pungent odour, detectable at concentrations less than 10ppm, which provides a warning against remaining in harmful concentrations. Ammonia is flammable in air at concentrations of 16% to 27%, and may form an explosive mixture.

Secondary refrigerants

A secondary refrigerant is one which is used as a heat transfer medium, with a change of temperature but no change of state. The secondary refrigerants used in marine plants today are brine and trichloroethylene.

Brine
Brine is a mixture of calcium chloride ($CaCl_2$) and water, and has a specific gravity associated to temperature shown in Table 3.

In refrigerated brine systems, severe corrosion can occur causing valves to jam open or shut, and pipe failure leading to loss of brine. To prevent corrosion the brine should be maintained slightly alkaline (pH 8.5 to 9.5) by the addition of an inhibitor, e.g. sodium chromate or dichromate.

One such inhibitor is 'Nalfleet brine treatment liquid', a blend of chromate inhibitors, together with

Table 3   Properties of calcium chloride brine ($CaCl_2$).

Specific gravity at 15°C	1.24	1.25	1.26	1.265	1.275	1.28
Percentage of CaCl2	25.77	26.59	27.66	28.0	29.0	29.35
Operating temperature °C	−21	−23	−26	−29	−32	−34
Freezing temperature°C	−30	−32	−35	−37	−41	−43

Note:
Specific gravity is measured using a hydrometer marked directly in specific gravity or marked in the Twadell or Beaume scales.

an alkaline buffering agent which generally eliminates the need to supplement the treatment with additions of caustic.

Ideally the brine pH should be maintained in the range 8.5–9.5 and the concentration of sodium chromate is based on the principle that the yellow colour of the chromate ion is a measure of its concentration. The colour is measured using a Lovibond comparator and chromate disc 4/35, in accordance with chemical manufacturer's test procedure.

Brine is normally used for temperatures down to −34°C, below which it is extremely viscous resulting in unacceptable pumping losses.

Brine is bitter to taste and will contaminate foodstuffs. Calcium chloride flakes readily absorb moisture to form a corrosive substance, so must be stored in sealed containers in a dry place.

As a safety precaution, eye protection and gloves should be worn when handling caustic soda or hydrochloric acid and great care must be exercised when mixing calcium chloride, as the chemical reaction generates a considerable amount of heat. Do not use small plastic containers to mix brine.

Tricholoroethylene
Trichloroethylene is used for temperatures down to −73°C. The gas, which is both toxic and heavier than air, has a maximum permissible concentration in air of 200 ppm. Trichloroethylene acts as a solvent to most synthetic rubbers and jointing materials. It is non-flammable and non-toxic. The liquid is both heavier than, and immiscible with, water, so any water in the system will freeze at temperatures below 0°C.

Refrigerants and the environment

Scientific evidence shows that the release of CFC refrigerants into the atmosphere is harmful to the environment. CFCs released into the atmosphere are broken down by photolysis to release chlorine atoms which catalytically destroy ozone, the stratospheric

Table 4   ODP and GWP values of marine refrigerants.

Refrigerant	ODP	GWP
R11 (CFC)	1.0	1.0
R12 (CFC)	0.98	3.05
R502 (part CFC)	0.23	5.1
R22 (HCFC)	0.05	0.365
Ammonia	0.00	0.00

gas which acts as a filter of ultra violet light from the sun. Scientists predict that increased UV light on earth as a result of ozone depletion will, amongst other possible consequences, cause skin cancer, interfere with immune systems, and harm aquatic systems and crops.

Furthermore, CFCs, along with other 'greenhouse gases', inhibit the release of heat radiated from the earth, thereby contributing to global warming. Scientists predict that if the average global temperatures continue to increase, the mean sea levels will rise, with catastrophic consequences in certain areas of the world.

To protect the global environment, an international agreement, the Montreal Protocol, signed in 1987, controls the use and production of CFC refrigerants and other ozone depleting substances throughout most of the world. It currently mandates that the production of the CFC refrigerants R11, R12 and R502, is to be phased out by 1997.

CFCs are characterised under the Montreal Protocol according to the extent to which they damage the ozone layer. The most damaging CFCs are given an 'ozone depletion potential' (ODP) of 1, and all other CFCs are then assigned an ODP between 0 and 1, according to their destructive potential relative to the most damaging CFCs. Likewise, CFCs are assigned a 'global warming potential' (GWP) compared to baseline R11. The ODP and GWP values of the refrigerants used in marine refrigerating plants are listed in Table 4.

Alternative refrigerants

Despite the considerable efforts being made to find suitable alternatives for R12 and R502, the choice is currently limited to R22, ammonia (R717) and R134a. R22 will continue to be the first choice for all new marine installations and is currently seen as a possible alternative for R12 in new refrigerated container systems. The long-term use of R22 is being questioned by environmentalists who claim that its contribution to the ozone depletion problem may be increasing.

Ammonia (R717) is receiving serious consideration as an alternative to CFC and HCFC refrigerants.

It has an ODP and GWP of 0, and can be used in certain marine installations provided that the required safety precautions are taken. As an added safety precaution, it has been recommended that ammonia be used only in indirect systems with secondary refrigerants.

R134a has been developed as an alternative for R12. Containing no chlorine, it has an ODP of 0, and a GWP one tenth that of R12. It suffers a drawback in being unsuitable for use with mineral oils, and is expensive. Synthetic oils have been developed but they too are expensive.

At present R134a is considered to be an acceptable refrigerant for small systems (below 5hp), operating at high evaporating temperatures and low condensing temperatures.

Reduction of CFC and HCFC emissions

CFCs and HCFCs only damage the environment if they are released into the atmosphere. It is therefore important that refrigerating systems are operated and maintained in accordance with the manufacturers' instructions, particular attention being paid to the reduction of leaks, and the elimination of deliberate emissions.

Reduction of leaks

A large percentage of the annual production of CFCs and HCFCs is used to replace losses from existing systems. The reduction of refrigerant leaks is therefore crucial to the prevention of further environmental damage, and will also result in improved plant reliability, and lower operating costs.

Systems should be routinely leak tested, with special attention being paid to pipe joints, shaft seals, valve glands, etc. The operation of the plant should also be monitored by keeping routine logs of pressures, temperatures, refrigerant charge etc., enabling any signs of refrigerant loss to be quickly detected. See *Leak detection*, page 289.

Elimination of deliberate emissions

High pressure refrigerant gases should not be used for cleaning the finned surfaces of air cooled condensers or air coolers, and R11 should not be used as a cleaning agent for flushing out systems after a hermetic compressor motor burn out. Other methods, more effective and less damaging to the environment, are available.

In carrying out repairs, the refrigerant charge should be pumped into the system receiver, or other suitable container, and not discharged to the atmosphere. Contaminated refrigerant should be stored in a container for recycling or safe disposal.

Recovery and recycling

Recovery and recycling of CFC and HCFC refrigerants has a potentially important role to play in reducing the overall use of these substances, and ensuring a source of supply for existing systems. Refrigerant manufacturers and other service companies now provide a recovery and recycling service, restoring contaminated refrigerants, wherever possible, to their original quality and specification.

Reclaim units are also available for use by maintenance personnel. These units require correct usage and proper maintenance to ensure the complete removal of the contaminants. The recycled refrigerant must be free of all contaminants before it can safely be re-used.

CONTAMINANTS

Moisture

The various refrigerants have different water solubility characteristics. For example, ammonia (R717) can hold large quantities of water in solution, whereas the CFC and HCFC refrigerants have much lower solubility limits, which decrease as their temperatures are lowered.

If the moisture present in a refrigerating system exceeds the amount that the refrigerant can hold in solution it will exist as free water. At temperatures of 0°C or lower, the free water will freeze into ice in the refrigerant control or evaporator, restricting the flow of refrigerant. To avoid freeze-ups, the moisture content in low temperature CFC and HCFC refrigerant systems must be maintained at a very low level.

A further effect of moisture in a system is to form corrosive compounds which may cause the following.

1. Pitting and other damage to valves, seals, bearing journals and other polished surfaces.

2. 'Copper plating' and staining of valve seats etc.

3. Premature fatigue failure of compressor valve springs and reed plates.

4. Deterioration of the lubricating oil, and the formation of metallic and other sludges which tend to clog valves and oil passages, etc.

5. A breakdown in the electrical motor winding insulation of hermetic compressors.

To prevent moisture related problems:

a) the system should be gas tight and dried thoroughly by evacuating it, before being charged with refrigerant;

b) drier units should be fitted in the liquid line, before the refrigerant control, in all refrigerant systems with the exception of ammonia;

c) the system should be inspected regularly for leaks and maintained gas tight to prevent the ingress of moisture laden air, or water from a water-cooled condenser, oil cooler, etc.;

d) when adding oil to the compressor, only clean oil from an airtight container should be used.

Oil

In refrigerating systems some oil is always carried over from the compressor into the condenser by the refrigerant gas, from where it is carried by the liquid into the evaporator.

The presence of oil in the circulating refrigerant reduces the heat transfer capacity of the various heat exchangers, the problem being greatest in the evaporator, since oil becomes more viscous and tends to congeal at low temperature.

To prevent oil related problems, the operation of the oil separator and oil rectifier (if fitted) should be checked regularly to ensure oil is being returned to the compressor lubrication system. The amount of oil added to the lubrication system should also be strictly monitored; an excessive amount indicates that oil is being trapped in the evaporator or suction line.

Ammonia (R717) is not oil miscible, so in ammonia systems the oil carried over by the compressor separates out and, as it is heavier than the liquid refrigerant, accumulates at the bottom of the condenser and evaporator. These vessels are usually fitted with drain points and should be kept drained of oil.

Air and non condensable gases

The presence of air and other non-condensable gases is detrimental to the efficient operation of a refrigerating plant, as these gases collect in the condenser, and so increase the condensing pressure. Abnormally high condensing pressures cause overheating of the compressor, excessive discharge temperatures, losses in compressor capacity and efficiency, excessive power consumption and possible overloading of the drive motor.

If air and other non-condensable gases are present, the saturation temperature, corresponding to the condenser pressure, will be considerably higher than the temperature of the liquid refrigerant. To prevent these problems, the system should be inspected regularly and, if found to contain air, must be purged and the leak found and repaired. In some plants, automatic purge units are fitted which operate continuously. These units should be carefully monitored, as their operation is a prime indication of the air leakage into the system.

Solid particles

The presence of solid particles in refrigerating systems can cause problems by blocking the control valves and damaging the compressor's bearings and other rubbing surfaces. To avoid these problems it is important to take stringent precautions when carrying out repairs, or during the installation of a new plant. The open ends of pipes, tubes and valves should be plugged to prevent particles of dust, metal filings, solder and weld spatter entering the system.

As an added precaution, it is good practice to fit a cloth filter in the compressor's suction strainer. The filter should be inspected after a few hours operation and replaced and this process repeated until no further particles are trapped. The cloth filter must not be left in the system as it will restrict the refrigerant flow.

EQUIPMENT

Compressor plant

Three types of compressors are used in marine refrigeration and air conditioning plants; reciprocating, rotary and centrifugal. The compressors can be further categorised, according to their construction, as open, hermetic or semi-hermetic. In an open-type compressor one end of the crankshaft extends through the crankcase house for connection, via a coupling or pulley, to an external drive motor. In the case of hermetic compressors, the compressor and its electrical motor are entirely housed in a gas-tight casing. The advantage of this design, in comparison with the open-type, is that the shaft seal, a potential source of refrigerant leakage, is eliminated. Semi-hermetic units provide access to the compressor and motor components for maintenance and repairs.

Reciprocating compressors

Most refrigerating compressors, from the smallest to the largest units, are of the reciprocating type. A typical multi-cylinder compressor, with the cylinders arranged in W formation, is shown in Fig 4.

Most manufacturers use an iron casting for the crankcase and cylinder housing, although one manufacturer employs an all-welded construction. The pistons may be aluminium or cast iron, and the crankshaft of steel or cast iron. The suction and discharge valves may be of the spring-loaded ring

1 stationary sleeve	13 delivery valve cage	24 oil filter
2 spring	14 delivery valve	25 oil filter cover
3 connecting rod	assembly	26 plug
4 gudgeon pin	15 cylinder liner	27 oil strainer
5 piston	16 cylinder cover	28 oil heater boss plug
6 suction inlet	17 delivery manifold	29 connections for oil
7 suction strainer	18 delivery outlet	differential pressure
8 suction valve	19 oil feed to	switch
9 unloading gear pin	unloading gear	30 safety disc cover
10 moving sleeve	20 crankshaft	31 oil level sight glass
11 suction valve	21 oil pressure relief	32 crankcase
guard	valve	33 suction stop valve
12 spring disc	22 oil pump	34 suction strainer
assembly	23 manual capacity	cover
	reduction control	

Figure 4 Reciprocating compressor: a) section; b) end view.

plate type, or reed valves (end clamped or free floating type) depending on compressor size. Most valve assemblies have spring-loaded safety heads to prevent damage in the event of slugs of incompressible liquid refrigerant, or oil, entering the cylinders.

Ammonia (R717) and R22 compressors are sometimes fitted with water cooled jackets around the upper parts of the cylinders to prevent excessively high discharge temperatures. The use of water-jackets also improves the efficiency of the compressor.

Open type compressors are fitted with shaft seals which normally consist of a spring loaded, self-lubricated hard carbon ring, bearing onto a steel collar, the seal to the crankshaft or crankcase housing being provided by synthetic rubber gaskets. Shaft seals are a common cause of leakage, and should be regularly inspected and leak tested. If fitted correctly and kept lubricated with uncontaminated oil, a shaft seal will give trouble free service.

Large compressors are generally provided with an unloading system which enables the compressor to start easily with no vapour pressure load in the cylinder, permitting the use of electric motors with low starting torques. Unloading is effected by holding the suction valves open, or by opening a bypass valve between the discharge and suction sides during starting. The unloading mechanism may be actuated hydraulically, mechanically or by solenoid valve.

The unloader system may also be used for capacity control by successively cutting in or out cylinders or cylinder groups. This may be controlled manually or automatically. Other methods of capacity control include varying the compressor speed, and 'hot gas bypass', which involved passing a proportion of the discharge gas from the compressor directly to the evaporator, bypassing the condenser.

Compressors are sometimes fitted with crankcase heaters as a safeguard against oil foaming. The heater keeps the oil warm during standstill periods, thus preventing refrigerant vapour migrating from the evaporator and condensing in the crankcase.

If liquid refrigerant is allowed to accumulate in the crankcase, it will vaporise at start-up and cause foaming of the oil, which results in an increased amount of oil being pumped out of the compressor, and loss of oil pressure. In extreme cases, oil foaming may also result in a total loss of the oil from the crankcase, and in slugs of incompressible liquid refrigerant and oil entering the cylinders, causing severe damage to the pistons, valves, connecting rods and crankshaft. Liquid refrigerant may also be carried over from the evaporator into the crankcase through leaking or wrongly set refrigerant controls. Such controls should be adjusted or replaced.

Two stage reciprocating compressors and intercoolers

As a rule, two stage or compound compressors are used in preference to single stage compressors in plants where the difference between the condensing and evaporating temperatures is of the order of 50K to 60K.

Two stage compression combined with intermediate cooling has the following advantages.

a) Lower cylinder pressures, hence lower bearing loads and wear;

b) lower discharge gas temperatures, preventing oil decomposition and valve damage;

c) increased volumetric efficiency.

Two-stage compressors may comprise separate low pressure (LP) and high pressure (HP) single-stage compressors, connected in series, or single compressors with LP and HP cylinders in one housing.

The function of an intercooler is to cool the gas from the LP stage before it enters the HP stage, resulting in lower discharge temperatures, and to subcool the liquid from the condenser before it enters the expansion control. The combined effect is to increase the refrigerating capacity and the coefficient of performance (CoP) of the compressor.

The types of intercooler systems found in practice are shown in Fig 5. Note, the injection cooling system is used only to cool the gas between the LP and HP stages.

Screw compressors

Two types of screw compressor are used in marine plants; double screw compressors and mono screw compressors. A double screw compressor consists of two rotors with matched helical grooves; a male rotor with four lobes which mesh with the corresponding six flutes on a female rotor (Fig 6). In modern designs the motor drive can be directly connected to the male or female rotor, the driving force being transmitted to the mating rotor by the thin layer of oil sealing the clearance space between the two rotors. The male and female rotors trap and compress the gas as they mesh and turn together. Suction gas is drawn into the compressor as the interlobe spaces of the rotors pass the inlet port. As they continue to rotate, a lobe of the male rotor progressively fills up the space which is available for gas between the female lobes, and the gas is forced forwards axially and compressed. The lobes continue to intermesh until the opposite end of the rotor passes the outlet port, and the compressed gas is discharged.

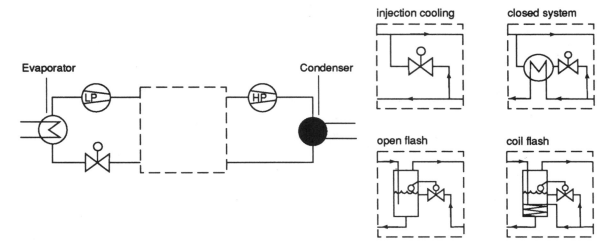

Figure 5   Intercooler systems.

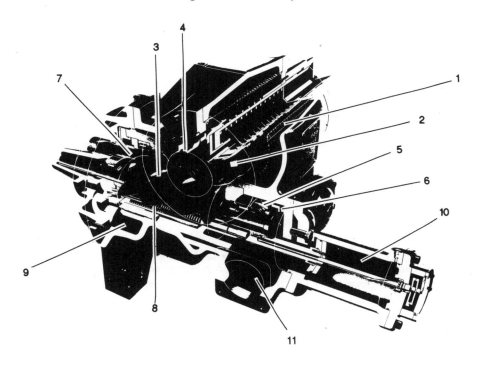

1	suction inlet filter	
2	automatic built-in suction throttle valve	
3	male rotor, 4 lobes	

4	female rotor, 6 flutes
5	thrust bearing
6	balance pistons
7	drive shaft seal
8	capacity regulating slide

9	capacity control, gas return port
10	capacity cylinder
11	discharge outlet

Figure 6   Screw compressor section.

A mono screw compressor consists of a single female rotor with six flutes. Two identical star shaped wheels, each with eleven teeth, mesh with the rotor and are symmetrically spaced around it. The driving motor is connected to the rotor. The principle of operation is similar to that of double screw compressors, the star wheels providing the same function as the male rotor, trapping and compressing the gas as they mesh and turn with the rotating female rotor.

To obtain efficient compression and pumping, oil is injected into the compressor to lubricate and seal the rotor mesh and seal the clearances between the rotors and casing walls. The oil also acts as a coolant. It removes some of the heat of compression from the compressed gas ensuring moderate discharge temperatures. The cooling effect reduces the thermal stress in the rotors and casing. The level of noise emitted by the compressor is also reduced by the dampening effect of the injected oil.

In the majority of screw compressors, capacity control is effected by means of a regulating slide valve mounted underneath the rotors, connecting via a bypass port with the suction inlet. When open, the valve allows some of the gas in the interlobe spaces of the rotors to return to the suction inlet. The regulating slide movement is controlled by a hydraulic piston, giving continuous regulation from 100% down to about 10% of full output.

In some designs lift valves are used, giving capacity regulation in five distinct stages; 100%, 75%, 50%, 25% and 0% of full output.

Economiser systems

The use of economisers with screw compressors provides an increase of refrigerating capacity by subcooling the refrigerant from the condenser. The subcooling takes place in a heat exchanger or open flash vessel (Fig 7).

The flash gas is led to an economiser connection on the compressor, positioned close to, but separate from, the suction gas inlet, enabling an additional charge of gas to be handled by the compressor. This is, in effect, a form of supercharging. The corresponding increase in power consumption is proportionally less than the increase of refrigerating capacity, the effect of which is to increase the coefficient of performance (CoP) of the compressor.

Centrifugal compressors

Centrifugal compressors operate on the same principle as centrifugal fans and pumps. They are used in marine air conditioning installations requiring large refrigerating capacities. A typical two-stage compressor, with R11 as the refrigerant, has a capacity of about 1400 kW.

Capacity control may be achieved by means of adjustable inlet vanes, speed variation, 'hot gas bypass', or by the use of a damper valve in the suction line.

Hermetic compressors

In this type of unit, the compressor and its electric drive motor are entirely housed in a gas-tight casing. The advantage of this design, in comparison with open-type compressors, is that the shaft seal, a potential source of refrigerant leakage, is eliminated.

Sealed units are housed in welded steel shells, and their use is limited to domestic and small commercial systems.

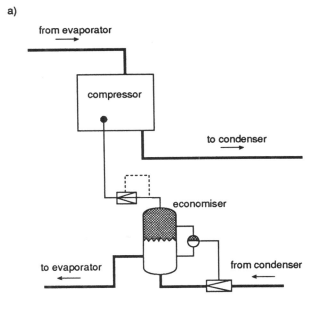

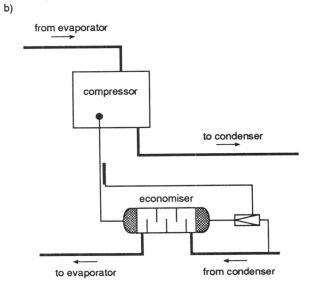

Figure 7 Economiser systems for screw compressors: a) open flash vessel; b) heat exchanger.

Semi-hermetic compressors have bolted casings, which provide access to the compressor for maintenance and repairs. This type of compressor is used in refrigerated containers and ships' provision stores.

An attendant danger with hermetic or semi-hermetic compressors is that the electric motor may develop a fault and burn out, so contaminating the refrigerant system. To guard against this, current or temperature overload protectors are installed in the rotor windings.

When a burn-out occurs, the system should be thoroughly purged to remove contaminated refrigerant and oil, and the compressor, liquid line filter drier and expansion valve should be renewed. A special burn-out filter drier should also be fitted in the suction line, immediately before the compressor. The system should then be commissioned, run for 6–8 hours, and the filter driers checked and renewed until no traces of contaminants are found. After some 24 hours operation an oil sample should be tested for acidity and, if clear (less than 0.5 acid number), the cleaning is acceptable. The burn-out filter drier should then be removed, and the liquid line filter drier renewed.

High discharge pressure is one of the most frequent reasons for motor burn-out. This pressure creates very high discharge temperatures which cause oil decomposition and the formation of corrosive acids which break down the motor winding insulation. It is important, therefore, to monitor the discharge pressure and temperature and to maintain them within safe limits. A high discharge pressure may be due to air in the system, a dirty condenser, or too high a suction temperature.

Oil systems

The primary function of oil in a refrigeration compressor is to lubricate the bearings and other rubbing surfaces. It is also required to:

a) seal the clearance spaces between the discharge and suction sides of the compressor;

b) act as a coolant, removing the friction heat from the rubbing surfaces and, in the case of screw compressors, part of the heat of compression from the discharge gas;

c) actuate capacity control mechanisms, and in the case of screw compressors, load the balance pistons;

d) dampen the noise generated by the compressor.

The oil for all these purposes is supplied from the crankcase or separate reservoir, and circulated under pressure by a pump or, in the case of some screw compressors, by the pressure difference existing across the compressor. Oil strainers and filters are fitted to prevent solid particles damaging the compressor and oil pump, and sludge blocking the system.

As a protection against too low an oil pressure, a differential pressure switch is fitted. If the oil pressure drops, the unit stops the compressor after a certain time has elapsed.

Small reciprocating compressors below 7.5 kW are generally splash lubricated. In the splash method of lubrication, oil in the crankcase is thrown by the crankthrow or eccentric up onto the cylinder walls, bearings and other rubbing surfaces.

Oil separators

Some oil is always carried over with the compressed gas and must be removed. This is:

a) to prevent it entering and fouling the internal surfaces of the evaporator and other heat exchangers; and

b) to ensure its return to the crankcase or reservoir, preventing failure through the shortage of oil.

Oil separators are placed in the line between the compressor and condenser, and consist of a vessel fitted with internal baffles and screens. The separation of oil is mechanical, the slowing down and change of direction of the gas/oil stream throwing out the oil. The oil separated from the gas collects in the bottom of the separator and is returned to the crankcase or receiver through an automatic regulating valve.

Heating elements are normally fitted as a safeguard against liquid refrigerant accumulating in the separator and passing into the compressor during standstill periods. The heater, by keeping the oil in the separator warm, prevents refrigerant vapour migrating from the condenser and condensing in the separator.

Oil coolers

The function of oil coolers is to remove the friction heat absorbed by the oil in lubricating the various rubbing surfaces and, in the case of screw compressors, heat from the compressed gas. Oil coolers may be shell and tube, or plate heat exchangers, water or refrigerant cooled, and are designed to maintain an oil outlet temperature of the order of 50°C.

Refrigeration oils

Lubricating oils for refrigeration compressors are selected for their suitability with the different refrigerant, compressor type and the plant's operating temperatures.

Refrigeration oils should possess the following properties:

1. Good chemical stability. There should be little or no chemical reaction with the refrigerant or materials normally found in the system.

2. Good thermal stability. They should not form hard carbon deposits at hot spots in the compressor (such as valves or discharge ports).

3. Low viscosity. This is the ability of an oil to maintain good lubrication properties at high temperatures and good fluidity at low temperatures, i.e. to provide a good lubricating film at all times.

4. Low wax content. Particularly important in the case of CFC and HCFC plants, operating at low evaporating temperatures, as separation of wax particles from the refrigerant–oil mixture may cause problems by blocking expansion and regulating valves.

5. Low pour point. Ability of the oil to remain in a fluid state at the plant's lowest evaporating temperature. The pour point is particularly interesting in relation to oils used in ammonia (R717) plants, as oils with a low pour point are easier to drain from the plant's low pressure side.

6. Moisture free. Any moisture added with oil may cause corrosion, and in the case of CFC and HCFC refrigerants would form as ice in a choked expansion or regulating valve.

When adding oil to a compressor, or doing an oil change, it is therefore important that only the type specified in the manufacturer's operating manual is used. The oil must be clean and have no moisture content. Oil should always be stored in tightly sealed containers, in a warm place, to ensure it does not absorb moisture from the atmosphere.

It is important that the procedures given in the compressor operating manual for changing and topping-up the oil are strictly followed.

Maintenance
To ensure trouble-free operation, it is important that the initial start-up procedures, the maintenance procedures and intervals between periodic services are all carried out in strict accordance with the manufacturer's instruction manual. As a general rule the following components require periodic examination and maintenance.

1. Reciprocating compressors:
   a) suction and delivery valves;
   b) top and bottom connecting rod bearings or bushes;
   c) pistons, piston rings, cylinders or cylinder liners.

2. Screw compressors:
   a) condition of the rotors.

3. Centrifugal compressors:
   a) condition of shaft labyrinth seals;
   b) condition of impellers.

4. All compressors:
   a) suction strainer;
   b) oil pump, strainer, filter etc., and checking the quality of the oil;
   c) oil cooler;
   d) drive coupling, belts or gear box;
   e) pressure switches and thermostats;
   f) capacity control or unloading mechanism;
   g) condition of bearings;
   h) shaft seals;
   i) oil heater and associated controls.

Condensers

The purpose of a condenser is to extract the total heat flow of the installation, which comprises the heat flow through the insulated surfaces, together with the heat extracted from the produce, and that introduced by fans, pumps and compressor drive motors etc.; a process which changes the high pressure refrigerant gas into a liquid.

Shell and tube condenser
This is the standard type of condenser used in marine plants, with sea water circulating through the tubes, and refrigerant condensing in the shell. A typical condenser is shown in Fig 8.

Marine shell and tube condensers are designed to resist corrosion, erosion or fouling. A typical shell and tube condenser for R22 has aluminium brass tubes threaded to increase cooling surface; these are expanded into copper alloy clad mild steel tube plates. Cast iron, cast bronze or mild steel end covers may be employed, and the water velocity is chosen to resist erosion. Corrosion plugs of iron are often fitted in the end covers to reduce the attack of sea water on the non-ferrous materials. To avoid erosion, the water velocity through the tubes should be kept below 2.5 m/s.

An air purge connection is fitted on top of the shell to facilitate the purging of air and other non-condensable gases. In ammonia plants, oil drain connections are also fitted to the bottom of the shell.

Maintenance
In general the following work should be done at regular intervals.

1. To prevent fouling of the inside of the water tubes with scale or marine growth, which reduces the heat transfer capacity of the condenser, the tubes should be cleaned by 'rodding' through with special brushes. Alternatively, a ready mixed inhibitive scouring acid can be used, with subsequent neutralization. Such agents must be suitable for

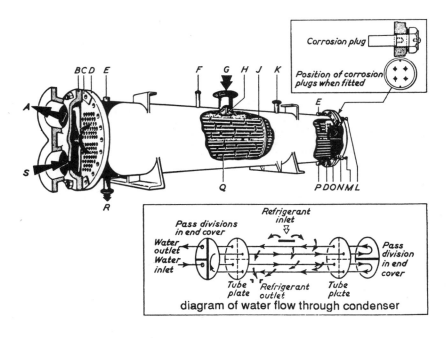

A Water outlet
B End cover (cast iron neoprene coated, or gun metal)
C Joint (neoprene)
D Tube plates (stainless steel clad cast iron or brass or gun metal)
E Air purges

F Branch for safety disc
G Gas inlet
H Gas baffle
J Tube support baffle (stainless steel)
K Vent connexion
L Air cock

M Drain cock
N End cover
O Joint
Q Tubes (aluminium brass or cupro-nickel)
R Liquid outlet
S Water inlet

Figure 8 Shell and tube condenser.

use with the tube materials, and applied in strict accordance with the chemical manufacturer's instructions.

2. The tubes and end cover should be inspected for wasting, caused by erosion and corrosion, and, where fitted, the corrosion plug should be replaced as required.

3. The water leaving the condenser should also be refrigerant leak tested regularly, to check for leaks between the water tubes and refrigerant side.

Air cooled condenser

This type of condenser is fitted in refrigerated containers and is also used in other small marine plants. The condenser consists of a finned tube coil encased in a metal housing with one or more fans to provide air circulation. The tube and fins are generally of copper.

Maintenance

In general, the following work should be done at regular intervals.

1. To prevent the accumulation of dirt between the fins, which reduces the heat transfer capacity of the condenser, the fins should be cleaned regularly by brushing or by blowing clear, using air or a water jet.

2. The tubes and fins should be inspected for damage, corrosion and refrigerant leaks. Damaged fins should be straightened by means of a 'fin comb'.

3. The lubrication, bearing alignment, and running temperature of the fan motors should be checked.

Evaporators

An evaporator is a heat exchanger in which liquid refrigerant is turned into gas, removing heat from the refrigerated space or product in the process.

Brine coolers

In marine plants shell and tube evaporators are normally used for cooling brine, or other secondary refrigerants, and may be operated with either flooded or dry expansion refrigerant flow (Figs 9 a and b). When the evaporator is operated 'flooded', the brine is circulated through the tubes and the refrigerant is contained in the shell. The maintenance of a correct working level of refrigerant in the shell is necessary to prevent either liquid carry over, or excessive superheat. Devices for controlling this level are described later. The behaviour of oil return from this type of evaporator is affected by the duty, e.g. with R22 there is a tendency for oil to collect after prolonged running on light duties. This oil can be retrieved by a brief run at higher duties.

When the evaporator is operated 'dry expansion', the refrigerant is expanded in the tubes and the brine is circulated through the shell. In this type of evaporator, the tubes are finned internally to increase heat transfer. The so-called 'innerfin' evaporator offers a more compact design, simplifies oil return, and permits the use of simpler refrigerant flow controls.

The construction of both evaporator types is similar, with steel shells and tubes of steel or aluminium brass.

Maintenance

As shell and tube evaporators are subject to low pressure, and do not suffer from the corrosive action of sea water as do condensers, they are generally a trouble-free item. Sources of trouble are most likely to be due to external atmospheric corrosion, particularly if parts are insulated, and the vapour seal is damaged permitting the ingress of moisture.

Air cooler batteries

Air cooler batteries comprise finned tube coils encased in a metal housing and at least one fan to circulate air over the coils. The coolers may be operated with either direct expansion or flooded refrigerant flow. In secondary systems, refrigerated brine is pumped through the coolers.

In large coolers the coils are formed by steel tubes and fins, galvanised externally for protection against corrosion. In small coolers the coils are formed by copper tubes and fins.

When operating at temperatures below 0°C, air coolers dehumidify the air causing frost to collect on the surfaces of the coils. This restricts heat transfer and air flow, thus reducing the cooling capacity of the cooler, and must be removed.

The various methods of frost removal are as follows.

Hot gas defrosting

Hot gas defrosting uses the hot gas discharged from the compressor to defrost coolers.

In large marine installations with multiple coolers, the hot gas is fed directly from the compressor discharge line into the outlet of the cooler to be de-

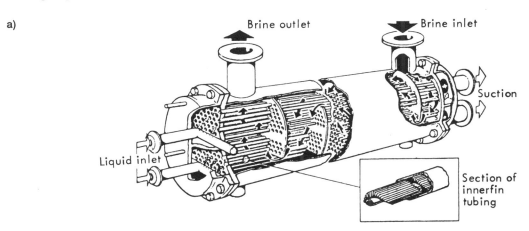

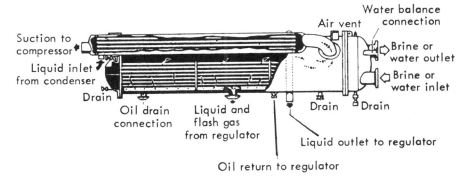

Figure 9 a) Sectional view of innerfin type brine cooler;
b) sectional view of shell and tube type brine cooler with liquid sub-cooling heat exchanger.

frosted. The hot gas is condensed by the defrosting process, and the resulting liquid condensate flows out of the cooler through the inlet header, bypassing the regulating valves to the receiver.

During the defrost cycle, the cooler on defrost is isolated from the main liquid supply line and suction line by automatic control valves.

Hot brine defrosting

In secondary systems, it is usual to circulate hot brine through the coolers. The brine is supplied from a separate hot brine system, comprising a heater (steam or electrically heated) and circulating pump. During the defrost cycle, the cooler on defrost is isolated from the cooling system, by automatic control valves.

Electric defrosting

Electric heating elements, inserted between the tubes, are used to defrost air coolers.

The drain trays and lines fitted under the coolers to collect the defrost water are also heated during the defrost cycle in order to prevent re-freezing of the water.

The defrost cycle may be initiated either manually or by an automatic device. The fans are stopped during the defrost period to prevent the heat of defrost and water being blown into the refrigerated space.

The maintenance procedures for air cooler batteries are the same as for air cooled condensers.

Surge drums or accumulators

In some flooded evaporator systems, the liquid refrigerant is circulated from a refrigerant reservoir called a surge drum to the various coolers by means of pumps or by gravity. The liquid in the coolers boils, and the resultant gas/liquid mixture returns to the surge drum where the excess liquid is separated from the gas. The gas then passes to the compressor by a separate suction connection, and the liquid is recirculated.

The liquid level in the surge drum is maintained constant by a low-side or high-side float control.

Auxiliary equipment

Heat exchangers

The functions of a heat exchanger are:

a) to subcool the liquid refrigerant and increase the efficiency of the plant; and

b) to superheat the suction gas and reduce the risk of slugs of liquid refrigerant entering and damaging the compressor.

Heat exchangers are fitted in the suction line between the evaporator and compressor. The liquid/gas mixture from the evaporator is superheated by the warmer liquid refrigerant from the condenser when passing through the heat exchanger. The heat transfer process subcools the liquid refrigerant, which results in a reduction of flash gas in the liquid line and an increase in refrigerating capacity.

Filter driers

The function of filter driers is to remove moisture from all refrigerant systems, with the exception of those using ammonia (R717), which has a high tolerance for moisture. Foreign particles, sediment, and the products of oil breakdown are also filtered out. The filter driers are fitted in the liquid refrigerant line from the condenser to prevent moisture and other contaminants entering and blocking the expansion valve.

Filter driers contain a desiccant, which is a moisture absorbing substance which will eventually become saturated with moisture and have to be replaced. Two widely used desiccants are silica gel and molecular sieves. Where rechargeable units are fitted, the desiccant can be removed and the drier casing refitted with a fresh charge.

Burn out filter driers are used to cleanse a refrigerant system after a hermetic compressor motor burns out. They contain a charge or core, which absorbs and holds the acids and other contaminants produced by the chemical decomposition of the refrigerant and oil, and the breakdown of the motor winding insulation.

Sight glasses

These are fitted so that the refrigerant flow may be observed. A full glass indicates that the system is fully charged, a stream of bubbles indicates a partially charged system, and rapid frothing of the liquid indicates a shortage of refrigerant.

Moisture indicating sight glasses have a colour indicator which changes colour when the moisture content of the refrigerant exceeds the critical value. The colour indication is reversible, changing back to the original colour when the plant has been dried by replacing or recharging the filter drier.

REFRIGERANT FLOW CONTROLS

Refrigerant flow controls are fitted to ensure that the correct volume of liquid refrigerant flows into the evaporator, and to maintain a pressure differential between the high and low pressure sides of the system. Correct functioning of these controls is essential to the efficient operation of the system, as the effects of a faulty control are cumulative and can soon cause complete failure of the equipment.

Flow controls have small orifices in order to effect the desired pressure reduction. They are prone to choking from any dirt in the system and are always protected by fine filters which should always be cleaned if any blockage is suspected. As the expansion valve is the first point in the refrigerant circuit at which the temperature falls, if the plant is operating at temperatures below 0°C any moisture in the refrigerant will freeze out, and the ice may choke the expansion valve.

A further situation which can cause erratic performance of a flow control, occurs if it is made to perform outside its 'normal' operating range. A flow control has to be sized correctly for a given application to obtain optimum performance. A refrigeration plant has to operate in different climates, so to produce various ranges of cold temperatures a wide variation in refrigerant flow through the valve is called for. To provide this flexibility of operation, some plants are provided with more than one flow control. Sometimes two valves are used in parallel, or a larger valve is brought into use for large flows.

Hand expansion valves

The simplest type of flow control is a hand-operated needle valve. This valve does not react to changes in load conditions, and must therefore be re-set manually in order to prevent either starving or overfeeding of the evaporator. These valves are used mainly as auxiliary flow controls, installed in bypass lines.

Thermostatic expansion valve

The thermostatic expansion valve is designed to provide an ample supply of liquid refrigerant to dry expansion evaporators, ensuring high heat transfer under varying load conditions, without allowing liquid to pass into the suction line and enter the compressor. The operation of a thermostatic expansion valve is based on maintaining a constant degree of superheat at the evaporator outlet.

The construction of a typical thermostatic expansion valve is shown in Fig 10. The thermostatic element, comprising the bulb and capillary tube, is usually charged with the same refrigerant as the

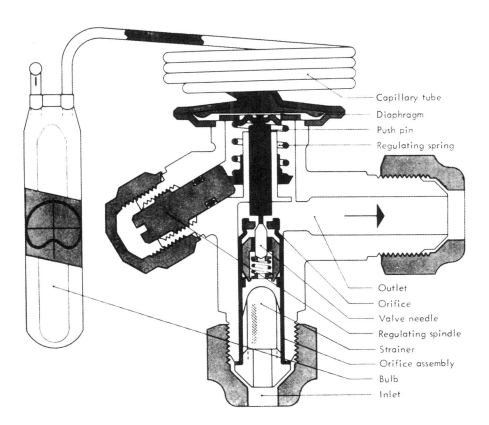

Figure 10 Thermostatic expansion valve section.

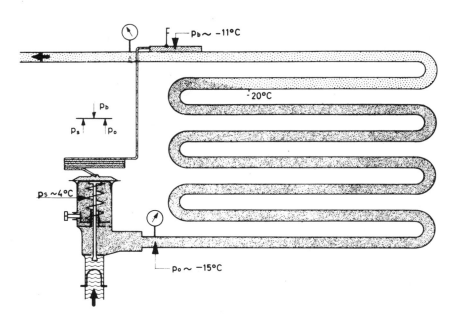

Figure 11 Thermostatic expansion valve arrangement.

system. To ensure the correct operation of the valve, the bulb must be securely clamped to the suction line, in accordance with the manufacturer's instructions.

With reference to Fig 11, the operation of the thermostatic expansion valve is governed by the interaction of three forces:

p_b Bulb pressure on the upper side of the diaphragm, tending to open the valve, where P_b is the saturation pressure of the refrigerant in the bulb, corresponding to the temperature of the gas at the evaporator outlet.

p_o Evaporator pressure on the lower side of the diaphragm, tending to close the valve, where P_o is the saturation pressure of the refrigerant at the evaporator inlet, and Δp is the pressure drop between the evaporator inlet and outlet.

p_s Pressure exerted by the regulating spring, tending to close the valve. The spring tension, set by the regulating spindle, controls the degree of superheat; a typical superheat value is 4°C to 6°C.

At any constant operating condition, these forces are balanced and $p_b = p_o + p_s$.

If the superheat starts to rise, the bulb pressure increases, $p_b > p_o + p_s$, and the valve is moved in the opening direction, admitting more liquid and restoring the constant operating condition. If the superheat falls, $p_b < p_o + p_s$, and the valve is moved to the closing position, reducing the supply of liquid.

In practice, to achieve the desired degree of superheat at the evaporator outlet, dry expansion evaporators require up to 20 per cent of their cooling surfaces to be available to superheat the gas, the precise area varying with demand.

Where thermostatic expansion valves are required to operate with evaporators which are subjected to large pressure drops, additional control is introduced by incorporating a pressure equalising connection. This connection eliminates further increase in the superheat temperature to compensate for the reduction in pressure, and so allows an increase in the effective area of the evaporator.

Maintenance

Once a plant is correctly set up, the superheat setting rarely needs adjustment. If a thermostatic expansion valve appears to be malfunctioning, one should first look for dirt or ice in the valve, and then the plant should be checked for leaks to ensure that the refrigerant charge is correct. Only after carrying out these checks should any adjustments be made, and then only in accordance with the manufacturer's instructions.

Electronic expansion valve system

The system is designed to provide precise, rapid and

remote control of the liquid supply to dry expansion evaporators, in response to the temperature differential between the evaporator outlet and inlet. This provides accurate control which allows maximum utilisation of the evaporator surface (high degree of filling), and a rapid response to changes in evaporator load. It is also unaffected by changes in condensing pressure, which allows the use of lower pressures in cooler climates, and hence reduced compressor power consumption.

The system shown in Fig 12 comprises three main components: expansion valve with electric valve actuator; electronic controller; and two plutonium 1000 ohm temperature sensors. The expansion valve is opened and closed by the actuator, Fig 13, which replaces the thermostatic element of the TEV. The actuator comprises a pressure reservoir, which holds a given amount of liquid, an electric heating element, and a negative temperature coefficient sensor (measuring resistance with negative coefficient). During normal operation the heating element keeps the liquid in the actuator at such a temperature (pressure) that stable equilibrium between the evaporator pressure under the diaphragm, and pressure in the actuator over the diaphragm is maintained.

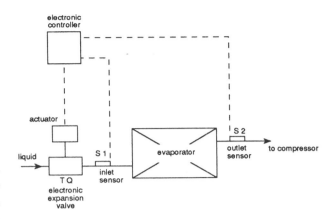

Figure 12   Electronic expansion valve system.

Operation

The measured temperature differential ($S_2 - S_1$) is compared in the controller with the required temperature differential (set on the controller). If the measured value deviates from the set value, power to the heating element is changed to cool or heat the actuator. The pressure in the actuator changes slightly, causing the valve to move in an opening or closing

Figure 13   Expansion valves with electric actuators.

direction, increasing or restricting the liquid supply, to restore the required temperature differential.

The proportional integration (PI) regulation of the controller ensures that the measured value ($S_2 - S_1$) does not deviate from the set value on variations in load, evaporating pressure, sub-cooling, and pressure drop across the expansion valve.

In the event of a malfunction, the system should be checked in accordance with the operating manual.

Evaporator pressure regulators

The function of an evaporator, or 'back' pressure regulator, is to prevent the pressure, and therefore the saturation temperature, of the refrigerant vapour in the evaporator from falling below a required minimum value. The regulator is fitted in the suction line between the evaporator and compressor.

Spring operated regulators which open when the evaporator pressure rises and close when the pressure falls below the set minimum value are used. The regulators are designed so that the pressure in the suction line has no effect on the operation of the valve.

In large installations, electronic temperature regulators are used to provide precise control of the air temperature in refrigerated cargo spaces, or water temperature in a water chiller, by regulating the evaporator pressure and hence the temperature.

The system, shown in Fig 14, consists of:

1. Main evaporating pressure regulating valve;

2. Motorised pilot valve;

3. Electronic controller and temperature sensor.

The main regulating valve is opened and closed by the pilot valve, which regulates the pressure on top of the piston in the main valve by means of a spring loaded diaphragm. The spring force can be changed by the electric motor which is able to move a push-rod up and down via a gear rack. In more modern plants, the motor is replaced by an electric actuator.

Operation

The temperature sensor measures the temperature of the cooled air leaving the evaporator. The registered temperature is continuously compared in the controller, with the pre-set reference temperature. As soon as a differential occurs between the measured and required temperatures, the controller sends electric impulses to the motor, which moves the spindle of the pilot valve up or down.

If, for example, the air temperature rises, the motor will move the spindle up. The spring force will de-

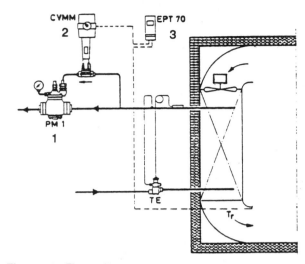

Figure 14   Electronic temperature regulator system.

crease, the pressure on top of the piston of the main valve will increase, and the valve will move open slightly. As a result, the evaporator pressure and temperature will decrease, the capacity will increase and the air temperature will fall again.

In the event of a malfunction, the regulating system should be checked in accordance with the operating manual.

Level control valves

These valves are used in connection with flooded coolers or evaporators to ensure that the liquid level remains constant, the valves being controlled by a float arrangement in the evaporator or condenser.

The simplest control of this sort is a direct acting, ball float valve. In larger plants electronic float switches are generally used.

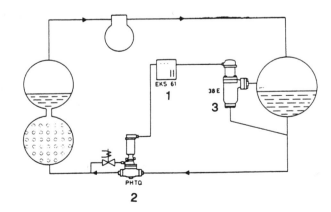

Figure 15   Electronic liquid level system.

A typical electronic liquid level control system is shown in Fig 15. It comprises:

1. An electronic controller;

2. An expansion valve with electric valve actuator;

3. A float switch (Fig 16).

Operation

When the liquid in the receiver moves up or down, the float, A, moves a rod through a magnetic core, B, causing a signal to be transmitted to the controller. This signal is compared with a reference setting on the controller. Depending on the variation in liquid level, the controller sends more or less power to the heating element in the actuator. The pressure in the actuator changes slightly, so that the valve moves in the opening or closing direction.

In the event of a malfunction, the system should be checked in accordance with the operating manual.

Float switches are also used to activate solenoid valves, and as a safeguard against high or low liquid levels by activating visible or audible alarms.

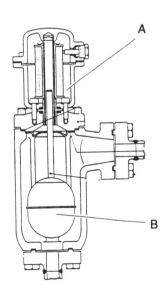

Figure 16 Float switch.

Crankcase pressure regulators

The function of this regulator is to protect the compressor motor against overload when the pressure in the evaporator is above the normal operating pressure for which the motor was selected, e.g. on start up after long standstills, or after defrost periods.

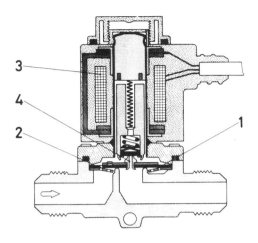

Figure 17 Solenoid valve.

The regulator comprises an adjustable spring-loaded valve, which is fitted in the suction line ahead of the compressor.

Solenoid valves

The solenoid valve is a servo-controlled electromagnetic valve which provides automatic opening and closing of liquid and gas lines.

In Fig 17, when the coil (3) is energised, the pilot orifice (4) is opened, and the diaphragm (1) moves into the open position (vice versa when the coil is de-energised).

A burnt-out coil, a damaged diaphragm, or blockage by dirt, will cause the valve to malfunction.

SAFETY CONTROLS AND DEVICES

Safety cut outs

Most of these controls are electric switches, actuated by bellows movement via amplifying leverage. The bellows move in response to pressure changes transmitted from the sensing point via a connecting tube. Electronic switching devices activated by pressure transducers are also used.

High pressure safety cut-out

This is used to protect against too high a discharge pressure, which will overload the compressor and may damage components. The control is usually set to cut-out and stop the compressor motor at a pressure of about 90% of the maximum working pressure of the system. Some controls restart the compressor automatically on drop in pressure; others have a manual reset mechanism.

Low pressure safety cut-out

This is used to protect against too low a suction pressure, which usually indicates a blockage or loss of refrigerant. The control is normally set to stop the compressor at a pressure corresponding to a saturation temperature 5°C below the lowest evaporating temperature. In some small plants, it is also used as a temperature control, stopping and starting the compressor to maintain the desired pressure and hence temperature.

Oil pressure safety cut-out

This is used to protect against too low oil pressure in forced lubrication systems. It is a differential control, using two bellows. One side responds to the low side pressure, and the other responds to the oil pressure. The oil pressure must always be greater than the low side pressure for the oil to flow. If the oil pressure fails, or falls below a minimum value, the control stops the compressor after a certain time has elapsed.

Thermostats

Thermostats are temperature-controlled electric switches, which can be used for both safety and control functions. When fitted to compressor discharge lines, they are set to stop the compressor if the discharge temperature is too high. Thermostats are also used to control the temperature in a refrigerated space by cycling the compressor 'on and off', or by 'opening and closing' a solenoid valve in the liquid line.

Three types of element are used to sense and relay temperature changes to the electrical contacts.

1. A fluid-filled bulb connected through a capillary to a bellows.

2. A thermistor.

3. A bi-metal element

The above controls should be set in accordance with the plant's instruction manual, and should be checked regularly for refrigerant leaks from the bellows and connecting tubes. The electrical contacts should be examined for signs of wear and arcing.

Pressure relief devices

Refrigeration systems are designed to withstand a maximum working pressure (MWP) which, if exceeded as a result of fire, extreme temperature conditions, or faulty electrical controls, may cause some part of the system to explode. To prevent this, compressors and pressure vessels are fitted with a pressure relief device.

There are three types of relief device.

1. Spring-load relief valves, which are set to open at the MWP and close when the pressure drops to a safe level.
   Relief valves must not be interfered with while in service, and must be locked or sealed to prevent unauthorised adjustment.

2. Bursting discs, which comprise thin metal diaphragms designed to burst at a pressure equal to the MWP.

3. Fusible plugs, which contain a metal alloy which will melt when the temperature in the system corresponds to the MWP.

Generally, the discharge from a relief device is vented direct to the atmosphere. In some plants, however, devices protecting components on the high pressure side are arranged to discharge to the low pressure side of the system.

REFRIGERATION SYSTEMS

The principal types of refrigerating plant commonly used in marine installations are those which cool directly, i.e. by 'direct expansion' (DX), and those which employ a secondary refrigerant (brine).

DX systems are considered to be cheaper to install and run than brine systems, and in recent years they have gained popularity as their reliability and accuracy have improved. Consequently, some very large reefer vessels of over 760,000 ft^3 capacity built in 1990, have been fitted with direct expansion systems using R22 as a refrigerant. The weight of refrigerant in the DX system is however, several times greater than in a brine system, which is, on the other hand, more bulky.

The principle of operation of the DX system is illustrated in Fig 18.

Direct expansion system

The refrigerant vapour from the air coolers is compressed to a higher pressure in order to raise the boiling point of the refrigerant to such an extent that it will liquefy again in the condenser. The vapour passes through the oil separator, where oil is separated and returned to the compressor crankcase and the vapour flows to the condenser. Sea water flows inside the tubes of the shell and tube condenser, and removes the heat from the hot vapour, which liquefies. The liquid drains to the receiver, passes through

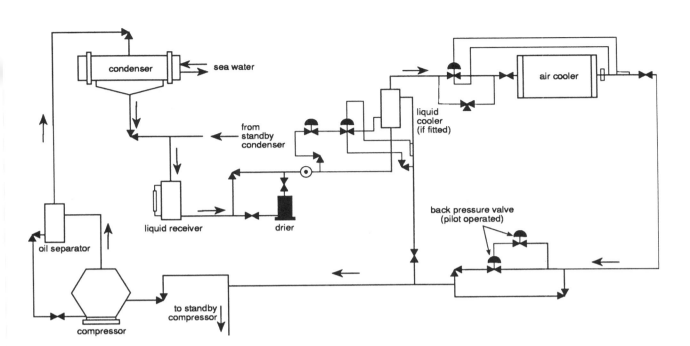

Figure 18   Principle of operation of DX system.

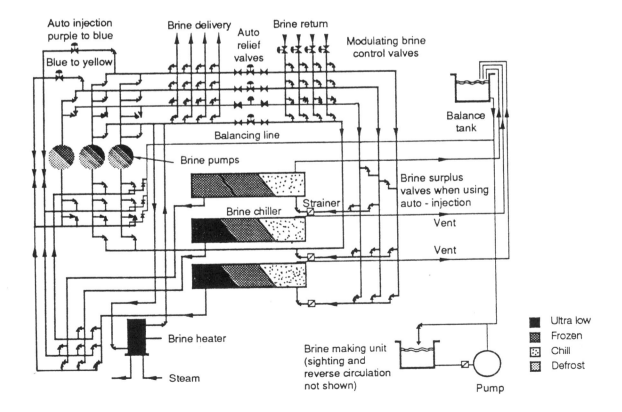

Figure 19   Indirect (brine) system.

the filter drier, is subcooled in the liquid cooler, and expanded in the thermostatic expansion valve into a low pressure liquid and vapour before entering the air coolers.

The air circulated in the cargo chamber passes through the air cooler. The liquid refrigerant vaporises, reducing the temperature of the air outlet by 3–5°C, depending on the type of cooler and the air velocity across it, the temperature of the chamber and the refrigerant entering the cooler. The air delivery temperature is controlled by a temperature sensor which regulates the refrigerant supply to the cooler by closing or opening the solenoid valve in the liquid line, depending on the demand. More precise control, to within ±0.2% of the preset delivery temperature value, can be achieved using a computer connected to the electronic expansion valves, and temperature probes fitted in the refrigeration suction line at the air delivery, as illustrated in Fig 12.

Indirect (brine) system

The system in Fig 19 incorporates three brine evaporators (or chillers), three circulating pumps and one brine mixing pump, the steam heater, the brine making and balance tanks, the brine delivery and return manifolds with valves, called the brine regulating stations, and the brine injection valves.

The system is entirely filled with brine and solely connected to the atmosphere through the balance tank placed at the highest point of the system. Such a system is known as a closed system.

The pumps circulate the brine from the evaporators through the delivery regulating station to the air cooler and back via the suction station to the evaporator. The brine temperature can also be regulated automatically by the use of brine injection which has an accuracy of ±0.1°C. The evaporators, however, can produce brine at different temperatures. Defrosting is achieved by circulating the warm brine from the brine heater to the air coolers and back to the heater. Steam is usually preferred as a heating media, but electrical heaters are sometimes used.

The brine regulating stations and pumps are usually located in a separate insulated room above the engine room which may also accommodate the brine evaporators. The brine expansion tank is equipped with a level switch, which allows for a low level alarm.

Controlled atmosphere

Controlled atmosphere is an inert gas system used to extend the storage life of seasonal perishable products and has been used for many fruits and vegetables; primarily apples and pears in the past, and now mainly for bananas.

To successfully store fruit for long periods, the natural ripening of the produce has to be delayed without affecting the eating quality. This is achieved by reducing the temperature of the fruit to the lowest level possible without causing damage through freezing or low temperature breakdown. To further delay ripening, the oxygen supply in the space is reduced to levels below that of the natural atmosphere. This level is below the level required to support human life.

The precise levels of temperature, oxygen and carbon dioxide required to maximize storage life and to minimize storage disorders are extremely variable, depending on type of produce, growing conditions and maturity. Optimum storage conditions can vary from farm to farm and from season to season.

On reefer vessels, oxygen (O_2) and carbon dioxide (CO_2) levels and relative humidity (RH) in controlled atmosphere zones (cargo chambers) can be independently controlled within close tolerances, irrespective of type, temperature and volume of cargo carried and the length of the voyage. A typical modern controlled atmosphere marine system would be expected to have flexibility to control gas levels within the following ranges:

$$O_2: \quad < 1\text{–}8\%$$
$$CO_2: \quad 0\text{–}15\%$$
$$RH: \quad 40\text{–}90\%$$

The required oxygen and carbon dioxide levels can be achieved in a number of different ways.

1. The oxygen level can be decreased by:
   a) injecting pure nitrogen as a gas or liquid from bottles or storage tanks;
   b) burning propane in an open flame burner, or a burner with a catalyst;
   c) generating gas (nitrogen with a low oxygen level) on board from compressed dry and clean air, using high pressure membranes, etc.

2. The carbon dioxide level can be increased by:
   a) injecting carbon dioxide gas;
   b) fruit respiration;

3. The carbon dioxide level can be decreased by:
   a) fresh air or gas injection;
   b) hydrated lime;
   c) carbon scrubbers;
   d) water scrubbing, etc.

4. Relative humidity can be increased by:
    a) injecting water mist;
    b) steam;
    c) evaporating water, etc.

It should be remembered that during transport fruit and vegetables are still living organisms absorbing oxygen and giving off carbon dioxide, water vapour and heat. If the chambers loaded with such cargo were absolutely air tight, the oxygen level would decrease and carbon dioxide level increase, but complete airtightness can not currently be achieved. Air leakage is to be compensated by injecting the required amount of gas to produce the desired result. The Lloyd's Register Provisional Rules for Controlled Atmosphere are applicable to any gas system, permanent or portable, gas generating or storage type, which would achieve the above goal.

SAFETY

It is necessary to draw attention to the potential hazards that could be encountered during installing, operating and maintaining the refrigeration plant. It must be emphasised that these notes are not exhaustive, and are principally intended to draw attention to the most important points for consideration.

Mechanical hazards

Personnel should be aware at all times that refrigeration systems contain liquids and vapours under pressure. Suitable precautions must be taken when opening any part of the system to guard against the pressure hazard.

Compressors must be operated within their design parameters, and should never be used as vacuum pumps or for compressing air. Personnel must not start the compressor until they have taken steps to verify that:

a) guards on coupling, belts drives, and fans are in place, and other personnel are not in positions that might be hazardous when the plant is in operation;

b) the compressor discharge stop valve is open.

Opening up part of the system will necessitate the loss of a certain amount of refrigerant to atmosphere. It is essential that the amount of refrigerant which escapes is kept to a minimum, and appropriate steps are taken to prevent hazardous concentrations of refrigerant accumulating. Under certain conditions,

liquid refrigerant at low temperature may be present. Contact with this liquid must be avoided.

When dismantling the compressor for maintenance, inspection or repair, the method of pumping out and opening up described in the operation manual should be followed with care.

When it is necessary to open up the compressor, e.g. when cleaning the oil pump suction strainer or changing the oil filter, caution must be exercised as the lubricating oil will contain a certain amount of refrigerant which will be released when subjected to atmospheric conditions.

Personnel stopping a plant must ensure that they do not shut pipe-line stop valves in such a way as to trap cold liquid refrigerant between valves. If this precaution is not observed, hydraulic expansion of the liquid will take place as the temperature rises, and eventually cause the liquid pipe or valves etc. to fracture due to the great pressure that will build up.

Electrical hazards

The electrical power used in this equipment is at a voltage high enough to endanger life. Before carrying out maintenance or repair procedures, persons concerned must ensure that equipment is isolated from the electrical supply and tests made to verify that isolation is complete. Whenever possible, precautions must be taken to prevent the circuit being inadvertently energised, i.e. withdraw the mains fuses, or, if this is not practicable, place a warning notice over the mains switch.

When the supply can not be disconnected, functional testing, maintenance and repair of the electrical units is to be undertaken only by persons who are fully aware of the risk involved and who have taken adequate precautions to avoid direct contact with dangerous voltage.

Chemical (primary refrigerants) hazards

Refrigerants R12, R22, R502 and R717 (ammonia), are the substances in general use.

Refrigerants R12, R22, R502, etc.
CFC and HCFC refrigerants, although not considered to be toxic, are damaging to the environment. For this reason refrigerant must not be allowed to escape into the atmosphere. Transfer into approved containers using a refrigerant recovery unit if necessary.

Contaminated refrigerant must not be reused: instead transfer it into special recovery vessels for return to the refrigerant supplier for possible recycling.

The maximum charge which the transfer vessel can accommodate must be observed, remembering oil/refrigerant mixtures have a lower density than pure refrigerant.

CFC and HCFC refrigerants can present a danger to life by excluding air. Inhalation of very high concentrations of the vapour, even for short periods, must be avoided since this may be dangerous and can produce unconsciousness or prove suddenly fatal due to oxygen deficiency. The refrigerant vapour is heavier than air, and in static or poorly ventilated situations may be slow to disperse. Anyone suffering from the effects of inhalation of the vapour should move, or be moved, to the open air. The use of adrenalin or similar drugs to aid recovery must be avoided.

Care must be exercised before entering any area where the presence of high vapour concentration is suspected. The vapour will displace air upwards out of cargo chambers, ships' engine rooms, etc., and tend to collect at deck level and in pits and trenches. Should accidental escape of the refrigerant occur indoors, adequate fan assisted ventilation must be used to disperse the vapour, preferably by extraction at ground level, before entering the area. When any doubt exists it is recommended that breathing apparatus should be worn.

These refrigerants are non-flammable, but refrigerant vapour coming into contact with temperatures of 316°C (600°F) and above (burning cigarettes, gas burners, electrical heating elements, etc.), will decompose to form phosgene, hydrogen fluoride and hydrogen chloride. These compounds have extremely harmful physiological effect on human beings, as well as being highly corrosive, causing rapid breakdown of electrical and mechanical equipment. Naked flame and smoking must be prohibited in the presence of refrigerant vapour, and refrigerant must be purged from pipes or vessels before carrying out cutting or welding operations.

As these refrigerants can, under certain conditions, create hazardous concentrations in enclosed spaces it is essential that systems are maintained gas tight.

Approved methods of leak detection only should be used. If a halide test lamp is used, remember that the heating or combustion effect will produce toxic by-products which could be dangerous if inhaled.

Liquid refrigerant in contact with the eyes or skin will cause freezing and injuries similar to a burn, thus it is essential when loosening a connection on any part in which refrigerant is confined, for goggles to be worn to protect the eyes. Care must be taken when opening pipes or vessels which may contain liquid.

Ammonia (R717)

Ammonia is normally considered to be the most dangerous of the primary refrigerants and has inherent material and physiological hazards. A limited range of ammonia/air mixtures (16–27% ammonia by volume) can be ignited by flame and an explosion may result. Ammonia must not be allowed to come into contact with iodine, bromine, chlorine, hypochlorite or mercury; there is an explosion hazard in each case.

Anhydrous ammonia must be treated with respect. It is not a cumulative poison, but, because of ammonia's high affinity to water, the immediate harmful effects of exposure are as follows:

Vapour

Low concentrations may cause only irritation and discomfort: high concentrations can destroy body tissue. The action is more pronounced on moist tissues: eyes, nose, breathing passages, and moist areas of the skin may be burned by high concentrations.

Liquid

In this form ammonia can cause severe burning of the skin and eyes. As the eyes are particularly delicate organs, even small amounts of ammonia can be harmful. The full effects of ammonia on the eyes may not be apparent for 8–10 days but, ultimately, blindness may result.

Because even low concentrations of ammonia gas constitute a health hazard, it is essential that systems are maintained gas tight.

Maintenance procedures must not be carried out unless adequate ventilation has been provided to avoid risk of explosion and physiological harm. Naked flames must not be permitted in the area. The pungency of ammonia will usually warn personnel against remaining in locations where dangerously high concentrations of vapour exist. Personnel must not be permitted to work without wearing a gas mask, even for short periods, in a concentration which causes any discomfort to the eyes or affects breathing.

When a line containing ammonia is broken, do not rely solely on an isolation valve for protection, but use a blank flange as well. Rubber gloves and goggles must be worn. Gas masks suitable for protection against ammonia must be immediately available, preferably already worn. All vessels and pipelines should be thoroughly purged of ammonia before starting operations likely to produce sparks or flames (e.g welding). In addition, precautions should be taken to prevent a dangerous build up of ammonia vapour during these operations.

Exits and gangways and engines rooms where ammonia is used or stored, must be kept clear and unobstructed to ensure that they can be rapidly vacated in the event of a serious escape of ammonia. If a leak occurs, open all doors and ports leading to the open air to accelerate ventilation.

Gas masks fitted with cannisters suitable for use with ammonia must be kept available for emergencies, and personnel must be trained in their use. For rescue work in high concentrations of ammonia, self-contained breathing apparatus (transparent, rubber type), rubber boots and gloves are essential. Gas masks are effective only for relatively short periods and in low concentrations of gas only.

Under no circumstances whatsoever should ammonia be discharged into drains, scuppers, or overboard when in port.

Transfer and storage of refrigerant

When adding refrigerant to the plant, it is essential that the content of the cylinder is verified to prevent charging with the wrong substance which could cause an explosion or other accident.

Contaminated refrigerant must be returned to the manufacturer for possible recycling. On no account should it be reused or discharged into the environment.

Refrigerant containers must be disconnected from the system immediately on completion of transfer of refrigerant. Cylinders must not be overfilled. Frequent determination of the weight of refrigerant must be made and the permissible quantity of refrigerant for the cylinder never exceeded. The permissible weight is calculated from the equivalent water capacity which is stamped on the cylinder.

Substitution of the system refrigerant charge for another refrigerant must not be made without the approval of the authority concerned, the manufacturer, the installer or other competent person, and the user.

Notices detailing the safety precautions to be taken, and preferably illustrating emergency first aid treatment, should be displayed in areas where refrigerant is used or stored.

Spare refrigerant must be stored in approved containers, and the quantity held in the plant room limited. Cylinders and drums of refrigerant must be treated with care. Above all:

a) keep away from heat;

b) do not drop;

c) ensure that blanked connections are tight;

d) never attempt to check the contents of a refrigerant cylinder by 'smell'.

First aid

Injuries caused by R22

Frost-bite
Direct contact with liquid refrigerant may result in frost-bite, due to the rapid evaporation of the liquid. Refrigerants are not usually caustic.

Eye injuries
Refrigerant vapours are not usually harmful to the eyes. However, should liquid refrigerant squirt directly into the eyes, ensure that the injured person is taken to hospital or a doctor immediately. Avoid rubbing the eyes.

The following first-aid should be administered. Drop the eyes with sterile mineral oil (refrigerating machine oil or liquid paraffin) and then rinse thoroughly with water. If the irritation continues, rise the eyes with a weak boric acid solution.

Fainting
There is a risk of suffocation, due to lack of oxygen, if a large quantity of refrigerant escapes into a poorly ventilated room. Take the affected person immediately out into the fresh air, and loosen close-fitting clothes. Artificial respiration should be given immediately and continued until an expert can administer pure oxygen. Rinse the affected area thoroughly with water. An inhalator should be used immediately.

Injures caused by R717 (ammonia)

Breathing problems due to inhalation of ammonia vapours
The patient should be moved to a heated room where he must lie down with head and shoulders slightly raised. Loosen clothing on the upper part of the body to relieve coughing and help the patient to breath more easily. Pure oxygen is necessary if the patient has inhaled a large amount of ammonia gas. The patient must also be kept calm and quiet. Unconscious persons must never be given water or other liquid to drink. If the patient is conscious, water or orange juice diluted with sugar and glycerine may be given.

Eye burns
Raise the eyelid and rinse the eyeball thoroughly with water for at least 15 minutes. If the patient is in a great deal of pain, treat the eyes with a few drops of castor oil or another pure and neutral oil (refrigerating machine oil).

Skin burns

Rinse thoroughly with water, for at least 15 minutes—before removing clothing if necessary. Never cover burnt areas with clothing, bandages, oil or liniment. The injured person should be treated by a doctor as soon as possible.

Swallowing liquid ammonia

Give the affected person plenty of water to drink, preferably a mixture of vinegar and water (1 part vinegar to 5 parts water). Milk, perhaps with the addition of a raw egg, also has a neutralizing effect.

THE OPERATION OF A REFRIGERATING PLANT

The refrigerating capacity of any refrigerating plant is at its maximum when the greatest possible quantity of refrigerant is evaporated in the air cooler to obtain the required cargo chamber temperature, or in the evaporator to obtain the required brine temperature. This maximum capacity can be achieved as follows.

The evaporating temperature and hence pressure must be kept as high as possible consistent with the temperatures and, sometimes, humidities to be maintained in cargo chambers. For a given design this means ensuring that all heat transfer surfaces are kept clean, so that the temperature difference across them is at its minimum. It is also essential to ensure that evaporator surfaces are supplied with liquid refrigerant at the correct temperature and in the correct condition.

The condensing temperature must be kept as low as possible so as to keep the compressor delivery pressure to a minimum. This again means keeping all heat transfer surfaces clean and ensuring the correct flow of cooling water or air through the condenser. It is also important to keep air out of the systems as, being non-condensable, it will collect in the condenser vapour space so raising the effective compressor delivery pressure artificially, i.e. by Dalton's law of partial pressures, the delivery pressure is the sum of that due to the air and that at which the refrigerant is condensing. Air in the condenser will be indicated by an excessively high condenser gauge reading in relation to the temperature of the cooling water or air; air can be purged out of the top of the condenser, though some refrigerant will also be lost with it.

A rule of the thumb is that a reduction in the suction saturated pressure of 1°C would reduce the compressor capacity by approximately 4% and similarly an increase in the condensing saturated pressure of 1°C would decrease this capacity by a further 0.9%.

The compressor must be maintained in the best possible condition. This means that suction and delivery valves must not leak and piston clearance must be kept to a minimum. The correct operation of unloading devices is also important, as the partial operation of these can affect compressor performance. Valve leakage or excessive clearance both result in re-expansion of gas from delivery to suction pressure, and hence in reduced pumping capacity.

The temperatures at inlet and outlet of each side of the heat exchanger, if fitted, must be correct to ensure correct superheat and sub-cooling temperatures.

The refrigerating capacity of a plant is directly proportional to the weight of refrigerant evaporated in the evaporator. This in turn is directly related to the weight of vapour pumped by the compressor. The latter is the sum of the flash gas formed at the expansion valve and the vapour evaporated in the evaporator; it is therefore important to keep the flash gas to a minimum.

The weight of refrigerant vapour pumped by a given compressor depends directly on the temperature and hence pressure difference between the evaporator and the condenser, and this must be kept to a minimum. Furthermore, the density of the refrigerant vapour varies directly with the evaporating pressure and hence temperature, and it is therefore important to keep the evaporating temperature as high as possible in relation to the required load conditions. The swept column of a given compressor at a constant speed is constant, and the volume pumped varies relatively slightly for normal plants, although for a given condensing temperature it drops rapidly at low evaporating temperatures, i.e. the volumetric efficiency of a compressor is directly related to the pressure ratio between the compressor suction and delivery, which in turn corresponds to the temperature difference between the evaporating and condensing temperatures. A rise in condensing temperature has much less effect on the refrigerating capacity than a corresponding drop in evaporating temperature; both affect the volumetric efficiency, but lowering the evaporating temperature also reduces the density of the gas entering the compressor suction. It is wrong, therefore, to assume that a lower evaporating temperature will improve the refrigerating capacity.

While heat transfer may be improved in the evaporator, this is much more than counterbalanced by the reduced weight of gas pumped by the compressor, due to its reduced density as well as to the reduced compressor volumetric efficiency.

MAINTENANCE

The importance of maintenance cannot be overemphasised. Specific examples have been included in *Equipment*, page 266.

Experience has shown that most problems with marine refrigerating plant involve refrigerant shortage caused by leakage. In those cargo holds where frozen or chilled cargo below 5°C is carried, it is necessary to keep air coolers free from frost. Cleaning of filters is also important.

In cases where equipment of different kinds is opened up, neither air nor moisture must enter the refrigeration system, as either will cause trouble, e.g. in the form of increased condensing pressure. To avoid moisture, filter driers are installed in CFC and HCFC plants. Some are small, throw-away filters, and others have exchangeable drying agents.

When filters that can be serviced are fitted, it is recommended that packings of a size to suit the filters available on board are procured. Suitable packing size is also relevant to compressor oil, which easily absorbs moisture.

If there is moisture in the plant, this is indicated by the formation of copper plating. Copper plating arises in two stages:

1. Copper is dissolved in the oil

2. Copper is precipitated on metal surfaces.

The first stage occurs in the presence of water, whereas the second may occur with no water present. It is usually assumed that there is a direct correlation between water and copper plating. To prevent copper plating, it should be emphasised that:

a) the system should be clean;

b) the system should be dry;

c) the system should be free from air;

d) the working temperature should be kept down.

The drying agent should be changed every time any part of the system is opened. This also applies when charging with oil or refrigerant. Oil should not be filled from vessels that have not been tightly closed.

In CFC and HCFC systems, it is sometimes difficult to return the oil which continually circulates in the system to the compressor. The various reasons for this are:

1. The oil level drops quickly at the start.

This may be due to refrigerant being dissolved in the oil. At evaporation the oil is drawn with the refrigerant into the system. Fill the system with a small quantity of oil, as the ejected oil will gradually come back.

2. The oil level drops slowly because:

a) the plant is operated at lower evaporating temperature than usual or the refrigerant charge is too small;

b) refrigerant leakage in the system, by which the level in the evaporator has become too low;

c) condensing temperature is too low, by which the oil rectifier is not supplied with a sufficient amount of heat; the minimum condensing temperature should be maintained;

d) the cooling demand is too low, so the gas velocity becomes too low and the oil remains in the system.

A leakage-free refrigerating plant does not consume any oil. The oil which has disappeared from the crankcase or oil separator is always somewhere in the system.

In those plants with piston compressors which have oil separators, the shut-off valve in the oil return line should always be kept closed for about ½ hour after compressor start in order to avoid the carriage of condensate from the oil separator to the crankcase.

In those cargo refrigerating plants where brine serves as the heat transfer medium, it is of great importance that the correct brine specific gravity for the required cargo temperature is maintained. When bananas only are transported for nine months or more, for example, some ship owners or operators reduce brine specific gravity to save on power consumption by pumps. If this specific gravity is not checked, functional problems may occur when the frozen cargo is carried.

Maintenance can be divided into daily maintenance, periodic and planned maintenance. Daily maintenance should be done every day to avoid unpleasant surprises. Periodic and planned maintenance should be done according to the suppliers' instructions and your own planning based on experience over time and your ship's working area.

Daily maintenance

The daily maintenance for a R22 installation should be completed as follows.

1. Check that condensing pressure and evaporating

pressure are correct, and that the oil pressure drop across the oil filter is within the specified range.

2. Inspect the compressor unit and check that there are no abnormal noises or vibrations.

3. Check the discharge and suction temperatures, and the oil temperature. Discharge temperature depends on refrigerant and compressor type, e.g. for a reciprocating compressor, using R22, the maximum discharge temperature is 130°C; for a screw compressor, the maximum is 105°C. Suction pipe temperature must always be higher than suction pressure recalculated to temperature. How much higher depends on type of system and type of compressor. A guide value is approximately 10°C, but 20°C may sometimes be tolerated. Oil temperature is also different for different compressors but should not be more than 30°C over room temperature.
The highest allowable oil temperature is approximately +60°C. Oil temperature must never be below room temperature. At a lower temperature R22 liquid accompanies the suction gas to the compressor. The oil temperature follows the suction pipe temperature and can be increased with higher superheat of suction gas.

4. Check the oil level.

5. Check the tightness of the shaft seal. Oil leakage can be tolerated whereas gas leakage can not.

6. If an oil separator is installed, check that oil is returned to the crankcase, and that the oil return line is warmer than the crankcase.

Periodic maintenance

Periodic maintenance depends on operation time and is different for different types and makes of compressors. One manufacturer requires the following.

For reciprocating compressors; 1450–1750 rpm

1. For every 5000 hours of operation:
   a) check operating valves and replace damaged or worn out parts.
   b) change oil and clean crankcase, oil level sight glass and oil strainer.
   c) check unloading mechanisms and replace o-rings and cuff rings. Clean strainer for capacity control system.
   d) inspect cylinders for scratches and seizures and also pistons if there is damage in the cylinders.

   e) check function of monitoring devices.

2. For every 10,000 hours of operation:
   a) replace operating valves.
   b) inspect bearing surfaces.
   c) check piston ring gap.

For compressors with speed lower than 1,200 rpm, the periodic times may be increased to 7,000 days and 14,000 days respectively.
For cargo refrigerating plants, the maintenance prescribed by the classification societies has to be added.

For screw compressors

1. For every 1,000 hours of operation check the function of monitoring devices.

2. For every 2,500 hours of operation:
   a) check alignment of compressor-motor
   b) clean all filters.
   c) lubricate the bearing of electric motor.

3. For every 5,000 hours of operation the bearings of the oil pump must be checked.

4. For every 10,000 hours of operation:
   a) change the oil.
   b) check the elastic coupling between compressor and motor. If cracks are present in the rubber the coupling has to be replaced.

5. For every 40,000 hours of operation, disassemble the compressor for total overhaul and replace axial bearings.

The following general service measures should be performed in order to obtain optimal operating results.

Leak detection

Refrigerating plants must be gas-tight to prevent refrigerant leakage and air entering the low-pressure side when under a vacuum. Systems which have been modified, or opened to the atmosphere during repairs, must be pressure tested for mechanical strength and leaks before charging with refrigerant.

Pressure tests

Pressure tests are normally carried out pneumatically. In the case of CFC and HCFC refrigerant plants, the test medium should be dry oxygen-free nitrogen. Commercial quality nitrogen or air may be used in ammonia plants. Water or other fluids must not be used as a test medium. The plant's compressors must not be used to pressurise the plant.

Prior to testing, any item that may be damaged by over pressure should be isolated from the system. All solenoid, pressure regulating check or other control valves should be opened and the circuit checked so that the system can be pressurised. Relief valves should be removed and the openings capped or plugged. The compressor stop valves should also be closed during pressure testing.

Typical test procedure

1. Do a strength test by filling the entire system with the test medium and gradually increasing the pressure until the test pressure, equal to 1.5 times the maximum working pressure of the system, is obtained. This pressure should be maintained for about 10 minutes.

   As a safety precaution, all personnel must be evacuated from the area of risk while the system is being strength tested, and the nitrogen or air cylinders must be fitted with both a pressure regulator and relief valve.

2. Reduce the pressure to the maximum working pressure and hold for a period of 24 hours, during which the existence of leaks may be indicated by a fall in pressure in the system. Any suspect joints, welds, seals, etc. should be leak tested using a solution of soapy water. Each joint, etc., must be examined thoroughly for signs of air bubbles which indicate a leak. After sealing any leaks, pressurise the system again with the test medium and some refrigerant as a trace gas, and repeat the leak test using an electronic leak detector, etc. It is imperative that all leaks are found and sealed before the system is charged with refrigerant, as even the tiniest of leaks can result in the loss of the whole refrigerant charge.

Leak detection equipment

Electronic leak detectors
Electronic leak detectors are the most sensitive and accurate method of leak detection. There are many instruments for detecting CFC and HCFC refrigerants and ammonia on the market. The most commonly employed operating principles are the semiconductor, ionization or corona formation, and infrared detection.

The detector contains an internal pump that draws air into a probe, or tube. If refrigerant gas is present in the sample, the electrodes in the sensing element generate a current, and an output signal is obtained.

In modern refrigerated cargo installations, leak detection sensors fitted in the holds and machinery spaces activate audible and visual alarms located in the control room in the event of a refrigerant leak.

Leak detector torch
Leak detector torches are used to locate leaks of CFC and HCFC refrigerants. This method is based on the colour of a flame that surrounds a glowing copper element. The flame turns blue-green if the air being consumed contains the refrigerant.

These torches should only be used in well ventilated spaces and must not be used to search for combustible gas leaks.

Sulphur candles
The lit candles, indicate the presence of ammonia gas by giving off a cloud of dense white smoke.

Litmus, or other indicating papers
The paper, when wet, indicates the presence of ammonia gas by change in colour, e.g. red litmus paper turns blue.

Routine inspections

Leak detection should be carried out every 1,000 hours of operation, special attention being paid to brazed joints, welded joints, gaskets, flanges, valve stems, compressor shaft seals, and areas where there are signs of an oil leak. The high pressure side of the system may easily be tested with the plant running, but it may be necessary to stop the compressor, and allow the pressure in the low pressure side to rise sufficiently. The amount of refrigerant in the system should also be strictly monitored as a drop in level may indicate the presence of a leak.

In the event of a major leak, the initial leak test should be made using the soap bubble method.

Safety

To prevent the risk of being overcome by fumes during leak testing, never enter an unventilated area alone. A second person should always be in attendance in the entrance to the area.

Refrigerant charging

In refrigerating plants, refrigerant may be lost through leaks or when carrying out repairs. When such losses occur the plant must be charged with refrigerant. It is imperative that the correct refrigerant is added to the plant, as charging with the wrong substance could cause an explosion or other accident.

Pre-charging procedures

Refrigerating plants must be free of all contaminants before being charge with refrigerant.

Systems which have been modified or opened to the atmosphere during repairs should be flushed through to remove solid particles, and evacuated to remove moisture and non-condensable gases.

Flushing

1. Fit a fine mesh filter or sock in the strainer in the compressor suction inlet.

2. Charge the system with the pressure test medium, and run the compressor to circulate the gas through the system. To prevent blockages, the expansion valve and other regulating controls with small orifices must be bypassed.

3. Stop the compressor at intervals and clean the filter, repeating this procedure until no particles are found.

Drying by evacuation

This method of removing moisture is based on the fact that the boiling point of water decreases with falling pressure. In the course of evacuation, any water or ice in the plant will evaporate, and is carried away by the vacuum pump.

1. Connect a vacuum pump to the system using a short length of large bore pipe, and open all valves in the system (expansion valves, solenoid valves, etc., may have to be jacked open).

2. Evacuate the system to a pressure of 6mm Hg or less. If possible, carry out the evacuation at ambient temperatures above 10°C.

3. Close the line between the system and the vacuum pump. The pressure in the system may not rise more than 2mm Hg within five minutes. A rise of more than 2mm Hg indicates the presence of water, and/or a leak. Where water is present, the system will be colder than its surroundings.

4. Check for water and/or leaks, carry out any repairs, and repeat the evacuation procedure until the pressure rise is less than 2mm Hg. When this is achieved the system is free of moisture and non-condensable gases and ready for refrigerant charging.

Charging procedures

Refrigerating plants should not be overcharged with refrigerant, as this may overload or damage the compressor. To ensure that the correct amount is added, the refrigerant should be weighed during charging.

Large plants

In large plants, the liquid refrigerant is decanted from the cylinder into the system via a charging valve on, or just after, the receiver, or after the expansion valve.

Procedure

1. Connect the cylinder to the charging valve, (cylinders without internal dip tubes must be inverted) and purge the line of air. Ammonia cylinders have internal 'gooseneck bends', and must be laid horizontally with the valve spindle facing upwards.

2. Open the charging and cylinder valves, and run the compressor.

3. Allow the liquid to flow into the system. If liquid is charged without a compressor running, the cylinder must be slightly warmer than the system.

Note the following:

a) liquid refrigerant must never be charged directly into the compressor suction;

b) ensure that properly tested charging hoses are used, and that non-return valves are fitted when charging into the high pressure side of the system.

Small plants

In small plants refrigerant gas is drawn into the system, via a 'back-seating' service valve in the compressor suction line.

Procedure

1. Connect the cylinder to the charging valve. Ensure that the cylinder is standing upright to prevent liquid carry-over, and that the charging hose is purged of air.

2. Open the charging valve and 'crack' open the cylinder valve.

3. Run the compressor to draw the refrigerant gas into the system. The suction pressure should be maintained just above atmospheric by regulating the cylinder valve.

If the refrigerant capacity of a plant is not known, or when filling a partially charged plant, the system should be approaching full charge when:

a) the refrigerant flow in the sight glass becomes a full stream without bubbles; or

b) the liquid level gauge on the receiver shows one third full.

Condensers

The condensers are far too often neglected. Anti-corrosion plugs, for example, should be inspected for the first time after the plant has been in operation for three months. Further inspections should be carried out when judged necessary. Anti-corrosion plugs may not be worn out more that two-thirds of their thickness.

Once a year, the tubes should be cleaned with a tube brush in order to remove deposits which would cause a high condensing pressure. The gaskets must be glued to the condenser end plate with good contact. If the partition wall gasket. is not properly installed, there is a risk that it will 'blow', leading to an excessively high water velocity and to damage to the tube plate. Such damage can be repaired, if discovered in time, using 'Prestolite' or a similarly commercially available compound. The water velocity should not exceed 2.5 m/s. It is essential that due attention be paid to the above points in order to ensure that both the condenser and the shell-and-tube evaporator will have a long service life. If a tube has become defective, it does not have to be replaced immediately. Up to 10% in each flow direction can be plugged, without jeopardizing the effect of the apparatus.

Oil coolers

Screw compressors may be equipped with watercooled oil coolers. These must be cleaned at regular intervals to keep the oil temperature within the prescribed limits. Cleaning is best done with tube brushes, but if the oil coolers are severely fouled, they may also be cleaned chemically using a solution of hydrochloric acid. The oil side is cleaned with a grease solvent. The suction strainer is made of fine-gauge steel gauze, which can be washed in white spirit.

Filter and driers

The various filters in the plant must be checked at regular intervals. This applies to the entire system (water side, refrigerant side, oil system, and air side). It is difficult to specify how frequently this should be done but, as a guideline, the check should be performed at least in conjunction with checking the compressor. The desiccant in the drier filter must be replaced whenever the plant has been opened and, in more severe cases of moisture, be checked and changed several times until the plant is dry.
When it is not known how much moisture there is in the plant it is best to evacuate it. Moisture in the CFC and HCFC plant can cause copper plating (page 287), or problems with the expansion valve, which freezes up.

Sight glass

There must be a sight glass in some form in all plants. Gas bubbles in the sight glass are a direct indication of a shortage of refrigerant and this always results ultimately in a shortage of oil.

Defrosting

Another task which may be regarded as maintenance is to keep frost deposits on provision and cargo refrigerating plants under control. Frequent defrosting assures that the plant will cause few problems. The plant will need a minimum of care and maintenance if it is kept:

a) free of moisture;

b) free of impurities;

c) free of freon leaks;

d) free of frost.

The need for defrosting arises when operating with cargo temperatures close to 0°C. The rise of delivery air temperatures in cargo chambers under normal operating status of the entire cooling plant would be the first indication of the frost build up on the air cooler coils. Visual examination of the cooler should confirm that the frost is excessive, e.g. 4 mm or above.

As the frost builds up the overall heat transfer coefficient between air and refrigerant will be reduced, and the compressor suction pressure may gradually decrease resulting in a loss of refrigeration capacity. A heavy frost on the coil will also reduce the air flow through the cooler and the number of air changes in the cargo chambers. It is therefore very important that defrosting by one of the methods described above is always carried out at the correct time interval. The defrosting procedure is normally performed manually, but some modern installations make provision for automatic commencement and termination of defrosting.

The sequence of events during a typical hot gas defrosting procedure in a DX system is shown in Fig 20. In brine systems (Fig 19), hot brine at approximately 40°C is pumped from the steam brine heater to the coolers being defrosted.

Regardless of the system, it is important that the cooler fans are not started before the air cooler coil temperature is reduced, by circulating low temperature brine or refrigerant, and the defrosting cycle is completed as quickly as possible.

Table 5   Trouble shooting chart.

Category	No.	Trouble observed	No current—main switch not coupled into the circuit	Fuses blown—loose e1 connections	Voltage too low	No pilot current	Excess voltage relay open—reset	Pilot current circuit open	Pump/fan not started	Welded contacts in motor starter	High pressure control has interrupted—reset	Low pressure control has interrupted	Low pressure control difference too small	The oil pressure control has interrupted—reset	Wrongly adjusted capacity regulator	Defrosting timer breaks the current	Oil charge too small	Compressor capacity too high during starting	Oil pressure too low—adjust oil press regulating valve	Oil is foaming in the crankcase	Overcharge of oil	Foul oil return—oil in evaporators
Compressor	1	Compressor fails to start	●	●	●	●	●	●	●		●	●		●		●						
	2	Compressor starting and stopping too frequently										●	●		●							
	3	Compressor starting, stops again immediately		●			●	●			●	●	●	●	●	●	●			●	●	
	4	Compressor runs continuously								●												
	5	Compressor abnormally noisy																		●	●	●
	6	System short of capacity													●		●			●	●	●
	7	Compressor knocks—during start																●		●		
	8	Compressor knocks—during operation																				
Pressure	9	Condenser pressure too high									●											
	10	Condenser pressure too low																				
	11	Suction pressure too high													●				●			
	12	Suction pressure too low											●		●							●
Temps.	13	Discharge pipe temperature too high											●									
	14	Discharge pipe temperature too low																				
	15	Oil temperature too high																				
Oil	16	Oil in crankcase disappears																●		●		●
	17	Oil in crankcase foams																●				
	18	Oil pressure too low													●			●		●	●	
	19	Crankcase sweating or frosted																●		●		
Sundries	20	Bubbles in liquid sight glass																●				
	21	Low refrigerant level in receiver																				
	22	Impossible to evacuate the plant									●											
	23	Capacity regulator hunting													●			●	●	●	●	

Cause of defect →	E1 supply	E1 connections	Automatics	Oil

Table 5 (contd)   Trouble shooting chart.

Fault categories (column legend):

Refrigerant
1. Restriction of refrigerant supplt
2. Refrigerant charge too small
3. Refrigerant vapours in liquid line
4. Leaky refrigerating plant
5. Overcharge of refrigerant
6. Liquid in suction line
7. At low temp operation, filling degree in evaporator rises

Condenser
8. Insufficient cooling water/air to condenser
9. Temperature of cooling water/air too high
10. Non-condesable gases in condenser
11. Fouling of condenser
12. Too much cooling water, air to condenser
13. Water valve does not function

Expansion valve
14. External pressure equalization of expansion valve closed
15. Expansion valve partially blocked (ice, dirt etc.)
16. Expansion valve has lost the charge
17. Expansion valve bulb wrongly placed
18. Leaky expansion valve
19. Expansion valve gives too small superheat
20. Expansion valve gives too large superheat

Sundries
21. Filters in liquid/suction line clogged
22. Solenoid valve in liquid/suction line closed
23. Solenoid valve leaks
24. Frosting up or clogging of evaporator
25. The cooling air is recirculated (restricted)
26. Too much loading of the plant
27. Refrigerant collects in cold condenser (close by-pass)
28. Improper adjustment of coupling or loose coupling

Compressor
29. Defective oil pump
30. Worn out or defective bearings
31. Defective piston rings or worn cylinder
32. Defective or leaky discharge valves
33. Defective or leaky suction valves
34. Compressor by-pass open—leaky safety valve
35. Clogged oil filter in compressor
36. Defective capacity regulator
37. Too high compressor capacity during start
38. Solenoid valve in oil return obstructed/defective
39. Clogged filter in oil return
40. Too high compressor capacity
41. Too low compressor capacity
42. Defective heating element in crankcase

Row	1	2	3	4	5	6	7	8	9	10	11	12	13	14	15	16	17	18	19	20	21	22	23	24	25	26	27	28	29	30	31	32	33	34	35	36	37	38	39	40	41	42
1																																										
2	●	●	●	●								●		●	●	●				●	●	●									●	●		●		●				●		
3																					●	●							●	●						●						●
4	●	●		●											●						●			●								●	●								●	
5						●																						●	●	●	●	●	●					●				
6	●	●	●	●							●			●	●	●	●			●	●			●	●	●					●	●									●	
7						●											●	●	●					●																●	●	●
8	●		●			●											●		●																							
9					●			●	●	●	●		●																													
10		●				●																							●	●	●					●					●	
11						●								●						●										●	●					●				●		
12	●	●	●								●				●	●					●	●	●		●	●										●						
13	●	●	●					●	●	●	●			●	●					●	●						●					●				●						
14						●									●									●									●									
15														●	●	●	●			●										●			●									
16						●																								●										●	●	●
17						●													●																					●		●
18						●																							●	●					●							
19						●												●	●																					●		
20	●	●	●																		●	●																		●		
21		●		●			●															●					●															
22															●																●	●	●	●	●						●	
23																													●								●	●	●			

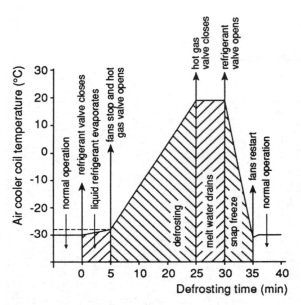

Figure 20   Sequence of events in hot gas defrosting.

TROUBLE SHOOTING

When problems are incurred in a refrigerating plant, these can be attributed in most cases to a shortage of refrigerant. Bearing this in mind, always commence trouble-shooting by checking the refrigerant charge. For example, in the case of CFC and HCFC plants, too little refrigerant prevents the oil, which always circulates in the system, from being returned as the gas velocity is low, and this leads to various functional troubles.

A trouble-shooting chart cannot be made complete until the design of the refrigerating plant is known. The comprehensive trouble-shooting chart (Table 5) should make it easier to locate the fault and its cause in the event of malfunction of a modern DX refrigerating plant.

In investigating trouble, there are certain things to which attention should always be paid in the first instance:

a) the temperature of the refrigerated space;

b) evaporating pressure;

c) condensing pressure;

d) suction pipe temperature;

e) discharge temperature;

f) liquid line temperature;

g) compressor running time;

h) noise from compressor, motor, expansion valve, etc.

REEFER VESSELS

Modern fully refrigerated vessels, or reefers as they are frequently called, are completely flexible multipurpose vessels, suitable for carrying any refrigerated cargo, palletized or in bulk, all over the world (Fig 21). The reefer must have a sufficient capacity to precool bananas, citrus and deciduous fruit, even meat if required, and be able to maintain a range of temperatures from –30°C to 13°C, some at close tolerances, in different temperature zones. They must also be able to carry most general cargoes on their return voyages. The reefer must provide facilities to carry integral containers on deck and be able to handle a 40 ft loaded container (30 tons weight) using her own fast operating cranes. The typical speed of a modern reefer is 19–20 kn, or 22 kn at the banana draft. The speed of unloading is of paramount importance and to facilitate fast unloading of cargo, large wide hatches or side loading designs are very popular. It is claimed that a medium size 'pallet friendly' reefer of 3000 pallet capacity can be unloaded in 8 hours. The speed of unloading bulk cargo, i.e. bananas, etc., is achieved by fitting side ports in the upper decks and hatches in the remainder for conveyors and escalators (Fig 22).

The main features of a modern, 450,000 ft³ reefer vessel are as follows.

1. Four holds with 4 or 5 cargo decks, each with the same clear head of 2.2m to minimize lost load space when storing standard pallets (1.2m long × 1.0 m wide × 2.1 m high maximum). These decks are arranged usually in eight air tight temperature zones, with the air coolers placed along the bulkheads serving one or sometimes two decks. Variable speed fans are placed above the coolers forcing air through, under the grating then vertically from bottom to top through the cargo and back to the coolers in so called 'ductless systems' (Fig 23).

2. The square shape of the holds prevents pallets from crashing at sea and improves the air flow through cargo, thus minimizing short circulation of air. In the forward end of the vessel, where the sides of the holds may have a flare, inflatable bags or sliding shutters are used.

3. Obstruction free decks and strengthened metal or plywood gratings enable fork lift trucks to work with pallets.

4. Wide hatchways, which facilitate easy handling of palletized cargo (six pallets or more can be discharge simultaneously), and side ports and/or deck hatches for banana elevators.

Figure 21   Modern reefer vessel.

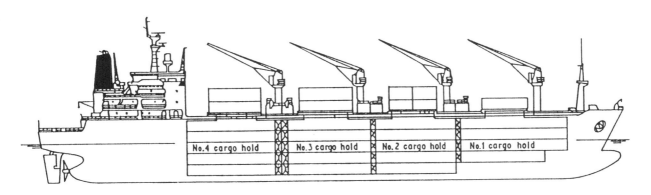

Figure 22   Arrangement of cargo holds and containers on board a modern reefer.

5. Four fast cranes able to handle a 40 ft container laden, for example, with frozen meat.

6. Space for eighty or more integral containers on the weather deck, and space for fork lift trucks and pallet cages.

Air circulation and refreshing

Between 90 and 120 air changes of the net volume per hour is usually provided in holds. Such volume flow guarantees good and uniform cooling rate of palletized and bulk cargo and allows for imperfect storage. This air rate will be reduced on completion of cooling down and when frozen cargo is carried.

Air refreshing rates to remove carbon dioxide, ethylene and other volatiles, can be two or three air changes per hour. In order to precool hot outside air some ships are also fitted with air to air heat exchangers.

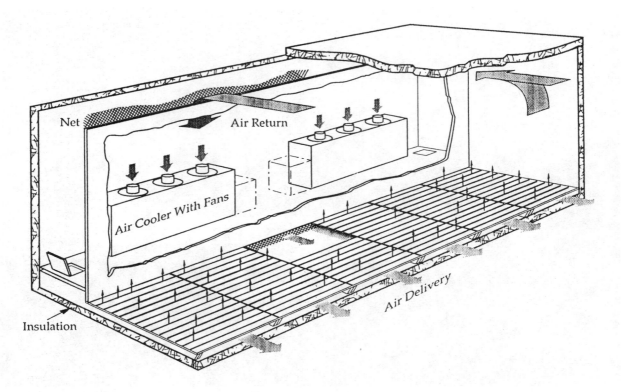

Figure 23   Ductless air circulation system.

Refrigeration machinery

In recent years most reefers have been fitted with 3 or 4 identical prefabricated package units incorporating double screw compressors with variable volume ratio to secure optimum efficiency at high as well as at low suction temperatures (Fig 24). With recent lower fuel costs, the idea of combining screw and reciprocating compressors or a number of different sizes of screw compressors on the same vessels in order to save energy has been less popular. Reliability of the installation and freedom from maintenance, where possible, is the prime object of the owner. In some cases surplus refrigeration capacity for various duties which a plant is expected to fulfil, has been more generous than ever before. Allowance is usually given for deterioration over a period of time, possible inefficient operation and higher than designed ambient and sea water temperatures in the Gulf ports in summer.

Insulation

Traditionally, cargo spaces of reefers have been insulated with rock wool or fibre glass slabs on ship sides and bulkheads and high density polyurethane slabs on decks and tank tops. Timber supports, suitably protected against rot, are placed between steel structures and inner face lining, such as aluminium, stainless steel, PVC or marine plywood to eliminate heat bridges. In recent years, the trend was to apply sprayed *in situ* polyurethane to ribbands, corners and complicated areas to reduce the heat transfer. In some modern designs polyurethane is sprayed on steel sides and frames before glasswood slabs are pinned to the sides. These slabs are covered by mesh wire and sprayed with polyurethane again to a thickness of 50mm before plywood lining is applied. Such an arrangement should prevent glass wool from setting down and getting wet in the event of damage to or inefficient lining and vapour barrier.

In other designs, polyurethane is simply injected between the ship side and plywood lining, or prefabricated polyurethane panels 60–100mm thick are fitted with mineral wool between the frames (Fig 25). In installations where mineral wool is not fitted, pressure equalising valves are applied to prevent the panels' collapse in the event of rapid cooling of chambers or temperature fluctuation in the void space between the panels and ship side.

An overall coefficient of heat transfer for a modern reefer vessel, regardless of the type of insulation fitted varies between 0.45 to 0.52 W/m^2 °C, with a tendency towards the lower figure.

Figure 24   Prefabricated package unit.

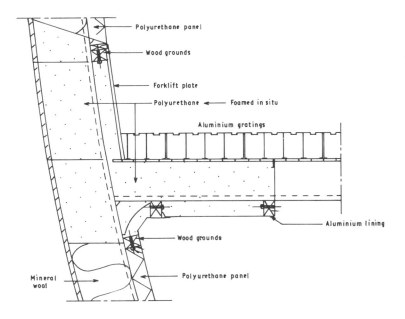

Figure 25   Detail of ship side and deck insulation.

MARINE CONTAINERS

Although refrigerated containers first made their appearance in the early 1930s, they were neither standardised nor intermodal and it was only in the late 1960s that ship design permitted the transportation of large numbers of refrigerated containers in any one vessel. The late 1960s and early 1970s were a period of marked development in methods of carrying refrigerated as well as general cargoes in containers, as is witnessed by the numerous patents taken out, particularly in the USA and the UK. The success of these developments was evident in the spread of refrigerated containerisation around the world, and the affect on the design of both the containers and the vessels carrying them.

The advantages of containerisation are simple and obvious:

a) the conversion of marine transportation from a labour intensive to a mechanised industry;

b) the avoidance of multiple handling of cargo and the ability to transfer between alternative modes of transport without physically handling the cargo.

Container types

Two basic types of refrigerated containers were developed for use in the international reefer trade.

1. The insulated box connected to the ship's central plant and a cold air circulation system; sometimes known as an isotherm container, or porthole container.

2. The insulated box incorporating its own 'plug-in' refrigeration unit within the standard module; usually known as an integral container.

Both types comply with ISO 1492/2, as revised in the 1987 edition, which endeavours to establish universally accepted standards for containers.

The containers most frequently found in practice are 20ft (6.097m) or 40ft (12.19m) long, 8 ft (2.4m) wide and either 8ft or 8.5ft (2.56m) high.

Early containers were insulated with polystyrene and lined with glass-fibre reinforced plastic covered plywood, but recently the trend has moved to rigid polyurethane with a metallic lining such as aluminium or steelplate. Occasionally, stainless steel is also used. The insulation thickness of the walls and overhead is 75mm and that of the floors and doors 100mm, giving an overall insulation heat transfer coefficient of approximately 27W/°K for an ISO 20ft container.

The container floor usually consists of T-sections and the air circulation may be either from bottom to top or vice versa, the former being more popular with porthole containers.

Some integral containers are fitted with a symmetrical air flow system. In this system the air is admitted along the entire length of one side of the container with extraction from the opposite side, thus guaranteeing an efficient and uniform temperature distribution. The overall weight of a container and its cargo is restricted by regulations in the UK and other countries, and is effectively limited to a gross of about 20 tonnes. The weight restriction virtually fixed the overall length of 20ft (6.097) for containers loaded with butter and meat, conforming with the standard container of the day. When loaded with frozen lamb in carcase, chilled meat in cuts, or fruit, container loads vary from about 9 to 13 tons, thereby giving some support to the case for using 40ft (12.19m) containers, although the same overall weight restrictions apply when travelling on the road.

The integral container will have an independent refrigeration unit which enables the container operator to carry cargoes in the temperature range –25°C to +20°C. These units are mostly electrically driven and are plugged in to appropriate power points on shore or onboard ship. Nowadays, a number of units are compact enough to allow for a removable diesel alternator set to be fitted when the container is travelling on the road, or sited in areas where a suitable 3-phase power supply is not available.

Although this type of container has become highly developed over the past 20 years, the basic principles have remained much the same, the main improvement coming through improved fans and electrical gear, temperature controls etc.

A typical specification for a 20ft integral container operating in the Far East service would be as follows:

Electrical supply	380–460V, 50 or 60 Hz
Power consumption	5–6 kW
Ambient temperature	+40°C
Container temperature	+20°C to –25°C
Temperature control	+0.25°C in range –4°C to 10°C, +0.5°C in remainder of range
Internal air circulation	60 changes per hour at an internal load resistance of about 10mm water gauge
Temperature difference evaporator to air delivery	–8°C at a container temperature of –18°C.

Fresh air changes	At least 1 per 4 hours
CO_2 sampling	Yes
Condensers	Finned copper or coated alloy if air cooled
Electric defrosting	3kW plus tray and drain heaters
Compressor	3.7 to 5.6 kW semi-hermetic 1500 or 1750 rev/min depending on frequency
Evaporator fans	Propeller 1800 m³/h, about 1 kW power consumption
Condenser fans	As for evaporator fans
Alternator output	12.5–15 kW to allow for locked rotor currents of minus 60–65 A.

There have been a number of variations on the above design, the most popular being a dual compressor system with either hermetic or semi-hermetic compressors.

Capacity control

Good control of the air temperature entering the container is obtained when the refrigerating capacity of the compressor can be reduced to meet the operation demand.

Capacity control may be achieved by any of the following methods.

1. On/off control
2. Variable motor speed
3. Cylinder unloading
4. Hot gas bypass
5. Hot gas injection to evaporator
6. Evaporator pressure controls.

Probably the most effective of the above systems, in terms of temperature control, will be (5) followed by (4) (Fig 26); also, of course, it is possible to use a combination of a number of them. Nevertheless, from an energy point of view, (1), (2), (6) and (3) are the most satisfactory, although there are few compressors made nowadays with cylinder unloading.

CONTAINER SHIPS

The first liner trade container ships for the carriage of perishable goods came into service in the 1950s from the west coast of North America to Hawaii and Alaska. Some of these early container ships were converted tankers and were capable of carrying dry

a)   b)

Figure 26 a) Hot gas bypass to suction with desuperheater; b) hot gas injection to evaporator.

cargo containers and integral unit refrigerated containers. At that time, the container in popular use from the USA ports had a length of 35 ft (10.66m) but many have since been lengthened to bring them into line with current international standards by the addition of a 5ft section.

By the mid 1960s it became apparent that traditional methods of carrying both refrigerated and general cargoes by sea was becoming increasingly expensive, and proposals were put in hand to containerise the service between Europe and Australia. Following this, a rapid growth was seen in container services from principle exporting countries such as Australia and New Zealand to Japan and South East Asia, and to the east and west coasts of North America. The Caribbean to Europe (CAROL) service was the first to use ships specially designed for the carriage of bananas, and pioneered the use of 40ft (12.192m) porthole containers. At the same time, bananas were transported in 40ft integral containers from Central America to the United States. Ten years later, additional services commenced between Europe and South Africa, Australia and the Gulf of Mexico and, more recently, between South America and Europe. A number of methods were proposed for carrying containers under refrigeration at sea and, in general, these have been developed to suit the particular operation circumstances in both exporting and importing countries. Each has several noteworthy features, but in all cases, the containers are held in place by a steel framed guide system.

Ship for the carriage of porthole containers

Insulated holds

The sides and bulkheads of the holds are insulated with 50mm thick slab polyurethane lined with aluminium. Hatch covers are insulated with at least 120mm foamed *in situ* polyurethane which is sprayed with two coats of fire retardant paint. The overall heat transfer coefficient is approx $1.4 \, W/m^2{}^\circ K$.

Insulated air ducts are permanently fitted to the bulkhead and may be disposed either horizontally or vertically. Horizontal ducts are normally built and insulated onboard and then connected to a large air cooler, which may serve up to 48 containers. The containers are connected to the air ducts by closable couplings. Special, efficient mixed flow fans are incorporated in a cooler house to ensure air distribution, even when the full complement of containers is not being carried. The first generation of these ships had a manually operated shutter to close unused couplings; later ships have an automatic closing butterfly valve incorporated in the design.

Vertical ducts are normally prefabricated with an air cooler house attached to the side or back. They are stringently tested at the makers' works for airtightness, quality of insulation, air distribution and against fan stalling. Some are designed for a container stack nine high, this being the maximum number of fully laden containers permitted by ISO and the limit of their frame structure.

Vertical ducts are probably more flexible, as the arrangement is such that each stack in a hold can have a different cargo temperature with the same brine inlet temperature to the hold. However, as the containers are not completely airtight, only compatible cargoes can be carried in the same hold.

Insulated holds are usually fitted with two or more air conditioners, each of which can maintain the hold temperature at a pre-set value, usually at $0^\circ C$. Air is circulated at the rate of 6 to 10 changes/hour and guarantees a very even temperature distribution at all levels of the hold. Such an arrangement practically eliminates sensible heat transfer through the container when fruit is carried, and therefore allows for much reduced numbers of air changes in the container, and is approved by both the United States Department of Agriculture (USDA) and the Perishable Products Export Control Board (PPECB).

With the exception of the girders, normal quality steel can be used for construction of the hold.

Uninsulated holds/partly insulated holds

These may be fitted with prefabricated ducts in a similar manner to the above, but large air coolers and bigger fans will probably be provided for the anticipated increase in the number of air changes in the containers.

The overall heat transfer coefficient of an uninsulated hold would be between 6 and $7 \, W/m^2{}^\circ K$ depending upon the construction of the double bottom, side tanks and container stack height. This arrangement generally increases the hold temperature which would be close to ambient temperature. The general argument for not fitting insulation in holds is that the containers had been subjected to higher ambient temperature ashore anyway prior to arrival at the ship.

Ships for the carriage of integral containers

The holds of these ships are normally uninsulated. In order to maintain the hold temperature below ambient, a very powerful ventilation system is fitted to forward and aft bulkheads with air intakes positioned in the vicinity of each container integral unit. Fresh air may be supplied to the holds at tank top level or through openings in the vicinity of hatches.

As soon as the containers are loaded and positioned up to 6 high in guides, the refrigerating units are plugged to the electrical power supply and those containers having water cooled condensers are connected to fresh or sea water cooling systems permanently fitted onboard.

The fresh water is circulated in a closed circuit and is cooled by sea water in heat exchangers, its outlet temperature being 4 to 5°C higher than the sea water outlet temperature from the heat exchanger.

The fans of air cooled condensers will not be running. However, measurements onboard have proved that some 27% of total heat was rejected by natural convection when hot gas was passing through air cooled condensers.

Some ships can carry over 600 integral containers under the deck which, in practice, may create a colossal maintenance problem when it is appreciated that all of these units may differ in age, type and temperature.

At the design stage the diversity factor for calculating the total power demand for refrigerating units is taken as 0.8, i.e. it is assumed that only 80% of all containers onboard will operate at the same time, and this assumption proved correct in practice.

Stack factor (SF)

The stack factor is defined to be the effective container surface area and was taken initially as 67% when the first generation of container ships was built. It was thought that the temperature between the containers in a stack would be equal to the temperature in the side containers. Measurements at sea however have proved that the temperature between the containers is much closer to the temperature of the hold and depends on the type of air circulation, whether forced or natural, the height of the container stack and the type of container.

The stack factor may vary between 0.75 and 0.95. These measurements have removed any arguments about the behaviour of air trapped under the floor of the containers.

It was noted at the same time that the temperature of the insulated hold at the top and bottom of a six high stack may differ by 2°C to 4°C when the air conditioning system is out of operation, and will be maintained within 1°C with forced ventilation. On uninsulated vessels these temperature differences may be up to 9°C for a 6 high stack.

Refrigeration machinery

Refrigeration systems in porthole container ships are generally similar to those used in conventional reefers, i.e. the primary refrigerant—usually R22—is circulated through compact shell and tube evaporators with refrigerant flow being controlled by conventional thermostatic expansion valves.

The brine, when cooled to the appropriate temperature, is circulated through finned tube air-to-brine heat exchangers, with some form of bypass valve to maintain the air at the prescribed temperature. It is advisable to keep a mean temperature difference between brine and air of 3°C to 4°C, so that relative humidity within containers is maintained at a high level of approximately 90%.

Defrosting of coolers is usually achieved by circulating hot brine, the time taken being about 30 minutes.

The centralised brine room is still in common use. This invariably results in long pipe runs to individual coolers. Perhaps the increasing trend towards full automation, including automatic defrosting, will result in some changes in this area of ship operation.

A direct expansion system was first used on the early Columbus container ships for the East Coast of North America service. It utilised a number of small 7.5kW or 10kW semi-hermetic compressor sets connected to a series of air coolers. These compressors were mounted in tandem with a common suction manifold, making the starting and stopping procedure very simple. The control of air delivery temperature was achieved by switching off compressors and each set had about 25% standby capacity in case of one machine failure.

AIR CONDITIONING

Comfort

In each environmental situation the organism loses a certain quantity of energy due to the emission of sensible heat by convection and radiation and to the emission of latent heat by respiration. The quantity of emitted heat depends on the temperature and humidity of the environment, physical condition of the individual, his activity, etc.

The human being has a natural ability to adapt within certain temperature limits. The graph shown in Fig 27 gives recommended indoor temperatures in relation to the ambient for the crew of merchant ships, in order to avoid thermal shock in summer in particular. A number of different air conditioning systems are installed on reefer vessels today, some

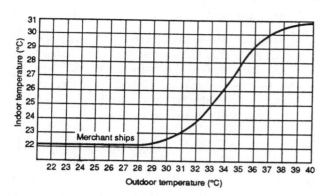

Figure 27 Recommended indoor temperatures for crew comfort.

Air handling unit (AHU)

The outside and recirculated air (50% or above) is mixed in the section of the unit fitted with dampers. It is then filtered and passes through preheaters and humidifiers in winter (cold) conditions, or through an air cooler in summer (warm) conditions. The fan distributes the conditioned air via a low velocity duct to cabins which are fitted with reheaters. Hot water, or steam is used for heating, and chilled water or refrigerant for cooling purposes. The rectangular or spiro ducts are insulated and connect the air handling unit with the cabin units fitted with reheaters.

Refrigerating plant

The refrigerating plant may utilize either a centrifugal or screw compressor (with the latter currently more popular), an shell and tube condenser, a liquid receiver and a shell and tube evaporator for chilled water. Air coolers may be fitted in the air handling

with individual temperature regulation in cabins, some without. It is likely that for a middle size reefer vessel in the worldwide trade, a single duct system with local reheating would be chosen. Such a system is illustrated in Fig 28.

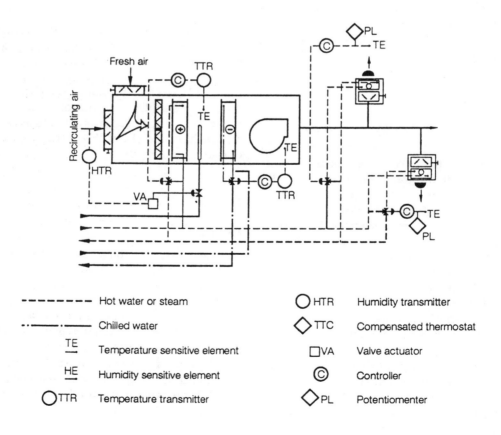

– – – – – – – Hot water or steam	◯ HTR	Humidity transmitter
–·–––––·––– Chilled water	◇ TTC	Compensated thermostat
T̲E̲ Temperature sensitive element	☐ VA	Valve actuator
H̲E̲ Humidity sensitive element	ⓒ	Controller
◯TTR Temperature transmitter	◇ PL	Potentiomenter

Figure 28 Single duct system with local reheating.

unit of smaller reefer vessels. R22 is used exclusively as a refrigerant. The plant may be fitted with a microprocessor based control, to increase efficiency and reliability of automatic operation at sea.

Self contained units

There are certain rooms in ships, such as control rooms, computer rooms, radio rooms, etc., where a specified temperature and humidity must be kept regardless of the main air conditioning plant operation. These rooms are usually conditioned with self contained units which operate as a complement to the main cooling plant, or as a standby.

CLASSIFICATION SOCIETY REQUIREMENTS

The part played by the classification societies in the development of refrigerated transport, although not particularly well documented, is nevertheless an important aspect and the following gives a brief account of the part played by Lloyd's Register of Shipping.

As the trade in refrigerated transport began to expand, the value of the cargo increased to such an extent that any failure of the refrigeration machinery or the insulation arrangements meant that the cargo underwriters faced very heavy losses. This loss of quality did not normally occur with general cargo provided the vessel was sound in construction and the cargo correctly stowed.

It was apparent to the owners and underwriters that a technical assessment of the cargo containment system—especially in view of early failures—by a reliable independent organisation with impartial status was necessary.

With such an assessment in mind the owners, underwriters and shippers approached the committee of Lloyd's Register of Shipping who finally agreed, in 1898, to undertake the task of immediately preparing the 'Rules for Refrigerated Cargo Installations'.

Lloyd's Register had on its staff an engineer surveyor, Mr Robert Balfour, who had considerable refrigeration knowledge and who produced a comprehensive report on the contemporary technology, on which rules could be formulated. The required rules were framed by a special sub-committee in consultation with the leading firms involved in supplying refrigeration equipment on board ship, and in 1898 the first set of classification society rules related to shipboard refrigerated carriage were approved and adopted by the technical committee of Lloyd's Register of Shipping.

These rules gave general satisfaction to all the interested parties and ensured that the refrigeration machinery, its installation onboard and the installation arrangement were of a quality and adequacy to give confidence in the successful carriage of the produce.

To show that the installation was built and installed to the satisfaction of Lloyd's Register of Shipping, the class notation ✠RMC (Refrigerated Machinery Certificate) was assigned in the Register Book. The first ship to have the notation ✠RMC was the *Wakool*, the survey of which was actually carried out before the Rules were finally approved. In 1910 the notation ✠RMC was amended to ✠Lloyd's RMC, a notation which is familiar to all engaged in marine refrigerated transport and which today is held by more than 520 installations, ranging from 21,000 m³ capacity down to a few hundred cubic metres.

Rule requirements

In order to maintain its RMC notation, any classed refrigerated cargo installation must undergo satisfactory periodical surveys as follows.

Annual survey

This is required at intervals of 12 months after the date of initial classification. Its purpose is to establish that the condition of the installation as a whole is satisfactory and the machinery is operating reliably and may be expected to continue to do so for the ensuing 12 months.

With a view to minimising interference with operational commitments, the survey requirements have been framed to avoid any opening up or dismantling unless the ship's records or external examination indicate the presence of some fault requiring attention. In general, refrigeration machinery with electric motors, air coolers and piping, insulation of cargo chambers, low temperature pipes and thermometers will be subjected to a visual inspection. The voyage logs will also be examined.

Special survey

This is to confirm the findings of examinations at the annual surveys by opening up plant and machinery every five years for the purpose of establishing that no concealed defects have developed. In general, refrigeration compressors operate under favourable conditions and are inherently reliable. It will be necessary to open up the compressors, shell and tube condensers and evaporators, examine carefully air coolers, pressure vessels and piping, and to remove some insulation from the refrigerant pipes to verify that it has not been affected by external corrosion. The cargo chambers' lining and insulation may be required to be removed for inspection purposes and foamed *in situ* polyurethane may be checked for shrinkage and absorption of water. Mineral wool does have a tendency to settle down in service and evidence must be seen that this is not the case on the inspected vessel.

'Condition of Class' may be recommended when objects are found which cannot receive immediate attention, but which do not jeopardize the operation of the installation for the required duty.

Loading port survey

This may be carried out at any time on one or more chambers to certify their condition prior to loading of a refrigerated cargo. The chambers must be clean and free from odour, and fitted with thermometers in working order. The electrical generating plant is inspected and refrigeration machinery is seen in operation. The temperature of each cargo chamber subjected to survey is noted and entered on the Certificate.

Loading port surveys are not mandatory and do not imply that the temperatures noted are necessarily suitable for the cargo which is to be carried. Nevertheless they clearly protect the interest of the shipowner, the cargo owner and the underwriter.

REGULATIONS

United States Department of Agriculture (USDA)

Since the early part the 20th century, sustained low temperature has been used as an effective method for the control of the Mediterranean and other tropical fruit flies. If infested fruit is continuously exposed to temperatures of 2.2°C or below for a sufficient period of time, so the various insects can be killed effectively. Procedures have been developed by the USDA so that this cold treatment quarantine method can be effectively applied to fruit while in transport.

USDA requires 'adequate' refrigeration, insulation and temperature control, but does not give a detailed specification. Equipment must be classified under the rules of an internationally recognised classification society, and there are special requirements for checking the calibration of the temperature recording system, which has to be accurate to ±0.15°C in the range −3°C to +3°C. The number of sensors required depends on the compartment volume, from a minimum of 4 for spaces up to 283 m^3 up to 10 for a space of 1981 m^3–2830 m^3. In containers, a return air sensor and two pulp sensors are sufficient, but these must be at prescribed positions in approved equipment and must be connected to approved temperature recorders.

All maintenance, repair and checks carried out on the equipment must be recorded in the work log book. Correction tables for the temperature sensors must be kept in the work log book.

Cold treatment temperature requirements depend on the species of fly to be controlled. Full details are given in the USDA PPQ Treatment Manual, with maximum permissible pulp temperatures of 2.22°C. In each case there is a range of alternative times and temperatures, and as an example the range for *Ceratitis capitata* (Mediterranean fruit fly) is as follows:

Necessary time (days)	Maximum temperature (°C)
10	0.00
11	0.55
12	1.11
14	1.66
16	2.22

For this treatment, it must be emphasised that if the pulp temperature exceeds the limit at any time, the whole quarantine period has to start again, e.g. in port. Alternatively, it may be possible to use an alternative fumigation treatment at port of entry.

Perishable Product Export Control Board (PPECB)

The PPECB requirements drafted by the South African Authorities apply to fruit and vegetables exported in containers. They require that the set air temperature within the container should not vary by more than 1°C. This may, depending on the container type and temperature difference between cargo and ambient, necessitate an increase in the air circulation rate from, say, 40 to 60 changes of air per hour within the container.

An additional requirement is to maintain the relative humidity within the container at a high level which PPECB defines as the temperature difference between the air leaving the air cooler and the surface temperature of the air cooler. This is essentially a water vapour pressure difference with its lower limit depending on the surface area of the cooler and its upper limit largely governed by water conditions at the surface of the particular fruit at the prescribed storage temperature.

Similar requirements apply to fruit and vegetable cargo transported on board reefer vessels.

The Agreement on the International Carriage of Perishable Foodstuffs and on the Special Equipment to be used for such carriage (ATP)

This agreement defines standards of insulation and refrigeration equipment performance for transport vehicles and containers. It also defines maximum temperatures for frozen and chilled produce, however it does not include fruit and vegetables.

The agreement applies to sea voyages shorter than 150 km.

Chapter 9
Steering Gears

Dr J Cowley

INTRODUCTION

The first steering systems were oars attached in various ways to the after quarters of boats propelled by oars, sail or a combination of both. When only a single wide bladed oar was used it was lashed or passed through a metal ring on the starboard (steerboard) after quarter. As the systems evolved, the blade of the oar became the rudder, the shank became the rudder stock and a tiller was added to facilitate a turning moment.

Remote transmission of power permitted a helmsman on the after deck to both see ahead and steer the ship. This was first achieved by the use of a rope attached to the tiller running on pulleys at right angles to it before passing twice round the drum on which the steering wheel was mounted. As the wheel was rotated, one turn paid out as the other wound in and the tiller moved to port or starboard depending upon the direction of movement of the wheel.

With the advent of steam, it became possible to move the position of the helmsman to amidships; steam engines provided the power and chains replaced ropes for rotating the tiller. A number of designs of steam steering gears were later developed and some are still in use. Following the introduction of electricity, systems utilising an electric motor through reduction gearing to a quadrant attached to the rudder post were introduced, with varying degrees of success. The problems of control of motor speed led to the introduction of electro-hydraulic steering gear systems. Today, the great majority of merchant vessel steering gears are of this type and there are no indications that this situation will change.

The design of the rudder is a matter for the naval architect and it is presumed that its area and proportions have been matched to the size and form of the vessel in each case considered. It is the job of marine engineers to design (and maintain) a steering gear of sufficient power and construction to control the rate of movement and position of the rudder accurately in all circumstances.

THE BASIC REQUIREMENTS FOR STEERING GEARS

In brief, a steering gear is required to:

a) be continuously available;

b) move the rudder rapidly to any position in response to the orders from the bridge during manoeuvring, and hold it in the required position;

c) have arrangements for relieving abnormal stress and returning the rudder to its required position;

d) maintain the ship on course regardless of wind and waves.

The manner in which these requirements are met will be discussed in greater detail, but note that the first three points are now governed by complicated statutory requirements and the last is of particular interest for economic reasons.

Continuous availability

Continuous availability depends upon reliability and the alternative arrangements available for maintaining continuity of steering capability. Complicated regulations prescribe the alternative arrangements required according to the size and type of vessel and, following the *Amoco Cadiz* disaster and the loss of some 230,000 tonnes of crude oil in the English Channel, the requirements for oil tankers are particularly severe. Reference to the statutory requirements will only be made in the context of running and mainte-

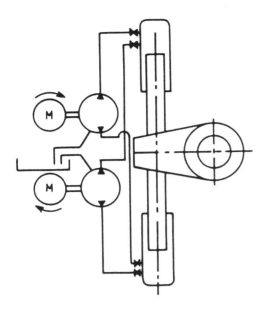

Figure 1 Steering gear permissible for all ships except tankers of 10,000 gt and upwards.

nance or general knowledge required of a marine engineer officer, and not as more than an introduction to the SOLAS regulations as amended in 1981.

Figure 1 is useful in discussing these points and introducing the terms adopted in regulations. It shows a two ram single acting electro-hydraulic steering gear in diagrammatic form which is acceptable for the category which includes new ships except tank-

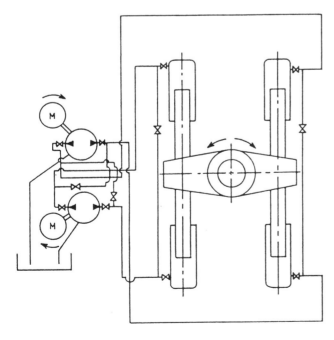

Figure 2 Permissible for all ships except tankers of 10,000 gt and upwards.

ers of 10,000 tons gross tonnage and upwards. The principles under discussion and the regulatory aspects are equally applicable to other electro-hydraulic designs (Figs 2 and 3) which also meet the requirements for this category. Purely for convenience in introducing the principles of availability, these figures show the steering gears with closed hydraulic systems and variable delivery pumps. In practice, fixed delivery pumps may be fitted and the hydraulic circuits may be open or closed.

The gear shown in Fig 1 is provided with duplicate identical power units (an electric motor and connected pump in duplicate) and duplicate piping with isolating valves. It thus meets the requirement that a single failure in its piping system or one of its power units can be isolated so that steering capability can be maintained or speedily regained. Neither the tiller nor the rudder actuator (hydraulic cylinders and rams) need be duplicated although ships fitted with ram type gears in this category (and particularly passenger ships) commonly have four ram gears which give a more even turning moment and a greater

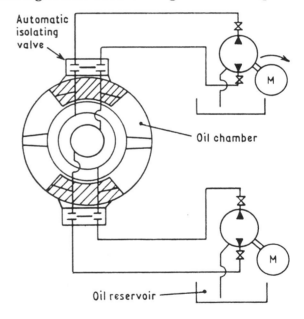

Figure 3 Permissible for all ships except tankers of 10,000 gt and upwards.

degree of duplication. Such an arrangement is shown in Fig 2 which shows the two power actuating systems comprising duplicated rudder actuators, power units (pump and motor) and the associated pipes and fittings. In the event of failure of either rudder actuator or its associated pipes, the effect can be isolated and steering continues using the unaffected power actuating system with the isolating valve between the cylinders of the defective system opened. A ro-

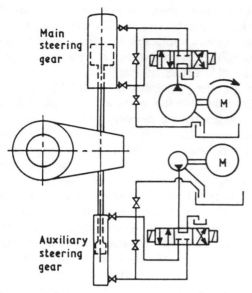

Figure 4 Permissible for all ships except tankers of 10,000 gt and upwards, and ships of 70,000 gt and upwards.

tary vane unit is shown in Fig 3. Again, a single failure in defective piping or a single power unit can be isolated manually and steering capability recovered. However, the weakness of all the arrangements in this category, and the lower category where the single failure criteria does not apply (Fig 4), is that the hydraulic fluid may be lost, resulting in uncontrolled rudder movement from a single failure in the common hydraulic system. Thus, damage not reparable at sea may occur before any effective remedial action can be taken. Against this weakness, however, must be set the extreme practical difficulties in simultaneously operating two independent hydraulic systems on the same rudder actuator (e.g. tiller) due to any differences in pump output or control mechanism, or leakage when responding to the common signal from the bridge for a given position of the rudder.

Tankers of 10,000 gt and upwards must, amongst other requirements, be provided with arrangements for regaining steering capability within 45 sec following a single failure of any part of the piping system or in one of the power units. Figure 5 shows one such arrangement suitable for all ships except tankers of 100,000 tons dwt and upwards. The upper unit is shown in operation. In the event of a leak outside the rotary vane actuator, the automatic isolating valve closes and rudder movement is prevented by the oil within the unit. The loss of oil outside the unit causes a reduction in the level of oil in the upper tank which can be detected and arranged to start up the other power unit within the 45 sec stipulated time limit.

Other requirements for hydraulic steering gears (Fig 10), include the provision of a low-level alarm for each hydraulic fluid reservoir, to give the earliest practicable indication of hydraulic fluid leakage (audible and visible alarms are required both on the navigating bridge and in the machinery space where they can be readily observed), and a fixed storage tank having sufficient capacity to recharge at least one power actuating system including the reservoir. The storage tank (ST) has to be permanently connected by piping such that the hydraulic systems can be readily recharged from a position within the steering gear compartment and must be provided with a contents gauge.

In the interests of continuous availability, regulatory authorities must ensure that all the steering gear components and the rudder stock are of sound and reliable construction, and that special consideration has been given to the suitability of any essential component which is not duplicated, such as the feed back from the rudder to the pump control mechanism (commonly called the hunting gear). Every essential component must use anti-friction bearings such as ball bearings, roller bearings or sleeve bearings, which must be permanently lubricated or provided with lubrication fittings.

The design pressures, used in calculations to determine the scantlings of piping and other steering gear components subjected to internal hydraulic pressure, must be at least 1.25 times the maximum working pressure to be expected when the rudder is put hard over port to starboard, when the ship is at her maximum seagoing draught and running ahead at maximum service speed. The regulatory authority may require that fatigue criteria be applied for the design of piping and components, taking into account pulsating pressures due to dynamic loads.

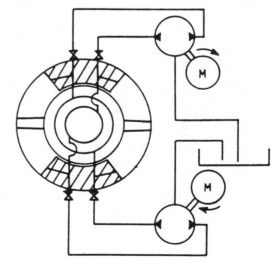

Figure 5 Permissible for all ships except tankers of 100,000 tdwt and upwards.

Rapidity of response, holding power and relief arrangements

Since the oil used in electro-hydraulic steering gears is virtually incompressible, discharge commences as soon as the control system (i.e. the system which transmits the orders from the navigating bridge) fractionally moves the stroke control on the pump (or pumps). As the pump and motor are already rotating, there is no loss of time in running up to speed and overcoming inertia effects, and the pump's output is immediately available to move the rudder.

The feed back arrangement will bring the rudder to rest at the desired position, where it will be held by the hydraulic pressure with the pump off stroke. In the event of leakage and consequent movement of the rudder, the feed back arrangement will put stroke on the pump and restore the rudder to the required position. The speed at which the rudder moves is regulated by the requirement that the main steering gear must be capable of putting the rudder over from 35 deg on one side to 35 deg on the other side with the ship at its deepest seagoing draft and running ahead at maximum ahead service speed and, under the same conditions, from 35 deg on either side to 30 deg on the other side in not more than 28 sec.

The regulations also require an auxiliary steering gear of adequate strength (since it has to operate in the same hostile environment following failure of the main steering gear), capable of steering the ship at navigable speed and of being brought speedily into action in emergency. It must be capable of putting the rudder over from 15 deg on one side to 15 deg on the other side in not more than 60 sec, with the ship at its deepest seagoing draught and running ahead at one half of the maximum ahead service speed or 7 kn, whichever is the greater. Figure 4 shows a permissible arrangement of a main steering gear with an open circuit, with a uni-directional pump and directional control valve and double acting piston. The auxiliary steering gear is similarly arranged but with a small power unit. In accordance with the amended regulations, the main and auxiliary units are completely independent. With this arrangement, the bypass valve between the ends of the cylinders of the auxiliary steering gear would have to be kept wide open during normal operation.

However, auxiliary steering gears as such are not commonly fitted since the regulations allow that where the main steering gear comprises two or more identical power units, (for tankers over 10,000 gt and other ships over 70,000 gt this is mandatory) an auxiliary steering gear need not be fitted, provided that in a passenger ship, the main steering gear is capable of operating the rudder from hard over to hard over as indicated above, while any one of the power units is out of operation. For a cargo ship, the main steering gear need only be capable of operating the rudder from hard over to hard over in 28 sec whilst operating with all power units. For all ships so fitted, the main steering gear must be so arranged that after a single failure in its piping system or in one of the power units, the defect can be isolated so that steering capability can be maintained or speedily regained.

The steering gear is safeguarded against abnormal loads by relief valves in duplicate such that excessive pressure on one side is bypassed to the low pressure side. The rudder will not correspond with the position of the helm immediately, but will, once the external load has passed, return to the required position under influence of the control system.

Sensitivity and economy

For a given passage, the distance actually travelled (and fuel consumed) will depend upon a vessel's ability to maintain the desired course. For a given sensitivity of autopilot, the ability to maintain course depends upon the sensitivity of the steering gear. The rapid and accurate response of well maintained electro-hydraulic steering minimizes the distance travelled and results in an economy of operation far in excess of other systems. Since ships spend most of their time on passage where close course keeping is important, modulating arrangements may be incorporated in the control system to provide a soft start, i.e. low flow rate at small rudder angles and a high flow rate at the larger angles required during manoeuvring.

Steering gear testing and drills and examinations

Under international (IMO, SOLAS) regulations the Master must, within 12 hours before each departure (except for ships on short voyages on which the tests must be carried out weekly) ensure that the steering gear is checked and tested in order to be sure that it is working satisfactorily. The requirements for steering gears depend on the age and size of the vessel, which may not have all the equipment included in the list of tests and checks, so the words 'where applicable' are included in the regulations, an extract from which follows.

'The test procedure shall include, where applicable, the operation of the following:

a) the main steering gear;

b) the auxiliary steering gear;

c) the remote steering gear control systems;

d) the steering positions located on the navigating bridge;

e) the emergency power supply;

f) the rudder angle indicators in relating to the actual position of the rudder;

g) the remote steering gear control system power failure alarms;

h) the steering gear power unit failure alarms; and

i) the automatic isolating arrangements and other automatic equipment required for steering gear.

The checks and tests shall include:

a) the full movement of the rudder according to the required capabilities of the steering gear;

b) a visual inspection of the steering gear and its connecting linkage; and

c) the operation of the means of communication between the navigating bridge and the steering gear compartment.'

It is too late to start tracing lines and ascertaining the functions of valves at the time of an emergency and all relevant staff should be familiar with the operation of the steering gear and the disposition and purpose of the isolating and bypass valves for emergency use and be aware of the procedures to be followed in the event of any failure. The regulations require that emergency steering gear drills be carried out at least every three months. These drills must include direct control from the steering gear compartment, the communications procedure with the navigation bridge and, where applicable, the operation of alternative power supplies. Simple operating instructions with a block diagram showing the change-over procedures for remote steering gear control systems and steering gear power units must be permanently displayed on the navigation bridge and in the steering gear compartment.

Under United Kingdom legislation, implementing the SOLAS regulations given above, the date and place of carrying out the mandatory drills, checks and tests must be entered in the log book. Non-compliance could lead to fines of up to £1,000 on summary conviction or, on conviction on indictment, imprisonment up to two years or a fine, or both.

The procedures in conducting the mandatory tests listed above will vary with the actual equipment provided. The system may be provided with unidirectional or variable delivery main pumps, auxiliary pumps, a variety of automatic isolating and control equipment, and open or closed hydraulic systems. Regardless of the system provided, any manufacturer's recommendations and owner's instructions should be strictly followed. The steering gears of many ships were installed before the mandatory tests were introduced and some general comments relating to routine operations following a normal shut down after arrival in port are given below.

Prior to the tests, the deck department should be informed and it should be verified that there are no obstructions in way of the rudder. In excessively cold ambient temperatures, the heating system in the steering gear compartment or the oil heater (only supplied at owner's request) should be used. In any case, at ambient temperatures lower than 10°C, as the oil warms up the gear should be inched over using the remote control handwheel in the steering compartment to gradually heat the oil in the system. The power units should be run for some thirty minutes before departure to raise the oil temperature and occasional rudder movements made to facilitate a uniform system temperature.

The oil level in the supply tank should be checked and topped up to about 75% of its capacity (see *Maintenance*) and where arrangements are provided for testing low level alarms these should be operated. The engineer officer should check over linkages to ensure that they are free and will not be impeded or prevented from operating satisfactorily, check that sliding surfaces are properly lubricated, and check for leakages from the system. Rams should be lubricated with system oil, and the engineer officer should check that individual grease nipples or the central greasing system, if fitted for the ram guides, are full and providing lubrication. The connecting pin should be removed from the steering from its navigating bridge position and inserted into position for control of the steering gear (by 'trick wheel') from within the steering gear compartment. The rudder should be moved hard over to hard over using each power unit in turn before cutting off the power to test the audible and visible alarms on the bridge. At the same time, the position of the tiller as indicated in the steering compartment should be checked against the position indicated on the bridge by the rudder angle indicator using (testing) the communication system provided and it should be verified that the light provided on the bridge to indicate the running motor of the power unit is working.

With the connecting pin replaced in position for telemotor steering, the tiller should be operated from the bridge by (say) the port power unit. Disconnecting the power supply to that unit would test the automatic start-up arrangements (if provided) for the starboard unit which could otherwise be started manually from the bridge. The test should be repeated using the starboard motor. With both power units running, opening the power supply breaker and then closing it would check the automatic restart arrangements. Each control system provided should be tested and, in the case of electric systems, the power supply should be interrupted to test the audible and visible alarms on the navigating bridge. If a hydraulic system is fitted, the level of the hydraulic fluid should be checked.

In the case of ships built since September 1984, having rudder stocks over 230 mm diameter in way of the tiller, an alternative source of power capable of operating the rudder from 15 deg on one side to 15 deg on the other side must be provided automatically within 45 seconds, either from the emergency source of electrical power or from an independent source of power (e.g. a diesel engine driving a pump and used only for this purpose) situated within the steering gear compartment. For ships over 10,000 gt and upwards, this alternative supply must last for at least 30 minutes; in smaller ships, for at least 10 minutes. If this source is taken from the emergency generator, one of the two exclusive circuits required to power the steering gear will normally be led through the emergency switchboard and the other directly from the main switchboard. Isolating the direct supply line and opening the breaker between the main and emergency switchboards would test the automatic starting of the emergency generator and supply power to the steering gear.

For many existing ships, the steering gear regulations were not comprehensive and the 1978 SOLAS Protocol regulations, which entered into force in May 1981, applied to oil tankers only and were not made retrospective in their entirety. Similarly, the SOLAS Amendment regulations made in 1981 after the *Amoco Cadiz* casualty were mainly concerned with oil, gas and chemical tankers and retrospective requirements only applied to such ships from September 1988 (the requirements for new ships entered into force in September 1984). However, many ships are provided with equipment over and above the mandatory requirements and the testing and drills regulations apply equally to mandatory and non-mandatory equipment. It is for each master and chief engineer to ensure that all equipment is checked and tested and that 'all ship's officers concerned with the operation or maintenance of steering gear shall be familiar with the operation of the steering systems fitted on the ship and with the procedures for changing from one system to another'.

OPERATION OF STEERING GEARS

The great majority of ships are fitted with two identical power units and it is common practice to operate with one unit in open water.

Arrangements have normally been provided whereby an audible and visible alarm is given on the navigating bridge in the event of power failure to any power unit, the power unit(s) in operation automatically restarts after a power failure, and the idle power unit can be brought into operation either manually or automatically in the event of failure of the running unit.

Automatic starting gives continuity of steering capability which is advantageous in confined waters. Manual operation has a considerable advantage in that it provides an opportunity to examine the hydraulic system to avoid inevitable damage to the standby power unit, in the event of the hydraulic fluid being contaminated by particulate matter.

It is possible, of course, to operate the power unit starting arrangements in such a way that automatic start will only occur in confined waters.

International regulations now require that, in areas where navigation demands special caution, ships must have more than one steering gear power unit in operation when such units are capable of simultaneous operation. The philosophy is that if one unit should fail the other unit would already be operating the gear. It also provides a higher rate of rudder movement and, for most ships, a faster rate of turn. However, it must be mentioned that in view of the above provisions, this requirement has been criticised and, in the event of certain failures, may result in accidents if correct procedures are not followed in the attempts to recover steerage.

Figure 6 illustrates both the possible consequences of a defect in the system which can lead to loss of steering capability, and the principle of the control system. Essentially, it shows only those parts of the hydraulic circuit needed to illustrate the consequences of a control valve sticking, i.e. relief valves, make-up arrangements and filters have been omitted for clarity. In the figure, PV1 and PV2 are spring loaded solenoid operated pilot valves controlled by a remote control system. Movement of the helm imbalances a potentiometer to activate the solenoids of the pilot valves and move them in the direction needed to cause the steering gear to move the rudder into the position required by the bridge. As the rudder re-

a)

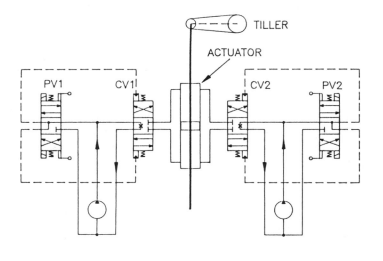

b)

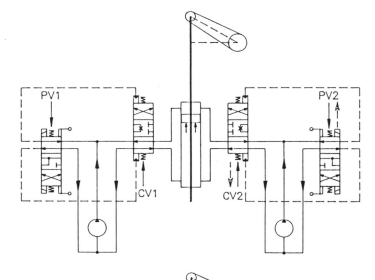

c)

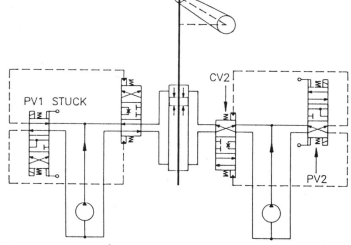

Figure 6   Hydraulic lock due to seized pilot valve: a) normal operation with two pumps running, no helm applied; b) as a), but turn to port required; c) turn to starboard required, PV2 responds and opens CV2 for downward movement of actuator.

sponds, the feed back arrangements correct the imbalance of the potentiometer and return the pilot valves back to their neutral positions, leaving the system in hydraulic lock at the required angle of helm.

If any problems are experienced with the helm control, there is an alternative electrical circuit to the solenoids of the pilot valves on a non follow-up facility. The pilot valves are necessary because of the control valves CV1 and CV2 which in turn direct the output of the uni-directional pumps so as to move the actuator in the required direction. The actuator is shown, for convenience, as a simple double-acting piston arrangement but should be taken to represent the actuator of any type of hydraulic steering gear.

Figure 6a shows the situation with the rudder and actuator in mid positions and all valves in neutral positions. The two uni-directional constant delivery pumps are discharging through the control valves and back to the suction side. No helm is being applied.

Figure 6b shows the situation with the rudder being moved to port through clockwise rotation of the tiller. Both pilot valves have moved downwards under solenoid control in response to the helm movement, and have admitted oil to the underside of the control valves. The output from the pumps has consequently been directed to the underside of the actuator piston. The arrows adjacent to the valve notations indicate the initial direction of the valves' movements from their neutral positions. If, say, pilot valve PV1 sticks in the position shown, by the time the helm reaches the desired position, the feed back arrangements will have removed the potentiometer imbalance and PV2 will be in the neutral position but CV1 will still be under the control of PV1 and the rudder will move hard over to port. Operation of the override through the alternative supply to the solenoids of the pilot valves will be ineffective since PV1 is stuck. Movement of the helm to give full starboard helm (as shown in Fig 6c) will not move the rudder since the system is in hydraulic lock.

The navigating staff will not know which power unit is defective. To quickly remedy the situation, both units should be switched off and then each one started in turn to establish which one is defective. Steering can then continue on the good unit.

A similar situation can occur in systems using variable displacement swash plate pumps operated by servos if the linkage or one of the directional control valves sticks and the buffer springs are not powerful enough to overcome the friction. H R Selby has described an incident in which a sticking directional control valve was considered to be the major contributory factor to a collision and subsequent loss of a vessel.[1] The steering gear in question was a rotary vane unit but the same control system is used on ram type gears using a variable displacement pump with a shuttle valve on the servo system to change the direction of the pump's displacement. In such cases, the shuttle valve may be activated either by the telemotor gear through linkage, or by a direct electric solenoid. In such cases, jamming of the shuttle control valve or the linkage of one of two units operating simultaneously can cause stalling of the steering gear.

In the case described, the two hydraulic power units were separated by a telemotor control box.

'Each power unit consisted of an electric motor driving a variable displacement swash plate pump operated by a servo. The servo was controlled by a series of links attached to the telemotor shaft. Buffer springs were provided in the linkage to allow operation with one or two units. The sequence of events which caused the alleged incident was determined by analysis and was successfully simulated on several occasions.

1. An order to go to starboard was given and the rudder responded (Fig 7a),

2. When the ship was swinging, amidships was ordered. The telemotor moved to amidships and the linkage closed the starboard directional control valves and opened the port valves (Fig 7b),

3. As the rudder approached amidships the hunting gear moved the first stage of the linkage to amidships. The linkage on the port steering gear motor had stuck in the port position and the buffer springs were not powerful enough to overcome the friction in the linkage. As a result, the power unit continued swinging the rudder to port whilst the starboard came to the neutral position (Fig 7c),

4. As the rudder continued to swing to port, the hunting gear opened the starboard directional control valve on the starboard steering gear; but the rudder was swinging hard to port and the starboard unit could not overcome the port power unit. The wheel was put hard to starboard as the ship continued to swing,

5. In the final condition the rudder was hard to port with the wheel hard to starboard and the steering gear in an hydraulic lock (Fig 7d),

6. The ship swung to port and struck an anchored vessel which subsequently sank.'

Critics of the requirement to operate both power units simultaneously in close waters believe that it is

a)

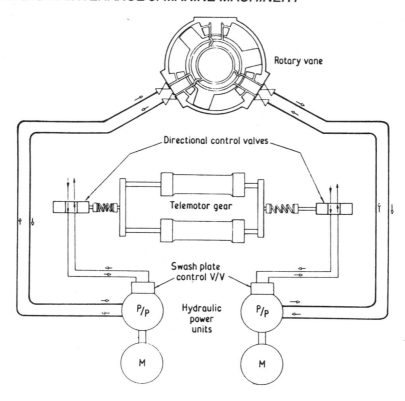

b)

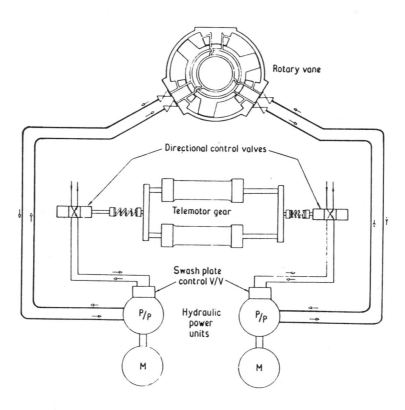

Figure 7   Sequence of events in incident where sticking directional control valve caused collision and loss of vessel: a) normal movement to starboard; b) returning to midships;

c)

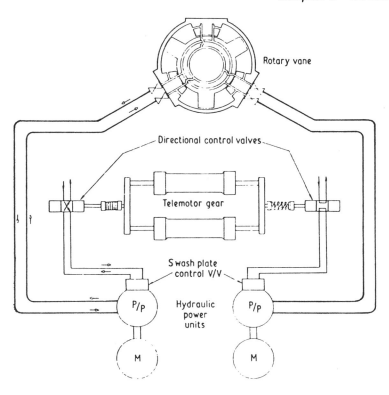

d)

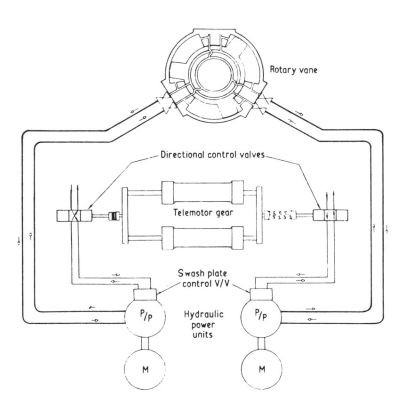

Figure 7 (contd.)   Sequence of events in incident where sticking directional control valve caused collision and loss of vessel: c) midships with port linkage jammed; d) rudder to port, telemotor to starboard (hydraulic lock).

preferable to operate only a single power unit in confined waters. There would then be no doubt in the navigator's mind if defects occurred. The running unit would be shutoff and the standby unit started. The critics claim, with some justification, that the time taken in changing to the alternative override electrical supply and then ascertaining which unit is defective is much greater than with one unit running. If it is necessary for the gear to be moved at the rate achieved by two power units acting simultaneously, they suggest that statutory requirements be upgraded so that the higher rate can be met by each power unit operating alone. This would not be too unreasonable for smaller ships but it would be extremely onerous for very large ships which have three or more pumps.

Whatever the merits of the argument, the importance of maintaining the cleanliness of hydraulic systems and the condition of linkages is paramount. The possibility of sticking of hydraulic components will be reduced if steering is switched from auto-pilot to hand control for a short period each day and some companies have standing orders to this effect.

Notice, in Fig 6, that the spring loaded pilot valves PV1 and PV2 may, in addition to solenoid control, be operated manually. Thus, in the event of loss of the control systems, the rudder can be operated from within the steering gear compartment. Orders from the bridge can be communicated to a person standing by the pilot valve who operates it manually in response to those orders. This procedure has been successfully used to overcome complete breakdown of the control system. Similar arrangements may be fitted on the servos of variable delivery pumps.

HYDRAULIC SYSTEMS

Maintenance

Steering gear manufacturers, recognising the problems of shipboard conditions, have designed gears which can be installed on board as complete units with their hydraulic systems virtually intact and often only hydraulic oil reservoirs need to be connected to the system during installation. Consequently, these general comments do not apply to initial installation nor to the extensive measures taken during manufacture and following assembly to ensure that they are free from actual and potential contamination from manufacturing processes.

It follows from the manufacturers' efforts to install steering gears as closed units that the system should not be opened up unnecessarily. It is preferable to rely on monitoring procedures to check the system's performance. These procedures may involve the monitoring of temperatures, pressures, vibration and noise as well as periodic sampling of the working fluid. If it is necessary to open up the system for maintenance or repair, temporary seals should be fitted at all openings to prevent the ingress of contamination. Special care should be taken, when removing sealing rings or gaskets, to avoid scoring surfaces with screwdrivers or similar implements. Replacement components should be inspected internally for contamination, corrosion, damage or other deterioration. The conditions during opening up and examination of components should be controlled. A special clean area should be established and no welding, chipping, drilling or dirt-generating operations should be carried out in the vicinity. If, during overhauling, components are found to have suffered wear, it is probable that the system oil is contaminated. It will be necessary to replace the oil otherwise the maintenance effort will be wasted. If specialist firms are employed in the case of major repairs or contamination, they will isolate sensitive components with jump leads and provide flushing rigs with external pumps and high capacity filters. If such assistance is not available, all practicable measures must be taken and special attention paid to the filters of the system following any disturbance of the hydraulic circuit.

When replenishing the system after repairs, guidance from the maker should be followed. The position of all the valves in the system should be checked to ensure that they are in accordance with the nameplate on the steering gear. The gear should be changed over from telemotor to local control by handwheel within the steering gear compartment and this handwheel should be used to control movements of the steering gear during the refilling operation. The oil supply tank level should be checked. Depending upon the particular system arrangement, the supply tank may be a reserve tank, or an expansion or similar tank within the hydraulic circuit. In the latter cases, provision for topping up from a reserve tank must be in place, including filtering arrangements. The objective is to completely remove air and fill the system with clean oil. If fluid is to be admitted other than from the tanks, for example to a rotary vane actuator cover, the surfaces surrounding the opening should be thoroughly cleaned and the fluid added through an appropriately sized filter (see *Cleanliness*). If, however, an emergency filling line is provided, the actuator should be charged through the stop valves on the unit with the bypass valve open, and air vented through the air release valves on the actuator and on the pumps.

Some systems provide for turning the pumps by hand by means of a bar inserted in holes in the flexible coupling between motor and pump. Then, with the motor stopped, the pump may be put on stroke by means of the local handwheel and the pump turned as the air release valves on the actuator are opened in rotation. The replenishing tank must be kept topped-up during the operation. When its level ceases to fall and only air-free fluid is escaping, the air release valves and the bypass should be closed and all valves returned to their normal running positions and the motor started. Under local control, the gear should be run slowly from hard over to hard over several times, using first one pump and then the other, whilst the air release valves are periodically opened to ensure that all air has been released.

On a hydraulic ram type gear, the air would first be vented through the pump air release arrangements as the casing and sump are filled. The air release valves on the cylinders would then be opened and the gear very gradually moved first in one direction and then the other. The travel of the rams should be gradually increased until air-free oil is discharged, and the rams should then be closed. The procedure is then as for the rotary vane system outlined above. In all systems, the gear should be turned over several times after a few hours and any remaining air should be vented from the system.

Piping

Steering gear piping and other components should be capable of withstanding the pulsating pressures which arise due to dynamic loads resulting from external forces on the rudder, and rapid demands during manoeuvring, as well as the stresses due to vibration. The piping should be adequately supported in order to minimise the effects of vibration and flexure under pressure, and any excessive vibration should be investigated and appropriate supports provided.

The piping should be examined for cracks, particularly carefully around attachments to flanges. The flexible pipes of pinned actuator steering gears should be examined for damage and replaced in cases of doubt regarding their suitability. Furthermore, as the weight of piping may impose significant loads on the connecting flanges, the securing arrangements should be periodically examined and any broken or corroded studs should be replaced with new studs to the original specification.

At the same time, the tightness of the bedplate holding down bolts and other attachments, nuts and keys should be checked and the necessary remedial measures taken.

A thorough examination should also be carried out whenever it is suspected that the installation may have been affected by rudder contact.

Recorded observations of the hydraulic pressure, in comparative circumstances (oil temperature and depth of loading), are a useful indication of the condition of the gear, and higher than normal pressures could indicate jamming within the gear, misalignment of the rudder or, in the case of a gradual increase in pressure, excessive wear of the rudder bearings.

The system should be periodically inspected for leaks, particularly at seals and joints. Exposed working surfaces (e.g. rams) should be kept clean.

Oil reservoirs

Depending upon the particular system, the functions of the reservoir include the following.

1. Providing a safe working level and a continuously available source of oil for the pump suction on open loop systems, and a make-up supply and receiver for excess fluid due to expansion in closed systems.

2. Receiving the oil returned from the system and removing the air from it. For this purpose it should have about 25% excess capacity above its normal working level so as to present a free surface to clean atmospheric air.

3. Dissipating the heat generated in the pumps in systems not fitted with coolers.

4. Providing a long residence time for the oil to enable larger contaminants to settle out.

5. Housing alarm and control arrangements for coping with leakages from the system.

From the above functions it will be evident that fluid level in the reservoir should be maintained at a level of about 75% of its capacity. If an excessive fall in level occurs, suction vortexes may be formed which draw air into the system, resulting in deterioration of the oil and noisy operation of the plant. Prolonged operation with a low oil level may result in temperatures over 80°C and consequent deterioration of the oil. Furthermore, the residence time with the reservoir for the settling-out of particles will be reduced.

Special care should be taken when topping up the reservoir to ensure that contaminants around the filling connection do not enter the system.

The inside of the oil reservoir should be inspected periodically at the intervals stated in the manufacturer's handbook, or at 5 yearly intervals, or according to previous experience of operating the system. If the internal surfaces have deteriorated, they should be descaled and treated with corrosion resistant paint.

Cleanliness

In recognition of the problems which will inevitably arise if hydraulic fluid of appropriate cleanliness is not provided, the SOLAS Amendments have introduced a mandatory requirement that 'arrangements to maintain the cleanliness of the hydraulic fluid taking into consideration the type and design of the hydraulic system' shall be provided. Regulatory authorities are left to decide how this requirement is enforced but it is difficult to see how the problem can be solved by specific regulations since electro-hydraulic steering gears currently operate at pressures varying between 60 bar and 280 bar. High pressures mean smaller and lighter systems but the range of components is limited and they require superior operating and maintenance conditions than are generally available on ships. Conversely, low pressure systems permit the choice of a wide range of components but need large cylinders to transmit the power and correspondingly large valves, piping and pumps to move the high volume of oil required. Low pressure systems are generally operated as open loops. Rotary vane units come within the lower pressure range (60 to 75 bar) because of sealing difficulties at higher pressures. In general, the higher the working pressure with consequential smaller working clearances and smoother working surfaces, the greater will be the sensitivity of the components to contamination. Whilst low pressure radial pumps (e.g. Hele-Shaw type) will operate with oil level contamination up to 100 microns, axial piston pumps require filtration at 10 microns and may fail if subjected to particles of nominal size of 20 microns. At this point, it must be mentioned that the rating of filters is complicated. For example, a nominal rating (as used in this chapter for convenience) of, say, 10 microns does not mean that the filter will stop all particles of greater size and let pass all smaller ones. The particular specification must be consulted, e.g. the filter may be specified as being capable of removing, under test conditions, 98% by weight of all particles of stated contaminant larger than 10 microns at a certain high concentration. The disadvantages of nominal ratings are that they do not specify the maximum size of the particles which may pass through the filter and the high concentration of contaminants used in the test is not typical of the conditions in practical systems.

Other standards specify the proportions of particles of given sizes which will pass through the filter under given test conditions. For example, Abex/Denison pump manufacturers specify for their axial piston pumps that filter micron sizes should be chosen to meet or exceed the NAS 1638 cleanliness levels (Table 1).

These brief introductory comments are provided for background information and an appreciation of the complexity and importance of filtration. The designer will certainly have chosen the level of filtration with care and, from safe operational considerations, it is essential that engineer officers ensure that replacement filters are ordered to the original specifications. A lower level of filtration may lead to rapid deterioration of the system whilst use of finer filters may lead to flow reductions, cavitation at pump suctions, rapid clogging of filters and bypassing of contaminants or unnecessarily frequent cleaning or replacement of filters.

Contamination may:

a) be taken into the system during manufacture, assembly or installation or during repairs;

b) be taken into the system during service;

c) result from mechanical wear and erosion; or

d) arise from chemical reactions in the system.

Precautions taken by manufacturers to avoid 'built in' contamination have already been mentioned, as has the need for care in topping up reservoirs. Pouring in oil from open containers such as buckets should be avoided if possible and many systems are provided with permanently connected hand pumps to prevent contamination from this procedure. Steering gear manufacturers have said that even new fluid may not meet the 10 micron standard required by the system. Since oil which has been handled or stored in reserve tanks may include contaminants or corrosion products, an appropriately sized filter should be included in the filling line. Attention to leaks will lessen the possibility of contaminants being added with the make-up oil. If a filter is not provided in the reservoir air pipe, solid air-borne particles may enter the system.

The area around air cocks, sampling points and filter bodies should be kept clean and dust free to prevent ingress of dirt during routine operations.

Opening up the system (see *Maintenance*) presents the greatest potential for ingressed contamination and if it is essential to work on hydraulic pumps and

Table 1   NAS 1638 cleanliness levels.

Particle size (microns, m)	Maximum allowed in 100 ml sample	NAS 1638 class level
5-15	128,000	9
15-25	11,400	8
25-50	2,025	8
50-100	360	8
over 100	64	8

control systems in the unsuitable conditions on board ship or in most shipyards, every precaution must be taken and reference made to the manufacturer's literature. In particular, if it should be necessary to drain down the system without renewal of the oil, sufficient scrupulously clean containers and effective sealing arrangements should be provided.

System generated contamination arises from the abrasion of seals and bearing surfaces. The solid contaminants will, if not filtered out, cause further abrasion and progressive deterioration. Small particles may, during period of agitation, form agglomerations (e.g. 100 microns or more) which are of greater size than the working clearances.

In addition to their abrasive effect, the solid particles deplete the oxygen inhibitor of the oil and thus increase the potential for corrosion.

Chemical reactions can occur due to:

a) presence of water (e.g. condensation in reservoir following shutdown or during maintenance);

b) salt (from sea water cooler leaks, spray droplets during maintenance or fluid passage over dry salt-covered surfaces);

c) oxygen;

d) a combination of the effects of two or three of water, salt and oxygen.

Corrosion products formed within the system can lead to a progressively deteriorating condition of the system. Their abrasive action exposes clean metal surfaces to further corrosion and the corrosion inhibitor of the fluid becomes depleted.

Oxidation of the hydraulic fluid is accelerated when it becomes locally overheated within the pump casing or when the oil temperature rises generally due to prolonged operation with a low reservoir level. The oil may develop a brownish black appearance, lose viscosity, become acidic and, in extreme cases, form sludges.

Fluid samples should be taken regularly to determine the condition of the fluid. Analysis will determine whether the pH value is satisfactory, or the fluid is breaking down chemically, or indicate the presence of particulate matter.

The sizes of solid particle contaminants in hydraulic systems are usually expressed in micro-metres (μm) or microns. This unit is 10^{-6} metres, i.e. about 0.04 thousands of an inch. For comparative purposes, the unaided human eye can resolve particles of about 40 microns and steering gear manufacturers are specifying filtration levels of 10 microns for the main hydraulic circuit and 3 microns for the servo systems. This comparison indicates the extremely small size of

the contaminating particles and the corresponding care required when oil is added to the system, when filter elements are replaced, or when maintenance is being undertaken.

The level of filtration required for a steering gear installation depends upon the contamination sensitivity of the individual components in the hydraulic circuits. A single suction side filter of 100 microns or more may be satisfactory for a low pressure radial piston pump whilst several filters may be required in complicated systems with high pressure axial pumps. Control systems may be provided with filtration levels down to 3 microns.

Particles greater in size than the working clearances (chips) can cause catastrophic failure whilst smaller particles in the range 3 to 15 microns (silt) can conglomerate and cause sluggishness and wear and lead to intermittent failures in operation. All engineer officers should be aware of the position of the filters which will have been determined from practical considerations.

The inlet side of pumps is always provided with a filter capable of removing chips and suction side filtration levels are normally between 50 microns and 100 microns mesh strainers but it is sometimes necessary to provide even finer filtration for the protection of the bearing surfaces. However, if possible, silt filters are sited elsewhere in the circuit because of the high pressure drop due to the viscosity of the fluid. This pressure drop could cause cavitation and conse-

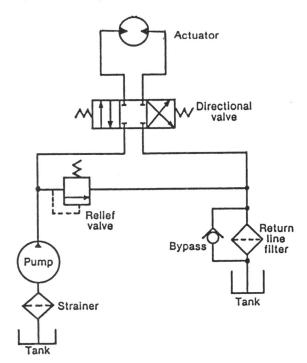

Figure 8 Open loop system with bypass return line filter.

a)

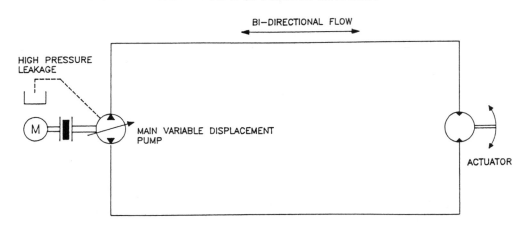

b)

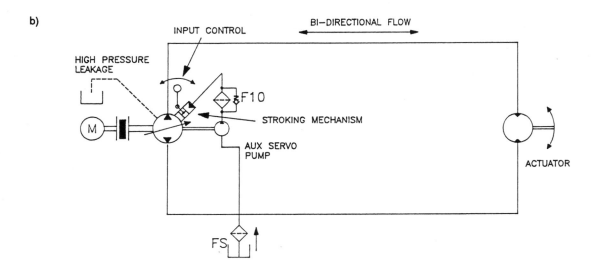

c)

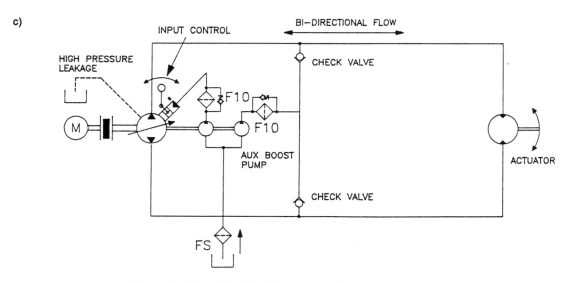

Figure 9 Closed circuit build up of parts of the system of a high pressure circuit:
a) basic circuit; b) pump displacement control added; c) boost flow added.

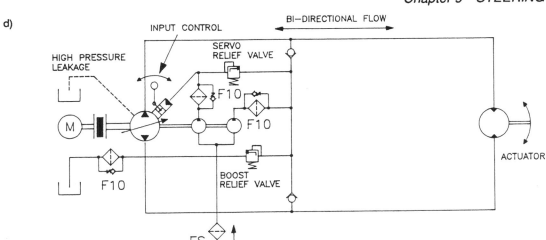

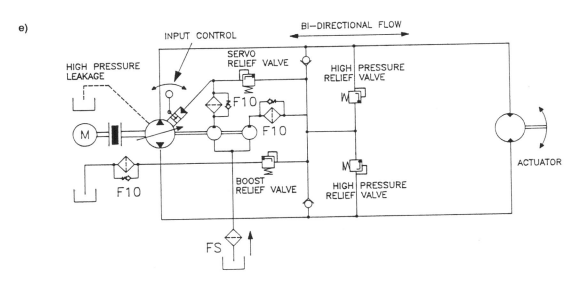

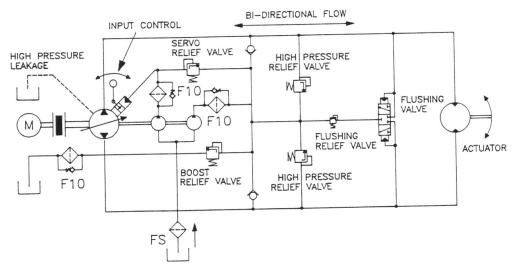

Figure 9 (contd)   Closed circuit build up of parts of the system of a high pressure circuit:
d) servo and boost relief valves added; e) high pressure relief valves added; f) flushing valve added.

quent damage to the pump and a bypass arrangement would be necessary to prevent starvation at the pump entry during cold starts.

In open loop systems, a silt filter in the return line to the reservoir would intercept all the oil subsequently to be returned to the system (Fig 8). In partially open loop systems a proportion of the charge pump discharge is generally passed through a return line filter to control the silt generated in the system.

In systems fitted with single uni-directional pumps, full flow silt filters with automatic bypass at pressure differences of around two bars may be sited in the pump discharge.

Closed systems with surcharge (boost) pumps serving variable delivery main pumps would normally have a full flow silt filter in the surcharge pump discharge. Where variable delivery pump sensitivities permit, filters on the surcharge pump discharges are fitted in this manner to avoid the high pulsating pressures on the discharges of the main pumps. The positioning of filters is also discussed in the following description of high pressure hydraulic circuit build up, and Fig 9.

It is not possible to state specific periods for filter element cleaning or renewal, but spare elements should always be available and action must be taken when clogging indicators show increased pressure drops. If filters begin to choke, servo-systems will become sluggish and this may be noticed by the deck department during manoeuvring.

Particular attention should be paid to the filters following repairs or in new systems during the running-in period of, e.g., the sealing arrangements of rotary vane gears. If contamination is present the filter should be cleaned at short intervals until it stays clean. Even in the absence of excessive pressure drops, it is good practice to examine the silt filters annually as a check on the condition of the system. Chip filters in reservoirs should not require examination more often than annually, or even only when the tank is opened up for examination.

It must be emphasised that filter elements should be replaced before they give rise to unacceptably high pressure drops which may lead to failure of the filter medium or opening of the by pass valve if fitted, and that, before opening up filters, the area around the joining surfaces should be thoroughly cleaned.

Highly powered closed loop circuits

Reference has been made to the rule requirement to operate with two power units in operation in confined waters, and when one power unit is in operation, the need to rapidly be able to change-over power units, the prevention of windmilling of the idle pump by the running pump, and the ability to restore steering capability immediately on restoration of power following a blackout.

These are onerous requirements for a highly powered installation and this section briefly describes how a hydraulic circuit might be arranged to meet these objectives of ready availability. Hydraulic circuits are complicated due to the number of components. Therefore, for descriptive reasons, a closed circuit build-up of parts of the system of a high pressure circuit is presented in Figure 9.

Figure 9a shows the basic closed circuit in which a constant speed motor M is driving a high pressure variable delivery axial pump controlling the movement of a steering gear actuator. The dotted line represents high pressure leakage from the pump back to the tank.

Figure 9b shows the addition of pump displacement control which is hydraulically powered by the auxiliary servo pump. This servo pump is shaft driven by the same motor as the main pump. A 10 micron filter (F10) with pressure bypass is indicated on the servo pump discharge and a chip strainer (FS) is indicated at the tank.

In Fig 9c, an auxiliary boost pump and check valves have been added to the basic closed circuit of Fig 9a. The boost pressure oil is fed through the check valve on the low pressure side of the actuator circuit whilst the other check valve prevents high pressure return flow. A 10 micron bypass filter is indicated on the auxiliary boost discharge pump.

Figure 9d shows the addition of a servo pump relief valve discharging into the boost pressure line and a boost pressure relief valve discharging through a 10 micron return filter, with pressure bypass.

Figure 9e shows both boost and servo control sub-circuits together with pressure control of the main circuit. The high pressure relief valves limit the pressure in the actuator circuit by discharging through the boost pressure check valves opening into the low pressure side of the actuator circuit.

In Figure 9f, flushing has been introduced whereby the flushing relief valve controls the flow through the pressure operated flushing valve by discharging into the boost pressure line and through the boost pressure relief valve and bypass return filter to the tank.

System with axial piston pumps

All the above features are included in Fig 10 which shows one of the circuit designs of the specialist steering gear manufacturing firm, Brown Brothers. This hydraulic sub-circuit related to a four ram electro-hydraulic steering gear fitted with Hagglunds Denison Gold Cup pumps.

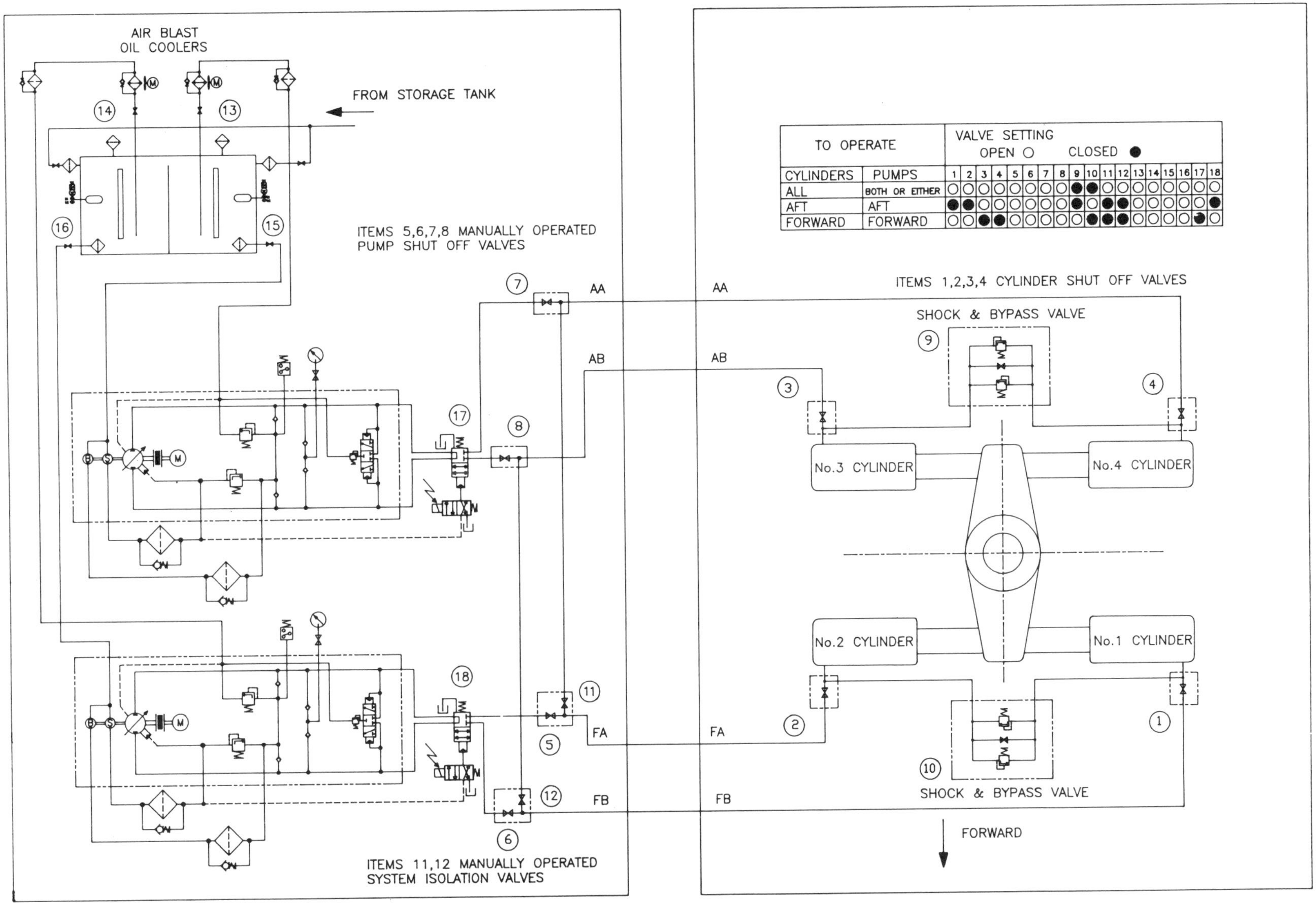

TO OPERATE		VALVE SETTING OPEN ○ CLOSED ●																	
CYLINDERS	PUMPS	1	2	3	4	5	6	7	8	9	10	11	12	13	14	15	16	17	18
ALL	BOTH OR EITHER	○	○	○	○	○	○	○	○	●	●	○	○	○	○	○	○	○	○
AFT	AFT	●	●	○	○	○	○	○	○	●	○	●	●	○	○	○	○	○	●
FORWARD	FORWARD	○	○	●	●	○	○	○	○	○	●	●	●	○	○	○	○	●	○

Figure 10 Hydraulic subsystem.

Each power unit of the system includes a 440V squirrel cage main motor suitable for direct line starting, rated at 82 kW at 1800 rev/min and main pump driven through a flexible coupling. This axial piston variable delivery pump incorporates an electro-hydraulic stroker for servo control. The integral boost (B) and servo (S) pumps discharge to their relevant systems through by-pass filters.

The stroker, which provides a proportional rotary servo position proportional to the input electrical signal, is interfaced with the bridge electrical control system. Also incorporated in each main pump package are automatic hydraulic locking/cartridge valves, which are operated through an hydraulically controlled valve from boost pressure, a torque limiter, a system pressure gauge, positive zero-swash control on start-up, and a scavenging shuttle valve.

The oil cooler, which is located between the main pump and the main motor, comprises a series of cooling tubes set between two headers. The tubes are air cooled externally by means of a fan, which is driven by an independent 0.25 kW electric motor. Return oil from the pump casing enters the cooler at the bottom connection and leaves through the top connection on its return to the oil tank via a return line filter.

The hydraulic oil tank contains a baffle plate to provide an independent oil supply to each power unit. In operation, each side of the oil tank is filled to three quarters full on charging (tank capacity at normal level is 110 litres total) as shown in the sight gauges (two gauges per side). An oil filler/air breather, a suction strainer and a drain plug are also fitted to each side of the tank. A low oil level switch is fitted to each side of the tank which provides a signal to the ship's alarm system.

The hydraulic sub-system includes the following valves.

1. Pump shut-off valves (17 and 18) which automatically isolate each pump from the system.

2. Manually operated pump shut-off valves (5, 6, 7, 8) to isolate each pump from the system.

3. Manually operated system isolation valves (11 and 12) which isolate each side of the system.

4. Shock and bypass valves (9 and 10) which relieve excessive pressure in the system due to abnormal rudder loading or other overload condition. The bypass valve enables one pair of cylinders to idle whilst the other pair are operational.

Operation of the shut off valves for automatic isolation of the pumps

If effective means such as the automatic pump isolating valves (17 and 18) shown above are not provided, the pressure oil from the working pump of a system with duplicated variable stroke pumps will 'windmill' the standby pump (which is on-stroke ready to be brought into immediate use). The power of the working pump will thus be dissipated in motoring the pump rather than turning the tiller and severe damage may result to the motor consequently being driven as a generator.

In Fig 10, both power units are stopped but the system is otherwise in operating condition with valves 1 to 16 open except for cylinder bypass valves 9 and 10 which are closed. The actuating rams are isolated from the power units by the isolating valves 17 and 18. In the absence of oil pressure supplied from their respective servo pumps, S, through their solenoid control valves, the isolating valves are held in their 'lower' position by the spring pressure. If, say, the forward (lower) power unit is started up, the solenoid control valve of isolating valve 18 will move to the right. The boost pump will supply the main pump which cannot, however, discharge to the actuating cylinders until the pressure from the servo pump is sufficient to overcome the spring pressure of valve 18. When this occurs, the forward power unit is directly connected to the four actuating cylinders and no 'windmilling' of the pump of the after power unit can take place since valve 17 remains in its 'lower' position.

If the after unit is also required, it will not, on start up, be subjected to any load due to pressure from the forward power unit. Even though both units may be on stroke, any discharge from its main pump will circulate through isolating valve 17, in closed circuit until the servo pump pressure is sufficient to overcome the pressure of the spring of isolating valve 17.

Blackouts

The effect of a blackout on the hydraulic circuit is the same as switching off the motors of the running pumps. In particular, the spools of the transfer valves are subjected to the force of the return springs and isolate the pumps from the hydraulic cylinders and prevent excess movement of the rudder. Restoration of power is the same as re-starting motors which have been shut off manually, i.e. the system can be automatically put back into operation without hydraulic load being imposed on the motors of the power units.

STEERING GEAR PUMPS

This section is intended to cover some aspects of three types of pumps: variable delivery axial piston; fixed delivery vane and gear. Since steering systems are generally well maintained, pump failures are comparatively rare. Consequently, some experiences within other industries using similar pumps are included. (For further details of pumping systems, refer to Chapter 10.)

AXIAL PISTON VARIABLE DISPLACEMENT PUMP

Figure 11 is intended to illustrate the pumping action and show the essential components of the pumps used in the hydraulic circuit diagram (Fig 10). The pumping action is achieved by varying the angle of the rocker cam within the stationary cradle, which coincidentally varies the stroke of the pumping pistons within the rotating barrel. The axes of the pistons are thus parallel to the drive shaft axis. In the position shown, oil is being delivered through the port plate by the lower piston and oil from the boost pump is entering the upper piston. From this position, the pump output may be continuously decreased from maximum delivery (at 19 degrees tilt or swash angle) through the lower part of the port plate to zero at zero tilt and continuously increased to maximum delivery (when the tilt angle reaches 19 degrees on the opposite side of the vertical) through the upper port. At any swash angle, x, on either side of the vertical, the piston stroke will be $D \tan x$ where D is the pitch circle diameter of the piston bores. The volume discharged per revolution will thus be the product $DAn \tan x$ where A is the piston area and n is the number of pistons. Neglecting leakage etc., the volume Q, discharged per minute at N rev/min would be given by:

$$Q = DAnN \tan x$$

Movement of the rocker cam in its vertical plane is achieved by means of a stroking vane (Fig 12) which is constrained to move in a circular arc within a sealed vane chamber having the same curvature as the rocker cam's cradle. According to the direction of rudder motion required by the navigating bridge, and the corresponding position of the servo valve, control oil from the servo pump is directed to either the upper or lower section of a vane chamber to operate the stroking vane. The control box shown adjacent to the servo valve contains all the control valves shown within the broken line rectangle enclosing the pump unit in Fig 10.

The servo and boost gerotor pumps are driven by a small auxiliary shaft splined to the cylinder barrel. It will be recalled that in closed hydraulic circuits, due to internal leakage within the pump, replenishment oil from the boost pump is essential to avoid starvation at the pump suction.

A feature of this design is the relatively small diameter drive shaft splined to drive the cylinder

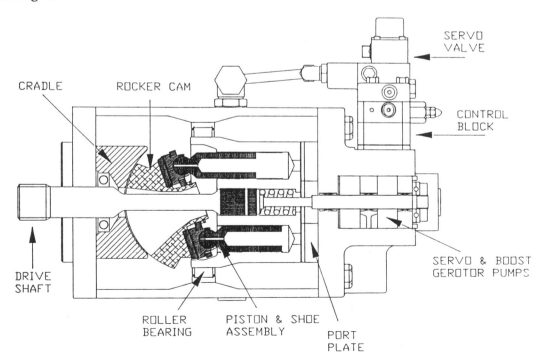

Figure 11 Essential components of a variable delivery axial piston pump.

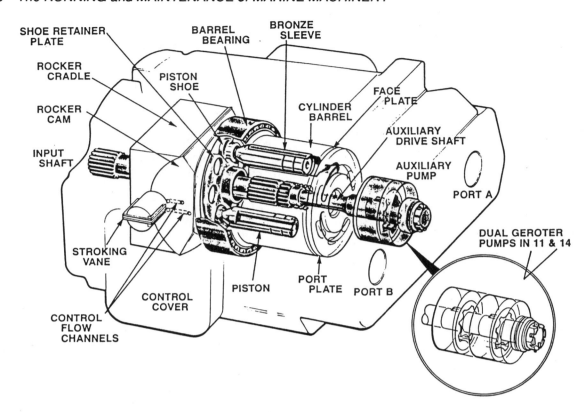

Figure 12   Rotating components of a variable delivery axial piston pump.

barrel. This is practicable due to the provision of the large diameter roller bearing which prevents whipping of the shaft due to centrifugal force and also prevents the barrel from tipping (causing greater leakage) at high speeds and pressures. If the bearings were placed conventionally at the ends of the shaft, the shaft diameter and consequently the barrel diameter and pitch circle diameter of the pistons would have been considerably greater resulting in increased losses due to heavier moving parts, greater windage with more oil stirred up and higher heat generation.

In this design, the piston shoes rotate on a flat annular creep plate fitted against the flat surface of the rocker cam. In operation, this creep plate rotates at about half the barrel speed due to oil drag. The piston and shoe assembly is maintained in position by a thrust plate and retaining snap ring fitted over the snout of the rocker cam. The thickness of the retaining ring should be such that the maximum clearance between the creep plate and shoe faces is between 0.050 mm and 0.125 mm. Lubrication for the piston shoes and creep plate surfaces is by means of holes drilled through the pistons and their shoes.

The sketch of the Hagglunds Denison pump (Fig 12) illustrates the internal configuration in a different perspective, with the servo and boost gerotor pumps shown in an insert. Seven steel pistons with bronze shoes operate within the bronze sleeves of the steel cylinder barrel.

The critical clearances in axial piston pumps are between swash plate and piston shoe (already mentioned), piston and cylinder block, and the cylinder block and valve port plate.

The most common types of piston pump failure are contamination and cavitation.

Contamination type failure

1. Wear on the bottom surface of piston shoes as a result of oil carrying contamination flows across sealing, lands from inside of the piston through the oil feed hole.

2. Imbedded particles in piston shoes causing sear in ball and socket joints.

3. Large particles becoming jammed between piston and bore causing seizure or partial seizure of pistons resulting in excessive clearance of ball and socket piston and shoes joints, or tearing the shoe completely from the piston.

4. Wear on port plate and barrel faces. The Hagglunds Denison pump (Fig 12) has a renewable faceplate

on the barrel face. This provision eliminates the need to rework or scrap the barrel because of damaged sealing faces.

Cavitation type failure

1. Low inlet or boost pressures quickly cause excessive clearance on piston/shoe/ball and socket joints. This occurs because the piston shoe has to pull the piston down the bore instead of the correct boost pressure pushing the piston down on the shoe.

2. Erosion of the port plate at the inlet lands.

3. Erosion of the underside of the bronze piston shoes.

Generally, cavitation type failures happen quite quickly. The pistons move from low pressure to high pressure once per revolution, any initial small clearances being rapidly increased by the continuous pounding effect.

Faults in the pump or the system may be brought to the attention of the operator by their symptoms. For example, a noisy pump may be symptomatic of the presence of air in the fluid or cavitation due to: the fluid being too cold, viscous or heavy; the boost pressure being too low; or the suction strainer being too small or too dirty. These faults may result in erosion of the pump barrel ports and port plate and the breakdown of the periphery of the piston shoe.

Low inlet pressure to the pump can rapidly result in damage, the mechanism being illustrated in Fig 13. The effect of good inlet pressure is to push the piston and shoe onto the creep/swash plate (Fig 13a) with normal clearance within the spherical point. With low inlet pressure, the piston is pulled down the bore by the piston shoe and the spherical joint is opened up (Fig 13b). The bottom of the shoe may be lifted off the swash plate, and at the commencement of the discharge stroke, be driven back at an angle to the plate so damaging both the shoe and the plate due to the hammering action. Figure 13c shows the unaltered (normal) clearance in the spherical joint of the shoe with good inlet conditions. The excess clearance caused by low inlet pressure is shown in Fig 13d.

Apart from the increasingly noisy operation and progressive opening out of the spherical socket of the shoe, the excess clearance on the suction stroke allows the introduction of any particles in the oil into the spherical chamber in the area shown in Fig 13e. On the discharge stroke, the piston sphere presses the particles into the bronze shoe resulting in rapid wear of the shoe and the steel pistons. The particles also enter the balance chamber of the piston shoe from

a)

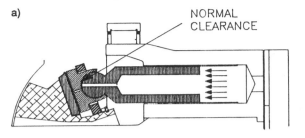

GOOD INLET PRESSURE. PISTON IS PUSHED DOWN BORE ON TO SPHERICAL JOINT

b)

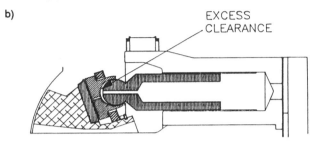

LOW INLET PRESSURE. PISTON IS PULLED DOWN BORE BY PISTON SHOE AND OPENS UP SPHERICAL JOINT

c)

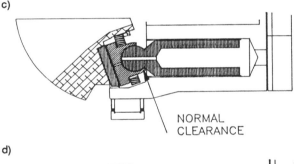

d)

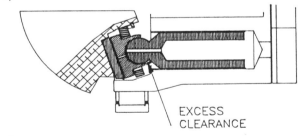

e)

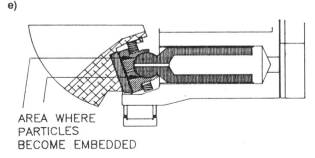

Figure 13 Low inlet pressure to the pump, resulting in damage: a), b) suction stroke; c), d), e) discharge stroke.

which they are ejected by the pressure causing radial grooves in the annular surface bearing on the wash or creep plate. This destroys the carefully calculated balance force leading to reduced pump performance.

Noisy operation may also be the result of misalignment of the shaft due to distortion of the mounting, faulty coupling, or faulty installation; or mechanical faults within the pump such as bearing failure, piston and shoe looseness or eroded or worn parts in the displacement control.

Overheating of the pump may be due to air in the fluid or the fluid being too thin. It may also be caused by excessive pump leakage due to excessive wear or improper assembly. Alternatively, the reason may be insufficient heat transfer in the heat exchanger due to mud or scale deposits; cooling water temperature too high or water flow too low; or restricted air flow in air blast coolers.

High wear rates in the pump may be caused by improper repair; water in the fluid due to condensation; faulty air breather in reservoir, water in make up fluid or heat exchanger leakage; fluid being too thin; chemical ageing of fluid and destruction of additive effectiveness and breakdown. However, as previously stressed, most significant are contaminants in the fluid due to the addition of make up fluid containing particle sizes and numbers beyond specification; inadequate precautions during repairs to the system; improper filter maintenance; and contamination introduced at shaft seals and reservoir breathers.

In concluding this section, it must be emphasised that careful attention to oil quality and correct operating procedures will avoid the problems considered above.

Vane pumps

Vane pumps may be employed in open circuit systems in conjunction with directional control valves at pressures up to 240 bar.

Simple vane pumps consist of a rotor with a number of radial slots containing vanes which, due to centrifugal action, slide outwards and press against the walls of the pump chamber in which the rotor is eccentrically located. The greater the eccentricity, the greater the pump output. However, if only single suction and discharge ports were provided, due to the difference in pressure at inlet and outlet, an unbalanced side thrust would be produced on the rotor and its bearings with consequential effects on their working life. Such pumps are thus unsuitable for high pressure applications.

Radial imbalance is avoided with the configuration of Fig 14 in which oil enters the pump chamber at suction ports diametrically opposite each other, and similarly leaves at diametrically opposite discharge ports. In fact, to ensure good inlet conditions, oil entering the pump is fed through ports on both

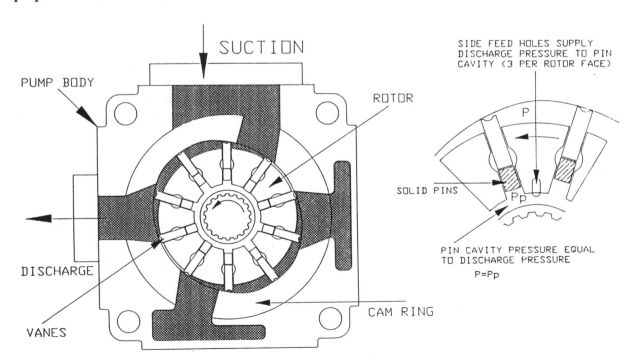

Figure 14 Vane pump.

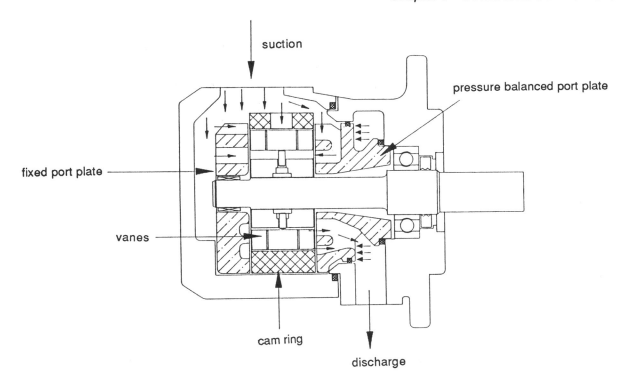

Figure 15 Pressure balance of a vane pump.

sides of the cartridge and to the large ports at each suction ramp (Fig 15). The two discharge outlets from the pump chamber are combined within the pump casing and leave through the common discharge.

The pressure in the over-vane and under-vane areas is equalised by radial holes through the vanes. An additional firm but light force against the vane is necessary to ensure smooth cam tracking by the vane. This additional force is provided in this design by pins (under the blades) whose small cross sectional area is subjected to the discharge pressure acting on the pins (P_p). Oil from the pump discharge is let through side feed holes which supply oil to the pin cavity (Fig 14). The vanes are thus held in continuous light contact against the fluid film which separates them from the cam ring as their radial position changes to follow the cam profile. In some designs, the additional force on a vane is provided by three springs each set in a locating hole in the rotor coincident with holes in the vane. The lips of the vanes have a relatively thin surface to ensure maximum sealing.

The rotor is separated from the side plates by the fluid film. The side plates are clamped axially by an over-balance of the internal pressure forces in the pumping cartridge. They accommodate dimensional changes due to temperature and pressure. Figure 15 shows the manner in which this is accomplished, one port plate being fixed whilst the other is subjected to the discharge pressure. The rotor and cam ring are constructed of tough, through-hardened steel to contribute to long service life.

The critical clearances in a vane pump are between the vane tip and cam ring (which, for a constant speed, depends upon the oil pressure and its viscosity) and between the rotor and side plate. In designs where the front plate is pressed against the cam ring by the pump's discharge pressure the clearance is equal to the difference in thickness between the cam ring and the rotor, i.e. a clearance between 0.01 mm and 0.02 mm. The minimum radial clearance between the cam ring and rotor is about 1/200 of the rotor diameter.

Vane pumps should be full of oil before starting since, in general, they cannot evacuate air from the suction circuit. Overheating will start from the centre of the rotor even though it has the lowest peripheral speed because it is the least lubricated due to the small amount of oil remaining in the pump. Seizure may occur in a matter of minutes. Other causes of failure (which should not occur in the well designed systems given in this chapter—subject to competent operating practices) include foaming of the oil and dirty or unsuitable oil.

Foaming may be caused by cavitation due to high vacuum at the suction port possibly due to a clogged filter, oil polluted by water, the reservoir level being too low especially in very heavy weather or oil returning to the reservoir above the free surface of the oil. All return lines must be well below the oil surface or air can be pulled in by the jet from the return pipe.

In cavitation, the small bubbles formed by the evaporation of the gas and aromatic essences of the oil, reach explosive pressures and erode exposed metal surfaces creating craters. The detached metallic particles may cause seizure between the moving parts. A cavitating pump is noisier than in normal operation and may result in instability due to the variable compressibility of the fluid. The vanes are hydraulically balanced to avoid damage to the cam ring due to the pressure variations occurring during the cycle. During the suction phase, the under vane pressure is less than the tip pressure and this difference is normally compensated for by the spring pressure. However, during cavitation, the spring (or pin force) may be insufficient to compensate and the vanes will then bounce within the slots creating indentations in the cam ring profile.

The same result may be caused by foaming oil due to water contamination in excess of 2,000 parts per million. In this case, there is the additional problem of corrosion.

Dirty or unsuitable oil is the major cause of failure in vane pumps due to rapid wearing resulting in possible seizure. Particles in suspension greater than half the total clearance between the sides of the rotor and end plate will be pushed by pressure force into the clearance space and form a wedge. One effect on vane operation of a high concentration of fine particles is shown in Fig 16. The vanes are subjected to a heavy tangential strain due to the thrust of the pressure in the opposite direction to the rotation. If the oil is contaminated, instead of moving radially sup-

Figure 17   Extreme example of slot wear.

ported on a layer of oil, the blades are abrased by the contaminating particles. This results in a wearing of the slots in the rotor especially at the contact points at the trailing edge of the tip of the vane and the leading edge of the slot in contact with the bottom of the vane as illustrated in Fig 16. This action may lead to excessive wear, an extreme instance of which is shown in Fig 17.

Gear pumps

A number of characteristics of simple external gear pumps may be considered in conjunction with Fig 18a. The pump has been designed to operate without external timing gears. The anti-clockwise rotation of the externally driven lower gear drives the upper gear and contacts between the teeth thus limiting backflow between the discharge and suction sides of the pump. At the design stage, backflow is limited by minimising the radial clearance between the teeth and the chamber and increasing the number of teeth. Thus, gear pumps must have a minimum of two teeth (e.g. specially designed elliptical lobe pumps with externally timed gearing) to limit backflow between suction and discharge and a sufficient number to limit peripheral flow over the tips of the teeth. However, the greater the number of gear teeth (for a given outside gear diameter and tooth form), the smaller the displacement volume of the pump.

Figure 18a also shows that the gears entering into mesh close the spaces before the spaces are completely empty. If no special measures were taken, the trapped oil would be compressed, causing very high local pressures resulting in noisy operation and hard pulsating running of the pump. Various unloading arrangements are employed, such as arranging for relief from the area of the common centre line of the gears to the discharge port. Some other means of

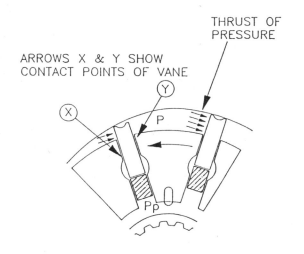

THRUST OF PRESSURE

ARROWS X & Y SHOW CONTACT POINTS OF VANE

Figure 16   Forces on vane.

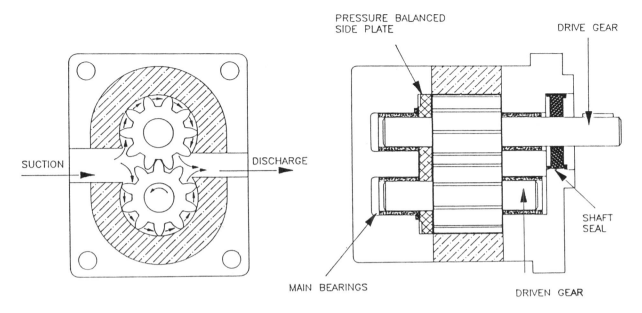

Figure 18   Gear pump.

meeting the problem are through the use of 'herring-bone' gears, which allow the trapped oil to flow in an axial direction to a region of lower pressure, or by allowing the oil to leak away by making generous clearances.

Another source of backflow from the pressure to the suction side of the pump is over the flat end faces of the gears through the side tolerance play. There is an optimum tolerance play. If it is too great, leakage will be excessive whilst too low a value will result in excessive friction. To compensate for increased pressure loss due to wear, the pump design may incorporate a pressure balanced side plate which is subjected to the discharge pressure (Fig 18b). In this way, tolerance play adjusts to system pressure.

Simple gear pumps of the type described above are suitable for operating pressures up to 250 bar and achieve displacement volumes in the range 0.35 litre to 1.0 litre per revolution.

CONCLUDING REMARKS

The steering gear is undoubtedly the most important single item in the ship. Whilst some twin screw machinery installations may permit a degree of manoeuvrability by judicious application of engine movements, in the majority of vessels loss of steering capability could result in grounding on a lee shore in the event of steering gear failure. Hence the introduction of the current stringent requirements including,

for example, the concept that (excluding the rudder actuator) a single failure should not result in loss of steering capability in the case of tankers between 10,000 gt and 100,000 dwt. The exclusion of the rudder actuator is dependent on the provision of arrangements whereby steering capability can be regained in 45 seconds following a single failure in any part of the piping system and power units and a special stress analysis of non-duplicated rudder actuators. Yet properly operated steering gears are probably the most reliable of machinery items.

Some 90% of the failures which have occurred could probably have been avoided by maintaining cleanliness in hydraulic circuits, paying attention to makers' handbooks and competent watchkeeping. One analysis showed that failures due to slackening back of fastenings (which thorough inspections would have revealed) were 50% greater than those due to pump failure. The vibration of unsupported pipes has also resulted in many unnecessary breakdowns. However, failures need not have catastrophic consequences as conscientiously completed drills and tests together with a thorough understanding of the steering gear system will normally ensure a rapid diagnosis of the problem by the ship's staff and the speedy restoration of steering capability.

REFERENCES

1. J Cowley, '*Steering gears: new concepts and requirements*', Trans IMarE Vol 94 (1982).

Chapter 10
Pumping Systems

Professor S G Christensen

INTRODUCTION

A ship cannot function without the various pumping systems placed in or controlled from the machinery spaces. The pumping systems are of major importance and they are many and varied. Some systems supply coolant and lubricants to the main machinery, and without this supply the main propulsion machinery will be quickly brought to a halt by safety devices in the control system. The machinery would be badly damaged if safety devices did not function to bring it to a halt. This illustrates the importance of machinery support systems, and the safety devices used to protect machinery in the event of a pumping system malfunction.

An equally important pumping system is used to pump out loose water from cargo and machinery spaces, which must be kept clear of water to prevent damage. In extreme cases, if loose water is not removed it could eventually collect at some point where the stability of the ship would be adversely affected and lead to capsize or sinking.

Machinery of either steam or internal combustion type requires clean fuel, free of water. The fuel transfer system is used to bring fuel from the bunker storage spaces into settling tanks where water and heavy dirty material are removed. In motor ships the fuel requires further purification treatment. This treatment is carried out in the fuel cleaning or separation system.

When cargo operations are in progress the ballast system may be used for ballasting or deballasting to maintain draught, trim, and a safe stability, and sometimes to keep hull stresses within safe limits.

Other systems supply feed water to boilers, cooling water to refrigeration machinery and allow liquid cargoes to be discharged from deep tanks in ordinary dry cargo ships, or from the cargo tanks in crude oil or liquid products tankers, and liquefied gas carriers. Other systems supply hydraulic fluid to the steering gear, to the cargo pumping system in chemical tankers, and to the control system for opening and closing of ramps and doors on ferry boats and ro-ro vessels, and so on. More systems supply the creature comforts necessary to sustain life for passengers, crew, and officers sailing on the vessel and to maintain the cargo in a safe and marketable condition.

From this it is easily understood that the various pumping systems in use play an important role in the safe and economical operation of both merchant ships and naval vessels. It is necessary to understand them to their fullest extent in order to obtain safe and economic ship operation.

It is therefore an incumbent duty of every engineer officer on joining a vessel to locate the pumps and valves controlling each separate piping system, together with their cross connections allowing different systems to be combined or used in emergencies. Due to the fast turnaround of ships, little more than a brief examination of the mimic board to locate starters, pumps, and valves associated with the propulsion and electrical generating machinery may be all that is possible in the time available. However, as soon as time becomes available, engineer officers should familiarise themselves with the various parts of each pumping system. This will involve making a note of the suction and discharge connections on each pump and tracing the piping runs both above and below the engine room floorplates.

Tracing pipelines or piping runs is facilitated if the pipes are painted or colour banded with distinguishing colours indicating the contents of the pipe. Knowledge of the contents of a pipeline is necessary when making important decisions affecting the safety and protection of the ships personnel before breaking pipe flanges and removing valve covers. The Interna-

a)

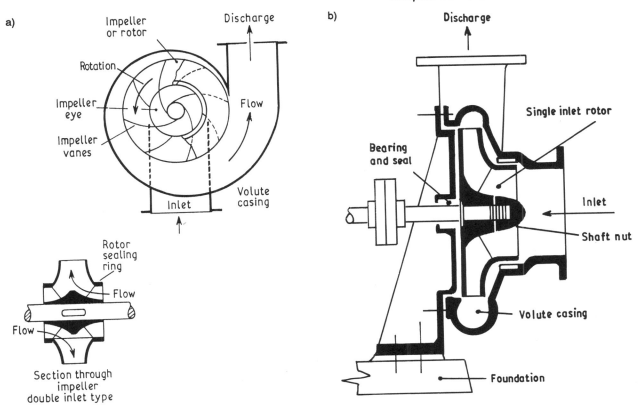

Figure 1 Centrifugal pumps: a) with double inlet rotor; b) with single inlet rotor.

tional Standards Organisation publishes a code giving the colours used on piping runs to indicate the contents of the pipe.

PUMPS

Before a fluid can be moved around any piping or trunking system, energy is required to overcome the inertia of the fluid, the frictional resistance imparted by pipe or trunk surfaces and the resistance to flow created by pipe bends and valves. Energy is also required to overcome the pressure at the discharge end of the system when it is higher than at the suction end. For example, in the boiler feed system energy is required to bring the inlet pressure at the pump suction branch to a pressure high enough at the delivery branch to enable the feed water to pass through pipe bends, branches, valves, and feed water regulators before overcoming the boiler pressure and entering the boilers. The pump discharge pressure will then be considerably higher than the pressure at the pump entry branch. In a similar way, energy is required to overcome the head difference when pumping ballast water from double bottom tanks to a higher level through the ship's side overboard valve.

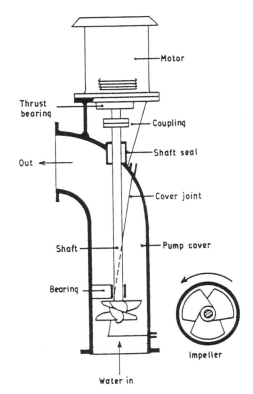

Figure 2 Axial flow pump.

a)

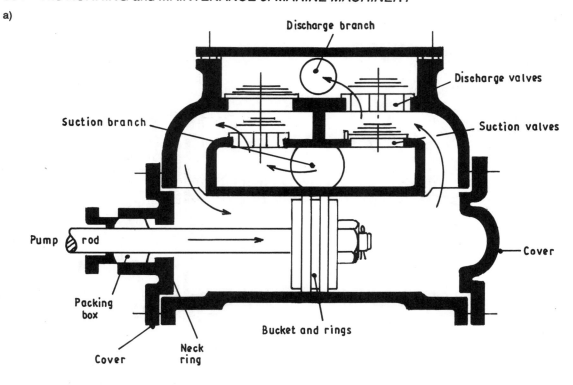

b)   c)

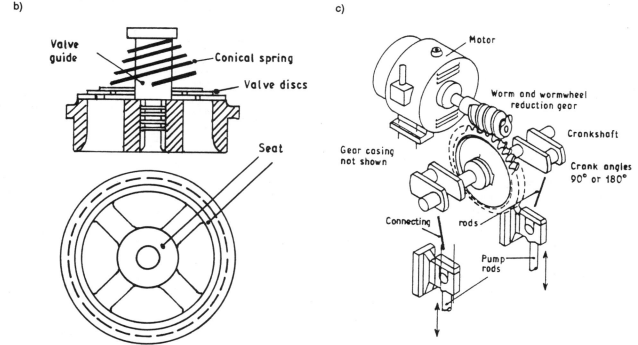

Figure 3   a) Water end of horizontal displacement pump; b) valve detail; c) electrical reciprocating pump drive.

The energy used to move a fluid is obtained from pumps or fans. Pumps and fans are usually driven by electric motors, but in some cases steam is used to supply the motive power, for reasons of safety, economics, or convenience.

Types of pumps and fans

Pumps are used to move liquids, known technically as non-compressible fluids, around or through a pumping system. Examples of liquids are water (sea,

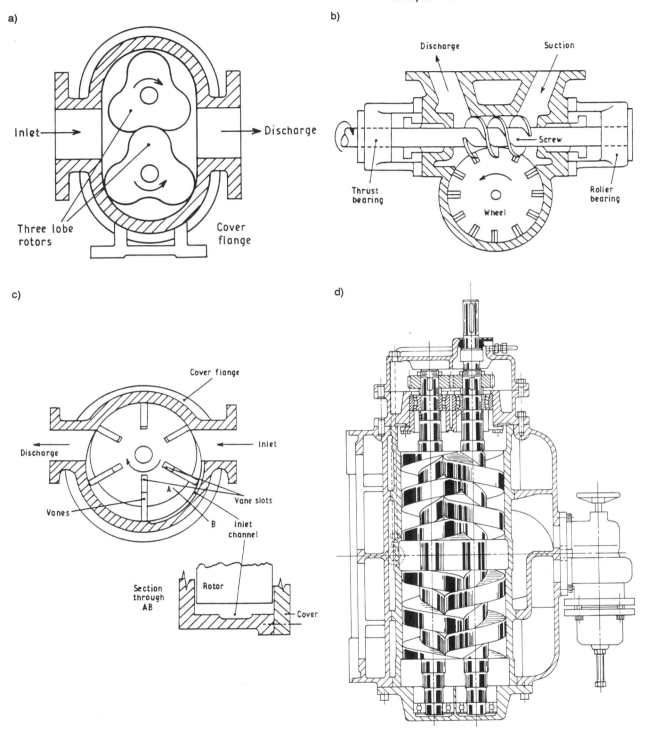

Figure 4 Rotary positive displacement pumps: a) lobe pump; b) screw and wheel pump; c) sliding vane pump; d) screw pump.

fresh, distilled and drinking or potable), fuel oil, lubricating oil, crude and refined oils, edible oils, latex, and the like. There are considerable differences in the ways in which various liquids behave. The various patterns of behaviour are covered in the rheological definitions for Newtonian fluids, non-Newtonian fluids, ideal plastic, and thixotropic substances. Most of this chapter applies to Newtonian fluids such as water, and mineral oils.

Fans are used to supply the energy to compress

and move low pressure compressible fluids (gases) through a trunking system. Examples are forced draught fans, the air trunking system to the fuel oil burning equipment on a boiler, engine room ventilation fans and the fans moving air through the trunking in air conditioning systems.

Compressors are used to supply the energy to compress compressible fluids to a higher pressure than is normally given by a fan. In some cases a compressor is used to compress a gas and to move it around the piping system. An example of this is the refrigerant compressor used to move refrigerant through refrigeration machinery. In other cases, after being compressed, air is moved through a system at the expense of its internal energy. An example of this is the starting air system of a diesel engine.

Pump classification

Pumps are usually classified by names descriptive of the type of pump. Each pump type then has some other distinguishing name or names indicating the sub divisions within the class.

Centrifugal pumps

These may be vertical or horizontal, of single stage or multi-stage type. They may be driven by an electric motor or a steam turbine. A centrifugal pump with a double inlet rotor is shown in Fig 1a, and a centrifugal pump with a single inlet rotor is shown in Fig 1b.

Axial flow propeller pumps

These consist of an impeller (similar to a ship's propeller) fitted in a casing. The axis of the impeller shaft is coincident with the polar axis of the pump casing. The casing is made in two pieces to give access to the impeller and the internal bearing. The drive is from an externally fitted electric motor, one of the motor bearings being arranged to take the impeller thrust. An axial flow water pump used for circulating the cooling water through a condenser in large turbine installations is shown in Fig 2.

Reciprocating positive displacement pumps

These are manufactured as vertical or horizontal, single acting, double acting, or differential types. The drive is by direct acting steam pistons working in cylinders, or by an electric motor and worm and worm wheel reduction gearing. The reciprocating motion is obtained from a crank and connecting rod.

The water end of a horizontal positive displacement reciprocating pump is shown in Fig 3a. Figure 3b shows a section through a suction or delivery valve. A vertical pump would be similar in detail but

the suction branch and the suction and delivery valve chest will be located on the front of the pump, with the valves placed horizontally.

An electrical reciprocating pump drive is shown in Fig 3c. The worm and worm-wheel are fitted in an oil tight casing and lubricated by splash from an oil bath.

Rotary positive displacement pumps

The type sub-divisions indicate whether the pump is of a fixed or variable displacement type. The pump is also classified by the type of its internal parts. These may be described as the helical type (screw type) having one, two or three helices; gear pumps; sliding vane pumps; flexible vane pumps; lobe type pumps; and screw and wheel type pumps. There are also other types of rotary positive displacement pumps used in shore based industry but they are not normally found in the marine environment. Figures 4 a–d show various types of rotary positive displacement pumps.

Liquid ring pumps

These pumps consist of a rotor working in an elongated circular casing arranged with a circulating water system. Figure 5 shows a liquid ring pump.

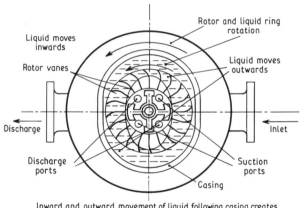

Inward and outward movement of liquid following casing creates suction and discharge effect in spaces between rotor vanes

Figure 5 Liquid ring pump.

Air compressors

These may be of the piston type, screw type, or liquid ring type. Figure 6 shows a two stage reciprocating air compressor.

Fans

These may be of the centrifugal type or axial flow type. An axial flow fan is shown in Fig 7.

Ejectors

These are sometimes called injectors, and consist of a

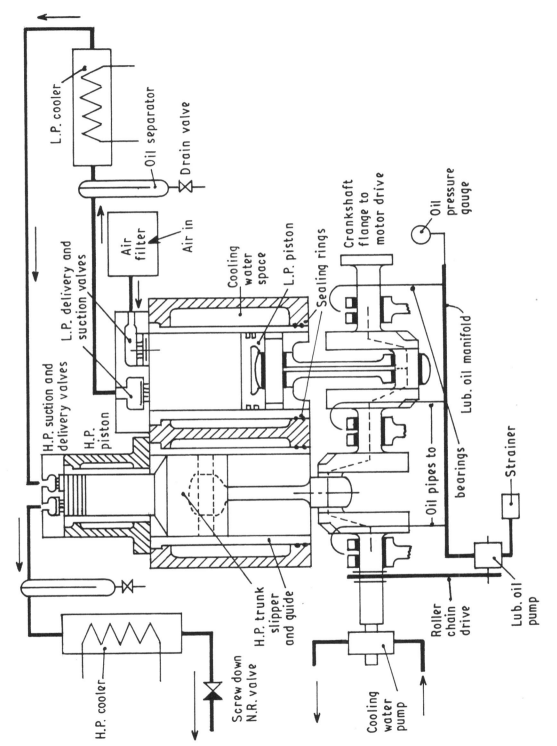

Figure 6 Two stage air compressor.

L.P. cooler

Oil separator

Drain valve

L.P. delivery and suction valves

Air filter

Air in

Cooling water space

L.P. piston

Sealing rings

Crankshaft flange to motor drive

Oil pressure gauge

H.P. suction and delivery valves

H.P. piston

Lub. oil manifold

H.P. cooler

Screw down N.R. valve

H.P. trunk slipper and guide

Oil pipes to bearings

Strainer

Roller chain drive

Lub. oil pump

Cooling water pump

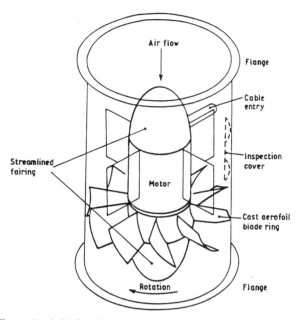

Figure 7 Axial flow fan.

jet discharging into a suction chamber into which is connected a suction line. The discharge connection is arranged on the same axis as the jet and opposite to it. Compressed air or water under pressure is passed through the jet, and the high velocity of the discharge creates a vacuum in the suction chamber and causes water to move into it. The water is then discharged through the discharge connection. Figure 8 shows an ejector.

axis may be arranged either vertically or horizontally and they are designed in sizes having capacities from less than 1 tonne/h up to approximately 5 000 tonne/h or more. These large capacity pumps are used for the discharge of cargo in very large crude oil carriers (VLCCs). Some pumps having a capacity of some few tonne/h are designed to suit the requirements of feed pumps used with high pressure boiler installations.

Figure 1a, showing a centrifugal pump with a double inlet rotor, is of a type used for many duties where a large capacity output is required. As the forces acting on either side of the rotor are the same, no thrust action is set up on the rotor shaft when this pump is in operation, except that due to the weight of the rotating parts in vertical pumps.

This type of pump, either vertical or horizontal, has a split casing. Provided the bearings are properly lubricated very little wear takes place, although over a time period some wear takes place on the sealing rings due to a combination of erosion and corrosion. When the sealing ring clearance has increased beyond some recommended amount they may be renewed when a pump is overhauled.

Figure 9 shows sealing rings of the split and solid types.

Figure 1b (page 333) shows a smaller type of centrifugal pump used in many locations where only a small capacity output is required. The rotor sets up an axial thrust to the right (on Fig 1b). This comes

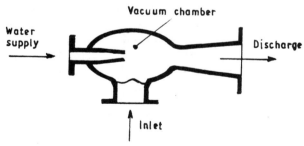

Figure 8 Ejector.

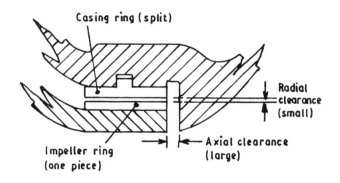

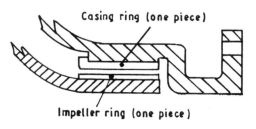

Figure 9 Wear rings, or sealing rings.

COMMON USES OF THE VARIOUS TYPES OF PUMPS

Centrifugal pumps

Centrifugal pumps are more commonly used for pumping liquids than any other type of pump. This is due to the small space they occupy and the ease with which they can be coupled to an electric motor without the need for reduction gearing. The pump

about due to the discharge pressure on the left hand side of the rotor being higher than the suction pressure on the right hand side.

Generally, centrifugal pumps are driven by an electric motor, exceptions being single or two stage boiler feed water pumps, where steam turbines are more commonly used. The exhaust steam from the turbines driving the feed pumps is used in the feed water deaerator to remove air and gases by heating the feed water.

For economic reasons, large capacity centrifugal pumps used for cargo discharge in oil tankers are usually driven by steam turbines. The steam turbine has virtually infinite speed control and is therefore considered to be safer for use with cargo pumps. The steam turbine is fitted in the engine room and the pump driving shaft passes through a self aligning gas and water sealing gland fitted on the pump room bulkhead. Where the design capacity of the boiler plant is limited, as on some diesel propelled tankers, electrically driven cargo pumps may be used.

Centrifugal pumps are not self priming, i.e. they are not capable of creating a vacuum enabling the suction line to fill with liquid and so allow the pumping action to be started. This disadvantage is overcome by using liquid ring vacuum pumps. When only a small number of centrifugal pumps are fitted in the engine room a vacuum pump may be fitted on each centrifugal pump. As the number of centrifugal pumps increases it becomes more economical to fit a central priming system.

Axial flow propeller pumps

Axial flow propeller pumps are sometimes used for circulating cooling water through the condenser in high powered propulsion steam turbine installations where scoop cooling has not been adopted.

Reciprocating positive displacement pumps

Reciprocating positive displacement pumps, both steam and electrically driven, may be found on older, smaller ships. They may be designed for use as boiler feed pumps for harbour duty or for auxiliary boilers in motor ships. They may also be used for bilge, or fuel oil pumping duty. Reciprocating pumps can be supplied as a simplex type pump, or a duplex type pump. They are designed or arranged for fitting in the vertical or horizontal position. They are sometimes used for ballast pumping duty when the capacity of the ballast system is relatively small. They may also be used as cargo stripping pumps for draining tanks when completing cargo discharge from an oil tanker.

Rotary positive displacement pumps

Rotary positive displacement pumps are commonly used for lubricating oil supply to both main and auxiliary diesel engines. They may also be used for the lubricating oil supply to main and auxiliary steam turbines. Rotary positive displacement pumps may be of the helical screw type utilising two or three screws, or of the gear type, rotary vane type, or the lobe type.

Figure 4d shows a helical screw rotary positive displacement pump of the type used in many steam turbine or diesel propelled ships for lubricating oil supply to bearings, gearing, and oil cooled pistons in diesel engines.

A pump with two helices has a set of timing gears arranged so that the surfaces of the helices never touch each other.

Variable displacement rotary pumps may be arranged with a series of radial cylinders and ram type pistons having a variable stroke. The stroke variation is brought about by fitting a pin in the end of the ram. The pin is fitted into two cod pieces which revolve in a circular slot. When the circular slot is concentric with the centre of the cylinders the rams have no reciprocating motion. When the circular slot is brought away from the centre position, movement of the rams takes place and the pumping action commences. If the slot is moved over in the opposite direction the pumping action is reversed. Another type of variable displacement rotary pump has the cylinders and rams arranged in an axial direction around the axis of the pump. The rams are connected with a swashplate. Movement of the swashplate sets up the movement of the rams and the pumping action. Either of these two types of pump are almost universally used with hydraulic steering gears. They have sometimes found favour for fuel oil transfer duty. Refer to Chapter 9, *Steering Gears.*

Small capacity variable displacement pumps are usually used to continuously supply a boiler with water treatment chemicals. The same pump may also be arranged for use as a hydraulic test pump for pressure testing a boiler. Larger, variable displacement pumps are sometimes used as the hydraulic power source to the cargo pumps in chemical and special products tank ships.

Positive displacement pumps have the ability to create a vacuum in the suction chest and suction lines to the pump; therefore, they are self priming. The clearances of the internal parts of the pump must be small so that slip of the liquid between the suction and delivery sides of the pump does not occur. If slip occurs the ability to create sufficient vacuum to effect

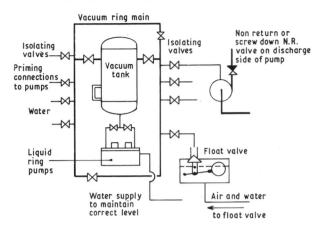

Figure 10   Ring or central priming system.

priming will be lessened. The pump output capacity is also reduced when slip occurs. Slip of the liquid occurs in other types of pump if the clearances of the sealing devices become excessive.

Liquid ring pumps

Liquid ring pumps are used to bring about and maintain the vacuum in steam plant condensers, and to create the vacuum in the vacuum tank forming part of the central or ring priming system used in conjunction with centrifugal pumps. They may also be used for compressing air in low pressure compressed air systems, particularly where the air must be oil free.

Figure 10 shows a ring priming system. In some cases a separate branch line is taken to each pump where priming is necessary. The system is then referred to as a central priming system.

Air compressors

Air compressors may be of the positive displacement type, using pistons operating in a cylinder or helical rotors operating in a casing. Air compressors supply the air to the starting air system in motorships and to the various compressed air systems fitted on modern ships for various duties.

Fans

Fans used for boiler forced draught duty are usually of the centrifugal type, as are the fans for circulating air in air conditioning installations. Fans used for air supply to machinery and confined spaces are commonly of the axial flow type.

Ejectors

Ejectors are used when completing tank cleaning operations to remove residue and small quantities of

water and cleaning materials not removed by pumps. The end of the suction pipe is used in a similar manner to a vacuum cleaner.

PIPING SYSTEMS

Bilge systems

The bilge system fitted in dry cargo and container ships is used to remove loose water from machinery, boiler and cargo spaces. It consists of a line termed the bilge main, passing along one side and around the forward and after ends of the engine room. Branches are arranged from the bilge main. These connect to the various pumps arranged for bilge pumping duty. Some of the other branches form bilge suction connections to the corners of the engine room. Each bilge suction branch is controlled by a screw down, non-return valve. The remaining branches are connected to group valve chests. Each branch from the lower side of a group valve chest is a bilge suction line connecting with an individual bilge space in a cargo hold. Each of these hold bilge suction lines is controlled by a screw down non-return valve fitted above the branch. Cargo hold bilge spaces may be located in the space formed between the tank margin plate and the ship's side. Where a flat tank top extends to the ship's side large drain hats or drain pockets are fitted in the tank top (inner bottom plating) of the cargo hold. (See also Figs 23 and 24.)

The group valve chests fitted on the starboard side of the engine room lead to bilge drain wells on the starboard side of the cargo holds; similarly, those on the port side lead to bilge drain wells on the port side of the cargo holds. The open suction ends of the bilge suction lines leading from the cargo holds are fitted at the after ends of hold spaces. Drain hats are similarly located in the after ends of cargo holds. As ships are normally trimmed by the stern loose water will drain to the after end of cargo holds and either to the port or starboard drain space if there is any list. Pumping out the loose water keeps the cargo hold spaces dry. The bilge suction lines connecting the group valve chests to the hold bilges usually run along the port and starboard bilge wings at each side of the hold and are covered by bilge limbers. In other cases they run through lightening holes fitted in the side brackets connecting the ships transverse framing to the floors under the tank top. In refrigerated cargo ships it would be imprudent to fit bilge suction lines under the insulation at the ship's side. In bulk carriers where cargo is discharged by grabs it would also be imprudent to fit bilge piping at the side of cargo holds because the piping would be quickly damaged by grabs when completing discharge.

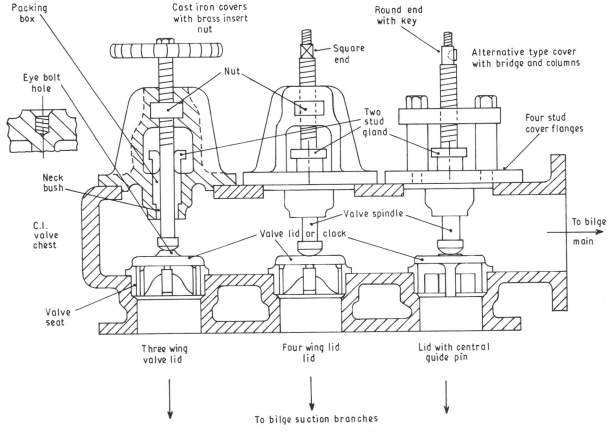

Packing box

Eye bolt hole

Neck bush

C.I. valve chest

Valve seat

Cast iron covers with brass insert nut

Nut

Square end

Two stud gland

Valve lid or clack

Valve spindle

Round end with key

Alternative type cover with bridge and columns

Four stud cover flanges

To bilge main

Three wing valve lid

Four wing lid lid

Lid with central guide pin

To bilge suction branches

Figure 11 Bilge group valve chest.

Figure 11 shows a group valve chest used in bilge pumping systems. Three different types of valve lid or clack are shown in the chest. One has three guide wings, the other four and the third has a central guide pin. The valve lids of any one valve chest are all of the same type. (See also Fig 40d.)

In bulk carriers and refrigerated cargo ships the bilge lines may be fitted in either duct keels arranged about the longitudinal centre line of the ship or in piping ducts fitted within the double bottom space towards the port and starboard sides of the ship. When piping ducts are fitted it is usual to fit a transverse duct at the forward end of number 2 double bottom space. The transverse duct connects the port and starboard ducts. Sometimes an access trunk is fitted. This leads from the weather deck down to the transverse duct. This duct may be used for ventilating the pipe tunnels before personnel enter them.

Where deep tanks are fitted forward or abaft the engine room in dry cargo vessels, and liquid cargoes are carried in these tanks, precautions must be taken to prevent the inadvertent loss of cargo. The precautions taken consist of blanking off the bilge suction lines to the deep tanks by changing over the position of spectacle blanks or turning the position of elbows in the bilge suction lines. After the changes are made, the bilge lines from the deep tanks become completely blanked off. If anybody mistakenly opens up a bilge valve to the deep tank, cargo cannot be introduced into the bilge pumping system and lost over the side. When the bilge lines are blanked off prior to receiving liquid cargo, and reopened again after discharge of the cargo, appropriate entries must be made in the engine room log book recording the date, time, and nature of the change made. The entry should be initialled by the engineer officer responsible for making the change.

Generally, all the valves in a bilge pumping system are of the screw down non-return type, including valves fitted in group valve chests and individual valves in the system. Non-return valves are necessary as a safety measure to prevent water flowing back into, and flooding, the various spaces connected through branch lines to the bilge main.

If the hull shell in way of the engine room space is breached, large amounts of water may flow into the engine room. In order to reduce the risk of a major casualty, the largest capacity pump or pumps fitted in the engine room are arranged with direct suction connections to the tank top or drain wells. In steam ships the largest capacity pump is often the main condenser circulating pump; in motor ships it may be the ballast pump. In some cases a combination of pumps may be arranged for emergency pumping duty.

An emergency bilge suction valve is shown in Fig 26. To operate the valve in an emergency the valve spindle is opened the full amount and the sea suction valve is closed down until water is taken from the bilges or off the tank top. After the quantity of loose water is reduced to a safe level and the level is being maintained, the sea suction valve position is adjusted to suit the inflow of water through the breach or source of leakage.

In motorships, there may be more than one emergency bilge suction valve. In an emergency they should all be brought into operation until the situation is under control and then one may be shut down if it is not required.

The engine room bilge pumping system in oil tankers and product tankers is not connected to any external space. This is for reasons of safety, preventing low flash point oils, or dangerous liquids entering the machinery space, and creates hazards if pipelines or pumps containing low flash point oils or dangerous liquids are opened up. The volatile nature of low flash point oils creates a danger of explosion or fire. If toxic liquids are present it will expose the engine room staff to health hazards which could be fatal.

The bilge main fitted in tanker engine rooms usually passes across the forward end and has a line running aft connected to the aft drain well. The main pump room bilges are usually pumped out with a steam driven reciprocating pump fitted in the pump room. It will be arranged to discharge overboard through an oily water separator, or into slop tanks. The forward pump room is usually fitted with a fuel transfer pump forming part of the fuel transfer system, and a ballast pump for use in filling and emptying the fore peak tank. These pumps will also be used for clearing water or oil leakage from the deck of the pump room.

Figure 12 shows a bilge pumping system, as found in many types of cargo vessel. On joining a ship an engineer officer should study the locations of the strainer devices used to prevent a bilge suction line becoming choked with muck.

The strainer plate is usually fitted in a mud box situated at floor plate level. In other cases its location is not always so definite, but in order to prevent problems arising when pumping bilges it is necessary to know the location of the strainers.

Automatic bilge pumping arrangements controlled by float switches require attention to the float controls and the strainers. In the engine room it is good practice to hose off the engine room tank top at regular intervals, determined by experience, and then to clean the strainers after the hosing and water removal is completed.

Sometimes maintenance is carried out by chipping and painting pipelines fitted below or near the engine room floor plates. Paint and rust chips may cause considerable trouble with bilge pumping systems. Therefore it is essential that all rust and paint chips are swept up and removed at the end of each work period and before hosing down the tank top.

Automatic pumping arrangements fitted in the bilge spaces in dry cargo ships should be checked out and the strainers cleaned whenever cargo holds become empty. The equipment should be tested after cleaning by filling the bilge space with water from a hose and observing that the water is pumped away. This ensures that any disturbed gaskets are not leaking air and causing malfunction. When this work is carried out it is essential that a log book entry is made after the testing is completed.

Ships carrying more than twelve passengers come under the jurisdiction of government appointed authorities. The actual government department controlling the safety of passenger ships depends on the laws of the country concerned. In the United Kingdom the Department of Transport is responsible; in the United States, the US Coast Guard. In passenger ships all bilge pumps and lines must be inboard of one fifth of the ship's breadth (i.e. within the B/5 line). When the ship suffers damage, to a specified extent, at least one pump must be available to pump from any compartment. This is provided by distribution of the bilge pumps throughout the watertight compartments, or by the provision of a submersible type pump within the B/5 line, as the regulations assume that collision damage occurs to this degree. This submersible type pump must be capable of operation when the space in which it is situated is flooded, so that it can operate in other compartments. The pump and its connections must be capable of being operated from a point outside the engine room. Its power source is obtained through the emergency switchboard. Bilge suction valves to some of the spaces where water may drain are sometimes arranged with extensions or reach rods so that they can be operated from above the bulkhead deck. The regulations covering the bilge system in passenger vessels are contained in the publications covering the survey of passenger ships issued by the government authority in the country concerned.

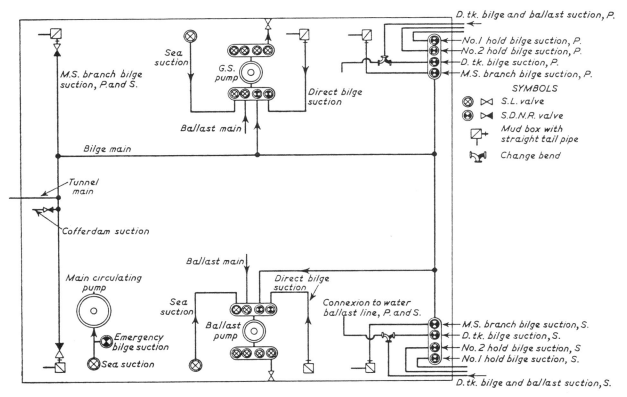

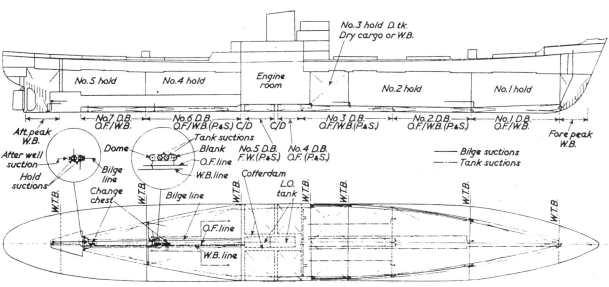

Figure 12 Bilge pumping system.

Oily water separators are used to remove oil from engine room bilge water before it is pumped over the side. They are an important piece of equipment and must be used carefully within their designed throughput capacity and kept in proper working order.

An oily water separator of a common type is shown in Fig 13. This type of oil separator will not remove all the oil from bilge or ballast water. Where the water must have a low number of parts per million of oil it is necessary to fit a coalescer filter to remove the remaining oil particles before the water is pumped overboard.

If the overboard discharge valve is lower than the separator, an anti-vacuum valve is fitted at the high-

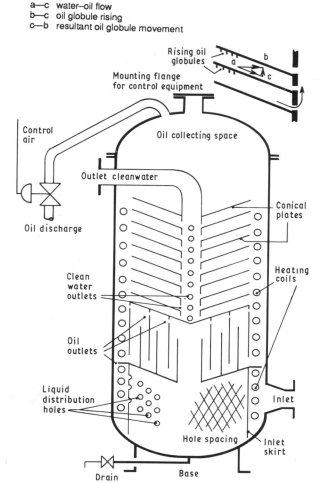

a—c   water–oil flow
b—c   oil globule rising
c—b   resultant oil globule movement

Rising oil globules

Mounting flange for control equipment

Control air

Oil collecting space

Outlet cleanwater

Oil discharge

Conical plates

Clean water outlets

Heating coils

Oil outlets

Liquid distribution holes

Inlet

Hole spacing

Inlet skirt

Drain

Base

Figure 13 Oily water separator.

est point of the discharge line. It is necessary to keep this valve in good working order. Should it fail to function, it is possible for the contents of the separator including the oil to be siphoned overboard, resulting in damage to the ecosystem and, possibly, severe financial penalties.

The vector diagram of flow velocities shows that if the throughput is increased above the designed figure the vector **a-c** increases. If it increases to an amount such that point b is level or in line with the outlet hole, oil globules will pass out of the separator. The designed throughput of an oily water separator must never be exceeded.

On modern ships the overboard outlet is monitored for oil content. An alarm is activated if the oil content approaches the allowable figure.

Problems with bilge pumping systems
The most common problem experienced with bilge

pumping systems is loss of, or reduction in, vacuum in the suction lines due to ingress of air at some point within the suction side of the system. A reduction in vacuum reduces the output of the pump and the rate of removal of bilge water. Increasing vacuum loss eventually causes the pump to lose its suction and the pumping action ceases. When this occurs the main suction valve of the pump working on the bilge system should be closed and the vacuum on the suction side of the pump noted. If the vacuum registered shows an increase, and returns to normal, the pump and the priming system is in order. It then becomes necessary to find the point of air ingress.

The most common way that air ingress occurs is through dirt being drawn into the piping systems and then lodging under a valve lid in a valve chest. The dirt or foreign material lodged under the valve lid prevents proper closure of the valve and air flows into the suction side of the system. The inflow of air causes the pump to lose its suction and pumping ceases.

In order to find the opened valve it is necessary to open up the group valve chests and find the valve with the foreign material lodged under it. Obviously, if pumping bilges has proceeded satisfactorily and the bilge pump loses its suction, the bilge valve last in use should be opened up for examination as this is most likely to be where the fault exists.

Another cause of air ingress is seal failure at strainer casing or mud box covers. When the covers are removed to clean out the strainer plate and dirt collecting space, they must be carefully replaced, preferably with a new joint or gasket if there is any doubt about the gasket removed. If the cover is fastened down with a number of nuts they must be pulled down evenly to prevent the cover lifting on one side and allowing air to enter through the opening.

Valve wheel spanners, wrenches or keys should never be used to close bilge suction valves. Their excessive use causes bent valve spindles and distorted valves. A bent spindle deforms the gland packing and allows air ingress down the side of the packing, this being more likely to occur if the packing is old and has become hard. If bent spindles are suspected to be the source of an air leak a small amount of engine oil fed with an oil feeder to the spindle and gland quickly shows if air ingress is present. The oil temporarily seals the air leak and the vacuum is then seen to rise on the vacuum gauge fitted to the suction side of the pump.

The non-return winged valves in bilge valve chests must be very light in weight to reduce the vacuum required to lift them. Being light, they have little strength to resist a load placed on them and buckle very easily if their spindles are screwed down with a wheel spanner.

Leaks in the bilge piping due to internal and external corrosion may also be found in older ships. This form of leakage is usually found on the lowest point of the piping. It is sometimes possible to hear the leak from the noise created by the inflow of air, but in many cases background noise in the engine room renders the noise of the leak inaudible. Sonic testing devices must then be used to locate the leak. If the leak cannot be found, the various sections of the bilge piping system will have to be isolated and blanked off. Each pipe is then back flooded by filling the line with water under pressure. This may be done by removing the bilge suction valve on one of the pumps and flooding back from the sea. Extreme care must be exercised to ensure that the various sections of the bilge piping are properly blanked when finding leaks in this manner. This method may be used in the engine room at any time. In dealing with cargo hold bilge lines it can only be used when the holds are clear of cargo. When back flooding engine room bilge suction lines extreme care must be taken to ensure hold bilge valves are properly closed, to prevent water flooding back into the hold and damaging cargo.

It should be realised that once a pipe is shown to be corroded in one location, other nearby corroded locations often come to light soon after making a repair. When problems are experienced the search should begin near the first repair. The usual form of repair is to make up a pipe clip and fit it over the hole to blank it off and prevent air ingress. Care must be used when tightening the clip to prevent a weakened pipe collapsing if the clip is made up in a material section heavier than required. If a soft rubber patch is fitted under the clip it is only necessary to tighten it lightly to hold the patch in place. Epoxy resin repair kits are also used to repair leaking bilge suction pipes.

Bilge pumping problems with hold bilges are sometimes experienced after a vessel has carried a bulk cargo. If the bilge drainage spaces have not been properly secured with gunny cloth, cargo may fill the drainage space or the bilge space and seal off the end of the suction line, preventing the flow of water to the pump.

Bilge pumping troubles in the engine room are often experienced after shore contractors have carried out engine room repair work. After the completion of repair work the tank tops, bilge drain wells, mud boxes and strainers should be inspected. Foreign matter such as rags, cotton waste, planks, packings, old joints or gaskets and the like should be removed. The mud boxes and strainer plates should be cleaned.

Before sailing the bilge system should be tested and any loose water removed must be discharged overboard through the oily water separator or pumped into a bilge holding tank.

When the bilges and tank top are cleaned and tested prior to sailing the possibility of bilge pumping problems in the engine room is removed, allowing better attention to be given to the main machinery in the critical period of operation immediately following repair work.

Ballast water systems

Requirements of the ballast system
The design of the ballast system is governed by the requirements of the type of ship the system is serving.

When a vessel must proceed between two ports without cargo or only partially loaded, it may become necessary to take on ballast for any one of, or combination of, the following reasons.

a) To reduce the vessels freeboard and give sufficient immersion of the propeller to reduce slip and possible propeller-excited vibration;

b) to give better rudder action due to the greater depth of water flow around the rudder;

c) to trim the vessel so the depth of water forward is such that the possibility of pounding (slamming) damage is reduced to a minimum when heavy weather is experienced;

d) to provide satisfactory stability conditions;

e) to assist in better weight distribution, thereby reducing hull stresses;

f) to give the ship better sea-keeping qualities in heavy weather.

In some cases the cargo loading requirements are such that a ship may be tender on sailing from a loading port, and as oil fuel is consumed from the double bottom tanks the stability may decrease until the ship takes up an angle of loll. In this condition the ship may 'flop' from side to side and possibly become dangerous. Double bottom tanks must then be filled to increase the bottom weight and obtain the desired degree of stability. The order in which either a port or starboard tank is filled is of great importance. In general, a tank is filled on the low side of the ship before the ship is brought upright. However, double bottom tanks are not filled haphazardly but only after all the requisite facts have been studied and instructions are passed on by the chief engineer.

If the requirements for fuel and ballast water capacity in double bottom tanks are such that a deficiency will arise in one or the other, certain double bottom tanks are made suitable for the dual purpose of fuel storage or the carriage of water ballast. When double bottom tanks are designed for dual usage the interface between the fuel transfer system and the ballast water system must be arranged with change over connections which are positive in their action. This is to prevent fuel oil being inadvertently pumped overboard through the ballast water system. When a ship is arranged with dual purpose double bottom tanks the capacity of the oily water separator must match the capacity of the ballast pumps and will be larger than that required for bilge pumping duty.

If a cargo ship is fitted with heavy lift cargo gear a part of the ballast system must be designed to accommodate the rapid changes of heel and stability which occur during heavy lift operations. The port and starboard ballast tanks must then be capable of being very rapidly filled, emptied, or transferred from port to starboard or starboard to port. A deep tank fitted forward of the engine room and divided into a centre tank and port and starboard wing tanks is sometimes used for this purpose. The two wing tanks giving the maximum amount of leverage when ballasted are then used during heavy lift operations.

Large stability changes come about when the weight of the heavy cargo is taken up by the lifting winches, particularly when the derrick has a large outreach over the side of the ship; when heavy lift cargo is first lifted from its stowed position on deck or in a hold; when it is swung outboard on the heavy lift derrick; and when the cargo weight is landed.

The ballast system in bulk carriers will reflect the arrangement and location of the cargo holds and the ballast spaces. For example, bulk carriers with hopper side tanks and cantilever wing tanks will have a different piping arrangement when compared with bulk carriers fitted with two longitudinal bulkheads and wing ballast tanks. The side tanks have a dual purpose and may be used for either water ballast or the carriage of grain or similar cargoes. Their use will be dependent on the density of the cargo carried and the volume it occupies.

Ballast pumping systems are shown in Fig 14.

Ore–bulk–oil carriers (OBOs) are often arranged with a deep double bottom tank system located in the central space formed between two longitudinal bulkheads. The wing spaces on the outboard side of the longitudinal bulkheads will be used for the carriage of oil or grain cargoes. The cargo space above the high double bottom is used for the carriage of heavy ore, grain, or oil cargoes. The wing spaces on the outboard

side of the longitudinal bulkheads extend down to the outer bottom plating. If the wing spaces are used for ballast following the carriage of oil the water ballast will become oil contaminated. The double bottom tanks are therefore often used exclusively for ballast purposes. This prevents ballast water becoming contaminated and allows discharge of ballast at a loading berth, either prior to or during loading operations without damage to the environment and the risk of a heavy penalty arising from oil pollution.

As there are considerable differences in the arrangements of bulkheads and double bottom spaces in this class of vessel, engineer officers must carefully study the ballast water system so they can handle it in a safe and efficient manner.

Oil tankers commonly use the ship's cargo tanks for ballast purposes. When they are used for ballast purposes before cleaning, the ballast water becomes oil contaminated and cannot be pumped directly overboard without serious pollution. Any ballast water contaminated with oil from cargo tanks is usually separated in cargo and slop tanks and discharged under controlled conditions to ensure that the rate of oil content of the discharge overboard does not exceed 60 litres per nautical mile.

An oily water separator of a type used in oil tankers is shown in Fig 13. They are much larger than those fitted in a dry cargo ship for bilge pumping duty. The discharge is monitored for oil content so that an audio alarm is given in the cargo pump control room when the oil content approaches the allowable figure.

It is usual to fit the separator on deck and connect it into a bypass fitted on the stern discharge line. If cargo is discharged through the stern line it passes straight through by closing off the bypass. If ballast is being discharged it passes around the bypass and through the separator.

After cargo tanks have been washed and cleaned they may be reballasted with clean sea water.

Vehicle and train ferries, and roll-on roll-off vessels (ro-ros) carry ballast water in a double bottom tank system similar to that in many other vessels. The ballast capacity is sometimes increased by fitting wing ballast tanks extending from above the outer or inner bottom plating up through to a lower deck level. These tanks may then be used for trimming purposes to correct a list with the least amount of water. This comes about because of the greater leverage obtained when water is placed in a wing ballast tank compared with the leverage obtained when water is placed in a ballast tank extending outboard from the centre girder to the side of the vessel.

Container ships may have a double bottom ballast tank arrangement together with separate wing ballast tanks extending up to the lowest longitudinal

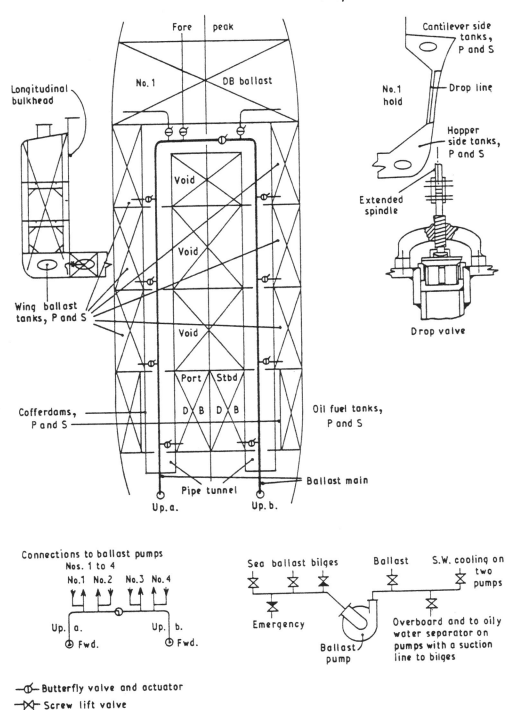

Figure 14 Ballast system for a bulk carrier.

walkway similar to those in some ro-ros. Again, there are variations in the arrangements of ballast tanks, dependent on the size of the ship, the extent of the container stowage width relative to the ships beam, and the fuel storage locations.

Capacity of ballast pumps

The designed capacity for the ballast pumps will be governed by the minimum time requirement for filling or discharging ballast prior to, during, or after cargo operations.

Cargo liners and general traders with comparatively low rates of cargo loading and discharge do not require as large a ballast pumping capacity as a bulk carrier, where the loading rate may go up to some few thousand tons/h. This is reflected in the size and type of pump or pumps used. Older ships in cargo liner service requiring only a low capacity ballast pumping output may use a steam or electrically operated duplex reciprocating pump. Modern ships, irrespective of type, use centrifugal pumps for ballast water duty. When a large pumping capacity is required, as in bulk carriers, then more than one ballast pump may be used. The use of a multiple number of ballast pumps of the same size allows a large degree of pump and motor standardisation to be achieved. Then many of the pumps used, irrespective of their duty, are of the same size. If minor changes are required in pump characteristics the changes may often be made by varying the diameter of the centrifugal pump rotor while retaining the same size of pump casing and motor frame.

In oil tankers and OBOs the cargo pumps may be used for ballasting purposes, but it is common practice to fit a ballast pump in the cargo pump room. This allows the ballast pump to be retained exclusively for clean ballast or for clean ballast from cargo tanks after cleaning operations have been completed.

Ballast tank capacity

The increase of welding and replacement of riveting in vessel construction has greatly decreased the lightweight displacement of ships. Modern cargo liners and general traders of all welded construction require, for satisfactory operation in ballast condition, a ballast displacement of approximately twice the lightweight displacement. Some of the weight requirement to obtain the ballast displacement is sometimes obtained by taking oil fuel.

In bulk carriers and similar classes of vessel, where cargo may only be carried in one direction, the ballast capacity is often greater than that for cargo liners and general traders.

In tankers when cargo tanks are used for the carriage of ballast the only limit to the quantity of ballast water carried is the loaded displacement of the vessel.

The arrangement and capacity of the ballast tanks in bulk carriers should be such that the stability in the fully or partially ballasted condition does not result in a ship that is excessively stiff. Past ship designs have shown that cost savings in this area have sometimes resulted in much greater operating costs for a variety of reasons.

It must always be remembered that the carriage of excess amounts of ballast results in a slower passage and an attendant waste of fuel.

Ballast piping arrangements

The ballast piping in cargo liners and similar classes of vessel consists of a ballast main fitted in the engine room and branch piping leading from group ballast valve chests to the various double bottom ballast tanks. In many cases separate branches, each controlled by its own valve, are led to the after inboard side of the ballast tank adjacent to the vertical keel, and to the after wing as near to the ship's side as possible. This arrangement allows tanks to be completely drained if the vessel has no rise of floor. During deballasting operations the vessel is slightly listed to one side or the other. Each group valve chest has its own connection with the ballast main.

Within the engine room the configuration of the ballast piping system is very similar to the configuration of the bilge pumping system. There are often cross connections fitted so that bilge pumps may be put onto the ballast system and the ballast pumps put onto the bilge system. There is, however, a great difference in the ballast water piping system external to the engine room.

The ballast piping leading from the group valve chests is placed within the confines of the double bottom tanks, whereas the bilge piping is normally fitted outside the double bottom tanks. Figure 12 shows a ballast system found in a dry cargo ship, where double bottom tanks may also be used for the carriage of oil fuel. Figure 15 shows the change over devices used to prevent cross contamination between tanks used for oil fuel and those used for water ballast.

Ballast tanks must be capable of being filled and emptied; the ballast main and branch lines must allow water flow inwards to the tank for tank filling and outwards from the tank when deballasting. The valves in the ballast system are therefore of the screw lift type to allow water flow in either direction.

The ballast piping arrangement in bulk carriers with hopper side tanks will be similar to that mentioned for cargo liners and similar type vessels. When cantilever side tanks are fitted under the main deck between the hatch sides and the ship's side they may be fitted with their own filling and emptying lines. For simplification, single main pipelines are led forward from the engine room bulkhead through the port and starboard cantilever tanks just under the deck level. A branch line is led from the main line down to the bottom of each tank. A gate valve is fitted on each tank branch line and is opened or closed by a reach rod passing through the deck. Indicators fitted on the reach rods show whether the valve is opened or closed. In other cases cantilever side tanks are filled with hoses connected to the wash deck and fire lines. A drop line is led from the bottom of each

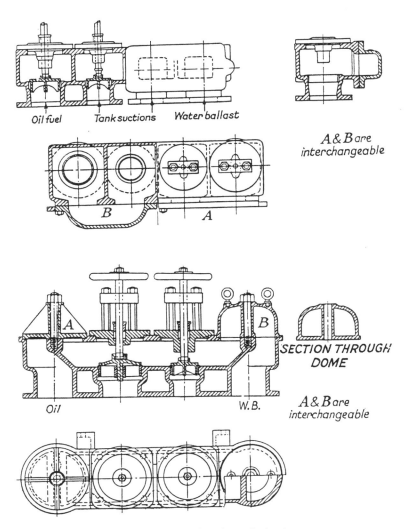

Oil fuel   Tank suctions   Water ballast

A & B are interchangeable

B   A

SECTION THROUGH DOME

Oil   W.B.   *A & B are interchangeable*

Figure 15 Changeover devices for tank chests.

cantilever side tank down to the hopper side tank. A screw lift valve is fitted at the top end of each drop pipe. The valve is controlled by a reach rod passing up through the main deck. The tanks are emptied by opening the screw lift valve and allowing the water to drain down to the hopper tanks and/or the double bottom tanks. The water is pumped out through the double bottom tank ballast water lines (Fig 14).

Bulk carriers fitted with two longitudinal bulkheads use the centre hold for cargo and the double bottom tank under the centre hold for ballast. The wing spaces go down to the outer bottom plating and may be used either for the carriage of water ballast or grain cargoes. With this type of vessel, continuous pipe ducts are fitted in the wings of the port and starboard double bottom tanks, the ducts are connected with an athwartship duct in the forward part of the vessel abaft number 1 double bottom tank.

For handling water ballast into and out of the double bottom tanks and wing spaces a ring main is fitted.

The ring main extends across the forward part of the engine room, portions of it passing through the port and starboard pipe ducts, the ring being completed in the athwartship pipe duct forward. Branch lines connect the ring main with the individual ballast spaces in the double bottoms and wing spaces. The valves commonly used with this system are of the butterfly type fitted with pneumatic or hydraulic actuators. Globe type valves may also be used in conjunction with actuators but they are more costly, take up more space and are not so easily handled if they must be changed for overhaul or repair purposes. Butterfly or globe valves are fitted in the port and starboard crossovers at the forward and after sections of the ring main. The ring main may then be operated with separate port and starboard suction and filling lines. The ballast pumps, usually two or more in number, are connected with the main at the aft crossover in the engine room. This arrangement of pumps and piping is very convenient for ships as the control of ballasting and deballasting operations may be easily arranged to take place from some point in the engine control room. The arrangement of piping and the relative location of valves are shown on a mimic board covering the ballast system. The valve actuator and the ballast pump controls are located adjacent to the mimic board (Fig 14).

This form of ballast system is also used in container ships, ro-ros, ferries and similar type vessels. It may also be used conveniently in any vessel and is quite often used where the engine room is located at the after end of the ship.

Apart from simplification there is a considerable time saving in being able to control ballasting operations from some central point in the engine room. There is also considerable saving in weight with this form of ballast piping system, compared with the weight of a conventional system having multiple runs of long branch lines.

If the access into and through the piping ducts is difficult and inadequate, any advantages gained will be lost when the ship begins to age. If it is difficult or impossible to maintain the valves, piping, actuators, and actuator piping in a satisfactory and seaworthy condition, serious loss of time will come about during ballasting and de-ballasting operations, and the cost of repairs may become astronomical. This condition often begins in the design stage of the vessel when insufficient space is allowed for easy or reasonable access of maintenance personnel along the duct. It sometimes arises because the hull steel plans are finalised before the amount of space required for piping is fully known.

Ballasting and deballasting operations

There are no set rules for ballasting and de-ballasting a vessel but certain conditions must be carefully observed. These relate to trim, stability, pollution, reducing hull stresses due to hogging or sagging conditions and avoiding hull damage due to tank pressurisation.

Before double bottom tanks, wing tanks, peaks, and deep tanks are filled or emptied, the closing devices or the plugs and covers to air pipes must be removed so that air may freely enter or leave the tank as the volume of water in the tank decreases or increases. Failure to remove air pipe covers has sometimes resulted in serious damage to the tank plating and internal structure because of the increased internal pressure build up or the creation of a vacuum.

Generally it is desirable to use only minimal amounts of estuary and river water for ballast purposes. This is to prevent the build up of unpumpable mud and sandy material in double bottom and other ballast tanks. A build up of unpumpable material leads to a loss of cargo carrying capacity when carrying any dense cargo that does not become volume bound within the available hold space. The loss of cargo is due to an increase in the vessels lightweight displacement.

Another reason for using minimal amounts of estuary and river water is due to the possibility of this water being corrosive. Generally the amount taken in is no more than is required to get the vessel safely out of the port limits.

After the vessel is at sea away from areas of possible pollution, ballasting may be carried out. Care in the interest of safety must be observed. If the stability condition is such that the free surface effect of water in double bottom or other tanks creates an unstable condition, then it may be more opportune to list the ship by filling a tank on one side of the vessel before filling the tank on the opposite side. The study of the stability conditions when filling and emptying ballast tanks is normally carried out by the deck department, ballast filling and emptying operations only being started after receipt of written instructions to the chief engineer from the master. The officer responsible for the removal of air pipe covers must also be clearly established to eliminate or reduce the risk of accidents.

When it is safe to do so, river and estuary water is pumped out and replaced with clean sea water, and the ballast pumps are then washed out by pumping through with clean sea water before shutdown.

Sometimes the question arises as to whether ballast tanks should be run up from the sea or filled up (pressed up) by pumping. It must be remembered if tanks are pumped up and an overflow occurs, that the pressure head placed on the tank structure and tank top will be greater than if it is run up by opening the tank connections through to the sea and filling by gravity flow.

If a double bottom tank manhole situated in a cargo hold leaks, damage will be sustained by any cargo present when the tank is pressed up. Damaged cargo involves claims on the owner and his underwriters for the damage sustained.

Problems with ballast pumping systems

The problems associated with the removal of ballast water from a ship are similar to the problems associated with the removal of bilge water; vacuum loss due to air leaking into the system.

When the surface of the water in the ballast tank has a positive head above the level of the ballast pump, as in deep tanks, wing tanks and the peak tanks extending upwards to the main deck level, there is never usually any problem with deballasting the vessel. The problems commence when the level of the water falls to slightly above the level of the ballast pump and resistance to water flow in the suction lines causes a partial vacuum to exist at the ballast pump inlet branch. The pumping conditions now will be similar to when pumping ballast water from a double bottom tank. When any air leakage into the ballast suction line occurs it will be shown as a reduction in vacuum on the ballast pump suction gauge. As the vacuum is reduced, the efficiency of the pumping action falls away and the pumping action eventually ceases. If the vacuum is increased when the ballast pump main suction valve is closed it indicates that the pump is in order. If the pump is of the centrifugal type it also indicates that the pump priming devices are in order irrespective of their type.

A common problem with centrifugal pumps fitted with their own priming devices, consisting of some form of vacuum pump and float control gear, occurs when the water sump becomes dry. The sump is then filled from the water filling line and an attempt is then made to prime the pump. If this still results in failure then the float control gear and shut off valves must be examined. Another cause of apparent failure with centrifugal priming devices, irrespective of type, occurs if the non-return valve on the pump discharge connection becomes stuck open and allows air to flow back down the discharge line and destroy the vacuum (see Fig 10 for float control valve).

If these measures fail, the procedures must then follow similar lines to those used when searching for vacuum loss in the bilge suction pipelines and group valves.

There is one important difference between dealing with bilge pumping problems and ballast pumping problems. Except in a real emergency endangering the ship, or when preparing cargo holds for cargo, bilge pumping problems can usually be dealt with in a less hurried manner than ballast pumping problems. Ballast pumping problems arise when ballast is being removed, prior to, or when loading cargo. If ballast cannot be removed as desired it can result in considerable financial losses arising out of 'lost time' and involve further financial losses to the owner if charter party penalties are applied by the charterer and others who have incurred losses due to the delays made by the ship.

Before entering any double bottom space, pipe tunnel or duct, duct keel, peak tanks or any other enclosed space, it is essential that the enclosed spaces are properly ventilated (see *Safety*).

Fuel oil systems

Fuel oil systems comprise separate but connected systems. They are the bunkering and transfer systems, the storage system, the cleaning and separation system, and the boiler firing system. In motorships a clean fuel system separate from the boiler fuel system is also required. The bunkering system is used to receive fuel on board the vessel. The transfer system is used to direct the fuel into the correct location in the storage system during bunkering operations and for the transfer of fuel into the settling tanks. The settling tanks are part of the fuel cleaning system. From the settling tanks the fuel passes through the 'cold' filters and then into the fuel oil burning system associated with the boilers.

Motorships require a more elaborate fuel cleaning system. The fuel is taken from the settling tanks and passed through filters, heaters, centrifugal purifiers and clarifiers, then passing up to the clean oil tanks. The clean oil tanks holding the purified fuel are sometimes referred to as day tanks.

The fuel is taken from the day tanks to the engine fuel system which consists of fine filters, pumps and heaters, external to the engine. The pumps then pass fuel under pressure into the high pressure fuel injection pumps fitted on the engine. High pressure piping connects the fuel injection pumps with the fuel injection valves fitted in the cylinders.

The fuel transfer system is also used to move fuel around the vessel to correct trim and heel conditions.

Fuel oil storage

The values for the specific gravity and the viscosity of boiler fuel were formerly very much lower than the values found today. Ships propelled by diesel engines used distillate fuels. When double bottom tanks were used, either for the carriage of water ballast, boiler fuel oil or diesel fuel, major problems with sludge formation only occurred in exceptional cases. The settling tanks, together with the fuel separators in diesel propelled ships, were able to cope with removal of water and the cleaning of the fuel to prevent problems.

As oil refining techniques improved, so giving a greater yield of marketable distillates, the quality of residual fuels deteriorated.

Experience then showed that quite often stable unpumpable oil-water emulsions formed sludges in the tanks that were used alternately for either water ballast or oil fuel. Many ships are presently in service with pumping systems allowing either oil fuel or water ballast to be carried in double bottom tanks. The practice today is to retain a certain number of the double bottom tanks exclusively for water ballast when required, the remaining double bottom tanks then being used exclusively for the storage of oil fuel (Fig 13a). It is common practice for specialist ship types such as bulk carriers, container ships and the like to have deep tanks situated in the forward and after ends of the vessel. The deep tanks are used exclusively for storage of fuel oil.

Some dry cargo vessels and bulk carriers have a midships deep tank for fuel oil storage. Trim problems do not arise as fuel is transferred daily from the deep tanks.

Oil tankers are arranged with forward and after deep tanks for the storage of fuel oil. In some cases tankers and specialist ship types have wing tanks on the forward port and starboard outboard sides of the engine room. These tanks also form part of the space allocated for the storage of oil fuel. In many cases tanks used for the storage of fuel oil are referred to as bunker tanks. The term is a carry over from the days of coal burning steamships when the coal used as fuel was referred to as bunker coal and the storage spaces were referred to as bunkers.

Due to the viscosity of modern fuel oils, steam heating coils become a very necessary part of the fuel oil storage system. Without heating coils the fuel stored would quickly become unpumpable. The heating coils are therefore used to bring up to, or hold the fuel oil at a temperature where the viscosity of the oil is such that it is fluid enough to be conveniently handled by the transfer pumps.

Modern ships have a space for the storage of diesel fuel. This fuel may be used for diesel generator sets. In some ships the diesel fuel is blended with a heavier fuel in a fuel blender prior to use. The use of a blender reduces the cost of fuel for the generation of electricity.

In steam ships gas oil or diesel fuel is used for emergency generators and, when necessary, for raising steam from a 'dead ship' condition. The location of the diesel oil storage tanks will be governed by the required storage capacity.

Emergency diesel generating sets of high speed type use gas oil for the fuel. Motor ships have a clean diesel fuel tank incorporated into the fuel oil system for the main engine. This tank makes it possible to manoeuvre the main engines on diesel fuel or to flush out the engine fuel system with diesel oil before engine shut down. The engine fuel system and its parts are more easily worked on if the system is flushed through with diesel oil before 'finished with engines'.

When only a small storage capacity is required for diesel oil, the tank can be fitted externally to the engine room, in the emergency generator room or at some location on deck. In other cases, diesel fuel may be stored in double bottom tanks. In specialist ships ranging from bulk carriers through to oil tankers, diesel fuel is commonly stored in double bottom tanks below the machinery space.

Smaller capacity heating coils are sometimes fitted in diesel oil storage tanks to hold the fuel at pumpable temperatures and to prevent wax formation or fuel gelling if the ship is trading in locations where low temperatures may be experienced.

All fuel storage locations around the engine room, whether in 'loose' or 'built-in' tanks, are insulated to conserve energy, prevent engine room temperature rise and protect personnel. At locations in dry cargo ships where the tank top or sides of heated fuel tanks may come into contact with cargo, suitable insulation must be provided in the areas where cargo could sustain damage or where dangerous conditions could arise with certain cargoes.

The heating services for oil fuel storage locations are shown in diagrammatic form in Fig 16. The steam is supplied to the heating coils through reducing valves allowing the temperature of the oil in the tank to be maintained by adjustment of the steam pressure.

The condensate passing out of heating coils is passed through steam traps to avoid energy wastage. One or more leaking steam traps cause a large waste of steam and may in bad cases lead to a shortage of steam from the exhaust gas boilers. This then requires the boiler to be 'flashed up' and wastes fuel to maintain the desired steam pressures. In other cases fuel is also wasted when the boilers are fired by oil fuel.

Tank steaming out connections are often brought off the reduced steam pressure lines to fuel heating services. The connections should be left blanked off when not in use.

Some passenger ships and cruise ships experience stability problems if the top hamper arising out of the ships structure and the weight of the upper internals is high. Ships with this problem sometimes use an arrangement of the fuel storage system whereby the stored fuel is kept floating on water. As fuel is used from the upper parts of the double bottom tanks it floats on water put into the bottom parts. This arrangement of fuel storage keeps the tanks full and obviates any free surface effect and the stability problems that may arise when the fuel tanks are slack or only partially full. The arrangement may also remove the need to carry permanent ballast.

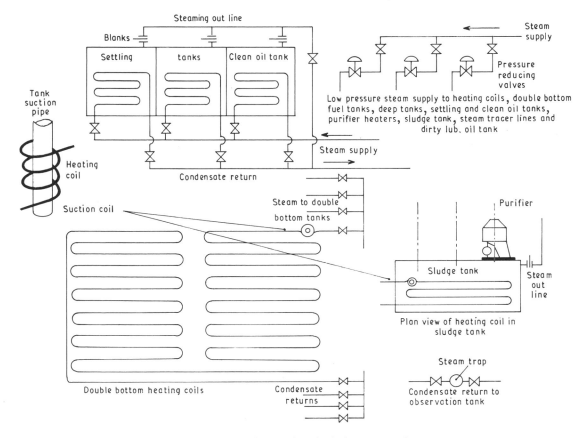

Figure 16 Heating services for fuel storage tanks.

Fuel oil bunkering and transfer systems

The oil fuel bunkering system and the fuel transfer system consist of pipelines, valves, strainers, transfer pumps and a system for quickly measuring the contents of fuel tanks at a centralised bunkering station. In order to speed up the receipt of fuel on board a vessel and reduce the risk of an oil spill when bunkering or transferring fuel, a tank overflow system is sometimes fitted in conjunction with the air piping fitted to the storage tanks.

Figures 17 and 18 show fuel transferring systems, and Fig 19 shows a tank gauge, used to determine the contents of the fuel tank.

In Fig 18, only one transfer pump is shown. Most ships are fitted with a standby transfer pump, others may incorporate the diesel oil transfer pump into the heavy fuel system as the standby. All heavy fuel lines within the confines of the engine room are fitted with steam tracer lines and insulated to maintain the fuel at a pumpable viscosity.

Transfer pumps are of the positive displacement type. Electrically driven gear pumps are often used for this service. Steam driven reciprocating pumps are also used. They have an advantage because they can be operated at very low speeds.

Positive displacement pumps require a relief valve on the discharge side of the pump. This is arranged to pass fuel back to the suction side of the pump. (The relief valve is not shown in Fig 17.)

The bunkering lines are usually fitted on the weather deck of a cargo vessel and run fore and aft along the deck with suitable port and starboard branch connections located forward, midships, and aft, so that fuel may be received on the vessel at any location with the least inconvenience, irrespective of whether cargo operations are in progress.

The bunker receiving lines on passenger ships usually consist of a receiving connection fitted on the port and starboard side of the ship located in a working cross alleyway served by doors fitted in the ship's side. A crossover line under the deck connects the port and starboard receiving points and leads down to the fuel transfer system in the engine room or boiler room.

Before fuel passes from the bunkering lines into the fuel transfer system and the storage tanks it passes through a strainer fitted at some convenient

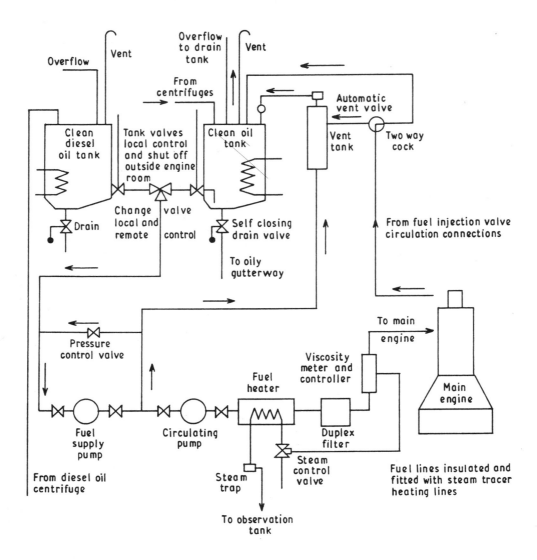

Figure 17 Fuel oil system for main engines.

location. Sampling connections are fitted at each inlet branch on the bunkering lines. Lifting facilities may also be provided to hoist the flexible bunkering lines from the dock side, supply vessel or bunkering barge.

The bunkering lines are connected into the fuel main located in the engine room. The fuel main is connected through valves with branch lines leading to the individual storage tanks located in the double bottoms and to deep tanks adjacent to or at the sides of the engine room.

In large bulk carriers, container ships, and tankers, where the main fuel storage locations are deep tanks extending up to the main deck or weather deck, the bunkering lines are connected directly into the deep tanks. Some specialist types of ship such as those mentioned may have a forward pump room in which

a fuel transfer pump is fitted. This pump is used to transfer fuel directly from the forward port and starboard deep tanks into the after deep tanks or the fuel main in the engine room.

Ships having double bottom tanks which may be used either for fuel or water ballast use a single pipeline between each valve in the group valve chest and the open end in the tank. This line is used for handling either fuel or water when filling or emptying tanks.

The group valves are of the screw lift type so that water or fuel may flow in either direction. The group valve chests have separate branches at each end of the valve chest. One branch leads to the ballast main and the other leads to the fuel main. Interchangeable connecting and isolating devices are fitted in such a

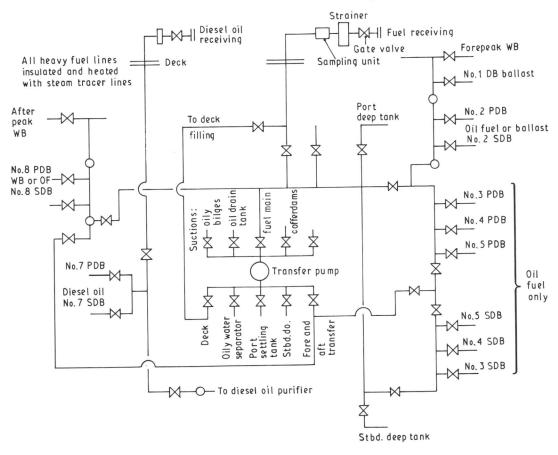

Figure 18   Fuel transfer arrangement.

manner that the valve chest is either connected with the ballast main and isolated from the fuel main, or connected to the fuel main and isolated from the ballast main.

If use of the double bottom tank is changed from ballast to fuel or fuel to ballast the isolating and connecting devices fitted on the group valve chest must be changed over accordingly. When the safety devices are changed over on any ballast-fuel group valve chest a suitable entry recording the change must be made in the log book. The entry should be initialled by the engineer officer supervising or making the changes.

The change-over devices fitted at each end of the group valves act as a safety measure to prevent pollution or inadvertent intermingling of oil fuel and ballast water except for the residue remaining in the tanks after draining. These safety devices prevent any loss of oil fuel by being pumped overboard through the ballast system when discharging ballast water, and also prevent a settling tank being filled with ballast water (Fig 14).

Where ships use any or all of the double bottom tanks and deep tanks exclusively for the storage of fuel oil it is only necessary to connect the main branches on the group valve chests with the fuel main. As there are no connections with the ballast system the isolating devices are redundant. The valves fitted in the group valve chests are of the screw lift type allowing oil to flow in any direction, either into or out of the storage tanks.

Pipelines passing through heated fuel tanks experience a wide change of temperature between the hot and cold conditions. Arrangements must therefore be made to accommodate the expansion and contraction that the pipes undergo when experiencing these changes. The pipes are therefore arranged with expansion bends or 'omega' loops to allow the expansion and contraction to take place freely and without damage to the piping (Figs 43 and 44a).

When heavy high viscosity fuels are used on a ship the transfer system piping in exposed positions in the engine room and boiler room requires thermal insulation, and steam tracer lines placed under the insulation.

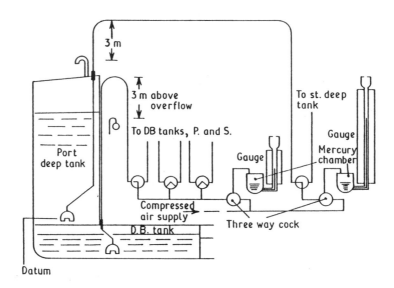

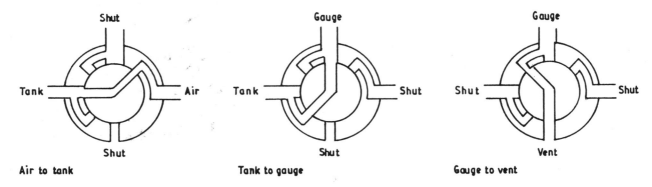

Figure 19   Tank gauges for oil fuel tanks, and positions for three way cock.

Heating coils

Any fuel oil storage location, including settling tanks and clean oil, daily-use tanks containing residual fuel or a residual-distillate fuel blend, requires the installation of steam heating coils. The heating coils maintain the temperature of the fuel, or heat the fuel to raise its temperature and give it a viscosity suitable for pumping. Heating the fuel in settling tanks increases the natural ability for the water, foreign matter and fuel to separate out from each other, and is referred to as gravity separation. The distillate fuels, such as some grades of diesel oil supplied today and expected in the future, will also require heating coils to maintain the fuel at a temperature above its cloud point and to prevent the formation of a gel.

The capacity of the heating coils must be sufficient to raise the temperature of the fuel and hold it at a temperature where the viscosity will allow it to be handled easily by the fuel transfer pumps.

The design of the heating coils requires a knowledge of heat transfer. The calculations start with the assumption that the heat transferred to the fuel from the coils must be equal to or, when increasing the temperature of the fuel, more than, the heat lost. The heat lost from the fuel passes through the boundary plating of the tank. These losses are calculated on the basis of a full tank by the usual methods covering conductive heat transfer.

The transfer of heat occurs through the inner surfaces of the tank plating in contact with the fuel and the outer surfaces of the fuel tank in contact with the moving sea water. When the ship is static the heat lost from the tanks to the sea water is reduced because of the 'thin film' which does not exist when the ship is moving.

The values for the conductive heat transfer to the sea through the tank boundaries takes into account the insulating effect of the oil that congeals on the inner sides and bottom of the tank. It is fortunate that as the sea water temperature falls the congealed layer slightly increases in thickness and so increases its insulating effect.

The heat lost through the tank top plating is also taken into account, but radiation losses are not usually considered.

The heat imparted to the fuel from the heating coils is calculated on the principles of conductive heat transfer through the tube surface during the same unit time period used in the heat loss calculations. As the fuel is heated the steam gives up its latent heat and condenses to water. The optimum length of a coil will be such that all the steam used in heating the fuel will be condensed to water at some temperature above the desired temperature of the oil. If the coil is made too long the last section of the coil will have little effect on heating the fuel because the sensible heat given up by the water is relatively small in amount when compared with the heating effect of steam giving up its latent heat. The water at the outlet end of the coil cannot give up much heat when it approaches the temperature of the fuel. If a coil is made too long the excess length plays very little part in heating the fuel surrounding it.

The design parameters are based on 'worst set' conditions; the lowest steam pressure and saturation temperature, the highest likely oil temperature and the lowest likely sea water temperature.

The temperature of the fuel in the fuel tank can be controlled by the use of a pressure reducing valve, by raising or lowering the heating steam pressure. A steam trap is fitted at the outlet end of the coil. The steam trap prevents live steam passing into the heating coil return lines. The steam pressure in the coils must be sufficient to lift the condensate from the coils up to the drain cooler or observation tank if a drain cooler is not fitted.

The heating coils are made up in sections, the sections being joined together with heavy four bolt flanges of the spigot and fossette type. This type of flange connection effectively holds the pipe joint or gasket in place and prevents it being blown out. It is usual to use very thick section lap welded mild steel (low carbon steel) between 50 and 100 mm bore for the piping sections, a common size being 75 mm nominal bore. The flanges are slipped on the pipe and fillet welded on both sides of the flange.

Older ships with transverse frames have the coils fitted thwartships, placed in between the floors and extending from the centre girder out to near the tank side margin plate. A helical coil of pipe is often combined with a section of the coils and fitted around the tail pipe on the suction line leading to the group valve chest.

Where longitudinal frames are used the coils run in a fore and aft direction and are located between the longitudinals. The coils are held in place by pipe clips welded to the tank bottom. They hold the heating coils 150–200 mm above it.

In deep tanks where the floor area of the tank bottom is not sufficient to place the total amount of coil required, the balance is then located on the lower parts of the sides and the ends of the deep tanks.

When heating coils are put in use there is always a danger present. Should the coils have leaked the possibility arises of oil finding its way into the boiler and settling on the heating surfaces. If oil finds its way into the boiler through the use of oil contaminated feed water the result is often disastrous and may easily lead to injury, loss of life or other serious consequences.

When oil gets on the heating surfaces the rate of heat transmission from the heat source to the water is greatly impaired. Where the heat source is at a relatively low temperature as is possible with the exhaust gas from an engine operating at slightly less than full power, the efficiency of the boiler is reduced. The boiler steam pressure then falls making it necessary to fire the boiler. When the boiler is fired the temperature of the combustion gases in the furnace and other gas passages is much higher, and the boiler pressure also rises. The heating surfaces then become overheated due to the reduced rate of heat transmission. In the overheated condition the strength of the plates and tubes is seriously reduced. The weakened plates or tubes then begin to be distorted by forces arising out of the steam pressure. Serious damage or an explosion will then rapidly ensue.

To overcome this danger an observation tank is used to view the condensate returns coming from the heating coils. If oil is present it is readily seen and steps must be taken to prevent oil-contaminated feed water entering the boiler.

Observation tanks are shown in Figs 20a and 20b. In order to reduce the chance of oil contaminated feed water entering the boilers, the observation tank is often incorporated with a cascade type oil filter.

The observation tanks used for the returns from cargo heating coils in some oil tankers and chemical cargo tankers carrying dangerous liquids are fitted external to the engine room in some well ventilated space to prevent dangers arising should heating coils leak.

The observation tank is a most important safety device protecting the boilers. It is often made in the form of a cascade type filter. If the amount of oil coming over with the condensate is small the cascade filter will retain the oil and allow clean condensate to

a)

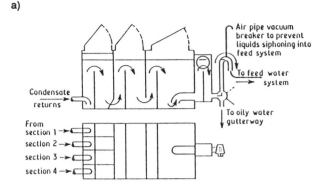

b)

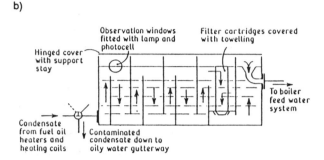

Figure 20 a) Observation tank; b) observation tank and cascade filter.

pass into the boiler. The retained oil is then drained off at set periods to the oily water bilge. The oil is separated from the bilge water in the oily water separator, the water passes overboard and the oil is returned to the fuel tanks. If the amount of oil in the condensate is more than the cascade filter can safely handle, all the contaminated condensate is drained to the oily bilge, and the oil is separated from the condensate and bilge water in the oily water separator. The oil may then be saved.

Some cascade type filters are fitted with sight glasses, a light source and a photo cell arrangement. If oil is present in the condensate the amount of light reaching the photo cell is reduced and an alarm condition is created.

When opening up the steam supply to heating coils the observation tank should be kept under observation. One must never feel secure because the steam pressure within the heating coils is almost always higher than the oil pressure outside; it is not always so if the steam supply to the coils is shut off or cut back in a tank when the correct oil temperature is reached.

Refer to Chapter 1, *Marine Boilers*, for more information on boiler failure.

To find a leaking heating coil, shut off the steam supply to each coil in turn and observe the conden-

sate returns from the coil. When there is no oil showing in the condensate returns the shut down coil is the one that is leaking. This process is time consuming and requires considerable patience.

Some ships are fitted with a sight glass arrangement in the return line from the drain cooler to the observation tank. Coil leakage shown in the sight glass may be sensed and used with warning devices.

Heating coils can be tested by hydraulic means. This gives positive results but should only be attempted after cleaning the tank and making it safe to enter. The location of the leak may then be found and the necessary repairs carried out as required.

Treatment of fuel oil

Fuel is treated in steamships by heating it in the settling tanks and allowing it to remain undisturbed in either the port or starboard settling tank for some time period, so that gravitational separation of water and heavy foreign material occurs. The water and foreign materials settle at the bottom of the tank and can be drained off through a self-closing valve into a tundish and an oily bilge.

The period of time allowed for gravitational separation to occur is related to the capacity of the settling tank and the fuel used in unit time. The minimum capacity of settling tanks often allows for a 12 h settling period, the run-down time being similar. In other cases the settling period may be increased to some multiple of 12 h, such as 24 h which is fairly common. In that case, the run down time will be 24 h.

A lengthy separation time is desirable although it can be seen that it is not necessary to extend it beyond the period when separation will be complete. Separation of the fuel proceeds faster when the fuel in the settling tank is heated and its viscosity and density are lowered.

The flash point of the fuel oil governs the temperature at which it is held in the settling tank. For reasons of safety the fuel must be held at some temperature lower than the flash point. The amount it must be held below the flash point is fixed by regulations, and for British flag ships is 14°C lower than the flash point of the fuel. Fuel oil having a flash point below 65°C is not normally used as fuel oil in merchant ships. This figure will be seen to differ under the regulations of different government authorities and ship classification societies. Engineer officers must therefore know the regulations that apply to the flag of the vessel they are serving on.

Stoke's Laws show how the gravitation force causing separation of foreign matter from fuels is affected by the differences in their specific gravities or densities, the importance of the resistance to separation being affected by viscosity. Obviously foreign matter will fall to the bottom of the settling tank faster when the fuel is hot and has a low viscosity. The separation forces will be greater when the difference in the specific gravity of the fuel and foreign matter is greater.

The treatment of fuel in motorships starts in a similar way to that in steamships. The fuel is first treated in settling tanks to reduce the content of water and heavy solid matter, but the high specific gravity of the fuel makes the separation of water and solid material more difficult to accomplish. The difficulties increase as the specific gravities of the fuel, water and other foreign materials approach each other. If soluble foreign matter, such as sodium and vanadium compounds, is present in the oil, the centrifuge will not remove it. However, sea water containing sodium compounds and other salts will be removed.

Following the initial treatment of the fuel in settling tanks the fuel is cleaned in the separation or purification equipment. This consists of pumps, heaters connecting pipe work and centrifuges. The fuel supply to the purification equipment is taken from either of the settling tanks through valves that can be closed from outside the engine room in the event of a fire causing engine room staff to leave the engine room.

After leaving the settling tank the fuel is pumped through a heater to raise its temperature, lowering its viscosity and density relative to the water. It then enters the first stage of purification by passing through a centrifuge set up as a purifier and is then pumped through the second centrifuge set up as a clarifier, the two centrifuges being connected in series. After treatment in the second stage the fuel is then pumped up to the daily use tank, or 'day tank'. On older ships the purifier will be of the automatic self cleaning type whereas the clarifier will most likely require manual cleaning.

On modern ships both centrifuges are often arranged as clarifiers in series, and cleaning is carried out with automatic control of the bowl cleaning cycle, sometimes called the dump cycle. When the centrifuges are arranged as clarifiers the amount of dirt and water in the bowl increases until a point is reached where extremely minute amounts of water begin to be discharged with the clean fuel oil or led back to the fuel supply through a separate circulating connection. Highly sensitive transducers capable of detecting the smallest amounts of water are used in the cleaning control equipment of the clarifiers. When a minute amount of water is detected by the transducer it gives out a signal, which is used to shut off the untreated fuel supply and activate the cleaning of the clarifier. When the upper and lower parts of the bowl separate, the periphery of the bowl is opened, and the solid matter and water in the bowl are quickly spun out under the action of centrifugal force. The open bowl then closes ready to recommence treatment.

An advantage is gained when centrifuges are arranged as clarifiers. In this manner, the use of sealing water in the bowl becomes unnecessary and heavier fuels having a specific gravity approaching, or slightly greater than, that of water may be treated at much higher temperatures without the problems of maintaining a water seal in the bowl.

When two clarifiers are arranged in series, some protection is afforded as the second clarifier safeguards any fall off in separating efficiency of the first stage clarifier.

The rate of passage of fuel through a centrifuge (purifier or clarifier) has a very important bearing on the efficiency of the cleaning operation. Slow purification rates are necessary to remove the maximum amount of dirt. The low cost fuel now used in many motor ships requires a very low rate of flow through the separation equipment for effective purification. In view of this, some ship owners and operators run two clarifiers in parallel, so halving the rate of flow. Others operate three clarifiers at the same time, with two of the machines being connected in parallel, the third machine in series with the other two. If the machines in parallel are operated as purifiers the third machine is operated as a clarifier. This is considered the safest way to clean low cost fuels. If an extra machine is installed to make this possible, higher capital investment is required for the fuel purification equipment and the piping system is slightly more complicated. Some older ships fitted with purifiers operate two purifiers in parallel to obtain the low throughput required. Some others direct the flow from the two purifiers in parallel to a clarifier. (See also Chapter 4, *Fuel Oil*.)

After passing through the final stage of purification the clean fuel is pumped up to the daily use tank (sometimes called the daily service tank or the day tank). The fuel is then ready for use in the engine.

Settling tanks and clean oil tanks form part of the ship's structure in modern vessels, and are often referred to as 'built in' tanks. They are located as high as possible within the engine room space, fuel then being able to flow down to the equipment being served by the action of gravity. When the tanks are located in the upper part of the engine room, a good head of fuel is available at service pump inlet branches.

Steam heating coils are provided in the settling tanks and daily use tanks to heat or to hold the fuel at the required temperature. The exterior surfaces of the settling and clean oil tanks are insulated to retain heat. The tanks are also fitted with thermometers for local readings and instrumentation to give a distant reading of the tank temperature in the machinery control room. Alarms may also be fitted to give a call out if the temperature in the tanks exceeds some selected safe value dependent on the flash point of the oil.

Drain valves are fitted for the removal of water from the settling tanks. The drain valves must be self closing and kept in good working order in the interest of safety.

A diagrammatic arrangement of a fuel cleaning system is shown in Fig 21. In the arrangement shown there are only two centrifuges, and they may be operated in parallel or in series. Many ships are fitted with three centrifuges, and another smaller capacity centrifuge for dealing with diesel oil. Some arrangements allow the overflow from the clean oil tank to be passed back to either of the settling tanks.

The sludge tank is often used as the foundation for the centrifuges and sludge passes directly into the tank. An alarm device is sometimes fitted at the sludge outlet and if the centrifuge begins to overflow an alarm is activated.

The positive displacement pumps fitted to supply oil to the heaters and the centrifuges have a common relief valve to pass excess oil back to the suction side of the pump. Some centrifuges have pumps mounted on them to pass oil to the heater and centrifuge. A pump on the clean oil outlet is used to pump fuel up to the clean oil tank.

The fuel cleaning centrifuges in modern ships are usually arranged to act as clarifiers and thus avoid the use of a water seal. Fuel with a density slightly greater than the density of water may then be handled by the fuel cleaning system.

The settling and clean fuel tank are fitted with self closing drain valves. The outlet valve from each tank is arranged for local control and to allow it to be closed from some remote point outside the engine room. Thermometers, high level alarms and high temperature alarms are also fitted. The clean oil tank or daily use tank is sometimes fitted with a low level alarm.

The piping system in the 'purifier room' has steam tracer lines fitted under insulation material surrounding the piping.

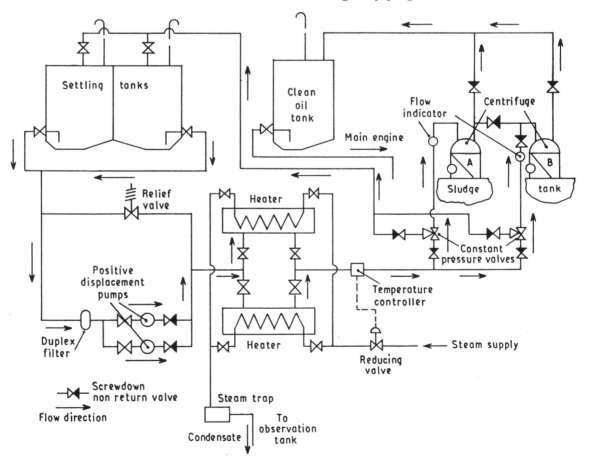

Figure 21 Fuel cleaning system.

Stoke's Laws apply to the treatment of fuel in centrifuges in a similar manner to their application when separation occurs by gravitational forces acting on the fuel, water, and dirt particles in settling tanks. When the fuel, water, and foreign matter is spun round in a centrifuge revolving at a high speed, the separation force is many times greater than the gravitational force, and cleaning takes place within a time period that is a minute fraction of the time required for gravitational separation.

Fuel systems in diesel propelled ships

The clean fuel system in a vessel propelled by a diesel engine consists of the clean daily service fuel tanks, a clean diesel fuel tank, surcharge or service pumps, circulating pumps, vent tank, fuel oil heaters, connecting fuel supply and return lines. The fuel supply and return lines are fitted with steam tracer lines placed under thermal insulation covered with a hard facing impervious to oil.

The flow path from the clean oil day tank is through a single valve identical to those fitted in the settling tank supply lines to the fuel separation equipment. The valves are normally operated from the engine room and also have reach rods, extended spindles or a tripping device allowing them to be closed from some point outside the engine room in the event of an engine room fire.

The fuel passes through filters to surcharge pumps, or through service pumps to fuel oil heaters. From the heaters the fuel passes through fine filters to the high pressure fuel injection pumps on the main engine.

Modern diesel propulsion engines have an arrangement in the fuel injection valve which allows fuel to flow freely through the valve body except at the time when fuel is actually being injected into the cylinder. When this type of fuel injection valve is fitted in the engine, circulating pumps are required together with a return line to lead the circulating fuel back into the fuel system. The returning fuel is passed into a vent tank allowing oil vapour to escape from the heated fuel back into the daily service tank. Alternatively the fuel may be passed directly back to the daily service tank. A drain line is fitted from the bottom of the vent tank and allows the fuel returning from the fuel injection valves to re-enter the fuel system.

This type of fuel valve when fitted on the engine allows the engine to be safely manoeuvred on heavy fuel. When running at slow speeds steam tracer lines heat and maintain the fuel at the correct viscosity.

The circulating fuel assists in maintaining the fuel injection nozzle at a safe temperature and the fuel valve cooling system becomes redundant.

When running under full away conditions the steam supply to the tracer line is closed. In some cases the fuel circulating pumps may be closed down and bypassed.

The fuel injection system on the engine is covered in Chapter 3, *Diesel Engines* (Fig 23, page 140).

AIR PIPES

All tanks, irrespective of their use, must have an air pipe unless they operate under a pressure or contain a highly dangerous or toxic material.

The air pipe allows the ingress of air or egress of air or vapours during tank emptying or filling operations.

The air pipes normally extend to above the weather deck. The open end of the pipe is made to face downwards by fitting a 'goose neck'. This prevents the entry of rain into the tank and reduces the inflow of water. When a vessel is fully loaded, or in heavy weather, the air pipes must be closed off by some device fitted at the end of the goose neck. The device may be a wooden plug, a canvas cover, or the pipes may be closed by screwing up a cover plate. In other cases a plastic float is fitted within the open end of the goose neck. If a sea is shipped the float rises and closes the open end of the air pipe, or the closing device prevents sea water from entering the tank through the air pipe.

Air pipes should be labelled with the name and number of the tank they are serving so that they may be identified easily.

If an attempt is made to fill a tank by pumping it up when air pipe plugs, canvas covers or the closing devices are in place, the tank will be subjected to an increasing pressure related to the performance characteristics of the pump. The tank or the ship's structure forming the tank may then be badly damaged due to internal pressure. Similarly, if an attempt is made to pump out a tank the increasing vacuum may cause the tank to collapse or badly damage the ship's structure forming the tank. An examination of claims made on underwriters over the years will show that this form of damage amounts to more than a few isolated cases.

When fuel tanks are emptied gases may form in the tank from the remaining fuel oil, and to protect the tank and prevent any ingress of flame, the open ends of air pipes must be covered by wire gauze made from a non-corroding material. The gauze is protected from mechanical damage by covering it with a much coarser, more open mesh gauze cover.

When air pipes are being painted, gauze covers often become coated with paint. They become ineffective and dangerous if the free flow of air into or out of the air pipe is prevented. If the gauzes are wiped over with engine oil before the air pipes are painted the chance of the paint drying is greatly reduced. The wire gauzes should be examined immediately after the air pipes are painted and cleaned.

The cross-sectional area of tank air pipes should be made larger than the cross sectional area of the filling pipe, or the aggregate area of the filling pipes if two pipes are used for tank filling. The rules of the various classification societies are not identical on the matter of air pipes or the relative areas of air and sounding pipes. Where figures are quoted the cross sectional area of the air pipes is usually 25% greater than the total cross sectional area of the filling pipe or pipes.

Sounding pipes

The contents of tanks are found by taking soundings of the depth of the liquid contained in the tank or ullages, showing the distance of the liquid level from the top of the tank or the sounding pipe. Sounding pipes are fitted to all tanks to enable soundings or ullages to be taken.

When the ullage or dip is known the volume of the tank contents is found from the tank calibration tables. If the volume of the fuel in the tank is known together with its density at the storage temperature, the weight of fuel in the tank is easily calculated as follows:

$$\frac{\text{tank}}{\text{contents}} = \frac{\text{fuel contents}\,(\text{m}^3) \times \text{density}\,(\text{kg/m}^3)}{1000}.$$

The density of the fuel is taken at its storage temperature.

In order to balance pressures within the sounding pipe and the tank a small hole is drilled through the sounding pipe wall just below the level of the top of the tank (Fig 22). If no hole is present and the pressure within the tank becomes greater than the outside air pressure the liquid in the tank will be forced upwards within the sounding pipe when the sounding cap is removed. False soundings will then be given, and in extreme cases liquid will be discharged from the sounding pipe.

Sounding pipes in machinery spaces are fitted with self closing cocks having a weighted handle or some other self closing device at their upper end, the purpose being to prevent flooding of machinery spaces when filling tanks if the sounding pipes were left open.

When soundings are being taken with a sounding rod the rod gains in velocity in its downward movement in a long sounding pipe, the velocity being dependent on the length of the pipe. The sounding rod hits the bottom of the tank with some force. This would cause heavy localised wear of the shell plating below the sounding pipe. A doubler, referred to as a striking plate, is welded on the bottom plating below the sounding pipe to protect the shell. When carrying out an inspection in a double bottom or similar tank the condition of the striking plate and its weld fastenings should be observed during the tank inspection. A striking plate is shown under the lower end of the sounding pipe in the hold bilge well (Fig 23). It is similarly located under the sounding pipes in double bottom tanks (Fig 24).

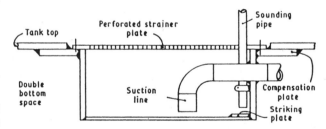

Figure 23   Hold drainage well.

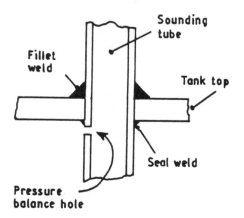

Figure 22   Sounding tube pressure balance hole.

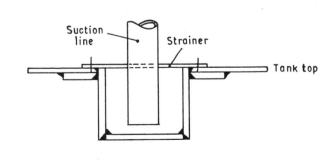

Figure 24   Engine room drainage hat box.

More expedient means of measuring the contents of tanks may be fitted to individual tanks, but sounding pipes are fitted to check the accuracy of the recordings.

It is normal practice to trim a ship by the stern, so air pipes are fitted to the forward ends of tanks and sounding pipes are fitted in the after end of tanks. In some cases an air pipe is fitted at the forward and after end of a tank. Obviously, if a vessel is trimmed by the stern the soundings obtained will be in error due to the greater depth of liquid at the after end of the tank. The tank calibration tables show the corrections required to obtain the true soundings relative to the amount the ship is trimmed by the stern.

In some cases sounding pipes are fitted at the mid length of the tank. The average depth of liquid in the tank is then shown and no corrections are required for the trim.

Many oil tankers are arranged with the tank hatch and ullage plug fitted directly over the centre of the tank in both the fore and aft direction and the thwartships direction. Provided the tank contents are not in contact with any part of the underside of the deck, the level in the tank remains with the same ullage irrespective of the list or trim. This saves considerable time when working out the contents of tanks without the aid of a computer as no corrections are required for list and trim.

Overflow systems

When the air pipes of fuel tanks extend up to the weather deck level, fuel could be spilled on to the deck, and possibly overboard, if the tank is overfilled when the vessel is receiving or transferring oil fuel. If an oil spill occurs the vessel may be subject to legal action and a large fine. To this must be added the cost of cleaning up the ship and the surrounding water, and the value of the wasted fuel, together with the costs for any time lost by the vessel as a result of the oil spill.

The bunkering time for a vessel may be greatly increased when the fuel storage system is to be completely filled, if fuel tank air pipes extend up to just above the weather deck. This is due to slowing up the rate of fuel reception to reduce the risk of overflow when topping up a tank. In order to reduce this risk, and so help shorten bunkering times when completely filling a vessel with fuel oil, an overflow system can be fitted to fuel tanks. The air pipes from the double bottom fuel tanks are led into a pipe running fore and aft on each side of the vessel. The starboard tank air pipes are connected into the line on the starboard side and the air pipes from the port side are connected into a line on the port side. In some cases a ring main is formed by connecting up the

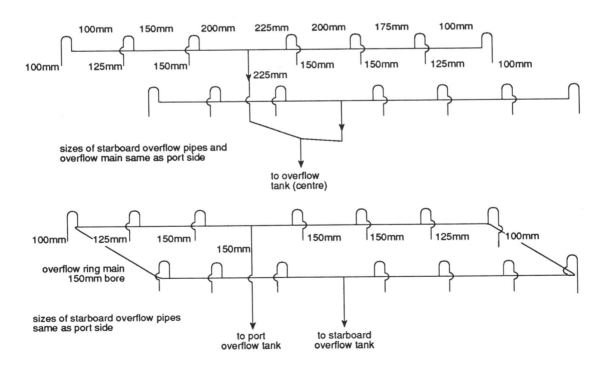

Figure 25 Oil fuel overflow systems.

pipes with a crossover at each end. In other cases a single crossover is fitted about mid length of the port and starboard pipes. Downcomers are led from the sides of the ring main or from the centre of the crossover, and these connect into the overflow tanks. If an overflow occurs during bunkering the oil passes into the overflow ring main or overflow lines and then passes down the drain lines into the overflow tank. Flow indicator switches are fitted in the downcomer, so that if an overflow occurs alarms are activated at the bunkering station and the control room.

Overflow tanks are safeguarded against excess pressures by air pipes leading up to some point outside the engine room. If the overflow tank becomes full, excess fuel spills onto the deck (Fig 25).

BUNKERING STATIONS AND BUNKERING

When arriving at a bunkering port or bunkering station it is essential for the delivery documents from the fuel supplier to be examined and compared with the instructions from the owner or charterer. The quantities and quality of the fuel to be supplied should be compared with the statutory requirements of density and viscosity required by the machinery. This allows any queries to be answered before fuel is received on the vessel.

Prior to receiving fuel oil from a shore based installation, barge or tanker it is necessary to take soundings or ullages of the supply tanks and to find the depth of any water bottoms. Without these figures it is impossible to pursue a claim for short shipment of fuel. It is also necessary to have accurate figures of the amounts of fuel remaining in each of the fuel storage locations on the ship. The overflow tank should be empty at the start of bunkering. If an overflow system is not fitted in the ship, receptacles must be placed under air pipes, and on older ships the scuppers should be sealed off to prevent oil going over the side if an overflow or spill occurs. While the shore or barge tanks are being checked a portable telephone is rigged by the bunkering connection on the vessel. Alternatively, suitable portable radio telephones may be used. In some vessels a telephone is permanently located at the bunkering station. The communication equipment should be tested prior to bunkering.

The group valves situated in the engine room controlling fuel flow into the fuel storage tanks are usually located at some central point adjacent or easily accessible to the tank contents or depth gauges for the fuel storage tanks. This point is often called the bunkering station.

When receiving fuel it is good practice to initially direct the flow into a port and starboard tank at the furthest location. When the port and starboard tanks are nearly full, the rate of flow into these tanks is slowed down by fully opening up the next pair of tanks to receive fuel. The rate of receiving fuel into the nearly full tanks can then be adjusted by partially closing the valves controlling fuel flow into the second pair of tanks. The slower rate of receiving fuel into the nearly full tanks gives a more precise control during the topping up procedure and reduces the risk of overflow.

The procedure for filling tanks is repeated until all the tanks are full with the exception of the last pair of tanks, or the overflow tank if it is to be filled. The rate of reception must be greatly reduced when the last tanks or the overflow tanks are topped off.

If fuel is being received from tanks at a distance from the ship it is not possible to shut off the fuel supply quickly without damage occurring. This is due to the amount of kinetic energy stored in the moving fuel by virtue of its total mass and its velocity in the supply line. If the fuel supply is shut off too quickly the kinetic energy causes a dangerous pressure rise at the shut off valve which may be high enough to cause a joint or gasket to blow out and consequent spillage of a large amount of fuel. In extreme cases, the shut off valve to the bunkering line has been known to fracture. If the height of the supply tanks is sufficient it is good practice to request the bunkering installation to go on to gravity supply when completely filling and topping up tanks. The rate of fuel reception is then greatly reduced as the final tanks are filled and topped up, and the supply at the ship may then be closed off more quickly. If the height of the shore based fuel tanks is insufficient to go on to gravity supply, so making pumping necessary, the pumping rate must be reduced when topping off fuel tanks. Telephone contact with the pumping installation must also be maintained.

When a vessel is bunkering it is desirable to keep new fuel supplies separate from fuel received earlier. This is not always possible and is dependent on a number of factors, such as the amount of fuel remaining, the amount to be taken and the number of tanks empty and available to receive fuel. Whatever the situation, the aim is to limit the intermixing as far as possible.

If the temperature of the fuel being received is lower than that at which it will be carried, some allowance must be made for its expansion when heating commences. If there is no expansion allowance the tank will overflow when the fuel expands.

During the time a ship is being bunkered, and in the absence of other instructions from the company's technical department, three samples of fuel oil are normally taken and the containers sealed. One sample is given to the fuel supplier's agent, for which a receipt note should be obtained. The other two are retained on board pending company instructions. In other cases the samples are taken by the bunkering agent and then given to the chief engineer, and a receipt note is usually demanded. The number of samples required is often given in the company's standing instructions.

Care must be taken when obtaining the fuel samples so they are truly representative of the main body of fuel being supplied. Some ships rely on a drip method of sampling where a small quantity of oil is bled into a large receptacle over the period of the bunkering.

In other cases a fuel sampling device is used. This meters small quantities of fuel by a rotating valve fitted in the bunkering line and actuated by the oil flow. The small quantities are stored in a container connected to the sampling device.

It is usual for the ships staff or the bunkering agent to draw off a sample in the presence of an officer. The specific gravity of this sample is measured with a hydrometer by one of the engineer officers for comparison with the stated density or specific gravity given on the delivery document. The weight of fuel received can be calculated once the volume is known.

It must be remembered that if the density stated on the bunker delivery receipt is too high, the weight of the fuel shown on the delivery receipt statement will be more than is actually placed on board. This will result in an overcharge for fuel cost to the owner or charterer.

Some ship owning companies or their managers send fuel samples from motorships to an oil testing laboratory immediately after bunkering. The fuel is tested for the presence of deleterious matter which could damage the engines. The company are notified of the results of the tests very shortly after the samples are received by the laboratory. If an adverse report is received action can be taken immediately so that damage to the engine is prevented. The chief engineer and master are then notified of any required action. This may only involve technical matters but in serious cases a diversion may be required to off load the fuel.

Fuel samples must be labelled properly and identified correctly. They must be retained carefully on board to protect the company in case of any problems and possible litigation arising out of any damage and delays.

Documentation given by the fuel supplier must give the flash point, and the quantity supplied. In some cases the specific gravity at a standard temperature and a brief analysis may also be given. A temperature correction must be used with the specific gravity figure given at some standard temperature when calculating the weight of fuel supplied.

COOLING SYSTEMS

Cooling systems are required in various parts of a ships' machinery installation.

Some of these systems may be relatively simple when compared with others. The cooling water system to the main condenser in a steam turbine propelled ship, is relatively simple when compared with some of the more complicated systems found in some motorships where the cooling system may be made up in three sections comprising the primary, the secondary and the tertiary systems. This type of cooling system is often called a central cooling system.

Condenser cooling systems

The cooling system for the main condenser in a steam turbine propelled ship consists of a regenerative condenser. This is a specialised form of heat exchanger designed so that one section condenses the water vapour and a further section or sections give extra cooling to the gases being removed from the condenser. Before being removed from the condenser by the air ejectors or the liquid ring air pump, the gases are directed over the surface of the condensate contained in the hotwell at the bottom of the condenser. The gases give up heat to the condensate enabling its temperature to approach the temperature at which condensation took place, which helps to prevent the condensate being undercooled to any great degree. Before passing out of the condenser the volume of the gases is reduced by further cooling in the other sections of the condenser. When condensate is cooled below the saturation temperature of the steam from which it was formed it is said to be undercooled. When any degree of undercooling occurs, sensible heat is removed from the condensate and wasted when passing overboard in the cooling water.

The condenser contains many tubes through which sea water is made to flow, with the aid of a pump, a scoop in the bottom of the ship, or due to the difference in static pressure of the sea water flowing into the propeller and on the outer surface of the hull at the forward part of the engine room. When either of the last two systems are used a standby circulating pump must be available for use when operating at

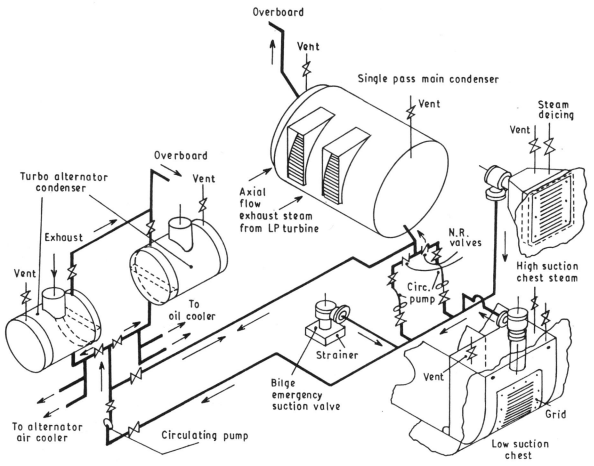

Figure 26   Condenser cooling system.

slow speed, in an emergency, or when warming through turbines and at shutdown.

The exhaust steam from the turbine is condensed when the latent heat of the vapour is removed by the cooling water after the vapour comes into contact with the cold outer surface of the condenser tubes.

A condenser cooling system in which cooling water is supplied to both the main condenser and the auxiliary condensers for the turbo alternators is shown in Fig 26.

Cooling water systems in motorships

The cooling services for the main engines and the auxiliary diesel engines in a motorship are usually made up of a primary and secondary cooling system, some motorships also having a tertiary system. The primary cooling system on the main engine is usually separated from that on the diesel generator sets but is similar to it in many respects.

A seawater cooling system for a main propulsion diesel engine is shown in Fig 27a. A central cooling system is shown in Fig 27b.

Jacket and cylinder head cooling systems

The parts making up the primary system consist of the inlet and outlet cooling water manifolds fitted on the engine, a heat exchanger for removing heat put into the cooling water by the engine, a steam heat exchanger for raising the cooling water temperature when preparing the engines for operation at sea or to maintain the temperature during a long standby, an expansion tank, and a cooling water circulating pump. A duplicate cooling water circulating pump is often fitted, one being retained for standby duty. The water discharged by the cooling water pump passes through a screw lift check valve to the heat exchanger, sometimes referred to as the jacket water cooler. The water then passes on to the inlet manifold on the engine.

The cooling space in the cylinder jacket and cylinder head are connected in series with each other. The cooling spaces through each cylinder unit are connected in parallel. The cooling water circulates through them and then passes into the outlet manifolds. The outlet manifold on the engine is connected

a)

b)

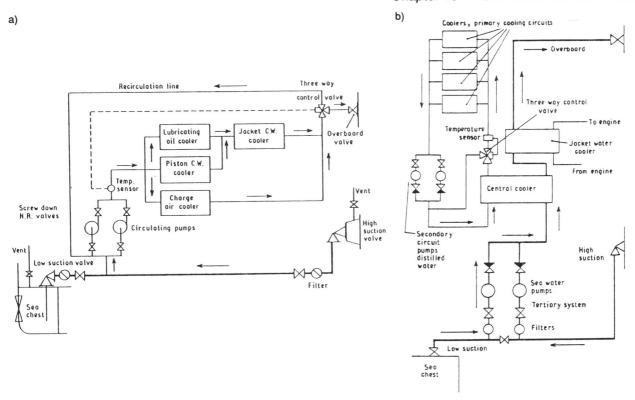

Figure 27 a) Main engine seawater cooling system; b) central cooling system.

with the suction side of the circulating pump to complete the closed circuit. A valve is fitted in the connecting pipe to the inlet side of the jacket, and another on the outlet branch from the cylinder cover. These valves are kept fully open when the engine is in operation and are only closed when removing the cylinder covers prior to lifting an engine piston for overhaul. This prevents loss of the cooling water from the system. The cooling water passes through a screw lift valve on the suction side of the pump.

The primary system has distilled water circulated through it, and is often called the jacket cooling water system, or JCW system (Fig 28). The distilled water is inhibited with chemicals to prevent corrosion in the cooling spaces of the engine, the connecting pipework, heat exchangers and pumps. This system is continuously circulated when the engine is in operation. In order to remove the heat passed into the primary cooling circuit from the cylinder jackets and cylinder heads the cooling water heat exchanger is circulated with sea water obtained from the secondary system.

The primary cooling water system is enclosed. The volume of water contained in the system is smaller when the system is shut down and cold than when it is in operation and warm. The difference in volume is catered for by including an expansion tank in the system. The expansion tank is fitted in the upper part

of the engine room, as high as possible. A pipe is led from the bottom of the expansion tank into the primary cooling water system where its pressure is lowest during operation. This point is at the suction entrance of the cooling water circulating pump and is the point where the connection to the expansion tank should be made. The expansion tank is sometimes referred to as the surge tank.

If air is entrained in the cooling water it could damage parts of the system due to bubble impingement. Outlets for air are often fitted at the highest part of the system. This may be either at the outlet branch of the cooling water pipe connecting the cylinder head to the outlet manifold, or at the end of the manifold. If the branch pipe goes downwards to the outlet manifold an air release branch is fitted into the highest part of the bend. The air release pipe from each cylinder head is then led to a rising common manifold leading upwards to a goose neck fitted over a tundish on the top of the expansion tank.

When the cooling water outlets are led upwards into the outlet manifold, a deaerator is fitted at its highest end, just before it branches downwards towards the cooling water pumps.

Normally the expansion tank is fitted at a height greater than the pressure head of the cooling water leaving the cylinders. Circulation of water through

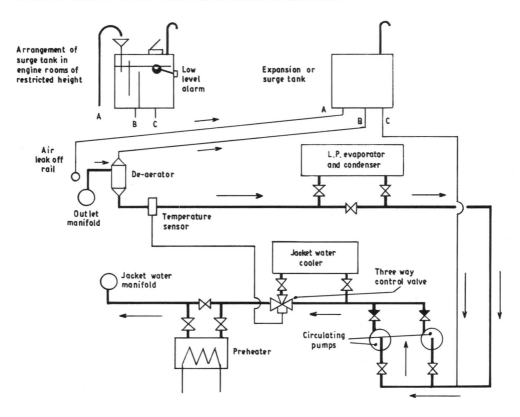

Figure 28   Jacket cooling water system.

the expansion tank cannot occur. Treatment chemicals must then be added to the system with a manually operated pump.

When the engine room is low, the pressure head at the highest end of the manifold will be greater than the height of the expansion tank above the engine, and water then circulates from the de-aerating connections or deaerator through to the expansion tank and back into the system. The expansion tank should then be made up as a cascade tank to separate any air brought into the system by the circulating water. Water treatment chemicals may be added to the system at the expansion tank when water circulates through it.

The primary cooling water system on diesel generator sets is similar to that on the main engines but the primary and secondary cooling water pumps will often be engine driven.

Piston cooling systems

The piston cooling system on slow speed main engines may be another primary system containing distilled water but unconnected with the jacket and cylinder head cooling system. With the exception of the expansion tank the piston cooling system will have similar parts to the jacket cooling water system. In other cases the piston cooling system may be an integral part of the crankcase lubricating oil system. The pistons will be cooled by lubricating oil circulated by the lubricating oil pump. Whichever system is used the heat removed from the pistons will be taken away by the sea water circulating through the secondary cooling system. Medium speed main engines for main propulsion use and auxiliary diesel engines forming part of the electrical generating sets are invariably of the trunk piston type. To prevent the crankcase oil system being contaminated with water, trunk piston engines have the pistons cooled with lubricating oil from the crankcase lubrication system. Piston cooling systems using lubricating oil is covered in *Lubricating Oil Systems*.

Piston cooling systems using distilled water
The piston cooling system begins with a holding tank large enough to hold the entire volume of water in the system. When the piston cooling water pump is shut down at the end of a passage the water in the pistons and telescopic pipes drains down into the holding tank. No water can then find its way into the crankcase and contaminate the lubricating oil in the drain tank.

The tank is fitted on the engine room tank top so that its cover is level with the floorplates. The piston cooling water pumps may be fitted on the tank cover with suctions led into the bottom of the tank or the pumps may be of the deep well or submerged type fitted on the tank bottom with a vertical shaft connected to an electrical motor mounted on the cover. A steam heating coil is fitted in the tank for heating the piston cooling water after a shutdown period prior to starting the engine or to maintain the piston cooling water temperature during a long standby period. In many cases the holding tank is arranged as a cascade tank to separate small amounts of lubricating oil that enter the cooling system from the scavenge space. This prevents oil entering the piston cooling system and settling out in the cooling water spaces of the piston. Should this occur the heat transfer from the hot side of the piston crown is retarded and the piston overheats. This will then lead to the deterioration of the sealing rings and in extreme cases may cause the piston to become overheated and lose its working clearance in the cylinder resulting in piston scuffing or seizure.

The piston cooling water passes from the circulating pump into the heat exchanger or piston cooling water cooler. From there it passes into the manifold fitted on the engine. A pipe is led from the manifold into the inlet telescopic pipe where it passes through a jet, which directs the water into the piston cooling space. After passing from the cooling space in the piston the water is led through telescopic drain pipes, down through a sight glass and into the drain manifold, which drains the cooling water back into the tank for recirculation through the system. The heat passed into the piston cooling water while passing through the pistons is removed by the sea water passing through the cooler from the secondary cooling system.

Secondary cooling water systems

The secondary cooling water system is usually made up of a sea water circulating pump with branches led to various parts of the secondary cooling system. There are no standard arrangements for this system. In some cases the secondary cooling water circuits in the main engine heat exchangers are connected up in series; in others they may be connected up in parallel or a combination of the two. By connecting up the secondary circuits in series some reduction in the sea water cooling pump capacity can be made. When heat exchangers are connected in series the system with the lowest operating temperature receives the secondary system cooling water before any with a higher operating temperature. Normally the temperature in the lubricating oil system is lower than the other systems, and the secondary cooling water will then pass through the lubricating oil cooler before passing into other coolers.

When the secondary cooling circuits of the heat exchangers are connected in series the bypasses for the secondary cooling water must be adequate enough to prevent cooling water starvation at points further down the system.

Tertiary cooling water systems

Some motor ships are fitted with a tertiary cooling water system. Where such a system is fitted, steam from the exhaust boilers is used mainly for fuel oil heating, domestic heating, and cargo heating so obviating the need for an exhaust steam condenser and a supply of sea water for cooling it. A drain cooler, sometimes called an atmospheric condenser, replaces the condenser but is much smaller.

The secondary cooling system then becomes an enclosed circulating system containing distilled water. It functions in the same way as a normal secondary cooling system but, being an enclosed system, none of the cooling water passes overboard. The heat passed into the primary system from the engines passes into the secondary system through the heat exchangers. The tertiary system cooling water is taken from the sea and circulated through a large heat exchanger forming part of the secondary system. This heat exchanger removes the heat from the secondary system where it is passed into the cooling water in the tertiary system, from where it passes overboard. It is claimed that when chemically treated distilled water is used in the secondary system, the amount of copper nickel alloy piping in the tertiary system is very much less, and the total cost of the three systems combined is less than the cost of a normal primary system and secondary system where copper nickel alloys are extensively used.

It should be noted that the term 'raw water' originally used in ships built for trading on the Great Lakes in North America has come into use for deep sea ships, and is used increasingly instead of the term sea water. If the opposite of 'raw' is 'cooked', it can be seen that the term is incorrect, even though its use may be fashionable. A central cooling water system for a main propulsion engine is shown in Fig 27b.

LUBRICATING OIL SYSTEMS

The lubricating oil systems for ships propelled by steam turbines is covered in Chapter 2, *Marine Steam Turbines*.

There are two lubricating oil systems in slow speed diesel engines. One caters for the lubrication of the engine cylinders, pistons, and piston rings where the special cylinder oils are used once only, and the other is a circulating system where the oil is used over and over again to lubricate the main bearings, bottom end bearings or big end bearings, crosshead bearings, crosshead slippers and guides, thrust journal bearings and main thrust bearing. These bearings are often called the crankcase bearings and the system is referred to as the crankcase lubricating oil system. The lubricating oils used in the crankcase system are sometimes referred to as system oils. In some cases the lubricating oil used in the crankcase system of slow speed engines is circulated through the piston cooling spaces to cool the pistons.

The crankcase lubricating system consists of the lubricating oil pumps (fitted in duplicate and usually of the positive displacement screw type), heat exchangers to remove heat from the lubricating oil and from piston cooling if the pistons are oil cooled, together with the connecting pipework and the lubricating oil drain tank forming part of the hull structure under the main engine.

Assuming that the pistons are oil cooled, the lubricating oil from the crankcase drains down into the drain tank. The oil returning from the pistons drains into a manifold after passing through the cooling oil sight glasses fitted on each piston cooling return pipe. The piston cooling return manifold is connected with the drain tank. The piston cooling oil then mixes with the oil returned from the crankcase.

The suction pipe to the lubricating oil pump is fitted with a vortex breaker and led from the aft end of the drain tank through a coarse filter or strainer and then through a screw lift valve fitted on the inlet side of the pump. After passing through the pump, the oil is discharged through a screw down, non-return valve, then passes, under pressure, through a self cleaning oil filter taking the full flow of oil. The oil

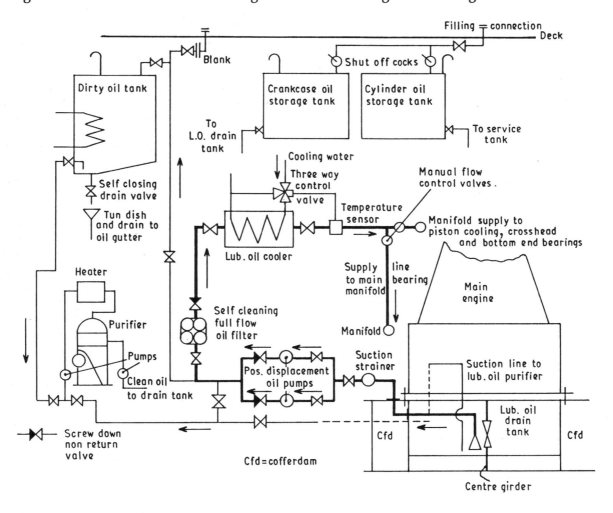

Figure 29   Main engine lubricating oil system.

then passes through the heat exchanger, and is led down to a branch piece where a part of the oil flow goes into the bearing oil manifold, the other part passing into the piston cooling oil manifold. After being circulated through the bearings and pistons, the oil returns to the drain tank.

Some engine builders prefer to lubricate the crosshead bearings with a supply of oil under very high pressure. In such cases the crosshead bearing high pressure lubricating oil pump is supplied with oil taken from the bearing oil supply manifold and pumps it into a separate high pressure manifold. From this manifold the oil passes through a swinging link arrangement directly to the crosshead bearings.

After some use the lubricating oil will become contaminated with dirt and wear debris together with water condensed from vapour in the air. The contaminants are removed from the lubricating oil by first heating it and then passing it through a centrifugal purifier. The oil cleaning section of the lubricating oil system consisting of pumps, heaters, and centrifuges, plays a very important part in maintaining the lubricating oil in a safe condition. In some ships an oil cleaning tank, sometimes called the dirty oil tank, is fitted in the upper part of the engine room. The tank is fitted with a steam heating coil and good drain connections. When the engine is shut down the lubricating oil may be pumped up to the cleaning tank where its temperature is raised. The oil is allowed to stand in the heated condition for some time. Heavy muck and water contaminating the oil then separates and settles on the bottom of the tank in much the same manner as water and dirt in the fuel oil settling tanks. After being retained in the cleaning tank the muck collected at the bottom of the tank is drained off. The lubricating oil may then be separated in the centrifuge. When treating a batch of lubricating oil in this manner the oil must be passed through the centrifuge at the slowest throughput the available time will allow. This brings the lubricating oil up to a good, near new condition.

During engine operation the lubricating oil is continuously treated in the centrifuges. The oil being treated may be taken from the discharge side of the lubricating oil pump before the oil passes through the heat exchanger. In other cases the centrifuges are fitted with supply pumps, which take the lubricating oil from the drain tank at some point near to the bottom of the tank at its after end, close to the main lubricating oil pump suction. When lubricating oil is being continuously treated, its throughput is adjusted so the maximum amount of dirt is removed during separation. The desired throughput is obtained by running the separator for, say, 6, 12 or 24 h.

After shutting down the purifier it is cleaned, and the amount of dirt removed is weighed. The separator is then operated with an increased throughput over the same time period, and the weight of dirt removed is again obtained. By repeating the experiment and adjusting the flow rate up or down, the throughput giving the greatest amount of dirt removal in unit time will be obtained. The aim of continuously centrifuging the lubricating oil is to remove dirt and contaminants at the rate at which they enter the oil during service.

A lubricating system found on main propulsion engines with oil cooled pistons is shown in Fig 29.

STEAM SUPPLY SYSTEMS

Steam is obtained from oil fired boilers in steamships, the system being designed to operate at the highest design pressure and temperature to give the best economic conditions possible after taking into account installation, running, and repair costs.

The boiler installation for a steam turbine propelled vessel is usually made up with one or two main water tube type boilers. Where only one boiler is fitted, a second smaller boiler may also be installed. The working steam pressure may be up to 95 bar and the steam temperature will be of the order of 510°C. Some ships have been built with boiler installations having a higher steam temperature but the tendency today (1991) is to keep the figure given as a maximum value because the high cost of suitable, high tensile, creep resisting alloy steel makes higher steam temperatures commercially unattractive.

The steam supply system in modern steam turbine installations is made up in two separate sections. They consist of the steam supply lines to the main propulsion turbines, called the main steam line or lines, and the other steam lines leading to the auxiliary machinery, called the auxiliary steam lines.

Certain parts of the steam system requiring low pressure steam are supplied with steam taken from an auxiliary steam line after passing through a reducing valve station.

When the vessel is at sea, low pressure steam requirements may in some cases be obtained by bleeding steam from any of the various stages of the main turbine. The stage chosen will have a steam pressure during operation suitable for the pressure requirement of the equipment or the heat exchanger.

Before coming to any final conclusion on how the steam system will be divided and how steam will be supplied to the various equipment locations, a heat balance sheet is drawn up. The aim of the heat balance sheet is to obtain the maximum amount of heat from the fuel used by using the steam produced in the most economical manner.

Among the various things studied are whether it is better to use steam bled from the main turbines for general auxiliary purposes, or whether to use it for purposes of boiler feed water heating, or for both. For example, there is no loss of latent heat (enthalpy of evaporation) from the system when bled steam is used for feed heating after doing work in the main turbine, whereas that steam which passes into the condenser loses its latent heat content overboard in the cooling water. Generally it is more economical to use steam reduced in pressure after passing through the higher pressure stages of a turbine than to use low pressure steam obtained through a reducing valve.

The design of the high pressure–high temperature steam lines is also carefully studied. This is to ensure the loads arising out of the forces and moments created by thermal expansion of the piping are not excessive at the boiler and turbine steam pipe connections.

In some cases when the steam pipes are made up they appear to be too short in their cold state. They are pulled together when being bolted up. The allowable stresses on the material of branch connections is greater when they are cold than when they are at their working temperature. As thermal expansion takes place the stresses caused when being bolted up are negated as the piping lengthens.

The amount the pipes are left open is referred to as 'cold pull up' and is shown on steam pipe drawings. When carrying out repair and survey work make up pieces must not be made and inserted to fill the open spaces.

The study in the design of steam pipes also involves the assessment of loads at the pipe supports, the required support springs and the effect of a ship rolling and causing the pipes to swing from side to side. A decision can then be made on the type of pipe supports that will be used and whether sway braces will be required to prevent sideways movement due to a rolling ship. These braces also prevent movement due to vibration.

All steam pipes should be arranged so they become self draining at one end only, or at each end depending on the relative heights of the start, the middle and the end of the pipe run. Downward loops in steam lines in which water may remain must be avoided or the risk of water hammer is greatly increased. Where a downward loop is unavoidable a drain cock or drain valve must be located at the bottom of the loop.

Normally high pressure–high temperature steam pipes are made up in as long a run as possible with circumferential welds to join pipe sections in preference to the use of flanges, except at the boiler stop valve and turbine connections. The bolts and nuts must be of special steel able to resist the high temperatures without stretching due to creep action. Stud bolts are used in these high temperature pipe flanges and, being made of special heat resisting steel, they must never be changed for nuts and bolts of an inferior grade of material.

The steam stop valves on the boilers are of the screw down non-return type. If a tube should burst on one boiler the non-return steam stop valve closes and prevents loss of steam from the other boiler by steam passing back into the boiler and through the burst pipe.

The temperature of the superheated steam must be carefully watched; the allowable operating temperature must not be exceeded. Alarm equipment for a steam temperature rise above allowable limits and steam temperature measuring equipment is important and must be regularly checked to avoid problems and the risk of accident.

If military spending is reduced around the world there is a possibility that the cost of the alloying elements will be reduced and the price for steel alloys capable of withstanding high temperatures will also come down. This will enable boiler pressures and steam temperatures to rise again and lower the fuel costs on high efficiency steam turbine installations.

The boiler installation for a motorship is not designed to work at such high pressures and temperatures. In high powered, diesel engine propelled ships the boiler installation may be of such a capacity that the heat in the exhaust gases is sufficient to produce enough steam to drive a turbogenerator set supplying all the electrical requirements of the ship. With such a turbogenerator set the savings will be considerable, because no diesel fuel is used to produce electricity, and the running hours on the diesel generator sets are reduced, so effecting savings in overhauling and spare parts' costs.

As the temperature of exhaust gases is relatively low, steam production can be increased by operating the steam system at two pressures. The exhaust gas is used initially in the higher pressure boiler and then used in the lower pressure section of the boiler. In other cases the exhaust gases are first passed through an exhaust gas boiler and then the lower temperature gases are passed through an economiser.

Large diesel engine propelled crude oil carriers having cargo pumps driven by steam turbines will have a boiler installation comparable with that in a large, steam turbine propelled ship. This comes about due to each cargo pump turbine having a power output up to approximately 4000 kW (approx 5400 hp) when pumping cargo at maximum output against a high static head.

Smaller ships fitted with lower powered diesel engines may have a simple steam supply system used only for oil fuel heating, accommodation heating, and similar services. In this case a composite fired boiler may be used. Exhaust gases will normally be used for steam production while at sea, but when operating at reduced power, or when in port, the boiler will be fired through the oil burning section of the boiler.

Sketches showing the various types of boiler used in steam systems are shown in Chapter 1, *Marine Boilers*.

To avoid the risk and dangers of water hammer when opening a steam valve on a shut down or cold steam line it is absolutely essential for the line to be drained of all water before opening the steam valve. The opened drain cock or drain valve is left open and the steam valve is 'cracked open' (opened a very small amount). Condensation formed when heating the line up to working temperature then drains away without damage.

After the line is thoroughly warmed through by the incoming steam, and the noise of the steam escaping from the open drain is continuous without the intermittent noise caused by the passage of water, the steam valve can be opened slowly to its fullest extent.

The opening of steam into a line is a common occurrence, which appears simple but is inherently dangerous. Opening up a steam valve to a steam line is extremely dangerous if 'water hammer' is not prevented by draining the lines of water prior to opening up the steam valve.

When water collects in a steam line and a steam valve is opened up, the collected water is moved forward, and the incoming steam condenses in the cold steam line creating a vacuum. The vacuum causes the water to be drawn backwards with increasing velocity. A small body of water may easily gain sufficient kinetic energy during its backward movement to strike the steam valve with enormous force. If the force is sufficient to fracture the valve a fatality usually occurs.

Figure 30 shows a deck steam valve fractured by the action of water hammer. The cover section landed on a boiler platform grating over two meters away. Some of the parts from the location of the fracture were never found. A donkeyman opening the valve was injured by flying debris and badly scalded.

Investigation revealed failure occurred some time after the valve was first cracked open, and although the immediate section of the line was drained, it was

Figure 30 Damage to deck steam valve through water hammer.

thought a body of water most likely existed in the deck steam line forward of the poop deck. Apparently this section was not drained prior to opening the deck steam valve situated in the boiler room. A drain connection fitted in the lower part of the line at the break of the poop deck was found to be in working order.

FEED WATER SYSTEMS

In order to reduce the amount of extra feed water pumped into a boiler system, the steam used is condensed within a condenser or within the heating coils in use. The condensate is then pumped back into the boilers as the boiler feed water. Using condensate reduces the amount of scale forming material put into the boiler and so reduces the quantity of water treatment chemicals required to keep the boiler water in a safe condition without scale build-up on the heating surfaces.

One of the design objectives carefully considered when arranging a feed system is to exclude air from contact with the condensate, so that the minimum amount of dissolved oxygen is present when passing into the feedwater deaerator. Condensate or feed systems designed in this manner are referred to as closed feed systems.

A diagrammatic arrangement of a closed feed system is shown in Fig 31. Only one turbo-alternator is shown, in order to simplify the diagram. Most steamships have two, unless two diesel-alternator sets are fitted and then only one turbo-alternator may be installed. The condenser hotwell level control on the turbo-alternator condenser has been omitted but will be identical to that shown for the main condenser. A condensate line from the deaerator to the

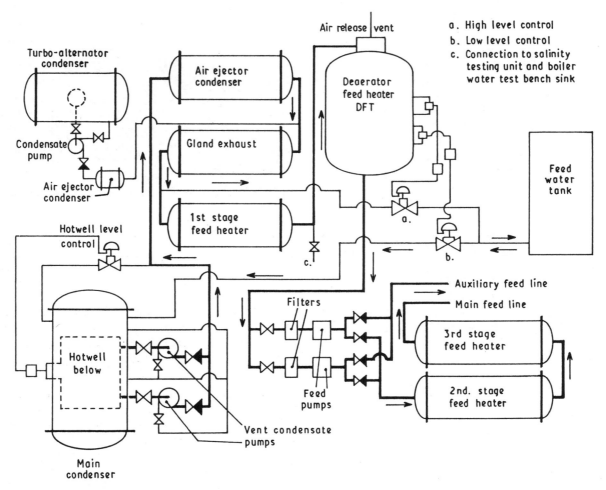

Figure 31 Closed feed water system.

harbour service feed pump has also been omitted.

This system appears to be complicated but can be understood by following the arrows indicating the path of the condensate from the main and auxiliary condensers through the various heat exchangers and thence to the feed pumps. The feed pump discharges are arranged with branches connecting with the main and auxiliary boiler feed lines which are separated.

The main feed line is connected to a feed water regulator on each boiler. The feed regulator is controlled by the level of the water in the boiler to which it is attached. The separate feed lines on the high pressure side of the feed pumps allow the auxiliary feed line to be available should a problem arise with the main feed line.

Each feed line is connected to each boiler through a screw down non-return valve. These are often referred to as the 'feed checks'. In the event of an emergency shut down by a feed pump, the water in the boilers is not discharged back into the feed system

when the system pressure falls as the pump is slowing down. Should a boiler tube burst, the non-return valve on the feed line prevents boiler water and steam being discharged into the furnace of the boiler where the burst has occurred.

A very important part of the closed feed system is the deaerator feed heater. This is sometimes called the deaerator, the de-aerating feed tank, or, in speech, the 'DFT'. Its purpose is to remove any dissolved oxygen and other gases which may enter the feed water in its passage from the condenser to the de-aerating feed heater. The removal of oxygen is necessary to prevent tube pitting and other problems due to oxygen attack in a boiler. The small amount of oxygen remaining in the feed water is absorbed by chemicals in the feed and boiler water treatment or by a treatment creating a thin protective film on the water side of the boiler. The thin protective film does not retard the heat transfer across the heating surfaces of the boiler or water wall tubes.

Air containing oxygen and other gases is removed when the water is heated up to the saturation temperature (boiling point) corresponding to the pressure. The gases cannot remain in solution in the feed water at this temperature. Breaking the water into a fine spray as it enters the deaerator allows the water to come up to boiling point more quickly. The heat is absorbed at a greater rate when many small particles are in contact with the incoming steam than when fewer larger particles are in contact. The total surface area of many small particles is greater than the surface area of fewer larger particles of the same amount of water. As the surface area in contact with the steam increases, so does the rate of heat transfer. Smaller particles require less heat to bring them to boiling point than larger particles.

When a deaerator is operated at a temperature corresponding to the saturation temperature of the incoming steam, and it is some few degrees higher than 100°C, some of the dissolved solids, although only a few parts per million, solidify and come out of suspension. Over time, they may build up in the form of a sludge. If this sludge is allowed to enter the feed pumps it may easily lead to pump seizure due to the small clearances in the sealing rings of the pump.

Multi-stage feed pumps with their longer shafts are more prone to this problem than pumps with a lesser number of stages and a stiffer rotor shaft.

It is essential that the internal parts of the deaerator are examined and cleaned as necessary. This becomes more pressing if the salinity content of the feed water, although within safe limits, is higher than normal over some time period.

The filters on the inlet side of the feed pumps should also be examined periodically to ensure the filtering media has not deteriorated so allowing foreign matter to pass through it. Feed pumps with water lubricated bearings should also have the water line filter to the bearings examined and cleaned at regular time intervals.

The procedure for starting up a steam plant and a closed feed system is not necessarily the same for each ship. The procedure will generally follow the description given but in all cases the instructions given by the equipment makers are paramount and must be followed.

Assuming we are starting up on a 'dead ship' with electrical power available from a shore supply or the emergency diesel generator, and the control and instrument compressed air or other control equipment is ready for use, steam is first raised on a boiler and then a turbo-alternator set is brought into use.

Before warming through the alternator turbine, the valves on the closed feed system are first lined up to ensure there is a clear path for the condensate through to the boiler. The condenser hotwell and deaerator water storage space levels are then checked and brought up to the required levels for start up, the condenser cooling water pump is started and sea water is circulated through the turbo-alternator condenser.

The condensate pump connected with the turbo-alternator condenser is then started and steam is supplied to the air ejectors to give a small amount of vacuum. Alternatively the liquid ring pump should be started. The lubricating oil drain tank is drained of any water and the standby lubricating oil pump is started. The turning or jacking gear on the alternator is then brought into use. Steam is put on the gland sealing system to warm through the turbine and prevent air leakage through the glands. The auxiliary or harbour service feed pump is then started up to feed condensate into the boiler. If only one boiler is in use the harbour service feed pump is usually used until steam is put on to the main propulsion turbine.

Once the system is started, the hotwell level control equipment on the condenser, and the level controllers on the deaerator water storage space, ensure there is sufficient water in the condenser hotwell to keep the condensate pump working without going dry, sufficient water going through the air ejector condenser to condense the air ejector steam, and sufficient water in the deaerator to keep the harbour service feed pump supplied.

Following the initial warm up period on the turbo-alternator set, the turning gear is disconnected, the standby lubricating oil pump is kept in use and the steam valve is opened enough to set the turbine rotor spinning slowly and continue the warming through process. After the required time period of warming through the turbine, the condenser vacuum is increased and the turbine is brought up to operating speed. The standby lubricating oil pump is shut down as the main lubricating oil pump pressure is built up. Cooling water is circulated through the lubricating oil cooler.

If the machine has been shut down for some period or the overspeed governor is due to be tested, it is good practice to check the overspeed governor emergency tripping device on the turbine. The successful completion of the test should be recorded in the log book and initialled by the engineer officer supervising the test.

After checking the overspeed governor for satisfactory operation and starting the turbine again, the alternator frequency must be synchronised with the shore supply frequency or the frequency of the emergency generator. When the frequencies are synchronised the machine is connected to the main bus bars through the main switchboard breaker. In modern ships this may be done through the control equipment.

The preparation of the main turbines for manoeuvring follows a similar procedure.

When the main turbine is sufficiently warmed through the turning gear can be disconnected. The main turbines are then put on to automatic standby control for bringing up the turbines to near their manoeuvring temperature.

In this standby mode of operation the control system puts steam on to the ahead turbine, and as soon as the propeller shaft starts to turn the steam is shut off. As soon as the turbine comes to a halt steam is put on to the astern turbine for a short period until the screw shaft starts to move in the astern direction. The process is continued automatically, and the turbine is held at a temperature ready for manoeuvring without fear of the high pressure rotor sagging.

Rotor sag comes about due to a combination of loss of strength of the rotor resulting from the high steam temperature, and the rotor remaining in one position when static, allowing the weight of the rotor to cause it to sag.

The small amount of propeller movement does not cause any load on the anchor cables or the ships moorings, but the propeller should not be turned without warning the bridge officer. He will confirm that the propeller is clear, after which permission is given for the propeller to be moved.

The main feed pumps are then started. Some feed pumps are fitted with recirculating water connections leading back to the deaerator for use when operating with a low throughput of water. In these circumstances, the recirculating connections may then be brought into use. Recirculation connections are not shown in Fig 32.

The condenser vacuum is brought up to operating level before accepting 'stand by' with a reply on the bridge-engine room telegraph, or placing the main turbines on bridge control. In some cases the vacuum is brought up to its full amount when putting the main turbine automatic control into the standby mode.

During the period of manoeuvring the main turbines, the quantity of steam passing into the main condenser varies over a wide range according to the turbine speed. The control equipment maintaining the level in the condenser hotwell and the deaerator water storage space then comes into play.

When the turbine is stopped or moving 'dead slow', the level in the hotwell falls. The condenser hotwell level control then allows water to be by-passed back to the condenser from the condensate pump discharge line downstream of the ejector con-

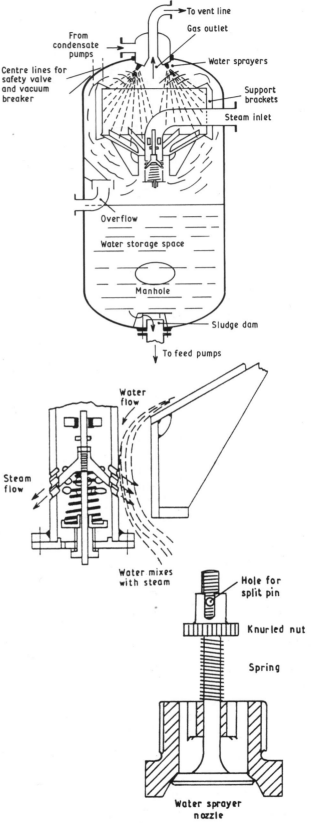

Figure 32   De-aerating feed water system.

denser. Water is then continuously circulated through the condensate pump and the air ejector condenser.

This prevents seizure of the rotor which easily occurs if the pump runs dry and also prevents overheating of the ejector condenser because of an absence of circulating condensate.

When the main turbine is stopped after running full ahead or full astern, the level of water in the boiler falls because there is less space taken up by steam bubbles forming in the water wall spaces and generating tubes. The feed regulators open and the water level in the boilers then rises until the feed water regulators take over control and slow down the flow of water into the boiler. The water level in the deaerator feed water storage space falls due to the amount of water pumped into the boiler and the reduction in the supply of water from the condensate pumps. When the level falls some predetermined amount the low level control takes over and opens control valve 'b' (Fig 31), allowing feed water to pass from the feed water tank to the main condenser. The system then balances itself again.

When the main turbine is started again the boiler steam pressure momentarily falls, bringing the burner control into action. This action allows more oil to pass through the burners. The increased oil flow increases evaporation in the boiler, steam bubble volume is increased, the water level rises and the feed regulators reduce the flow of water to the boilers. With more steam passing into the main condenser, the hotwell level control shuts off and a surge of water is pumped up to the deaerator so raising the water level. Eventually the high level control takes over and control valve 'a' is opened. This allows condensate to bypass the deaerator. The condensate passes through control valve 'a' directly into the feed water tank.

The feed pumps operate with a reduced throughput of water until the water level in the boilers is brought to the correct level. After this the feed water input to the boiler matches the evaporation rate and the system balances itself again.

Between the limits of the high and low level controls on the deaerator there is an area referred to as the 'dead band' in which the water level stands when the plant is running in a steady state condition. The level of water may change between the upper and lower levels of the dead band without the control valves being activated. The dead band prevents the controls 'hunting' from one to the other by continuously raising the water level and then lowering it.

Feed water regulators have a dead band giving some stability to the feed water regulators for the changes in boiler water level when the evaporation rate changes and a varying volume of the water space

is taken up by steam bubbles. Where the water space in the boiler is relatively small and the boiler has a high evaporation rate the rise and fall of water level over the range of evaporation may be outside of the dead band but within it during the normal higher rates of evaporation.

After full away with steady steaming conditions, even in ships with very tight steam and water systems, an unavoidable and gradual loss of water occurs. This causes the level in the deaerator to fall as the correct level of water in the boilers is maintained. When the lower level of the dead band is passed the low level control comes into action and extra feed water is drawn by vacuum through the control valve marked 'b' (Fig 31) into the condenser. This continues until the level in the deaerator rises to its normal operating level, at this point air holding the control valve open is released, allowing the valve to close and shut down the supply of extra feed going to the condenser.

There is also a control on the feed tank which causes a feed transfer pump to pump water into the tank when the level is low. It is pumped from either of the reserve feed water tanks. Should the level in the feed tank rise, an overflow branch allows water to run into the bilge or return to the reserve feed water tank.

The overflow connection on the feed tank, the feed transfer pump and its float controls are not shown on the diagram.

The level sensors in the control system are differential pressure cells. They operate a pneumatic control valve which allows control air to pass into or leak from the control valves fitted in the condensate lines. Air passing from the air controller to below the diaphragm opens the control valve. When air is leaked off to the atmosphere the valve closes under the action of a spring.

In some older ships float control valves are used instead of differential pressure cells to effect control of the closed feed system. A float control valve is shown in Fig 33.

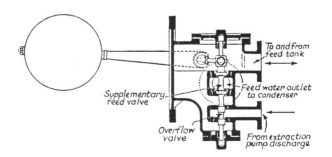

Figure 33 Feed control valve.

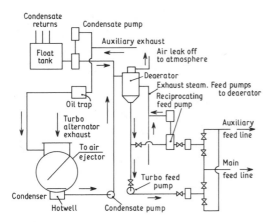

Figure 34   Simple feed water system.

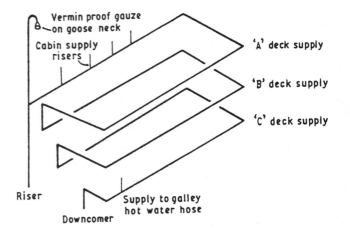

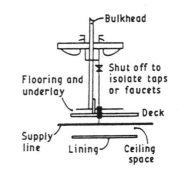

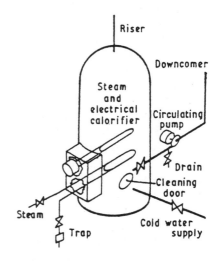

A simple feed water system incorporating a condenser is shown in Fig 34. The system shown could be used with an exhaust gas fired boiler, an economiser and a steam turbine alternator set. The condenser would then be of the regenerative type operating with a high vacuum.

Drain coolers

A drain cooler is a heat exchanger used to condense the steam flashed off from hot water passing under pressure through a steam trap. The temperature of the fuel in storage tanks is often such that the condensate from the heating coils passing through the steam trap is over 100°C. It then flashes over to steam after leaving the steam traps when the pressure is reduced. The steam and water vapour is condensed in the drain cooler before the condensate is passed into the observation tank. An air and gas outlet pipe is fitted on the cooler and is open to the atmosphere. The cooler can be circulated with sea water in simple steam plants but may be circulated with boiler feed water in more sophisticated systems.

DOMESTIC WATER SYSTEMS

At one time, three domestic water systems would be found on a ship: the domestic salt water system; the domestic fresh water system; and the drinking, or potable, water system. The salt water system is now redundant. The domestic water systems found on modern ships are the hot water system fed from the cold fresh water system (Fig 35), and the drinking water system (Fig 36). Since the advent of the low pressure, flash type evaporator which uses the heat contained in diesel engine cooling systems, there is

Figure 35   Domestic hot water system.

now such an abundance of fresh water that it is used for all purposes where sea water was previously used.

Most domestic fresh water systems consist of a pump, a pressure tank and the connecting pipework. The tank is only partially filled. Compressed air above the surface of the water in the tank gives a pressure head to the water causing it to flow to the most remote and highest outlet points of the system.

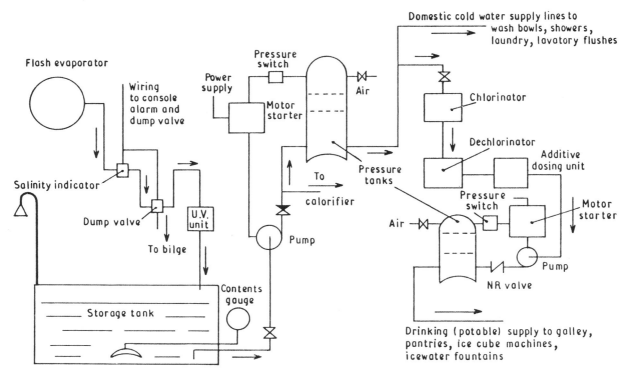

Figure 36 Domestic fresh water system.

As water is used, the level in the tank falls, as does the air pressure. Pressure switches are activated at some selected low pressure value and cause the pump to start. As the tank fills with water and the air pressure rises, another pressure switch set at some higher value stops the pump. Over time, air is lost from the tank and this is supplemented by air from a compressed air supply.

A supply connection is led from the water tank through to a hot water tank. The hot water tank is usually fitted with an electric heater and a steam heating coil. This enables hot water to be supplied at sea or in port or drydock when only one or the other of the heating sources is available. The hot water outlet is led from the top of the hot water tank (sometimes called a calorifier). The riser passes vertically upwards and returns from the highest point downwards through loops formed on each deck level to a downcomer connected into the lower part of the calorifier. This sets up a thermo syphon action so that hot water is quickly available without running off large amounts of cold water. If the hot water supply line from the top of the tank is not led upwards in this manner it is necessary to have a circulating pump so that hot water is immediately available.

The drinking water system and storage tank are usually supplied from the evaporator used for the production of fresh water. Since the temperature at which evaporation occurs is low, the water produced cannot be guaranteed to be sterile. Before being used as drinking water, fresh water is first subjected to ultra violet treatment, or chlorinated and de-chlorinated before passing into the storage tanks. A sampling device for detecting the presence of chlorides is fitted in the water outlet line close to the evaporator condenser. A dump valve is situated in the supply line downstream from the sampling device. If chlorides are detected at the sampling connection, the dump valve is activated and the water is led off to the bilges. This prevents contamination of the drinking water storage tanks, and other domestic water storage tanks, if priming or carry over occur.

When drinking water is obtained from a low pressure flash evaporator the evaporator must not be used in river estuaries or coastal areas, because of the possibility of the sea water being contaminated by bacteria or chemical contaminants. Non toxic treatment chemicals must also be used in the treatment of diesel engine cooling water when it is the source of heat in flash type, low pressure evaporators used for producing drinking water. This prevents toxic material entering the water supply if leakage of the evaporator heating coils occurs.

The drinking water supply system is similar to the fresh water system. Drinking water is supplied to the galley, galley dishwashers, bain-marie food dispensers, food steamers, and any other food processing equipment. A supply is also led to pantries serving saloon and dining areas, and also to the various decks where drinking water fountains are situated. Sometimes these fountains are fitted with a small tank and a refrigerator enabling ice water to be supplied.

CENTRAL PRIMING SYSTEM

The parts making up a central priming system consist of a vacuum tank, and working and standby liquid ring pumps, referred to as vacuum pumps, which are used for exhausting air from the vacuum tank. A ring main of piping is fitted around the engine room with connections to the various centrifugal pumps. The connections between the ring main and the pump are served by a stop valve and a float controlled check valve. The purpose of the float controlled check valve is to block off the system and prevent water entering into the connecting lines and the vacuum tank. When the centrifugal pumps fill with water, it lifts the float shutting off the line, preventing water entering the vacuum lines and the system.

To prime a pump the stop valve is opened. The pressure of the air or gases in the pump is lowered as the gases expand and flow to the vacuum tank. The external atmospheric pressure forces water up the suction line to fill the pump before it is started. After the pump has been started, and the discharge pressure is normal, the stop valve on the vacuum line connection to the pump may be closed.

Pressure switches are used to start and stop the vacuum pump. Screw down check valves are used on the discharge side of the pumps to prevent a back flow of air if the overboard discharge is above the water line and would allow air to flow back into the pump. A central priming system is shown in Fig 10.

SEWAGE SYSTEMS

The discharge of untreated sewage from ships while they are in the limits of port and coastal areas of many of the world's harbours is prohibited by law. If treated sewage is discharged overboard it must comply with certain limits governing the demand of oxygen, the amount of suspended solids and the amounts of certain coliform bacteria. Unfortunately these limits are not standardised and may vary from place to place.

The test for oxygen demand is called the biochemical oxygen demand test (BOD test). This is a laboratory procedure used to find the oxygen demand of the bacteria in a sample of sludge when held at some specified temperature over some time period. The test for suspended solids is done by filtering a liquid sample and noting the weight increase in the filtering media after being dried out. The test for coliform bacteria establishes the quantity of bacteria in a sample. Coliform bacteria are present in the colon and are sometimes referred to as colon bacilli. They appear rod shaped under the microscope.

The sewage treatment system must be capable of discharging an effluent that comes within the limits of the tests. Sewage can be treated biologically so that it may be discharged with minimal damage to the ecosystem. Biological treatment involves the use of living organisms to treat the sewage within the sewage treatment plant so the liquids and sludges discharged are within the standards specified.

Biological treatment plants are usually built up as a module and consist of various sections. Waste matter collected from the ships sanitary appliances is led through a sanitary piping system to the treatment module. The solid matter is broken up by passing it through a screen or a series of revolving cutters. The broken up solid material, together with the waste liquid, passes into a tank containing bacteria which require oxygen and a nutrient to propagate. The nutrient is contained in the solid waste material, and oxygen is supplied by bubbling compressed air through the broken up waste. The propagated bacteria change the waste material into a sludge by aerobic digestion. The sludge is finally treated to kill the coliform bacteria before it is passed overboard.

When a biological sewage plant is started up, such as when activating a new ship or after cleaning out the tank, a pellet containing bacteria is introduced into the tank. It takes approximately one week for the bacteria to propagate and make the system fully effective. The choice of sanitary appliance cleaners requires extreme care, as many cleaners are toxic to the active bacteria. Once a biological sewage plant is made active it should not be shut down. If it is it will have to be reactivated again because the bacteria will die without a supply of nutrients and oxygen.

Bacteria that require oxygen for their survival are referred to as aerobic. Aerobic bacteria are normally used in ships' sewage treatment equipment. Other forms of bacteria that do not require oxygen are referred to as anaerobic. Anaerobic bacteria are used in shore based sewage treatment works where methane is obtained as a by-product for use as fuel.

Cruise ships and passenger ships often have a holding system where the waste matter is retained on board in tanks while the ship is in port. The tanks are

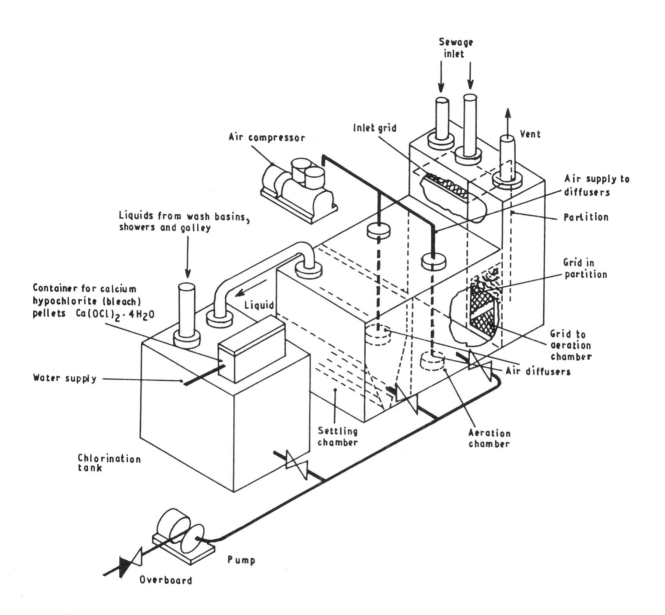

Figure 37 Diagrammatic arrangement of aerobic sewage treatment plant.

located in the lowest part of the ship, and are discharged at sea after passing outside of port limits. In some ports facilities are available enabling connections to be made up between the ship's sewage system and a municipal sewage system ashore. This allows waste matter to be discharged while the ship is in port.

When the ship is in dry dock the holding tank automatic discharge controls must be properly shut down to prevent sewage being discharged on the bottom of the drydock. An aerobic sewage treatment plant is shown in Fig 37.

LIQUID CARGO SYSTEMS

Liquid cargoes are carried in many different types of ships. Sometimes they are carried in drums or barrels in the cargo holds of dry cargo ships, when, with the exception of barrel slings, no special cargo handling requirements are necessary, other than those used for handling dry cargo. On the grounds of safety, certain types of cargo must be stored in drums manufactured to certain specifications.

Modern container ships also carry liquid cargoes. Certain types of liquid cargoes are carried in standard sized tank containers. Circular shaped tanks are built into a frame conforming with the dimensions of standard sized containers so that the frame can be loaded onto other containers, use standard container lashings or fit into the container guides located in the container holds. The length of the tank is approximately the length of the container. The ends of tanks fitted into container sized frames are reinforced and made strong enough to resist damage if the tank is only partially full and movement of the liquid (sloshing) occurs. If this happens, high fluctuating stresses may be set up and cause fatigue failure of the welded joints. Some restrictions based on safety are placed on the type of liquids allowed to be carried on container ships and in dry cargo ships.

Bulk liquid cargoes require tanks to store the cargo, a loading system to bring it on board and a pumping system to discharge it. Dry cargo ships often use the deep tanks for the carriage of smaller amounts of bulk liquid cargoes. Larger amounts of liquid cargo may be carried in specialised chemical, products, or parcel tankers designed to carry a number of different cargoes at the same time. Large shipments of liquid cargo such as crude oil, or a single refinery product, are carried in small, medium, large, or very large sized tankers. Petroleum and natural gases are carried in a liquefied state at a low temperature in very specialised gas carriers.

When trading to ports where certain types of safe liquid cargo are available, such as palm oil, ground nut oil, liquid latex, and similar cargoes, dry cargo ships often use the deep tanks for the carriage of safe liquids.

Before loading a liquid cargo in the deep tanks, the tanks must be cleaned of any residue from previous cargoes, including temporary coatings such as paraffin wax, or dunnage wood and mats. The tanks are then surveyed to ensure cleanliness and readiness to receive the next liquid cargo. If heating coils are required it is necessary for them to be installed and tested under steam for any leakage at pipe connections. The test is also witnessed by the surveyor. Blanking devices and change over connections for loading and discharge of the cargo are also checked.

If bilge and ballast water normally drain into a space between the tank margin plate and the ship's side it is usual to carry the inner bottom plating to the ship's side to take the place of the bilge limbers. The bilge space is then entered through manhole openings. When carrying a liquid cargo the manhole openings are closed off with manhole covers to prevent cargo entering the bilge space. When the ship's inner bottom plating extends out to the ship's side, totally enclosing the double bottom tank space, a hat

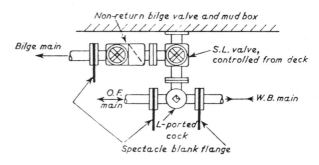

Figure 38   Isolation of deep tank suctions.

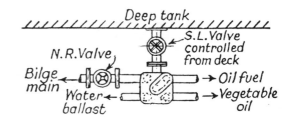

Figure 39   Combined changeover and blank flanging device for deep tank suctions.

box or drainage well is often arranged to take the bilge suction tail pipe, the tail pipe for handling ballast water or the tail pipe connection to the cargo pumps and filling connections. The bilge suction connections and ballast water connections, if fitted, are removed, and the lines sealed off with blank flanges (Figs 38, 39 and 40). Any cargo connections for loading and pumping out cargo are fitted, and new joints or gaskets should be used. The flanges must be checked visually and with a feeler gauge after being fitted. This ensures their tightness, and air leakage into the pumping system is prevented when draining and stripping tanks of cargo.

If liquid latex cargoes are carried, special type centrifugal pumps having connections for fresh water and ammonia injection are used. The tank sides, bottom and tank lid are also coated with paraffin wax. The paraffin wax is heated and brushed on to

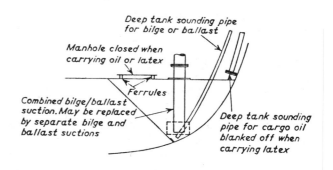

Figure 40   Connections in deep tanks.

the tank surfaces as a hot molten liquid. It congeals quickly, leaving a coating like liquid latex.

The safety devices and changes made to the piping system and any temporary coatings are also checked by the cargo surveyor. After these procedures are completed a certificate is issued to the effect that the tank is fit to receive cargo and loading may commence.

As trading companies became larger and international in ownership the quantities of liquids shipped in bulk have increased in size. This, with the gradual demise of general trading type cargo liners, has excluded many of the liquid cargoes formerly available from being carried in deep tanks, because the total carrying capacity of normal sized deep tanks is insufficient for the large amounts of liquid cargo carried as a single shipment.

Specialist type tankers having stainless steel lined cargo tanks, and other tanks coated with specialised coatings, are increasingly used instead of dry cargo ships with deep tanks.

These specially designed tankships often have separate individual cargo loading and pumping systems. The cargo pump is usually hydraulically operated and fitted in a hatbox or well on the bottom of the cargo tank. When the cargo handling pumps and the pipework for each tank are isolated from each other the risk of cross contamination between different types of cargo is prevented.

Large tankers or VLCCs (very large crude carriers) have a relatively simple pumping and loading system incorporating three or four cargo pumps each having capacities going up to 5,000 m^3/h or more. Their capacity and the number of pumps placed in the pump room depends on the size of ship and the required speed of turnround when discharging cargo. The design capacity of pumps is quoted in m^3 of water/h at some head in metres. In some cases the capacity is also quoted in Imperial and US gallons of water/min and feet head.

Some large tankers do not have the more normal suction lines but are fitted with gates similar to a water tight door. These gates are fitted in the lower part of the bulkheads separating the various cargo tanks. The suction lines to the cargo pumps are only fitted in the aft cargo tanks. Stripping lines from each of the tanks replace the normal larger suction lines. The bulkhead valves are opened as discharge proceeds but the discharging program for such ships is different to tankers with a normal arrangement of suction lines and stripping lines in the cargo tanks.

Some of the modern VLCCs are built with a duct keel. Pipe branches combined with a valve and an 'elephant's foot' are fitted to the duct keel. The pe-

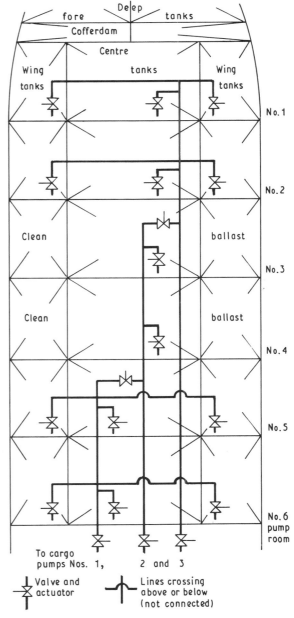

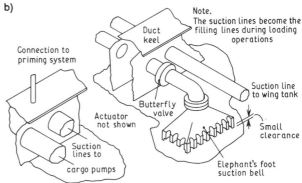

Figure 41 a) Cargo tank suction lines; b) duct keel suction line for VLCC.

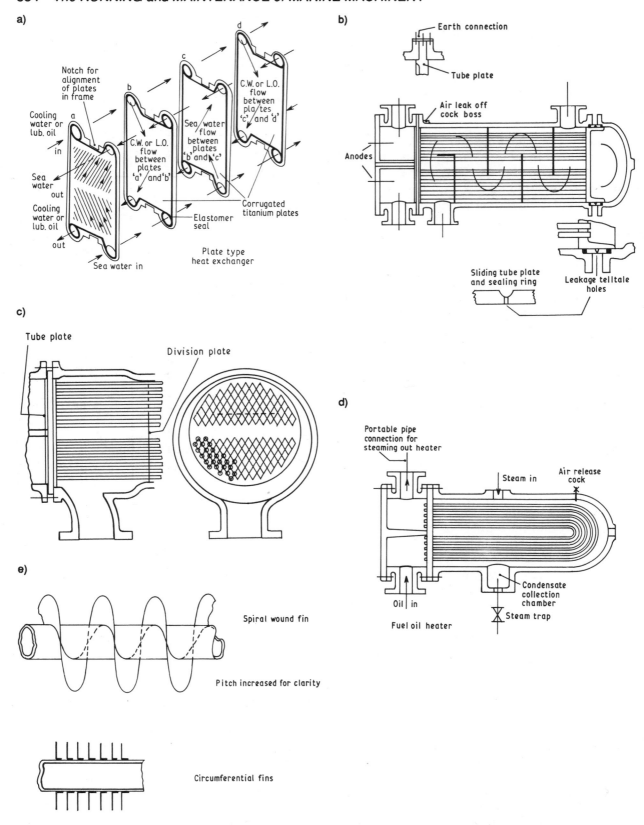

Figure 42   Heat exchangers: a) plate type; b) multitubular (can be mounted vertically or horizontally); c) multitubular (alternative arrangement of body branches); d) fuel oil heater; e) heat exchanger tubes with fins.

riphery at the bottom of the elephant's foot is very extensive. This allows it to be fitted quite near to the bottom plating. The product of the large periphery and the small clearance give a good flow area into the bell. The small clearance allows the remainder wedge at the aft end of the tank to be small in amount when pumping is completed in the tank.

Bells of this or circular type are fitted in all types of tanker, in the double bottom ballast tanks and fuel tanks in dry cargo ships and most other tanks.

The duct keel is then used as a common suction line to all tanks. The duct keel continues into the pump room and the cargo pump suction lines are connected into it. A special form of priming system incorporating either liquid ring pumps or air ejectors is used to keep the duct keel primed.

The discharge from the air ejectors or the priming pumps is a dangerous fire and explosion hazard. Pipe lines are led from the ejectors or liquid ring pumps so that the gases are discharged well above the deck level. They are then dissipated into the atmosphere without any danger arising.

Figures 41a and b show cargo suction piping systems.

HEAT EXCHANGERS

Heat exchangers form part of many piping and machinery systems. Some of the heat exchangers used may be specially designed for the service they will perform. Examples of this are the regenerative exhaust steam condenser and the refrigeration plant condenser and evaporator. Charge air coolers are also of special design and of the finned tube type. Other heat exchangers are of the plate type, the multitubular type, the bent or 'U' tube type, or the fin tube type. Figure 42 shows various types of heat exchanger. The plate type heat exchanger is being more extensively used than formerly. The materials used in the manufacture of heat exchangers are chosen after taking into account corrosion resistance, resistance against scouring action when velocities of liquid are high, ease of manufacture, weight, first cost, and maintenance costs.

Plate type heat exchangers consist of a series of thin plates, usually made of titanium, fastened between spacers having connections to inlet and outlet headers for the media being cooled and the coolant. The plates and spacers are held together with long bolts fastened on the end covers. The headers are arranged so that the media being cooled is circulated between the inlet and outlet headers on one side of the plate while the coolant is circulated on the other

side of the plate. Titanium is a very strong material, highly resistant to corrosion and scouring action. The plates separating the two liquids may therefore be stamped out from very thin material, and are given a corrugated form to increase the effective cooling surfaces. This, together with high liquid velocities, gives a very good rate of heat transfer and makes for an efficient cooler. Generally plate coolers have a high first cost but a low maintenance cost.

Heat exchanger bodies may be made in cast iron or fabricated from mild steel. The tube plates may be of bronze or brass, and the tubes of brass, aluminium copper, or nickel copper alloys. As heat exchangers are manufactured from a variety of different materials screwed plugs are fitted in the sea water side of the system. Anodes of zinc or soft iron are screwed into the inner side of the plug to protect the materials in contact with sea water. To give continuous protection, the anodes must be renewed as they become wasted. Anodes, when renewed, must be of the correct material. Many heat exchangers have a brass or copper plate fitted between the cover, the tube plates and the body or shell to give electrical contact between the various parts. These plates must be kept in a clean condition so that conductivity is not lost.

In order to increase the heat transfer rate in multitubular heat exchangers, fins may be fitted to the tubes. The fins may be put on to the tube by winding and crimping a long strip of metal in a helical form around the tube. In other cases discs of metal with a punched hole are forced down the outside of the tubes. The fins carry heat away in the circulating fluid and lower the temperature on the outside of the tube surface and increase the heat transfer rate.

Oil fuel heaters and charge air coolers are usually fitted with tubes having fins on the outside of the tube.

PIPING MATERIALS

The various factors considered when making a choice of material for use in a piping system are the corrosion resistance of the pipe material to the liquid it will carry; the allowable liquid velocity of the liquid being moved in the material under consideration; and the strength of the pipe material and the thickness of material required to withstand the internal pressure in the pipe. The weight of the system, and the possible use of suitable plastic coatings on cheaper pipe materials, are also considered together with the initial cost of the system and expected maintenance costs. If the pipe is used in a steam system subject to high temperature and pressure, special creep resistant alloy steels must be used.

For sea water services, galvanised mild steel, copper, aluminium bronze, and copper nickel alloys are commonly used. Sections of pipework made up of different material must be avoided because sea water acts as an electrolyte and will cause wastage of one of the materials.

Copper nickel alloys are increasingly used. Copper nickel alloys are hard and resist scouring or erosion. They have a high tensile strength so may be made thinner than copper and aluminium bronze, lowering the weight of the piping system. One disadvantage is that the required thickness of the pipe is such that it has little resistance to damage if small tools and lifting gear such as spanners, wrenches, and shackles are allowed to drop on the pipe. The indent formed in the surface of the pipe can set up cavitation and bubble impingement damage, leading to later leakage downstream of the interference to the water flow.

Plastic coated pipe may also be used for sea water service. In some cases the piping and the flanges are completely encapsulated in plastic. This protects both the inside and outside surfaces from corrosion. The allowable velocity of a fluid is lower than for copper nickel alloys so larger diameter pipes must be used to handle water at the same flow rates. Plastic coated steel pipes for sea water systems are therefore heavier than copper nickel systems. Plastic coated sea water piping systems are, however, the lowest in total cost. Experience over more than 20 years of usage shows that they last the life of the ship without renewals or other repair cost.

Ballast systems often use steel pipes which may or may not be galvanised. Plastic coated steel piping is also used and usually lasts the life of the ship.

Cooling water systems using distilled water invariably use steel piping, but when this is used the water must be treated to protect the pipe from corrosion. In other cases copper may be used. Lubricating oil systems also use steel piping.

Domestic fresh water systems may use plastic piping for the supply lines to the various locations in the accommodation. The connections from the supply lines to taps and faucets are often made from small bore copper tubing.

Drinking water supply lines are often made of plastic materials or copper. Normal cast iron and spheroidal graphite cast iron are also used for some piping systems.

VALVES

There are many different types of valve; some used more extensively than others in the various systems found aboard ship. The more common types are shown in Fig 43.

Generally, valves will be of a type where the closing device consists of a circular disc with some arrangement of wings, or a centrally located guide rod on the base of the disc. The wings, or the guide rod, guide the disc in its up and down motion in the valve seat bush fitted in the body of the valve. The disc is sometimes referred to as the valve lid, or the clack, and is the closing device that prevents flow through the valve. Valves having this form of closing device are often referred to as globe valves. Although this valve is commonly used, the change of direction to the fluid flow causes energy to be wasted when fluid passes through the valve. The energy wastage increases as the flow of fluid is restricted when the amount of valve opening is used to adjust flow rates.

Another type of valve, a gate valve, uses a wedge shaped closing device. The wedge fits into a wedge shaped opening in the valve body. Fluids pass straight through this type of valve without a change in direction so there is less energy loss. The gate valve is commonly used where a high rate of liquid flow is required, such as in condenser cooling water systems, tanker cargo pipelines and the like.

A third type of valve uses a ball or spherical shaped closing device. A hole is made through the ball. When the axis of the hole is in line with the direction of flow the valve is open. When the hole in the ball is at 90 deg to the fluid flow the valve is in the closed position. The energy loss is very low when fluids pass through this type of valve because the flow direction is not changed.

A fourth type of valve, the butterfly valve is also well suited as a closing device in pipelines and is used increasingly. Butterfly valves have a relatively low first cost in the various sizes. For smaller valves the initial cost is shown to be lower than the overhauling costs for many other types of valve. Smaller butterfly valves then become an expendable item. In larger sizes the overhauling costs are also low, overhaul usually consisting of nothing more than removing a rubber or elastomer lining from the inside of the valve and replacing it with a new liner together with renewal of the 'O' rings in the shaft glands. This work is normally carried out by the valve manufacturer or by some repair organisation approved by them.

Valves may be operated manually or by opening and closing devices known as valve actuators. Manually operated globe type valves have a screw and handwheel to open or close the valve. The thread of this type of valve is usually a single start thread as this gives a rapid enough opening or closing speed when the valve wheel is turned. The lid travel of this type

a)

c)

b)

d)

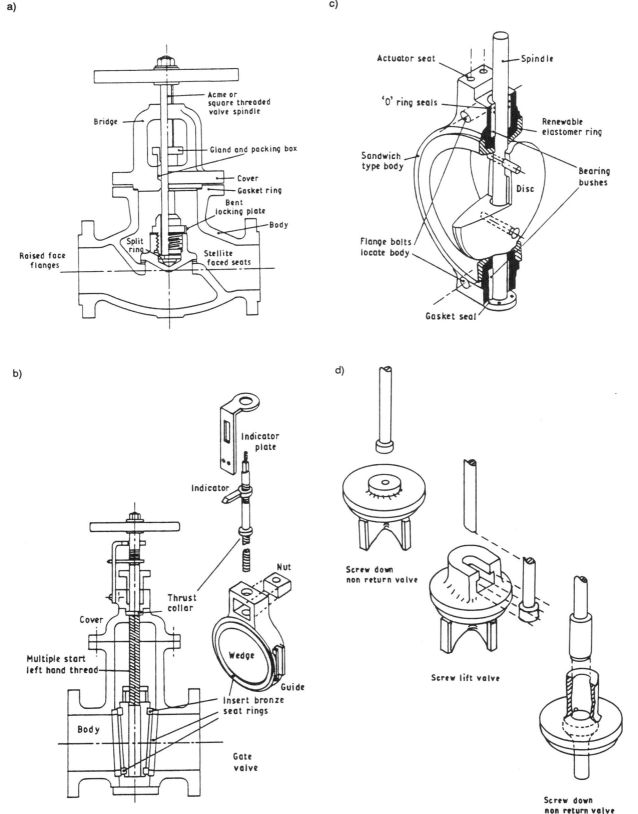

Figure 43 a) Globe valve; b) gate valve; c) butterfly valve; d) valve lids or clacks.

of valve from shut to open is approximately one quarter of the lid diameter, although some valves designed to have less flow resistance may have a larger amount of opening. The movement required by a gate valve wedge to go from fully open to shut is approximately the diameter of the circular landing face of the wedge, and this may be slightly more than the diameter of the piping connected with the valve. In order to increase the speed of opening, two start threads are used on smaller size gate valves while three start or multiple start threads may be used for the larger and largest sizes of gate valves.

Ball valves and butterfly valves are manually operated by a lever requiring a swing of approximately one quarter of a turn to open or close the valve.

As valves have become larger and ships machinery has become more automated than formerly, actuators are increasingly being used to operate valves. This requirement is brought about in some cases because the forces required to open and close large valves are beyond the limits for manual operation. The use of actuators also makes it possible to control valves from some central location such as the cargo control room in a tanker or the control space covering propulsion and auxiliary machinery.

Valve actuators come in various forms. One is as a piston working within a cylinder, arranged to operate on the double acting principle. That is to supply power on to the piston so that the valve may be operated in either direction without the aid of springs. In other cases a ram and spring are used to enable the valve to be operated in two directions. Actuators may also be of a form referred to as a servomotor. This type of actuator is used where a rotation of approx 90 deg is required, such as in a ball valve. Another type of actuator uses a double acting piston to obtain an up or down motion. At the bottom of the piston rod a small shaft is fitted which passes through the piston rod, but at 90 deg to it. The small shaft moves up and down following the motion of the piston. The piston and rod are prevented from rotating by making the small shaft reciprocate within a fixed vertical slot. Within the portion of the actuator carrying the vertical slot a sleeve is fitted. The sleeve is held between two ball thrust bearings, allowing it to revolve, but restricting any vertical motion. A double helix is cut in the inner sleeve and the small shaft moves up and down in the helices. This vertical movement gives the inner sleeve angular movement, allowing it to open and close a ball valve or a butterfly valve.

Valve actuators are powered by either compressed air or hydraulic fluid supplied under pressure. Where large amounts of power are required to operate valve actuators, hydraulic powered equipment is generally less demanding on space than pneumatic equipment. Generally pneumatic equipment is faster in action.

Electric motors are also used as actuators to open and close valves operated by threaded valve spindles. Damage to the valve is prevented by limit switches fitted to prevent the motor overriding the fully open or fully closed positions of the valve.

If indicators are required to show whether valves are open, partially open or closed, pointers showing the position of the valve are fitted and connected up mechanically with the actuator. If the valve is some distance from the indicator some form of feedback is required. This is often accomplished by electrical means using a form of Wheatstone bridge control or a variable electrical resistance. In many cases it is only necessary to know whether a valve is open or closed. In such cases the valve position indicator may be operated by limit switches covering movement of the actuator. In some cases feedback from the control lever for the valve actuator may be used to activate the limit switches. The indicator may be a pair of coloured lamps.

Sometimes fluids are only required to flow in one direction. To prevent flow in the opposite direction, usually on the grounds of safety, non-return or check valves are fitted in the piping system. These may be in the form of a globe valve fitted with or without a normal valve spindle. When fitted with a valve spindle, the valve may be held in a closed position when the spindle is screwed down onto the valve lid, or allowed to open when the spindle is screwed away from the valve lid and the pressure balance is correct. The lid, or clack, is opened when the downstream pressure under the valve is greater than the upstream pressure above the valve. If the pressure difference is reversed, the valve closes, and flow in the wrong direction is prevented. When check, or non-return valves are fitted with a spindle used to hold the valve closed, they are referred to as screw down, non-return valves, or screw down check valves. If a check valve has been removed for overhaul, great care must be taken when it is re-assembled in the pipeline to ensure fluid flow is only allowed in the correct direction.

Another type of non-return valve uses a clack fitted on an axle in the form of a hinge, and this is referred to as a hinged non-return valve, swing check valve or flap check valve.

In many cases of machinery operation the supply of fluid to a piece of machinery or through some piece of equipment must be controlled. Examples of this are the supply of steam to a turbine, the supply of cooling water to a heat exchanger, the supply of air to a control valve or the supply of steam to a feed heater and so on.

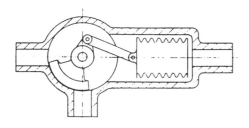

Figure 44 Wax element control valve.

Expandable fluids, such as steam and compressed air, are usually controlled by throttling the flow of the fluid across a partially opened valve. The control may be made manually, as in the case of a steam driven reciprocating bilge pump or fuel transfer pump. The steam valve is then opened or closed in varying amounts to control the speed of the pump. When necessary, the flow rate of expandable fluids is controlled by control valves actuated by compressed air of differing pressures acting on either side of a flexible diaphragm, or by compressed air acting on one side of a diaphragm for movement in one direction, with a spring causing movement in the opposite direction.

The valve giving the throttling action may be given various forms to obtain the required flow behaviour or characteristics. When throttling occurs, the velocity of flow may reach very high values and scouring of the seating surfaces of the valve may cause a rapid deterioration of the ability to control flow correctly without a hunting action. The important parts of control valves are manufactured from various materials to suit the rigorous conditions under which they operate and prevent scouring action.

For high pressure steam at high temperatures, special alloy steels or cobalt chrome tungsten alloys sold under various trade names, one being Stellite, may be used to weld a hard facing on the valve parts where throttling occurs. For small temperature change and low pressures, hard bronzes may be used for the valve parts. It is important that the correct material for the valve parts or valve trim are selected, because otherwise the valve will not give satisfactory service without continuous overhaul. The control of air to the diaphragm will be effected by pressure or temperature sensors fitted up or downstream of the control valve, or some other part of the system where control is required.

The flow rate of non-compressible fluids such as water and other liquids is usually controlled by diverting the liquid from one path into another path; commonly called a bypass. An example of this type of valve is the wax element control valve which is used with a heat exchanger in engine cooling systems. Another form of diverter valve is made up from two butterfly valves arranged with one actuator and lever arrangement so that as one valve is closing the other is opening. Diverter valves allow the total flow through a system to remain approximately constant. This is important when using centrifugal type pumps. Diverter valves allow the discharge pressure from the pump to be kept nearly constant so that the quantity of water discharged remains nearly constant. If throttling devices were used to control the amount of water flow, the pressure fluctuations on the discharge side of the pump would cause considerable variation in the total output of the pump and lead to an imbalance in the system. Diverter valves must be used on the secondary cooling water system when the secondary sides of heat exchangers are connected in series.

Automatic self-closing valves are required on fuel tanks. They are usually gate valves and must be capable of being operated at the fuel tank, or closed remotely from some point external to the engine room. In the event of an engine room fire making it necessary to evacuate the staff, the fuel supply lines from the fuel tanks may be shut from outside of the engine room. Self closing valves are constructed with each of the columns supporting the spindle bridge made up as two links. When the links are pulled out of line, a heavy spring forces the gate wedge into the valve body and stops the flow of oil. Angle globe valves with extended spindles, or reach rods, leading to some point outside of the engine, enabling them to be closed remotely, may also be used.

Valve bodies are usually made by casting in a foundry. For some high pressure steam systems the valves may be cast steel or forged steel. The materials used for castings may be normal cast iron, spheroidal graphite, or patent cast irons, brass, bronzes, normal steel or alloy steels.

The design of valves and their dimensions are covered by various standards drawn up by government or trade sponsored organisations such as the International Standards Organisation (ISO), the British Standards Institute, the American National Standards Institute (ANSI) or the Japanese Standards Institute, or similar national and trade bodies. The various valves are classified into various allowable working pressure and maximum working temperature groupings. The materials used for valves in the various groupings are specified together with the required physical tests for the materials and the pressure tests to which the valves must be subjected in order to comply with the specifications.

PIPE FITTINGS

When piping must pass through a watertight bulkhead, the integrity of the bulkhead is maintained by using a bulkhead piece. In some cases bulkhead pieces are made of cast iron, or fabricated by welding together shaped pieces. In modern ship construction the bulkhead pieces are a continuation of part of the piping system, and are assembled and welded into the hull module at the time of its construction in the steel fabrication shop.

Where branches, bends, tee pieces and cross pieces are required in steel pipework, forged pieces are available for fabrication purposes. These forged pieces are welded into the various pipes where they are required. Similar shaped pieces are also available in copper nickel and aluminium bronze materials for building up a pipe system. Bends and tee pieces may be made without flanges for fastening the piece into the surrounding pipework by silver soldering. In other cases the pieces are flanged and fitted into flanged pipework.

Reducers are important pipe fittings available in most materials. These are hollow truncated cones, with the smaller diameter in line with the larger diameter or offset from it. They are used where a larger diameter pipe must join up with a smaller diameter pipe such as at a centrifugal pump flange where the linear velocity of the liquid leaving the pump is greater than the desired linear velocity within the pipeline. The reducer prevents the formation of wasteful eddies by giving an easy transition between the two diameters.

Pipe flanges are forged or cast in various materials. Steel flanges are fastened to steel piping material by electric welding. Copper nickel and aluminium bronze flanges are fastened to piping of similar material by silver soldering. Copper piping and cast brass flanges are fastened together by brazing processes using gas torches. In selecting the filler for the fastening process care must be exercised if corrosion between the base metal of the pipe flange, the pipe and the filler is to be avoided.

When a piping system experiences any temperature change, expansion or contraction of the piping occurs. This creates stresses in the piping system if it has not been designed to accommodate the changes in the length of the piping. Piping situated on the upper deck, or in double bottom spaces near to the outer bottom plating of a ship, also experiences changing stresses due to the lengthening and shortening of the deck and ships bottom when the hull is bending in heavy weather. In order to guard against excessive stresses, bends of adequate amount may be placed in the piping system so that forces arising out of the change in length may be accommodated by the pipe or the equipment to which it is connected.

The equipment used to allow thermal expansion to take place from the cold, or to accommodate hull bending, are bellows pieces, piping loops or omega bends, and pipe expansion gland fittings. When these items are used it is usually necessary to anchor one end of the pipe holding the fitting, so allowing the other end of the pipe to move. When bellows and gland type fittings are used it must be remembered that the internal pressure within the pipe sets up a thrust action in the pipe tending to move the pipe ends outwards on both sides of the fitting.

The stresses arising in high pressure superheated steam piping between the boilers and turbine cannot be accommodated by using the fittings described. The design of the piping is usually arranged in the form of large radius bends and must be carefully studied. Sometimes stresses are created when the pipe is in a cold condition. This is done by making the pipes short so the flanges are left open in the cold condition; pulling them together when bolting up leaves the pipes in tension and subject to bending moments. The amount the flanges are left open is referred to as 'cold pull up'. Cold pull up is negated and relieves the tensile stresses and bending moments as the pipes expand when coming up to their working temperature. The set of calculations made to estimate the required amounts of cold pull up are the loads applied to pipe support springs, the estimated stresses in the pipe arising out of bending, and the forces and moments coming on the turbine and boiler steam stop valve flanges when in the operating condition. These calculations are submitted to the classification society for approval before the piping is manufactured and assembled.

Anchor points of piping are shown on piping plans. They should be examined periodically to ensure that their effectiveness is not lost.

Compression sleeve couplings are used to join two lengths of piping together without the aid of flanges. They consist of a sleeve which fits over the end of each pipe. A tapered groove is formed at each end of the sleeve, and a wedge shaped elastomer or rubber ring fits into the groove. A flange is fitted over each end of the pipes being joined. Through bolts pass through the flanges, and, when tightened, these compress the wedge shaped ring against the pipe and sleeve so that a pressure-tight seal is made. A stopper ring around the inner circumference of the sleeve at mid-length, or a stopper pin similarly located, prevents the sleeve working along one or the other of the pipes being joined. This type of coupling is known by its trade

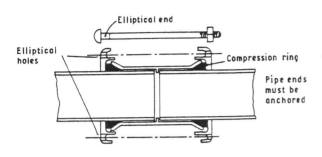

Figure 45 Compression ring coupling (Dresser).

name as a Dresser coupling (Fig 45). A similar coupling is also known by its trade name as the Dayton coupling.

Deck service lines for fire or wash deck use, together with ballast and bilge lines fitted in the double bottom, use these couplings in an efficient manner. Each pipe forming part of the system is anchored at mid length. A clearance is left between the pipe end and the stopper ring. Movement of the pipe due to thermal expansion or contraction, or due to the effects of the ship working, are easily accommodated by pipe movement within the sealing ring. The coupling may be encapsulated in plastic, and when used with steel pipe encapsulated in plastic, produces a piping system having a lower first cost and maintenance cost than the various alloy piping systems. It has been known for ballast and bilge lines to have to be renewed at the first special survey of a ship, at a great cost. The cost of protecting the pipe by encapsulating is a small fraction of the renewal and replacement costs.

Bilge line mud boxes are usually fitted at the suction end of a bilge line serving a particular bilge or hat box. There are two branches on the box and a cover. One branch faces downwards on the opposite side to the cover. A straight tail pipe is fitted to this branch and goes down into the bilge. The other branch is on the opposite end of the box at 90 deg to the cover face, and this branch is connected into the non-return bilge valve fitted in the bilge valve chest. A perforated plate, or strum, is fitted in the box to separate dirt particles and prevent them from entering the bilge system and causing blockage problems, or an air leakage problem if solid matter lands under a non-return valve.

A strum box consists of a cubic box with five sides (one side being left open), which are perforated plates to act as a strainer. The open bottom sits on the ships bottom plating, in way of the bilge. A hole in the top of the cube allows the tail pipe to pass through it. The

strum box acts in the same manner as the strum plate in the mud box. The strum box is sometimes called a rose box and the strum plate is also called a rose plate. When the bilge tail pipe serves a hat box fitted in a tank top the entry to the hat box is protected by a perforated plate serving the same purpose as the strum box.

Mud boxes and strum boxes are manufactured in cast iron or fabricated from steel plates. Steel mud boxes and strum boxes together with cast iron strum boxes and strum plates should be heavily galvanised as a protection against corrosion wastage. Strum boxes are manufactured so that they may be removed and replaced without disturbing the bilge tail pipe. Commonly used pipe fittings are shown in Fig 46–48.

When expansion bellows are fitted in a pipe line the internal pressure acting on the bellows causes a thrust to act outward from the bellows piece. This does not cause any problem in straight piping runs provided the ends of the pipe are anchored and there is sufficient freedom on the bellows convolutions to accommodate pipe expansion.

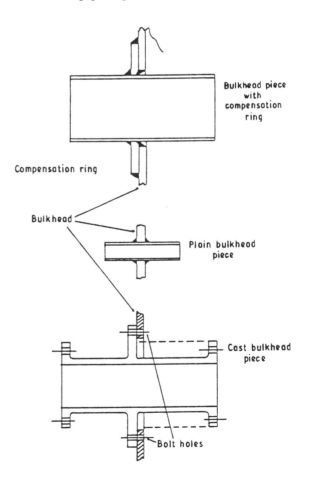

Figure 46 Bulkhead pieces.

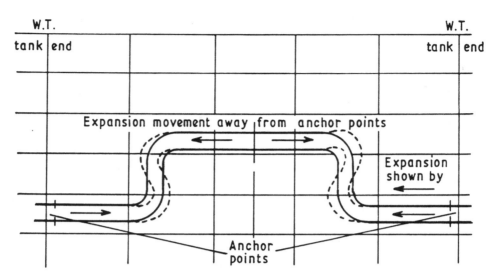

Figure 47   Piping expansion in double bottom tanks.

In cases where it is not possible to anchor the end of a pipe adjacent to a bend, the thrust set up may be quite high and cause an excessive bending moment on the pipe on the other side of the bend. If the bend is connected to a pump branch the bending moment may be more than can be safely resisted by the pump branch. In cases such as this a compensating arrangement of bellows pieces is made up as shown in Fig 48e. This arrangement compensates the thrust and brings the bending moment on the pump branch to zero.

Bellows pieces subjected to a large number of hot/cold cycles over time will suffer from fatigue after so many cycles have occurred. In critical situations the bellows piece may be given a life after which the piece must be renewed. The life may be extended by increasing the number of convolutions in the bellows piece so the stress range between the hot/cold cycle is reduced.

SAFETY

Constant vigilance must be exercised in ships' machinery spaces to prevent accidents and injury to personnel carrying out their duties. If vigilance and care are exercised, by thinking about the hazards of various operations, accidents can be prevented.

Staff are at risk when opening up steam valves and putting steam into steam lines. The hazard of water hammer has already been described (page 373). It is easily avoided by opening up the drain connections on the piping and allowing trapped water to drain completely out of the piping before the steam valve is opened. The steam valve should be opened slowly so that any steam condensed when the pipe is being warmed through can drain off before any accumulation occurs. After the piping is warmed through properly the steam valve may be slowly opened and afterwards the drain may be closed.

In some high pressure steam systems bypass lines are fitted around steam valves. The steam lines should be drained before opening up the bypass valve. The bypass valve should then be used to warm the steam line through before opening up the main steam valve. Some steam valves in high pressure steam lines are similar to gate valves. When steam pressure is behind the valve the friction created on the wedge makes opening the valve very difficult. When the pressure is balanced on both sides of the valve by using the bypass, only a small amount of friction is present, and the valve is easily opened.

Opening up valve covers and flange joints during disassembly operations next to, or near, a live steam section of the system, is also a dangerous operation if not carried out correctly. Normally, drain connections on steam lines should be used to ensure that there is no pressure present in the line. A cold line must not be regarded as an indication of an absence of pressure. It may contain condensate backed by live steam. Safe practice requires each nut on the studs fastening the cover in place to be slackened a very small and equal amount in the first instance. By closing the valve onto its seat, the cover will be lifted, and the cover joint will be broken. If a pressure exists above the valve, its presence will be heard immedi-

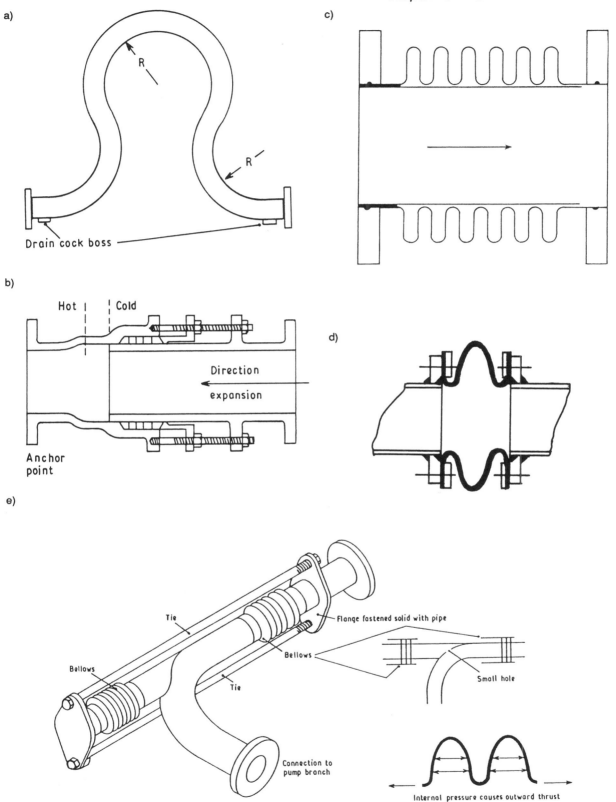

Figure 48   Piping fittings: a) expansion bend 'omega' loop type; b) pipe expansion gland; c) expansion bellows; d) rubber expansion bellows for water service; e) thrust compensated expansion bellows.

ately. If a pressure exists below the valve and the valve is opened very slightly, the existence of pressure will also be heard immediately. By working carefully in this manner accidents can be avoided. There are many cases on record of the disastrous consequences of removing all the cover nuts on a valve and the operative being killed by scalding when the gasket or joint gave way and allowed the cover to be blown off the valve body.

In a similar manner, if pipe flange bolts are being removed with burning gear, a new bolt should replace each old bolt as it is removed. The replacement should be tightened before burning out the next bolt. After the old bolts are all removed, the flanges may then be broken under full control in the same way as when removing a valve cover from the valve body; by slackening off each new bolt an equal and very small amount before using wedges to separate the flanges. If the steam line is for high temperature and pressure steam, every care must be taken to ensure that bolts of the correct grade material are used when finally making up the joint.

Painting pipelines in enclosed machinery spaces requires adequate ventilation during the time paint is being applied and during the drying or curing period. Failure to adequately ventilate the space has lead to operatives being asphyxiated. The fumes given off from some paint solvents are also found to be toxic.

Any enclosed space such as a double bottom tank, duct keel, pipe duct, peak tanks or similar space must be properly ventilated before entry is allowed.

These enclosed spaces may have an atmosphere depleted of oxygen through the absorption of oxygen by steel during rusting. Another source of danger may be the presence of carbon dioxide due to organic material rotting. One sad case involved the cleaning of bilge lines and the removal of grain from bilge piping in a pipe duct following the discharge of a grain cargo. Some of the grain was left in the pipe duct and remained there for some time after the duct entry doors were replaced. Some time later the duct was opened and people who entered were asphyxiated. Enquiry showed the grain when rotting had given off carbon dioxide and left the space unsafe for entry because there was insufficient oxygen present in the pipe duct to support life.

After properly ventilating an enclosed space nobody should enter the space without another person standing by outside to call for further assistance if the person inside the space experiences difficulties. The person standing by should not enter the tank to render assistance but should call other people to give aid as necessary.

Accident enquiries show that many people are injured through falls from spaces where hand rails, gratings or floor plates have been removed. If any danger is created when equipment is removed from areas where there is normally free access, the area where the danger exists must be roped off making access difficult. Notices should be posted at engine room entrances calling attention to the danger.

Safety helmets should be worn when working in a ship's engine room when repair work, dismantling engine parts, using lifting gear and the like are in progress. Safety shoes with steel toecaps should also be used when safety helmets are being worn.

It is essential that valves on fuel tanks should be operated at the tank, and from the remote position, at weekly intervals. Extended spindle universal couplings and shaft bearings should be lubricated regularly to ensure that they work easily, and do not seize up in the bearings. Wire cables on self closing valves should be protected with oil to prevent wastage by corrosion, and pulleys supporting the cables should also be lubricated. These tests are best carried out as part of the fire drill exercise at the same time as the testing of fire pumps. The test should be recorded in the engine room log book and a copy of the entry given to the Master for inclusion in the official log.

Chemical solvents, degreasing fluids, and inhibited, acid descaling liquids must all be used with extreme care. The instructions regarding their use must be studied and any safety recommendations strictly complied with; particularly with regard to protection of the eyes and skin. Special ventilation requirements when using industrial solvent and cleaners must also be strictly complied with.

PUMPING TERMINOLOGY

The axial centre line of a horizontal centrifugal pump rotor, the mid point of the rotor or the position of the entry eye to the rotor of vertical pumps are the datum points from which head measurements are taken. For other types of pump it is often taken as being at the centre line of the pump suction flange.

Discharge head is the distance above the datum that a pump will lift water, and is measured in metres or feet.

Suction head is the distance measured in meters or feet above or below the pump datum to the surface of the body of water from which the pump is receiving water.

If the surface of the water is below the pump it is referred to as negative suction head. It is therefore the height water must be lifted by atmospheric pressure to enter the pump.

If the surface of the water is above the pump it is referred to as positive suction head and water will flow into the pump under the action of gravity and atmospheric pressure.

These head measurements are also referred to as static heads.

When the surface of the water is below the pump, atmospheric pressure acting on the surface of the water causes the water to flow to the pump when a vacuum is created in the suction line. The action is similar to a mercury barometer. Air pressure supports the column of mercury within the barometer tube while a vacuum exists above the surface of the mercury. If a long barometer tube used water instead of mercury, the barometer would have a height equal to the height of the mercury column, multiplied by the ratio of the relative density of mercury (Hg) to the relative density of water.

Atmospheric pressure measured as the height of a mercury column is approximately 750 mm Hg; i.e. three quarters of a metre of mercury. Since the relative density of mercury is 13.5 and the relative density of water is 1, a barometer using water instead of mercury would have a height of 13.5 times 0.75 m, or approximately 10 m. This is the maximum theoretical negative suction head a pump could lift water. In practice, the maximum negative suction head a pump can lift water is approximately 6.9 m. This comes about because as the vacuum in the suction line increases, a point is reached where the water vaporises because the boiling point of water is lowered with falling pressures. The water vaporises and fills the suction pipe with water vapour and so destroys the vacuum. It follows that cold water can be pumped with a greater negative suction head than warm water.

The net positive suction head (NPSH) of a pump is a figure of the available head at the inlet to the pump. In theory, liquid cannot be drawn into a pump but only forced in by air pressure acting on its surface.

The NPSH of a pump is the total absolute suction head measured in metres at the pump datum, minus the vapour pressure of the liquid in metres absolute. In designing the suction side of the piping system leading to a pump, it is essential that the available NPSH (obtained by calculations beginning with the addition of the absolute atmospheric pressure and any positive suction head from which the friction and other losses in the suction line are subtracted) is greater than the required NPSH found by tests carried out on the pump by the manufacturer.

The NPSH values for a centrifugal pump are often plotted on the characteristic curves drawn up for a pump when it is tested.

Pressure measured as a head value in metres, or some other linear value, may be converted to pressures measured in bar or other values.

Chapter 11
Minimising the Fire Hazard

Dr J Cowley

INTRODUCTION

The regulatory bodies have established standards of protection from fire according to the hazards presented by the various spaces on board ship and the particular hazards of specialised ships such as oil, gas and chemical tankers and roll on/roll off vessels. As these standards are under continual review and revision, the fire protection arrangements for the same type of ship vary according to its age. These differences are discussed in this chapter only to explain the changes in fire protection philosophy and as an aid to understanding of the subject, and not as an introductory exposition of some of the regulatory requirements, a detailed discussion of which would occupy several volumes.

There are certain principles which apply to all ships both in respect of the provision of equipment and its use and limitations. All ships must, for example, be provided with arrangements to deal with a fire, in any one compartment, using sea water. Attention is directed to the reference to 'any one compartment' since the regulations are not formulated to deal with simultaneous outbreaks in separate compartments.

Proximity to any major fire is a frightening experience and, unlike ashore, it is not possible to run to call the fire brigade. Responsible behaviour by ships' personnel will minimise the possibility of fire, and the ready availability of fire appliances and their competent use will reduce the possibility of any detected fire from spreading. The importance of prevention or early detection and extinction of a shipboard fire cannot be over emphasised since the ships' personnel are required to act as both fire fighters and repairers of the damage caused.

All seafarers should be aware of the need when joining a ship to immediately familiarise themselves with escape routes from their cabin and the accommodation space, bearing in mind that, in the event of a fire, this might be their last opportunity. Being aware of the disorientating effects of smoke, they will count the number of cabin doors between their room and the exits. They will familiarise themselves with the position of the fire extinguishers and hoses; and consider their alternative courses of action if awakened by fire, smoke or alarms. The thoughtful man will resist the temptation to go to sleep without taking these precautions, even after a long and tiring journey to join a ship, knowing that a serious fire is just as likely to break out on that night as on any other.

The experienced seafarer will know that almost three times as many lives are lost in fires in the accommodation of ships as in their machinery spaces. Most of these deaths from fire occur on ships in port, often following a night ashore, when the senses may be blurred, prior to actions such as the preparation of hot food or toast or carelessness in the use of matches or cigarettes when, say, smoking in bed. Such fires should not occur. Familiarity with the location of fire extinguishing equipment may limit their consequences but one thing is certain—hundreds of lives would not have been lost in fire situations if everyone took the self-evident precaution of familiarising themselves with their living or working environment to the extent that they could find their way to the exits in conditions of zero visibility.

Immediately after joining a ship, new officers or ratings should be acquainted with the ship's muster list and their posts in the event of fire. Their attention should also be directed to the location of the ship's fire control plans. These matters are dealt with in more detail later. It is pertinent to first review the chemistry of fire to aid understanding of the thoughts behind the design and operation of the systems provided on board ship.

THE CHEMISTRY OF FIRE

Readers will be familiar with the fire triangle, with sides representing fuel, heat and oxygen. Removal of any side results in the collapse of the triangle and the extinguishing of the fire. Without contradicting this, it is more appropriate to use a fire tetrahedron (Fig 1) to illustrate the nature of fire and, in particular, the extinguishing action of modern extinguishing media such as halogenated hydrocarbons (halons) and certain dry chemicals. (NB Halons are to be phased out due to their ozone layer depletion effects).

The three sloping surfaces in the tetrahedron represent fuel, heat and oxygen and the base represents the chain reaction between the short-lived chemical species following ignition. As the temperature rises, the reaction rate increases resulting in a further rise in temperature. There is, however, an opposing influence due to the depletion of the fuel and its replacement by combustion products and in the case, for example, of fuel burning in an open tray, the rate of evaporation of vapour from its surface will control the rate of reaction. In the case of a flammable gas mixture, the speed of reaction is sufficiently high to result in explosions.

If the chain can be broken, the fire will be extinguished, i.e. the base of the tetrahedron (which may be considered as maintaining the sloping faces in place) is destroyed. The halon extinguishing agents and certain dry chemicals effectively break the chain reaction by attacking the structure of the active chemical species and preventing their reaction and so killing the flame sometimes in less than one hundredth of a second. However, halons have a minimal cooling effect, and if their concentration is not maintained until sufficient cooling has taken place or a cooling medium has been applied, and the three sloping sides of the tetrahedron are present, re-ignition may occur.

The fire hazard from liquid fuels is generally related to the flash point, i.e. the lowest temperature at which sufficient vapour is released to form a mixture which will ignite on application of a flame. Liquids which will form a flammable mixture at ambient temperatures are not permitted as fuels for machinery spaces, but other properties of fuels are important from safety considerations. Petroleum liquids will ignite without the application of a naked flame if heated sufficiently, e.g. when fuel or lubricating oil leaks onto hot surfaces. The temperature at which this ignition occurs is much lower for lubricating and fuel oils than for crude oil, petrol and kerosine. The ignition temperature, for a given substance (solid, liquid or gas) varies with the conditions of the test,

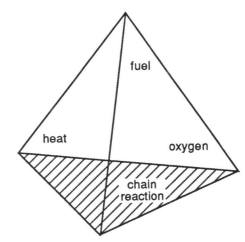

Figure 1 Fire tetrahedron.

e.g. the bulk of the substance and its surface area. For solid materials, it is estimated by heating a sample in an oven or on a hot plate. Typical ignition temperatures are: coal, 130°C; newspaper, 180°C; and cotton, 228°C.

Consequently, it is dangerous to place oiled or paint splashed overalls, rags or waste on hot pipes. Such oiled materials, initially at room temperature, may cause fires through heating due to the initial slow oxidation of the oil. This is an exothermic reaction within a good thermal insulating material which will continue as long as oxygen can diffuse inwards. The heat cannot readily escape and as the temperature increases so does the reaction rate until, in suitable conditions, the substances burst into flames. The exothermic reaction is referred to as self or spontaneous heating and the subsequent fire as spontaneous combustion. Therefore, oily or paint impregnated rags should never be stored near combustibles but should be retained in airtight tins and disposed of ashore.

Fire classification and extinguishing media

Table 1 lists the common extinguishing media and the fires for which they are suitable. For convenience in selecting appropriate extinguishing media, fires have been arranged in classes A, B, C and D according to the nature of the material undergoing combustion. Two similar systems are in use: ISO standard 3941; and NFPA 10 as shown in Table 2. In this chapter, NFPA 10 is used. The following general examples of the use of classification may be helpful.

Class A fires (i.e. flammable solids) are most effectively extinguished by cooling, i.e. water, although foam and dry chemicals may be used. Class B fires (i.e. flammable liquids and gases) are most effectively

Table 1 Extinguishing media and fires.

Extinguishing medium	Recommended for use on fires involving:
Water	wood, paper, textiles and similar materials
Foam	wood, paper, textiles and flammable liquids
Dry chemical (standard)	flammable liquids, electrical equipment and flammable gases
Dry chemical (multiple or general purpose)	wood, paper, textiles, flammable liquids, electrical equipment and flammable gases
Dry powder	combustible materials
Carbon dioxide	flammable liquids, electrical equipment and flammable gases

extinguished by a smothering agent, e.g. foam, water fog, dry chemical or carbon dioxide. Class C fires (i.e. involving live electrical equipment) are always combined with Class A or Class B substances. A non-conducting agent must therefore be used, e.g. carbon dioxide, as a smothering agent in suitable conditions or dry chemical powder (acting as a chain breaker). A dry chemical extinguisher which is suitable for Class A, B and C fires (e.g. monoammonium phosphate) may thus be referenced as dry chemical ABC extinguisher. In respect of powder extinguishers, the terms dry powder and dry chemical are often used synonymously but in this chapter dry powder refers to substances suitable for Class D fires, e.g. sodium chloride which forms a crust on burning metal. Dry

Table 2 Fire classification.

International Organisation for Standardisation (ISO standard 3941)	National Fire Protection Association (NFPA 10)
Class A: Fires involving solid materials, usually of an organic nature, in which combustion normally takes place with the formation of glowing embers	**Class A:** Fires in ordinary combustible materials such as wood, cloth, paper, rubber and many plastics
Class B: Fires involving liquids or liquefiable solids	**Class B:** Fires in flammable liquids, oils, greases, tars, oil base paints, lacquers and flammable gases
Class C: Fires involving gases	**Class C:** Fires which involve energised electrical equipment where the electrical non conductivity of the extinguishing medium is of importance. (When electrical equipment is de-energised, extinguishers for class A or B fires may be used safely.)
Class D: Fires involving metals	**Class D:** Fires in combustible metals such as magnesium, titanium, zirconium, sodium, lithium and potassium.

chemical refers to potassium compounds, e.g. potassium chloride (BC) and potassium bicarbonate (BC). Class D fires (i.e. combustible metal fuel) fires must be smothered and controlled by dry powder although sand has been used successfully in some instances.

Whenever possible when dealing with Class B liquid fires, the supply of fuel should be shut off but it is essential in the case of Class B gaseous fuel fires. If this were not done, the escaping gas may accumulate and be ignited resulting in an explosion more disastrous than the burning fuel.

The suitability of extinguishing media in fixed installations is also discussed under *Machinery space protection*. Table 3 refers to their use in portable extinguishers and covers each extinguisher's characteristics including its method of discharge; means of extinguishing a fire; operating peculiarities and limitations; merits and disadvantages; and the maintenance required.

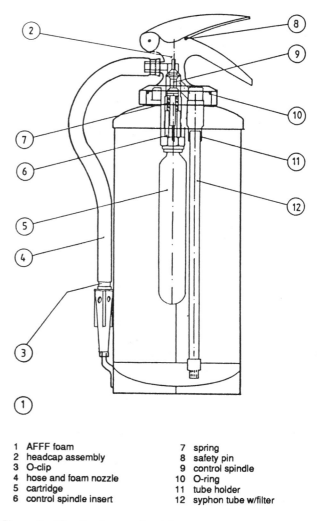

1	AFFF foam	7	spring
2	headcap assembly	8	safety pin
3	O-clip	9	control spindle
4	hose and foam nozzle	10	O-ring
5	cartridge	11	tube holder
6	control spindle insert	12	syphon tube w/filter

Figure 2 Nine litre foam extinguisher.

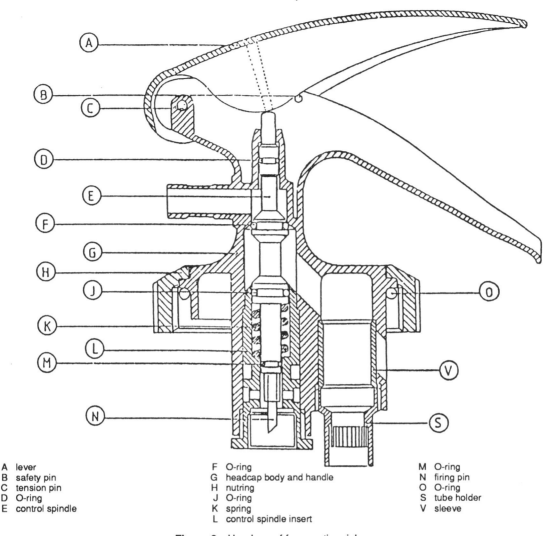

A	lever	F	O-ring	M	O-ring
B	safety pin	G	headcap body and handle	N	firing pin
C	tension pin	H	nutring	O	O-ring
D	O-ring	J	O-ring	S	tube holder
E	control spindle	K	spring	V	sleeve
		L	control spindle insert		

Figure 3 Headcap of foam extinguisher.

The information marked on each extinguisher should include the types of fire for which it is suitable, the type and quantity of extinguishing medium and the method of operation.

Table 3 is comprehensive in that it includes extinguishers which are discharged by chemically generated pressure (soda-acid and foam) and gas pressure operated (water and 'mechanical' foam) extinguishers.

Although almost all newly manufactured extinguishers are of the latter types and are operated in the upright position, chemical extinguishers are still in service and some require inversion for activation. It is therefore important to become completely familiar with the correct method of operation of all extinguishers on board.

A sketch of a Unitor 9 litre foam extinguisher together with a technical description is given in Fig 2.

The correspondingly sized water extinguisher (painted red) is almost identical in construction except for the design of the hose nozzle.

A sectional view of the head assembly for the water and foam extinguishers operated by gas pressure is given in Fig 3.

To operate the extinguisher, the safety pin preventing inadvertent operation is removed, and the hose is unclipped and appropriately directed. To commence discharge, the handle is squeezed. Discharge may be interrupted by releasing the handle.

Servicing and recharging

Shipping companies almost invariably employ manufacturers' representatives or specialist contractors to service fire extinguishers, but a ship's staff should be capable of recharging and making detailed

Table 3 Characteristics of portable extinguishers.

	Types of extinguisher						
	Water		Chemical foam		Mechanical foam	Powder	Carbon dioxide
Extinguishing medium used	Water with possible salts in solution		Basic water solution	Basic water solution with foam generating substances	Water solution containing foam generating substances	Dry chemical powders	Pressurised carbon dioxide
Expellant charge of the extinguisher (stored pressure or cartridge as indicated)	One basic and one acidic reagent; in general the basic reagent is a solution of sodium bicarbonate, and the acid reagent is a solution of hydrochloric acid or of aluminium sulphate	Carbon dioxide or other pressurised inert gases or compressed air (storage pressure or separate cartridge)	Solution of sulphuric or hydrochloric acid or aluminium sulphate	Water solution and acid reagent (e.g. solution of aluminium sulphate)	Carbon dioxide or other pressurised inert gases or compressed air (stored pressure or separate cartridge)	Carbon dioxide or other inert gases or dry air (stored pressure or separate cartridge)	
The discharge of the extinguisher is achieved by:	Opening of the valve. Generation of carbon dioxide (chemical reaction which develops inside the extinguisher)	Opening of the valve. Action of pressurised gas (opening of the cartridge)	Opening of the valve. Generation of carbon dioxide (chemical reaction between the acid in the cartridge and the basic solution of the charge)		Opening of the valve. Action of pressurised gas (opening of the cartridge)	Opening of the valve. Action of pressurised gas (opening of the cartridge)	Opening of the valve of the container constituting the extinguisher
The discharged extinguishing medium consists of:	Water with possible salts in solution	Water with salts in solution	Foam containing carbon dioxide		Foam containing the gas used	Dry chemical powders and carbon dioxide or other gas	Carbon dioxide
The discharged extinguishing medium causes the extinction of fire by:	Cooling of the burning material. Water evaporation and consequent formation of a local atmosphere (water/steam) which isolates the burning products from the surrounding air		Formation of a foam layer which isolates the burning products from the surrounding air			Inhibition of the combustion interrupting the chemical reaction. Some separation of burning materials from the surrounding air	Formation of a local inert atmosphere (carbon dioxide) which isolates the burning materials from the surrounding air. Smothering and cooling action of carbon dioxide

Table 3   Characteristics of portable extinguishers (contd).

	Types of extinguisher					
	Water		Chemical foam	Mechanical foam	Powder	Carbon dioxide
The electrical resistance of the discharged extinguishing medium is:	Very low	Very low	Low	Low	Very high. Under intense heat some powders may be electrically conductive	Very high
Operating peculiarities and limitations	The jet part of the extinguisher is to be directed towards the base of the fire		The jet part of the extinguisher is to be directed towards the base of the fire The extinction of the fire is achieved only when all the burning surface is covered by foam		Powder mixture subject to windage; they may have reduced effectiveness in the open or in ventilated spaces	Gas, subject to windage; they therefore have limited effectiveness in the open or in ventilated spaces
Disadvantages and dangers	Not to be used where there are electrical hazards		Not to be used where there are electrical hazards	Not to be used where there are electrical hazards. Malfunctioning of the reducing arrangmenets may result in dangerous overpressures	Generated powder mixtures may be suffocating. Powder can damage electrical contacts	Carbon dioxide may be suffocating
Maintenance	Extinguishers with copper or copper alloy body should not be polished with products of a corrosive nature which may cause wall thickness reduction. Such extinguishers should preferably be painted externally					
	The charge can freeze at temperatures of about 0°C (unless the charge is made non-freezable chemically)					
		Avoid installing the extinguisher in excessively warm locations where the internal pressure of the carbon dioxide in the cartridge might rise to very high values	The charge can freeze at about -5°C. The charge can be altered by elevated temperatures (about 40°C or more). Therefore the extinguisher should not be installed in positions where it may be exposed to high or low temperatures		Some types of powder may be altered by humidity; therefore avoid the refilling of the extinguisher in humid locations	
	When a carbon dioxide container is provided, avoid the installation of the extinguisher in excessively warm locations, where the internal pressure of the carbon dioxide in the container might rise to very high values					

inspections of most types of extinguisher. The useful life of foam solution depends on its location but extinguishers should be serviced annually and subjected to a discharge test and renewal of solution at least every four years.

If a cartridge operated extinguisher has been discharged, the pressure should be relieved by inverting it and (directing the hose nozzle away from the face) gently squeezing the operating handle. This will relieve the pressure without discharging the residual foam solution.

The nutring is then removed and the extinguisher washed out, the rinsings discarded and the interior of the extinguisher examined. Re-charge with new solution in accordance with the manufacturer's instructions, making an allowance for anti-freeze if freezing temperatures are expected. Check the operation of the headcap, and check the diptube, strainer and nozzle by blowing through nozzle with handle squeezed. Check the headcap for damage and reassemble with new CO_2 cartridge. Remember to add the date of recharge to the record label on the extinguisher.

FIRE PROTECTION AND INTERNATIONAL REGULATIONS

All ships must, as a minimum, meet the requirements of the Safety of Life at Sea Convention (SOLAS) of the International Maritime Organization (IMO) according to their age, type and size. Ships under 500 grt may be required to comply with national or classification society requirements. Although the regulations are extremely detailed, they are based on the general principles shown in Table 4. These principles express the intention of the regulations to national administrations and classification societies acting on their behalf, shipowners, shipbuilders and fire protection engineers. Readers may wish to refer to Table 4 to confirm that the principles are being met in their own ships.

These principles and the corresponding regulations take into account the potential hazards associated with the functions of the various types of ship. Not only must the nature of fire fighting installations and extinguishing media be appropriate to the hazards associated with the cargo, e.g. in gas, chemical and oil tankers, but the accommodation must be specifically arranged to protect the crew against possible cargo fires.

Equally, the differences between the protection of passenger ship and cargo ship accommodation and public spaces are reflected in the fire detection and structural fire protection and alarm requirements. This differentiation is necessary because passenger ships carry large numbers of passengers each of whom is a potential initiator of a fire; many may never even have used a portable fire extinguisher; some will be very old or very young or infirm; and, from time to time, some will be intoxicated. Consequently, in passenger ships carrying more than 36 passengers an efficient fire patrol system must be maintained, in addition to structural and equipment augmentation.

PASSENGER ACCOMMODATION SPACES

In a typical ten year period, some fifty lives were lost through accommodation fires in UK cargo and passenger ships compared with twenty lives lost in the machinery spaces.

Detection of a fire may be by fire patrol, individual observation or smell or by either of the following mandatory systems installed in each separate fire zone.

1. A fixed fire detector and alarm system utilising detectors operated by heat, smoke or other products of combustion or a combination of these factors; or

2. An automatic sprinkler, fire detection and fire alarm system together with a fixed fire detection and alarm system fitted to detect smoke in corridors, stairways and escape routes.

The United Kingdom administration has consistently advocated sprinkler protection since, without human intervention, it provides automatic extinguishing. Other administrations at IMO have argued that this only occurred when the fire was sufficiently

Table 4   IMO fire protection principles.

IMO fire protection principles
1. Division of the ship into main and vertical zones by thermal and structural boundaries.
2. Separation of accommodation spaces from the remainder of the ship by thermal and structural boundaries.
3. Restricted use of combustible materials.
4. Detection of any fire in the zone of origin.
5. Containment and extinction of any fire in the space of origin.
6. Protection of the means of escape or of access for fire fighting purposes.
7. Ready availability of the fire extinguishing appliances.
8. Minimisation of possibility of ignition of flammable cargo vapour.

intense to operate the glass detector head and that considerable volumes of asphyxiating smoke may have been generated before this happens. The new regulation referred to in alternative (2) above meets this eventuality. Furthermore all passenger ships must now be fitted with sprinkler systems by the year 2010 at the latest.

Any person seeing or suspecting that a fire has broken out should call out an alarm, inform other available crew members of the exact location, deck level and space and operate the nearest manual alarm. This will initiate a visible and audible alarm at the bridge control panel. Activation of manually operated call points (and automatic detectors) gives the location of the section where the activation took place. If a signal has not been acted upon within two minutes, it will cause an alarm to be sounded throughout the crew accommodation spaces, control stations and machinery spaces. Manual fire alarm call points are fitted at all exits and no part of a corridor is to be more than 20m from a call point.

If competent to do so, the discoverer may tackle the fire using a portable fire extinguisher or a hose reel (see below) immediately after ensuring that an escape route is available. An operator should never let the fire block the escape route, e.g. from a cabin or from the dead-end of a corridor. Sprinkler systems generally control accommodation fires with rapidity (e.g. by the opening of one or two sprinkler heads). If a sprinkler system is not fitted and the fire cannot be controlled with portable extinguishers, hose parties (with breathing apparatus if necessary) may be quickly assembled. Ventilation should be shut down and doors, windows, sidescuttles and other openings should be closed and not opened—at least until all preparations for entry are complete. Similarly, if the source of the fire is not evident, doors should not be opened to locate the source of smoke or smell until the fire party is ready. Indications of the location of the fire may be wisps of smoke, blistered paint or temperatures of bulkheads or decks, above or below, which are higher than normal. A fire which has been burning in an enclosed space will have reduced the oxygen level. As a result of opening a door, the fire is provided with a generous supply of air which may increase the intensity of burning to the extent that flames and hot gases are violently emitted. Precautionary measures should include cooling the door before approaching the handle from the side of the hinges and ensuring that nobody is standing in way of the opening. The fire can then be tackled using the fire hoses with nozzles attached, permanently connected to hydrants for ready availability, sited within or outside the accommodation. Administrations usually accept smaller diameter lined hoses (e.g. 45 mm) and nozzles which are more suitable for use within accommodation spaces (from ease of handling considerations) as alternatives to the unlined canvas hoses traditionally used in outside locations (63.5 mm). Also, subject to conditions, non-collapsible rubber hose reels are accepted. The latter are always fitted with a stop cock on the nozzle at the end of the hose which can be conveniently unwound with the pressure on by one person. On the other hand, the backup team using larger diameter hoses coupled to hydrants outside the accommodation would advance towards the fire fighting location with empty hoses due to the greater ease of handling them up and down ladders or around corridors. Full hoses are difficult to manhandle especially by firefighters wearing breathing apparatus and consequently the water would not be turned on at the hydrant until the backup team was in position for attacking the fire. At this stage it may be decided to open a ventilator to remove smoke and improve visibility. Although this will induce an air flow, if there is sufficient water available to extinguish the fire by cooling, the extra air will be unimportant.

Structural fire protection

Passenger ships are divided into main vertical zones not exceeding 40 m in length by 'A' class divisions (i.e. divisions constructed of steel which are capable of withstanding a specified fire test for 60 min without the passage of flame or smoke) extending deck to deck and to the shell. These vertical bulkheads and other bulkheads and decks bounding accommodation, public and service spaces are to be insulated to a level which, under test conditions, would limit the rise in temperature to 180°C at any point and to an average rise of 139°C. The standard designations for class 'A' divisions are A60, A30, A15 and A0 which signify that, with the insulation level provided, the divisions complied with the temperature rise limitations under prototype tests for 60, 30, 15 and 0 minutes.

The regulations include tables which state the level of fire integrity required between the various spaces on board ship according to the hazards they present. In this respect, the machinery space boundaries are required to be insulated to A60 standard because of the potential danger of a fire therein spreading into the accommodation. Figure 4 shows three methods of insulating a machinery casing from three tiers of accommodation. In each diagram, the ribands of insulation (shown hatched) are necessary to negate the effect of heat transfer from the machin-

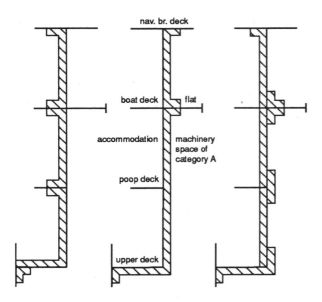

Figure 4   Three methods of insulating a typical machinery casing showing the ribands of insulation at the boundaries and intersections.

ery space along intersecting decks, flats or the ship's side. In the left hand diagram, the casing is insulated on the accommodation side except for the riband at the ship's side plating which could otherwise conduct heat into the accommodation in the event of a machinery space fire. Similarly, ribands are required on the accommodation side at all deck levels.

All the insulation is on the casing side for the centre diagram alternative and this arrangement avoids the need for ribands at the poop deck level. In the right hand diagram, the insulation is fitted on the vertical side of the casing within the accommodation and ribands are necessary at all deck levels.

Divisions between spaces may also be of 'B' class which must be constructed to withstand the passage of flame up to the end of the first 30 min of the standard fire test. 'B' class divisions are to be of

approved non-combustible materials and be capable of limiting average and maximum temperature rises to 139°C and 225°C respectively for 15 mins (B15) or 0 mins (B0).

All penetrations (for pipes, cables, ventilation trunks and access) in fire protection divisions are designed to maintain the integrity and prevent a fire spreading to adjacent spaces. Figure 5 shows the arrangement for penetration of an A60 bulkhead or a machinery casing by a steel pipe. It will be noted that collars of A60 insulation are fitted on the pipe at both sides of the steel bulkhead and its A60 insulation to limit heat transfer between compartments along the pipe. A less complicated arrangement is required for the penetration of a B-class bulkhead (Fig 6). Fire doors and their self-closing and securing arrangements when closed, and ventilator flaps should be checked on a regular and systematic basis. Whenever maintenance on pipes or cables is carried out, particular attention must be paid to ensure that the fire integrity of the system has not been impaired and that sealing arrangements have been replaced. A number of major fires have resulted from fires

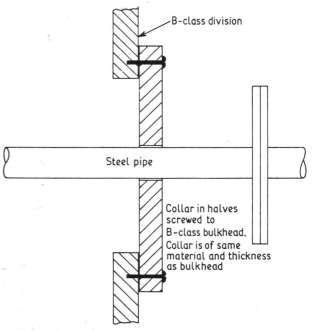

Figure 6   Steel pipe penetrating a B-class bulkhead. (N.B. for B15 division, pipe to be insulated with A15 insulation.)

spreading between compartments through openings because a disturbed system had not been restored to its original condition. Similarly, storerooms have been used for storing materials having a greater fire risk than was catered for in the original design and, on one occasion, a passenger ship became a construc-

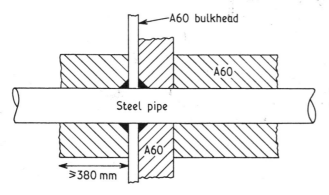

Figure 5   Steel pipe penetration of A60 bulkhead.

tive total loss when a machinery space fire ignited greased engine spares in a storeroom above. Fortunately, the fire was confined within the vertical zone by the transverse fire protection divisions and no lives were lost.

In addition to the prevention of spread of fire by 'A' and 'B' class divisions, limitations are placed on the volume of combustible facings, mouldings and decorative veneers and, in addition, exposed surfaces in accommodation, corridors and stairway enclosures must have low flame spread characteristics.

Automatic sprinkler, fire detection and fire alarm systems

Space limitations do not permit full discussion of fire protection arrangements but in view of the importance of automatic sprinkler systems for accommodation and control and service stations, an introduction to a system suitable for a passenger ship is provided and a schematic representation is shown in Fig 7. The protected spaces are fitted with a network of pipes at deckhead level pressurised with fresh water up to the sprinkler head bulb (3). Each sprinkler head covers a deck area of up to 12m². The sprinklers must be grouped into sections (3 sections are shown diagrammatically in Fig 7), each of not more than 200 sprinklers. Each section must be capable of giving, automatically, a visible and audible alarm on the navigating bridge or in the main (manned) control room following the fall in pressure when a sprinkler comes into operation.

The sprinkler tank pressure of about 5 bar is obtained from the top-up air compressor (10). The fresh water charge is half of the 5000l pressure tank (9) capacity. The minimum volume of this fresh water is to be equal to the amount of water which would be delivered by the sprinkler pump (12) in one minute. The pump and piping must be capable of maintaining the necessary pressure at the level of the highest sprinkler to ensure the simultaneous coverage of a minimum area of 280m² at an application rate of 5 l/m² per minute. The sprinkler pump must be sited remotely from machinery spaces of Category A and be provided with electrical power from the main generator and the emergency generator. One supply

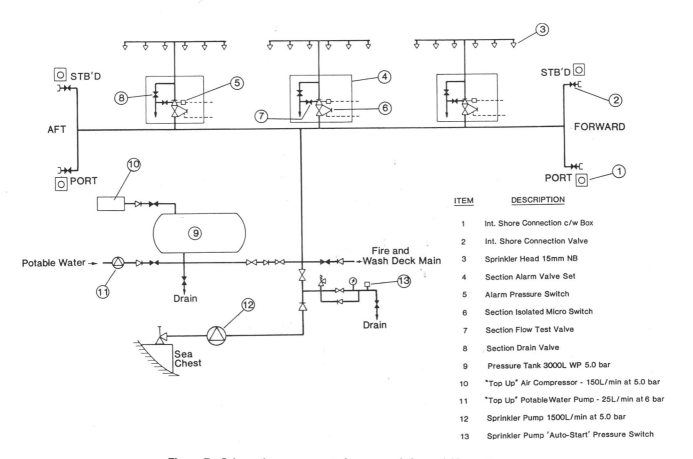

ITEM	DESCRIPTION
1	Int. Shore Connection c/w Box
2	Int. Shore Connection Valve
3	Sprinkler Head 15mm NB
4	Section Alarm Valve Set
5	Alarm Pressure Switch
6	Section Isolated Micro Switch
7	Section Flow Test Valve
8	Section Drain Valve
9	Pressure Tank 3000L WP 5.0 bar
10	"Top Up" Air Compressor - 150L/min at 5.0 bar
11	"Top Up" Potable Water Pump - 25L/min at 6 bar
12	Sprinkler Pump 1500L/min at 5.0 bar
13	Sprinkler Pump 'Auto-Start' Pressure Switch

Figure 7   Schematic arrangement of accommodation sprinkler system.

for the pump motor is to be taken from the main switchboard, and one from the emergency switchboard by separate feeders reserved solely for the purpose. The sprinkler bulbs are designed to operate within the range 68°C to 79°C except in high ambient temperature spaces where the operating temperature may be increased by not more than 30°C above the maximum deckhead temperature. In the glass bulb type, the bulb is filled with coloured liquid (usually having an alcohol base) of very high expansion ratio, leaving a small air bubble. As the temperature rises, the bubble becomes absorbed and the pressure of the liquid shatters the glass at the designed temperature. The pressure in the system forces out the sealing diaphragm, which was held in position by the intact bulb, and the water strikes a serrated plate from which it is deflected upwards and outwards in a fine spray. The water flow through the alarm valve results in operation of the alarm pressure switch (5) and the transmission of a signal to the bridge alarm panel. As the pressure in the system falls further, the sprinkler pump cuts in and supplies sea water to the affected section (a non-return valve prevents sea water entering the pressure tank).

The pressure fall in the pressure tank is sensed by the 'auto start' pressure switch (13) and the sprinkler pump discharges sea water into the system without contaminating the pressure tank. Sea water may also be supplied via a non-return valve from the fire and wash deck main from the ship's pumps or through the international shore connection.

After the fire is extinguished, the sprinkler pump is stopped and the relevant section valve is closed. The piping system is flushed through with fresh water through valve connections provided for the purpose. The sprinkler head(s) must be replaced by new bulbs of the same type and operating temperature. The section valve is opened and the piping system and the pressure tank are refilled with fresh water from the 'top up' pump (11). The system is bled of air through the release valves and checked for leakage. The tank is pressurised from the compressor. Finally the compressor and fresh water supply valves are closed.

Routine tests

The pressure tank level and pressure should be checked daily and topped up using the pump (11) and compressor (10) as necessary. It should also be ascertained that all valves are in their correct positions and that the pressure tank, fire and wash deck main and section valves are locked open. All alarms should be tested weekly.

At least monthly, the system should be checked by opening the section flow test valve (7) for a few seconds to ascertain that the alarm operates and that the correct section is indicated on the bridge control panel. In addition, the sprinkler pump and its automatic starting arrangements should be tested. During the test, the valve between the sprinkler system and the fire and wash deck main and the pump discharge valve should be closed and the drain valve opened. The pump output thus flows into the bilges and contamination of the system is avoided. After the tests, the level of water and the pressure within the sprinkler tank are restored and all valves must be reset to their correct positions.

It might be emphasised here that the system described above should properly be entitled 'automatic sprinkler, fire detection and fire alarm system' in contrast to the 'fixed pressure water spraying systems' used for the protection of machinery spaces, pump rooms and car decks. These systems are manually operated and the pipes between the spray nozzles and the section distribution valves are dry.

CARGO SHIP ACCOMMODATION SPACES

The comments made with regard to passenger ships also apply to cargo ships, except that for ships built before September 1984, virtually the only mandatory provision concerning structural fire protection arrangements and alarm systems, was that 'B' class panels should be fitted on corridor bulkheads with the objective of protecting the escape routes. In recent years (September 1984 and 1985) step changes in the standard of protection have increased to the extent that newly built cargo ships have systems as extensive as some older passenger ships.

Structural fire protection for a cargo ship is now achieved by one of three methods, 1C, 2C or 3C, depending upon whether:

a) the internal divisional bulkheading is of non-combustible material to prescribed standards (1C);

b) there is no restriction on internal bulkheading (i.e. chipboard may be used) but there is the compensation of a sprinkler system (2C);

c) there is no restriction on internal bulkheading except that no area not bounded by 'A' or 'B' class divisions may exceed 50m and a fixed fire detection and fire alarm system is provided (3C).

As in the case of passenger ships, tables are provided which indicate the fire integrity required for bulkheads separating adjacent spaces, there are regulatory restrictions on the volume of combustible material on exposed surfaces, special arrangements are prescribed for the protection of stairways and lift trunks, and doors fitted in machinery space boundary bulkheads must be reasonably gas tight and self closing. This last provision is negated if, as sometimes happens, boiler room doors are tied open. Serious accommodation fires have resulted from the spread of flames from machinery space fires through open doors.

Irrespective of the method adopted, machinery space boundaries must be of A60 standards, corridor bulkheads must be of at least 'B' class integrity, decks separating adjacent spaces must be of 'A' class integrity or higher, and all ships built since September 1985 are required to be provided with smoke detectors in corridors and over stairways within accommodation spaces.

In addition, for oil, gas and chemical tankers, the exterior boundaries of superstructures and deckhouses enclosing accommodation spaces and control stations have to be insulated to A60 standard for the portions facing the cargo area and on their sides for 3m from the boundary facing the cargo area. No doors into the accommodation must be fitted in this boundary, and sidescuttles and windows (except for wheelhouse windows) must be of a non-opening type. Windows must not be fitted in the first tier of superstructures. Sidescuttles in this tier must be fitted with deadlights, and there are restrictions on higher tiers. Also air inlets and other openings are not permitted.

For tankers there are restrictions regarding the location of spaces in SOLAS and, for gas and chemical tankers, in the relevant mandatory codes. For example, in oil tankers, machinery spaces and accommodation spaces, main cargo control stations and certain other spaces must be positioned aft of cargo tanks, slop tanks and cargo pump rooms because of the danger of flammable gases being ignited. Also, machinery spaces must be isolated from cargo tanks and slop tanks by cofferdams, cargo pump rooms, oil fuel bunker tanks or permanent ballast tanks because of the possibility of leakage through boundary bulkheads of flammable liquids or flammable vapours in sufficient quantities to form explosive mixtures.

In all classes of vessels, the regulations call for two means of escape from all accommodation, service spaces and machinery spaces, and require stairways and ladders to be provided to the open deck and thence to lifeboats. All seafarers should familiarise themselves with the means of escape from any space in which they may be employed.

DRY CARGO SPACES

When it was common practice for ships to be fitted with wooden hatch boards, many ships were provided with steam smothering systems intended for the extinguishing of fires in cargo holds. The value of steam in practical situations, principally due to condensation, is limited and it is not now acceptable for new ships. Under the current regulations, only ships carrying cargoes considered by an administration to constitute a low fire risk, may be exempted from the requirement for a fixed gas fire extinguishing system. This exemption implies that the cargo hold can be rendered relatively air-tight and that an outbreak of fire will die out or at least be limited in intensity by lack of oxygen. The regulations specify that if dangerous goods are carried, a fixed smothering gas installation must be provided and most ships carry some classes of dangerous goods during their lifetime. The extinguishing medium invariably chosen is carbon dioxide rather than a halon. The advantages of using halons lie in their rapid application and low production of toxic compounds, but these advantages cannot be realised in cargo holds and, for deep seated smouldering fires, a greater weight of halons than carbon dioxide is required for control.

If the cargo hatches are open, it may be possible to extinguish a cargo hold fire with fire hose spray nozzles to limit slack water effects on the ship's stability and unnecessary damage to cargo. Concurrently, preparations should be made for rapid closing of the hatches and subsequent release of carbon dioxide (if fitted). Should the fire be deep seated, the best procedure is to close the hatches and ventilator flaps and cover the cowls with tarpaulins which should be kept wetted.

If the hatches are closed when a fire is discovered, sufficient carbon dioxide for that hold would normally be admitted (provision is made for admission of variable quantities of gas). The hatches should not be opened until the temperature in the hold and at the bulkheads has been normal for at least 24 hours. Water should not be pumped from the hold since air may be drawn into the space and negate the smothering operation. In cases where the fire cannot be controlled with carbon dioxide the hatches should not, as far as possible, be opened until the ship is in port and the local fire brigade is available to assist.

Since carbon dioxide has limited cooling effect the fire may not be extinguished until the cargo has cooled down and, if hatches are opened, the air admitted may cause the fire to flare up. Consequently, only the minimum area of hatch opening should be used and fire hoses should be at the ready. Preparations for closing the hatches and re-admitting carbon dioxide should be made.

In ships not fitted with a smothering system, the hold should be completely closed down and the deck and any accessible bulkheads kept cool using hose water sprays unless, depending upon the type of cargo, it is possible to locate the seat of the fire from paint blisters or high temperatures and admit water directly onto the fire. However, it should be remembered that the damage caused by water is often greater than the damage caused by the fire itself.

There is, of course, always the possibility of the fire spreading to adjacent holds. Therefore continual local observations should be made for any indications of this and, if smoke detectors are fitted, continual attention should be given to them.

Once in port, trained firemen with breathing apparatus will attempt to reach the seat of the fire whilst the cargo is simultaneously discharged. Supplies of carbon dioxide will be available and if smoke and heat prevent unloading, the hatches may be closed and carbon dioxide injected through temporary connections if necessary. This procedure of alternately unloading and closing down and injecting carbon dioxide may have to be repeated several times.

The above description covers only substances which do not require special firefighting procedures and not those which, because of their high oxygen content (e.g. nitrates including saltpetre and chlorates), cannot be extinguished by carbon dioxide or steam or those which react violently with water (e.g. carbide, sodium, magnesium). Detailed procedures for dealing with these substances and bulk chemicals and gases are outside the scope of this chapter.

FIRES IN CONTAINERS

Fires in containers in holds should be dealt with in a similar manner as for general cargo holds, i.e. flaps in ventilator trunks should be closed and the refrigerating machinery and ventilation for any reefers stowed therein should be shut down. An appropriate quantity of carbon dioxide should be admitted and checks made on the temperatures of the boundaries and also those within the hold by means of thermometers lowered down sounding pipes.

The hold should be kept closed down for a least 48 hours and until the fire is likely to be totally extinguished. Arrangements should be made to have the local fire brigade present when the hold is unloaded.

If a fire breaks out in a container stowed on deck, the vessel should be turned to a course such that the flames blow away from it and speed reduced to the minimum navigable speed. The contents of the container will determine whether water spray, dry powder, or foam will be used for extinguishing purposes. Water should only be used in the form of a spray since strong water jets will spread burning material. Adjacent containers should be kept cool by water sprays during the operation. If necessary, a hole may be punched at the position of greatest heat in an exposed side of the container with, for example, the pike end of a fireman's hatchet. If the cargo therein is not exceptionally valuable and water is a suitable agent, the container may be completely flooded. In the case of very valuable cargoes, carbon dioxide may be discharged in sufficient quantity (say six portable extinguishers) and the hole plugged. The extinguishing gas would be topped up hourly and the exterior of the container and those surrounding it kept cool by water spray.

TANKER CARGO TANK PROTECTION

The precise requirements for cargo tank protection (and for fires on deck) for oil tankers are complicated but, broadly speaking, inert gas systems are required for all tankers over 40,000 tons deadweight and all other tankers with crude oil washing systems or using high capacity (over 60 m^3/h) tank washing machines.

Fires and explosions in unprotected cargo tanks of oil tankers can have a wide variety of causes. One specific instance is the use of high capacity tank washing machines and consequential generation of high levels of static electricity (which has been extensively investigated). However, regardless of the mechanism of the production of incendive sparks or potential source of ignition, it is impossible for a fire or explosion to take place in an intact tank in which the atmosphere has been rendered inert by the reduction of the oxygen level. This reduction is normally achieved by treating the flue gases from the ship's boilers and directing them into the cargo tanks to displace the gases in the tank atmosphere until the oxygen level falls below 8%.

It is important to recognise that the certainty of preventing ignition refers to a fire or explosion in an intact and inerted tank. Should an inerted tank be breached, then the concentration of hydrocarbon gases when diluted in the atmosphere could produce an incendiary mixture although the probability is less than for a non-inerted tank. Similarly, an inert gas system does not afford out of tank protection in the case of deck spills of cargo.

Inert gas systems

Figure 8 shows a flue gas system for inerting the cargo tanks. Flue gas is obtained from one or more boiler uptakes and passed to the scrubber. In the

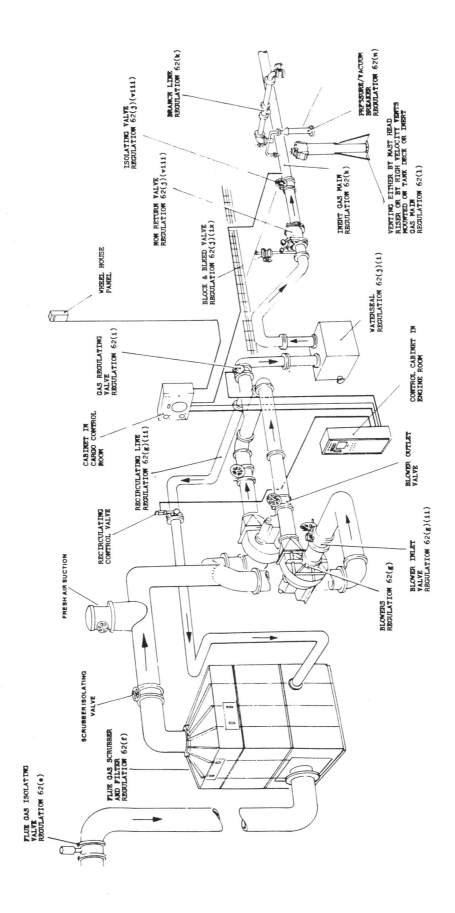

FLUE GAS ISOLATING
VALVE
REGULATION 62(e)

FLUE GAS SCRUBBER
AND FILTER
REGULATION 62(f)

SCRUBBER ISOLATING
VALVE

FRESH AIR SUCTION

RECIRCULATING
CONTROL VALVE

RECIRCULATING LINE
REGULATION 62(g)(ii)

CABINET IN
CARGO CONTROL
ROOM

GAS REGULATING
VALVE
REGULATION 62(i)

WHEEL HOUSE
PANEL

BLOCK & BLEED VALVE
REGULATION 62(j)(ix)

NON RETURN VALVE
REGULATION 62(j)(viii)

ISOLATING VALVE
REGULATION 62(j)(viii)

BRANCH LINE
REGULATION 62(k)

PRESSURE/VACUUM
BREAKER
REGULATION 62(m)

VENTING EITHER BY MAST HEAD
RISER OR BY HIGH VELOCITY VENTS
MOUNTED ON TANK DECK OR INERT
GAS MAIN
REGULATION 62(l)

INERT GAS MAIN
REGULATION 62(k)

WATERSEAL
REGULATION 62(j)(i)

CONTROL CABINET IN
ENGINE ROOM

BLOWER OUTLET
VALVE

BLOWER INLET
VALVE
REGULATION 62(g)(ii)

BLOWERS
REGULATION 62(g)

Figure 8 Flue gas system for inerting cargo tanks.

scrubber, the gas is 'washed' to reduce the sulphur dioxide and solid particles to an acceptable level and cooled. A demister or equivalent device reduces the entrained water before the gas is drawn into one of the two blowers. Normally, the blower output is led to the gas regulating valve and to a recirculating valve having a line connecting back to the scrubber. The gas regulating valve, in conjunction with the recirculating valve, controls the output of the plant and closes in the event of a fault condition. As the demand for inert gas falls, the gas regulating valve closes and the gas recirculating valve opens to allow a proportion of the gas to return to the scrubber and prevent overheating of the fan. The gas regulating valve must be located at the forward bulkhead of the most forward space into which the entry of hydrocarbon gases would produce hazards with regard to flammability and toxicity, through which the inert gas supply main passes.

The gas passing to the distribution system enters a deck water seal. This seal is necessary to allow the passage of inert gas to the tanks and yet prevent gases from the tanks passing in the opposite direction in the event of pressure being present in the tanks (which may occur particularly during the loading operation). In addition to the deck seal, a second non-return device is required (this is normally a conventional non-return valve having positive means of closure) to prevent liquids and higher vapour pressures passing back through the inert gas system. As an additional safeguard against the possible leakage of hydrocarbon liquids or vapours back from the deck main, means have to be provided to permit the section of the line between the non-return valve having positive means of closure and the gas regulating valve to be vented in a safe manner when the non-return valve has been manually closed.

The cargo tanks must be protected against both pressure and vacuum. Small volumes of vapour mixtures caused by natural aspiration of the cargo tanks are relieved by means of the pressure/vacuum valves set to operate at water gauge pressures of 1900 mm (positive) and 400 mm (negative) respectively. Protection against large volumes of vapour/air mixtures during cargo loading and ballasting or during discharging is provided, typically, by high velocity vents fitted on each cargo tank, high velocity vent valves fitted in the inert gas main, or by masthead risers.

Inert gas generators

Although inert gases for cargo tank protection are normally obtained from boiler uptakes, inert gas generators are sometimes fitted. For example, if the boilers are not capable of producing inert gas of the correct quality or if the purity restrictions on cargo quality cannot be met by flue gases, independent gas generators may be fitted. These generators burn light oils and, unless the above-mentioned considerations apply, they will normally be inappropriate from economical considerations as they burn about one kilogramme of oil for every 17 m^3 of inert gas produced. Gas generators are extremely valuable for 'topping up' purposes when inert gas used in cargo operations is obtained from auxiliary boilers not normally in use at sea.

Operational aspects

Crew training and motivation is of prime importance if the inert gas installation is to provide the protection expected of it. The system must be operated with complete understanding. It must be maintained to standards which will ensure its continued operation and reliability. Although careful design and choice of materials are essential it must be backed up by a commitment of shore management, clear operating instructions and considerable training of ships' staffs.

A major problem may occur due to the difficulty of obtaining an adequate supply of inert gas of low oxygen content from the existing boilers. In a modern well operated boiler on normal load the volumetric composition of the inert gas, after scrubbing, will approximate to:

nitrogen	80%
carbon dioxide	12–14%
oxygen	2–4%
sulphur dioxide	0.2–0.3%
carbon monoxide	trace
oxides of nitrogen	trace.

However, on low load in port when the back pressure of the discharge is low, it may be difficult to limit the oxygen content to 5% in the inert gas supply. It may therefore be necessary to put a load on the boiler by, for example, pumping water from the sea and discharging it overboard (taking great care, of course, to avoid pollution).

Every tanker must, under SOLAS regulations, carry manuals containing full details of the plant and covering its operations, safety and maintenance requirements, occupational health hazards (inert gas is highly toxic) and emergency procedures. Only a few general points can be made here. In brief, an inert gas pressure must be maintained in all tanks, which are not required to be gas free, at all times. The oxygen content in the tanks must not rise above 8% but a lower figure should be aimed for. During a loaded passage, a positive pressure should be maintained in the ullage spaces by topping up. The low pressure alarm should be regularly tested.

If the oxygen analyser in the flue gas measuring system becomes faulty or inoperative, arrangements for a replacement at the next port must be made and, until a repair is effected, the system should be kept in operation using portable oxygen meters.

However, if the inert gas system becomes defective and cannot meet the above requirements and a repair cannot be made, emergency procedures formulated by Industry and IMO must be observed. For crude oil tankers, it is essential that cargo tanks be maintained in an inerted condition due to the danger of pyrophoric iron sulphide being exposed to oxygen and the subsequent rapid exothermic oxidation heating individual particles to incandescence and causing an explosion. The iron sulphide is formed by the combination of iron oxide (rust) and hydrogen sulphide in atmospheres where the oxygen content is lower than that of the hydrogen sulphide. There is thus no alternative for crude oil tankers but to close down the cargo system and cease cargo operations until either the system is repaired or an external supply of inert gas is provided.

For product tankers detailed emergency procedures are listed which include severe restrictions on tank dipping, ullaging and sampling.

Maintenance, safety checks and log books for inert gas systems

The earliest attempts to introduce inert gas systems were unsuccessful because of the difficulties in maintaining them in a reliable condition. Even with the better system design and more appropriate materials, present day systems require continual maintenance. Details of the systems fitted on board are included in the statutorily required manuals. The following intervals between inspections are suggested as representative of good practice:

Every 6 months

Flame arresters and screens; pressure vacuum valves; blower impellers flushed and examined through inspection openings; scrubber water level regulators; scrubber alarm, probes, sprayers, baffles etc.; deck water seal level controls, valves and alarm floats; and internals of high velocity vent valves.

Every 30 months

Flue gas isolating valves; blowers opened up for survey of interior, impeller and bearing; scrubber opened up for examination of protective lining, weirs and packing; cargo tank isolating arrangements; pressure vacuum breakers; liquid breaker opened up

for internal survey and/or mechanical breaker dismantled for survey.

All these inspections should be recorded in the maintenance log book and signed by the appropriate officer or surveyor.

Statutory surveys

Intermediate surveys of the internal parts of the scrubber, deck water seal and pressure/vacuum release arrangements are not practicable when the system is in operation. Also, the back flow prevention function of the deck water seal cannot be tested whilst the cargo tanks are inerted. As an alternative to the test, the internal condition of the seal must be established by a thorough examination for corrosion and erosion and by verification of the structural dimensions necessary to form the required levels in the seal. This examination should be undertaken when the ship is gas free as it is probable that the deck isolating valve and the non-return valves are insufficiently tight to allow the operation to be conducted safely.

In view of these difficulties, surveyors will normally accept, in conjunction with their own observations of the system, an inspection report by the chief engineer officer which provides details of the operation, maintenance and repair of the system. However, all major items should be seen by a surveyor within any five year period.

Safety checks of inert gas systems

A safety log book should be kept which should include the date of the check and the signature of the responsible officer. Every month, freedom of movement checks of valves should include the following: deck isolating valve; deck non-return valve; pressure vacuum valves; and high velocity valves. The blowers should be checked for vibration and the casing drains proved clear. The operation of the gas pressure regulating valves should be checked.

In addition, the following alarms should be tested and the settings checked: high oxygen supply; high inert gas (ig) temperature; blower failure; scrubber low water pressure/flow; scrubber high water level; power failure to instruments and control systems; high and low ig pressure; and low deck water seal. Prior to discharge of cargo the calibration of the oxygen meter should be checked and it should be ascertained that the ig system shuts down on: failure of blowers; high ig temperature; scrubber low water level/flow; and scrubber high water level.

Operations log book

The operations log book should be completed daily when the cargo tanks are inerted and hourly when the inert gas system is in use. All entries should be initialled by the responsible officer. The information to be recorded should include: the date and time; the oxygen level in the supply main and in the tank; the tank pressures; the time the blower is in use and that the deck seal level has been checked.

Tanker deck fires

Tanker companies operate stringent procedures before and during cargo operations and fires on deck are fortunately infrequent but their effects may be disastrous. Consequently foam installations consisting of monitors and foam applicators are required on ships built after May 1981 and many older vessels are fitted with less comprehensive systems discharging low expansion foam.

It is essential when using foam to ensure that there is a sufficient supply of foam solution available to maintain an adequate rate of discharge to control the fire. If the supply is interrupted or otherwise inadequate, the heat will break down the foam blanket and the fire will burn back.

On the outbreak of a tanker deck fire, the general alarm should be sounded (and if in port, the ship's whistle would be sounded to alert shore personnel, and the local fire department's help requested). The cargo pumps and cargo valves must be shut down to reduce the supply of fuel and the foam system should be activated. Foam from the nearest foam monitor, on the windward side of the fire, between the fire and the accommodation block would be lobbed onto the near edge of the fire. The foam blanket would be steadily formed by side to side movement of the nozzle until the spill area is completely covered. Any areas shielded from the monitor stream would be covered by foam from the foam applicators. During the operation, the fire-fighters would be protected as necessary by a fine spray curtain from fire main hose nozzles which would not be allowed to dilute or otherwise destroy the foam blanket. In such situations, foam is the only medium which remains effective after it has been discharged. If the supply of foam is depleted before the fire is controlled, the action would be continued using as many hoselines and fine spray nozzles as could be manned from the windward side of the fire. The firefighters would advance only slowly and never so far as would endanger themselves through a possible flashback. The attack would be continued until all surfaces had been cooled down, the fuel supply shut down and the flammable liquid washed overboard.

Pumproom protection

Despite all possible precautions being taken to pre-vent leakages of pipe joints and pump glands, pumprooms must be treated as gas dangerous spaces. Any leakages into the bilges will result in toxic and flammable oil vapours, heavier than air, concentrating in the lower regions of the space where the main sources of ignition are situated. The space cannot be inerted since access by ship's personnel is necessary. Consequently, the space must be continually ventilated and should never be entered unless the fans have been running for a considerable length of time. In some companies, permanent notices caution that the pumproom must not be entered unless the officer of the watch has been informed and someone is standing by.

Effective maintenance is necessary to prevent overheating of cargo pump bearings which can lead to the failure of the pump glands providing both an ignition source and a flammable gas mixture.

Whilst the temperature of steam used in pumprooms is mandatorily restricted to well below the auto-ignition temperature of the petroleum carried, this is not a certain protection if the lagging becomes saturated with the heavy ends of petroleum. Oxidation will take place if air can obtain access to the wetted lagging and the exothermic reaction can raise the temperature to above the auto-ignition temperature and the spontaneous ignition may result in burning material falling into the bilges and causing a major fire should oil be present.

Carbon dioxide appears to be the most practicable total flooding system for pumproom protection. The customary precaution of ensuring that nobody is in the space before release must be observed. Also, the avoidance of its use for inerting the space in the presence of flammable mixtures is necessary because of the possibility of the generation of static electricity causing an explosion. The effectiveness of carbon dioxide depends upon the ability to seal the space effectively. Nevertheless, it is advisable to leave a door slightly ajar during discharge to release air and avoid overpressure blowing out the pump shaft seals. The door should be closed immediately injection is complete and the space kept effectively sealed until all heated surfaces have cooled.

MACHINERY SPACE PROTECTION

Statutory protective measures

Considering the conditions for the initiation of a fire or explosion, it will be readily appreciated that since the machinery spaces are habitable, oxygen will always be present. Furthermore, although care is taken to limit sources of ignition, it can never be guaranteed that incendiary sparks, heat and flame can be eliminated.

Fire prevention is consequently based on limiting the availability of fuel in a condition in which it may be accidentally ignited in the prevailing circumstances. The means of achieving this objective include the following.

a) Adequate ventilation to prevent the concentration of vapours reaching the lower flammable limit (LFL);

b) limiting the flammability of the oil fuel by restricting the flash point;

c) prescribing arrangements for the stowage, distribution and utilisation of the fuel and lubricating oil systems;

d) good operating practices.

The principal regulations are as follows.

1. The flash point of the oil fuel carried shall not be less than 60°C.

2. Oil fuel systems containing heated fuel at a pressure exceeding 1.8 bar gauge must be in illuminated locations so that defects and leakage can be readily observed.

3. Suitable drip trays must be provided around any pumps, filters or heaters from which oil may spill and arrangements must prevent spraying of oil onto heated surfaces.

4. Oil fuel tanks shall, where necessary, be provided with save-alls or gutters which will catch any oil which may leak from the tank; oil tanks shall not be sited directly above boilers or other heated surfaces.

5. Shut off valves outside the machinery spaces must be provided for the outlets of all fuel oil storage and settling tanks. In the event of evacuation of the machinery space, these valves would be closed to limit the possibility of oil feeding a fire.

6. Special arrangements must be made for measuring the amount of oil in oil fuel tanks. Sounding pipes are permitted only if their upper ends terminate in safe positions.

7. Provisions shall be made which will prevent overpressure in any oil fuel tank, oil fuel filling pipe or any part of the oil fuel system. Air and overflow pipes and relief valves must discharge to a position where there will be no risk of fire or explosion from the emergence of oil or oil vapour.

8. Every oil fuel pipe must be made of steel or other suitable material.

Additional requirements for ships with periodically unmanned machinery spaces

In addition to the above stipulations, for periodically unmanned machinery spaces, the requirements include the following.

1. Where necessary, oil fuel and lubricating oil pipelines shall be screened to avoid, as far as practicable, oil spray or oil leakages onto hot surfaces or into machinery air intakes. The number of joints should be kept to a minimum and, where practicable, leakages from high pressure fuel pipes shall be collected and arrangements provided for an alarm to be given.

2. In these ships every oil fuel tank that directly supplies the main propulsion machinery or its auxiliaries and which is arranged to be filled automatically or by remote control must be provided with means to prevent overflow and spillage. Every such tank and settling tank fitted with oil fuel heating arrangements must be provided with a high temperature alarm if the flash point of the oil therein can be exceeded.

3. In addition, the equipment (such as oil fuel purifiers) for preparing flammable liquids for use in boilers or machinery must have arrangements to prevent overflow and spillages and, so far as it is reasonable and practicable, be installed in a space appropriated solely for such equipment and their heaters.

4. An efficient fixed fire detection and fire alarm system complying with the IMO specification has to be fitted and satisfactorily tested under varying conditions of engine operation and ventilation.

Observations on the prevention and detection arrangements

Although the IMO regulations provide for the use of low flash point fuel, it must be emphasised that this is only permissible when special arrangements and procedures have been approved by the administration. Unauthorised admission or use of low flash point fuel is extremely dangerous.

For example, loss of life on a small UK registered coastal tanker resulted from an ingenious but unauthorised arrangement within the machinery spaces. Modifications to the fire and wash deck pump enabled a vacuum to be put on the deck fire main. A portable hose was then connected to a fire hydrant and used for stripping low flash point cargoes. Unfortunately, when the pump valve chest was opened up, a flammable concentration of oil vapour was released into the engine room and exploded. In oil tankers, serious explosions have occurred in engine rooms following leakage of crude oil and vapours from pumprooms through the bulkhead glands of cargo pump drive shafts. Unauthorised introduction of crude oil into the fuel oil system is an extremely dangerous practice which resulted in the deaths of 76 people in an oil tanker under repair, when the oil fuel bunker containing crude oil exploded following hot work on deck. In addition to their provision in periodically unmanned machinery spaces, fixed fire detection and alarm systems are required in ships where the propulsion and associated machinery is under continuous manned supervision from a control room. Smoke detectors are the usual choice, but they may need to be supplemented by other types of detectors because of smoke dilution, particularly in large machinery spaces when the height of the engine room crown above the deck below exceeds about 10 metres.

FIRE FIGHTING ARRANGEMENTS

Machinery spaces are provided with extinguishing equipment intended to cope with fires of various levels of severity. The first level of provision includes sand and portable and semi-portable extinguishers. The next level includes fire hoses with spray nozzles and portable foam applicator units connected to the fire main and provided with a portable tank containing at least 20 litres of foam-making liquid.

If it is not possible to extinguish a fire outbreak with the above equipment and the space has to be evacuated and closed down, one of the following fixed installations would be available:

1. a gas system; or

2. a high expansion foam system; or

3. a pressure water spraying system.

The regulations specify the requirements for each of these systems. It will be noted that steam smothering and low expansion foam systems are not now accepted as primary arrangements although they may continue to be used on existing ships. Whilst steam in its gaseous (i.e. invisible and uncondensed) state is a good extinguishing medium, in ships' systems it may rapidly condense to form visible water particles and is not always effective as a smothering medium.

Low expansion foam was a useful medium in the days when the major fire hazard was from tank top fires due to such causes as burning oil flowing from furnaces of smoke tube boilers. Today, with the preponderance of diesel engines, the principal fire hazards arise above tank top level (60% of fires are due to fuel and lubricating oil pipe failures). However, low expansion foam, having a maximum expansion ratio of 12 to 1, may be used even in new ships in addition to the prescribed primary systems, subject to specified conditions, including the discharge in 5 minutes of sufficient foam to provide a depth of 150 mm over the largest area over which oil fuel is likely to spread.

Total flooding gas systems

Fixed gas systems normally utilise carbon dioxide, which extinguishes fire by diluting the atmosphere to a point where the oxygen content will no longer support combustion. Halon gases e.g. halon 1301 or halon 1211 (which interfere with the chemical reaction of flame propagation in the burning material as described above) should no longer be fitted. With carbon dioxide, the aim is to clear the space of personnel, shut off supplies of air and fuel and inject the gases as quickly as practicable. Regulations require the provision of an automatic audible warning which must operate for a suitable period before the gas is released; 85% of the charge must be injected in 2 minutes.

Carbon dioxide installations are of either the high pressure multi-cylinder or the low pressure bulk storage tank type. The latter is particularly suitable where very large spaces are to be protected. Up to 50% saving in weight is possible together with lower cost and the merit of simplicity. However, bulk storage installations require ancillary equipment, e.g. duplicate refrigerating units (see below) and, in some trades, replenishment may present difficulties.

For multiple cylinder installations, arrangements differ according to the manufacturer but several aspects are common. All cylinders are fitted with an internal pipe to ensure that liquid only is discharged and freezing-up at the cylinder outlet is prevented. Since it would be impossible to manually open all the cylinders in the bank simultaneously, gas pressure is utilised. In one arrangement, the operator in the control position releases the gas from master cylinders in the CO_2 room by means of a manual pull wire. The CO_2 from these cylinders acts on the pistons of a gang release system. Movement of the piston actuates a system of levers attached to the cylinder head valves which, by means of a special cutter, release the gas to the manifold. The released gas then passes to a control valve at the control station and thence to the diffuser heads in the protected space. The operating arrangement for this valve should be arranged so that the control cabinet door cannot be closed with the valve in the closed position.

In all systems, concise instructions must be provided at the control position and a warning should be sounded when the cabinet door is opened. This door is usually locked and the key kept in a glass-fronted box adjacent to the control cabinet with a special hammer to shatter the glass attached. Notwithstanding this warning arrangement and the provision of a gas operated siren in the CO_2 discharge line within the machinery space, it must be emphasised that all persons should be accounted for before the gas is released.

The SOLAS requirements for CO_2 systems are not detailed and the statutory regulations for low pressure bulk storage carbon dioxide systems, in particular, depend on the national administration. The United Kingdom requirements include: an additional 5% over the calculated capacity (see below) because of possible non-availability of supplies; duplicated refrigerating units arranged for automatic standby duties; an automatic alarm, at no more than 2% loss of contents, powered from two sources (including the emergency source of power); one complete refrigerating unit powered by the emergency source of power; and duplicate relief valve arrangements on a change-over valve assembly to permit replacements during service whilst maintaining relief capability.

Storage of CO₂ smothering gas

CO_2 cylinders or bulk storage tanks should be stored in a space solely for that purpose. The space should be well ventilated and illuminated, dry, and accessible from the open deck by a person wearing breathing apparatus. It should not present hazards to personnel in the event of leakage, and the temperature should not exceed 60°C. It should not be accessible directly from machinery, accommodation or cargo spaces and there should be sufficient headroom and space for maintenance and servicing (e.g. weighing cylinders).

Capacity of CO₂ installations

For the purpose of calculating the amount of gas required to protect a space, the volume of free CO_2 is calculated at 0.56 m³/kg.

For machinery spaces the minimum volume of free gas, so calculated, must be the larger of the following volumes.

1. 40% of the gross volume of the largest machinery space so protected, the volume to exclude that part of the casing above the level at which the horizontal area of the casing is 40% or less of the horizontal area of the space concerned taken midway between the tank top and the lowest part of the casing.

2. 35% of the gross volume of the largest machinery space protected, including the casing.

By comparison, for cargo spaces (which can be much more effectively sealed) the corresponding minimum volume is only 30% of the gross volume of the largest cargo space to be protected.

One disadvantage of gaseous systems compared with water or foam is the possibility of inadvertent (and often undetected) admission to a space occupied by personnel. This has occurred with fatal consequences despite the preventative provisions in the regulations. Probably the greatest danger arises in port or in a shipyard when repairs and maintenance are being carried out and ventilation is shut down. In such circumstances, the leakage of colourless, odourless CO_2 into a machinery space may proceed undetected until personnel are overcome. As a precaution, blanks are often inserted into the gas discharge line to the space. On occasions, these blanks have not been removed before ships return to service and total losses from fire have resulted. It is essential, if blanks (or any similar measures) are taken, that responsibility for their removal is clearly allocated and a written statement referring to the measures taken is made in a log book to ensure that the installation is returned to service conditions.

Fixed pressure water spraying systems

These systems must be capable of ensuring an effective average distribution of at least 5 l/m² per minute in the protected spaces. In higher hazard areas substantially increased application rates are necessary.

The system must be kept charged and the pump supplying the water must start automatically on a pressure drop in the system. The pump, its air supply and power source and controls must be outside the protected space and must not be affected by a fire in that space.

Although the system may be divided into sections (the distribution valves for which must be outside the protected space), the pump must be capable of supplying all sections simultaneously.

The pump may be used for other than machinery space systems if the requirements for all protected spaces are met. Thus, water spray systems for the protection of special category spaces on passenger ships and vehicle decks may be supplied by the same pump as the machinery space pressure water spraying system.

High expansion foam systems

Any system fitted to comply with the fixed fire extinguishing system requirements must be capable of filling the greatest space to be protected at a rate of at least one metre depth per minute. The quantity available must be sufficient to produce a volume of foam not less than 5 times the volume of the largest space to be protected and the expansion ratio of the foam must not be greater than 1,000 to 1.

The arrangement of supply ducts for distributing foam, the air ducts to the foam generator and the number of foam-making units must be sufficient to provide effective foam production and distribution. The foam generator, its sources of power, foam-making liquid and means of control must be readily accessible, simple to operate and grouped in as few locations as possible not likely to be cut off in the event of fire. The arrangement of ducting for delivering foam must be such that a fire in the protected space will not affect the foam generating equipment.

High expansion foams have not found popularity in ships where there is difficulty in ensuring that the foam could fill the protected space without voids unless a large number of large supply ducts and foam making units were provided. The availability of sufficient crew members to operate the system in an emergency would also present problems.

Observations on fixed installations

The problems facing the ship's staff following an outbreak of a developing fire include deciding whether to use the system and close down the space and, having done so, when to re-enter the space.

The factors influencing a decision to continue to fight the fire will include the damage which a water drenching system would cause to equipment and its effect on stability; the loss of the charge of a gas installation and the loss of use of the machinery space and its systems until the space can be opened up, ventilated and the machinery put back into service.

With the benefit of hindsight when reviewing casualty reports, it is generally apparent when the decision has been delayed too long and the fire has developed rapidly to uncontrollable proportions despite the efforts to control it. On some occasions, the fire has spread outside the machinery space before the fixed installation has been operated. On the other hand, severe fires have been extinguished by use of fire hoses or foam applicators and a shut down of the machinery space has been avoided.

Virtually all ships' staff have attended fire courses and it would be presumptive to express opinions as to how they might act even when the suggestions are based on studies or reported incidents since no two situations are identical. Those responsible for the safety of the installation must be familiar with the lay-out of the machinery space and escapes, the position of all equipment and its controls and the potential hazards. With this knowledge, they would no doubt carry out exercises based on the potential hazards and consider their intended actions in the event of a serious outbreak. This prior consideration would undoubtedly increase the probability of effective action being taken rapidly in an actual outbreak.

Emergency fire pumps

Shutting down the machinery space will normally mean that the fire pumps therein are not available. However, the regulations provide that, in any ship, where a fire in any one compartment could put all the prescribed fire pumps out of action, there must be an alternative means, consisting of a fixed independently driven emergency pump capable of supplying at least two jets of water. Its capacity must be at least 25 cubic metres per hour.

To fulfil its emergency purpose, this pump should be truly independent and this has not always been the case. In some ships the pump has been sited in an adjacent compartment with direct entry which has been rendered untenable by heat and/or smoke. The regulations now require the provision of an air lock (with each of the doors being self closing) if it is impracticable to site the emergency pump elsewhere. The standard of structural fire protection for the compartment containing the pump is also prescribed.

On occasions, the cables of pumps powered from the emergency generator have passed through the machinery space and been damaged by the fire, leaving the ship without fire water.

Even if the pump is operating satisfactorily, water may not be available at the machinery space boundaries if the deck fire main cannot be isolated from the fire main in the machinery spaces. In the past, branches from the machinery space rising main have been taken fore and aft at various levels to individual hydrants outside the space in a so-called 'Christmas tree' arrangement. Then, if machinery space hydrants are left open when evacuating the space, or the piping system is damaged, water from the emergency fire pump flows ineffectively into the machinery space. To prevent this situation arising the fire main should leave the machinery space at one position and be fitted with an isolating valve outside the space. The deck fire main connections and branches to other hydrants should be made on the downstream side of the isolating valve. In an emergency, hydrants would then be available for cooling the boundaries to prevent the fire spreading from the machinery space, and for use when re-entering the space.

The factors to be borne in mind when re-entry to a closed down space is considered include the dangers from lack of oxygen; the possibility of re-ignition when air is admitted, particularly in the case of systems using gases (which have negligible cooling effect); and the dangers to personnel due to the toxic products of combustion, the toxic and irritant acid gases formed by the decomposition of extinguishing media and the suffocating and toxic media itself.

External factors will also influence the decision. No doubt less time would be allowed to elapse for cooling down before re-entry using breathing apparatus when heavy weather at sea was expected, than when at anchor or in port without such pressures. In reported cases, re-entry times have varied from 1 to 15 hours.

Fire hazards of machinery spaces

Machinery spaces are potentially dangerous, despite the continual improvement in fire protection, and the reason for the relatively low loss of life compared with accommodation spaces is most probably due to the lower numbers of people in the space. Serious machinery space fires still occur due to operator carelessness or defects in arrangements, when bunkering, transferring oil, changing over fuel oil and lubricating oil filters, leakage of oil from thermometer pockets and from makeshift repairs using Jubilee clips and plastic piping. The absorption of oil or oil vapours into lagging and subsequent spontaneous ignition (see *Pumproom Protection*) is another recurring cause of machinery space fires. However, as the number of steamships decreases, the traditional hazards from furnace leaks of burning oil onto tanktops and furnace explosions have been largely replaced by the major hazards from high and fluctuating fuel oil pressures, and vibration from diesel engines leading to fractures of both high and lower pressure pipes discharging high temperature oil onto hot surfaces, and auto-ignition.

Machinery is now more highly rated leading to smaller machinery (and machinery spaces) and distances between fuel piping and exhaust manifolds have consequently been continually reduced leading to greater probability of ignition of escaping oil. Turbo-chargers have added hazards, sometimes high in the machinery space. Fuel oils now need to be heated to above their flash points making it essential that piping and glands are kept tight and that there is no escape of vapour into the machinery space from settling and service tanks and that adequate ventilation is maintained. The use of 'hydraulically' operated systems and thermal heating oils has increased the potential for fires involving other than fuel and lubricating oil.

The above, and other factors, necessitate the highest standards of maintenance, cleanliness, safety consciousness, preparedness and training. In particular, the engineer officers should, through prior thought and tests, be fully aware of the practicalities of fighting a fire in the different areas of the machinery space using the equipment provided. For example, from access, visibility and air supply considerations, the feasibility of a fire party wearing breathing apparatus proceeding down the engine room steps to deal with a fire on the bottom platform should have been established during fire drills. The location of the fire fighting equipment should similarly have been given prior consideration so that effective action may be taken as soon as a fire breaks out. Unless rapid action is taken to deal with a fire in its early stages, more oil may be released and, furthermore, electrical power may be lost leaving the fire fighters dependent for water upon the emergency fire pump. This possibility is greater with an unmanned machinery space where the chance of extinguishing a fire with portable or semi-portable extinguishers is reduced.

Machinery space fires

In the event of a fire in a machinery space, the fire alarm must be sounded and the bridge informed of the location and severity of the fire. Efforts should be made, using localised fire fighting equipment, to contain the fire and to maintain essential services. Oil leaks should be isolated and non-essential oil fuel pumps and units should be shut down.

If the watchkeepers cannot contain the fire until the fire party wearing breathing apparatuses arrives, the space must be evacuated and secured closed. The chief engineer will take charge and decide whether the fire party should attempt to extinguish the fire or whether the fixed installation should be used. He will not wish to abandon the power centre of the ship lightly and, providing an escape route is available, will probably order that the attack be pressed home. It has been stated that, in about 50% of cases, analysis of incidents has shown that machinery spaces were abandoned unnecessarily and that continued action would have extinguished the fire. However, circumstances differ and his knowledge of the arrangements and estimate of the severity of the fire may lead to a decision to use the fixed CO_2 gas installation.

The instruction for operating such systems are concisely stated at the remote operating position but, before the gas is released all personnel must be evacuated, ventilator fans should be stopped and dampers and skylights closed, the main engine should be stopped, quick closing valves operated, pumps stopped and machinery space doors closed.

In the case of a high pressure CO_2 system it should be ascertained that the system has been discharged by checking in the bottle room that the required number of cylinders have been discharged by feeling the temperature of the bottles. The danger of minor gas leaks (due to the change in temperature on discharge) should be borne in mind.

The emergency generator should be run to supply essential services and the emergency fire pump started to provide boundary cooling. The screw lift isolating valve on the fire main outside the machinery space must be closed to prevent loss of pressure through machinery space hydrants left open or damaged piping. Checks should be made on adjacent holds and the accommodation to ensure that the fire has not spread out of the machinery space.

The chief engineer will decide when re-entry to the machinery space, at a lower platform level if possible, should be attempted, by a fire party wearing breathing apparatus.

Unprotected personnel should not be allowed into the space until it has been thoroughly ventilated. If early re-entry using breathing apparatus is decided upon, care must be taken to maintain the gas concentration by, say, the use of a flexible screen at the entrance. Cooling of hot spots within the space may be accomplished with coupled hoses from hydrants outside the space or from hydrants within the space supplied from the emergency fire pump.

SHIPBOARD ORGANISATION FOR FIRE EMERGENCIES

National and international regulations require the preparation, before a ship proceeds to sea, of a muster list which, amongst other emergency specifications and duties, assigns the duties of crew members in the event of fire. On cargo ships, at least one fire drill per month must be held to meet the statutory requirement that each crew member must participate in a fire drill at least monthly (fire drills must be held weekly on passenger ships). Details of the drills, which must be entered in the official log book, should include the date and nature of the fire drill and the nature of the on-board training given. Many prudent companies and experienced masters require fire drills at fortnightly intervals. Fire drills should be held simultaneously with the first stage of the abandon ship drill in which, following the general emergency alarm signal, passengers (if any) and crew proceed to

their muster stations. The second stage of the abandon ship drill, i.e. the muster and drill at the survival craft stations, follows the fire drill. In carrying out fire drills, potential fire hazards should be identified by the master or chief engineer and occasionally, although the time of the fire drill should be announced, no advance warning may be given of the actual location of an assumed outbreak. This will test both the preparedness of the personnel and check on the ready availability of the fire fighting equipment. Speed is essential since most fires can be extinguished with hand held extinguishers in their early stages. The emergency fire pump should always be tested for availability.

It is important for all staff to be encouraged to give consideration to potential hazards and to their reaction in the event of outbreak of fire both at sea and in port (where some of the most severe fires and greatest loss of life occur). Some fire drills should be conducted using the shore watchkeeping complements. The fire parties should be sent to the scene of the assumed fire. The hoses in the vicinity should be laid out and water should be played through them wherever practicable. The water supply should be taken first from the machinery space pump. The machinery space isolating valve should then be closed and the supply taken from the emergency fire pump. A number of portable fire extinguishers should be available and instruction should be given in the use of the type of fire extinguisher suitable for the assumed fire.

All personnel should be instructed and exercised in the closing of openings i.e. fire doors, ventilating shafts, closing flaps in the annular space within the funnel, side scuttles, skylights etc. so as to reduce the supply of air to a fire and isolate it from other parts of the ship, especially stairways and lift shafts. All persons should be made familiar with the position and operation of remote controls for ventilating fans, oil fuel pumps and oil tank valves.

Fixed installations for extinguishing fires, such as CO_2 or water spray in the machinery spaces, CO_2 in the cargo spaces, and sprinkler and fire alarm systems in accommodation should be tested. Checks should be made on relevant communication equipment and operation of watertight doors, and the emergency power system should be tested. The fire party should be exercised in the use of breathing apparatus and protective clothing, and axes and safety lamps should be available. Where the number of sets of breathing apparatus permits, persons using them should practice in pairs. Any necessary maintenance or defects should be remedied without delay, and any fire extinguishers used during the test should be recharged or replaced with a charged extinguisher immediately. Training in the use of fire fighting equipment, and particularly in the use of breathing apparatus is of major importance. The rapidity with which fire parties with members wearing breathing apparatus arrive at the scene of a fire can, say, make the difference between extinguishing a machinery space fire or having to evacuate the space, losing all power therein and having to use the fixed fire fighting installation.

Training sessions of, typically, one hour's duration without interruption conducted by senior officers, will demonstrate the company's commitment to fire safety and instil safety consciousness in the crew. Discussion will stimulate interest and indicate the extent of knowledge of the participants. Key points should be emphasised and illustrated by demonstration before the trainees handle the equipment and repeat the key points. The trainees should then demonstrate the use of the fire fighting equipment and be well prepared for the fire drills. Regular practice will alleviate the difficulties of carrying fire hoses into machinery spaces and up and down stairways and alleyways whilst wearing breathing apparatuses.

Although the exercises must be made as realistic as possible, on no account should a fire be started nor should training in the use of breathing apparatus be conducted in a dangerous atmosphere.

A summary of inspections, tests and fire drills is given in Table 5.

Fire parties and emergencies

Whilst the regulations specify that all personnel must be allocated specific duties and given instructions as to their actions and location in the event of an emergency, the actual arrangements and designations normally follow from company policy. The on-board decisions under the policy will be influenced by the personnel available and the type of ship but the choice may be on the following lines.

First fire party: mate, second engineer and three others.

Second fire party: second mate, third engineer and the remainder.

Utility party: catering staff or other persons able to tend injured persons.

In the event of a fire emergency, the fire alarm should be raised by means of fire bells and sirens sounding continuously until stopped from the bridge. If the system fails, the alarm should be raised by blasts on the ship's whistle or siren sounding seven short, one long blasts, three times in succession. The

Table 5   Summary of inspections, tests and fire drills.

Interval	Operation
Daily (at noon)	Fire alarm system and smoke detection alarm system if fitted.
Weekly (preferably on a specific day)	Log bulk CO_2 cylinder contents reading and check slave instrument reading. Check pressures and temperatures in CO_2 tank and cooling plant.
Fortnightly	Operate all ventilator stops. Check operation of 50% of engine room fire detectors. Run emergency fire pump. Test a fire hose, with fog nozzle, connected to fire main (in rotations). Test foam pumps using water. Check contents of bulk CO_2 system and master gauge reading. Fire drills for sea and in port preparedness. Each crew member to participate at least monthly.
Monthly	Inspect, operate and lubricate fire dampers, skylights and extended spindles. Smothering gas bottle systems: Check release arrangements, clamping of cylinders to prevent rotation, runs of wires, support of control piping, examine copper piping for fatigue fractures, or work hardening, grease piston rods of release cylinders, check liquid level of about 10% of gas cylinders. CO_2 bulk systems: Using CO_2 gas detectors or soap solution, check for tightness around stuffing boxes, valves, joints and manhole covers etc. All fixed gas installations: Check that alarm can be heard throughout machinery space when door switch on control panel is opened.
3 monthly	Check machinery space fire detector systems.
6 monthly	Check weight of portable CO_2 fire extinguishers.
Annually	Blow through smothering gas system piping with compressed air which should also sound the gas operated alarm. Extinguishers serviced. Mandatory annual survey conducted.
4 yearly	Pressure test to be carried out at 21 bars on portable and non portable fire extinguishers.
10 yearly	Internal inspection of bulk CO_2 tank.
20 yearly (maximum)	Hydraulic test of CO_2 cylinders.

watchkeepers should remain at their stations until relieved. Other persons should proceed to their allocated stations. The master would direct operations from the bridge, the radio room should be manned and the chief engineer should take up duty in the machinery space. The first fire party would be led by the mate or the second engineer depending upon whether the fire was in the accommodation or in the machinery space.

Other arrangements may involve the use of control, support control, No.1 emergency and No.2 emergency parties. Typically, the control party which may include the master, another officer and two men would take overall charge, direct emergency parties and maintain external communications. The support control party, formed by the chief engineer and two men, would maintain essential services and control emergencies in the machinery spaces. The two emergency parties, each consisting of a deck and engineer officer plus two or three men, would take the necessary emergency or fire fighting actions to remedy the situation, and the support party, consisting of one officer and three or four men, would supply the emergency parties with additional equipment and tend injured persons.

Fire control plans and maintenance manual

Whatever the arrangements and designations, all personnel should be familiar with the fire fighting equipment available, its location, and, above all, the fire control plans. In all ships over 500 gt, general arrangement plans must be permanently exhibited for the guidance of ships' officers. They must show clearly for each deck: the control stations; the fire sections enclosed by structural fire protection divisions; the fire detection and alarm systems; the sprinkler system (if fitted); the fire appliances; the means of access to different compartments and decks; the ventilating system including the position of dampers and fans serving each section. Alternatively, the same information may be included in booklets supplied to each officer and one booklet readily available on board. Plans and booklets must be kept up to date.

A duplicate set of fire control plans or booklets must be permanently stored in a prominently marked weathertight enclosure outside the deckhouse for the assistance of shoreside fire fighting personnel. The same IMO regulation requires, in addition, that instructions concerning the maintenance and operation of all the equipment and installations related to fire fighting and containment be kept under one cover in a maintenance manual or similar arrangement of documents, readily available in an accessible position.

Fire prevention in port

Several aspects of fire protection in port have been covered already but some basic concepts require

emphasis. Always, on arrival, fire hoses from the shore fire main should be connected fore and aft to the ship's fire main, unless the ship's services are to be maintained. Communications and liaison arrangements in the event of an emergency should be made with shoreside officials and it should be verified that the authority has a readily available counterpart to the ship's international shore fire connection so that water can be discharged into the ship's fire main when necessary. Arrangements for permitting smoking only in controlled locations should be made. Gas, chemical and oil tankers should take the precautions listed in the relevant industry guides.

In a shipyard, arrangements such as blanking off or locking the operating mechanism of the CO_2 system, must be made to prevent the inadvertent release of smothering gas into machinery spaces. Fire patrols should be set up to operate both during and outside working hours. The watchkeepers and patrolmen should be aware of how to contact sources of assistance.

Machinery spaces are particularly vulnerable to fire hazards and casualties when large numbers of shore workers and their equipment are on board. Temporary lighting and power cables (often improperly fused or connected, or having deteriorated insulation, or being subjected to chafing from portholes or doorways) present hazards and, along with air hoses, prevent the closing of doors and containment of a fire. Carelessness during burning and welding operations by uninstructed or indifferent operators has resulted in showers of sparks igniting oily waste and oil. On a UK ship in a foreign shipyard, 13 lives were lost in this way. On another occasion, a burning operation on rusty bolts at the vent pipe outlet from an oil bunker tank which contained low flash point cargo resulted in an explosion in the tanker which blew out the side of the bunker into the engine room and 76 lives were lost. Serious fires have also been caused by failure to check on the opposite side of heated deck or bulkhead plating, resulting in the explosion of acetylene gas bottles or ignition of flammable materials which should have been removed before work began. Both minor and serious fires originate in oily rags and waste, rope and rubbish, lagging, granulated and slab cork in insulated spaces which may have smouldered for hours following ignition from discarded cigarette ends or sparks from electrodes or burning operations. Patrolmen should therefore be informed of areas where such operations have been conducted, and the gas cylinders, piping and torches should be brought into the open air at night.

The consequences of a machinery space fire in port are severe because of the larger number of persons in the space, their unfamiliarity with the ship and the probable inadequacy of the escapes which may be designed for dealing only with the ship's normal complement or may be of a temporary nature. It is therefore essential that entrances and ladderways are not restricted and that obstructions are limited to the practical minimum.

The senior official responsible for safety should ensure that precautions are complied with, temporary wiring is protected against chafing and is not overloaded, adequate fire appliances are available, accesses for shore fire fighters are adequate, and a control centre with external communications is established as a focal point for patrolmen and the siting of breathing apparatuses, axes and keys to locked spaces.

It is essential that whether responsibility for fire safety rests entirely with shipyard or the ship, or whether there is some agreed division of responsibility, is clearly defined in a written agreement.

CONCLUDING REMARKS

Space limitations have restricted this chapter to selected aspects of fire protection. These topics have been covered in some depth with the intention of supplementing the reader's knowledge so that he is able to apply the principles and practices to other situations with which he may be faced. Knowledge alone is not a sufficient safeguard. Self discipline is essential and the fundamentals of fire safety must be put into practice and emphasised at all levels. No seafarer can afford to be unfamiliar with the ship's fire control plan, or the location and use of its equipment. Nor can he afford to dismiss fire drills as a statutory chore. A clear head, sound training and familiarity with the ship and its equipment will result in most fires being extinguished before they reach serious proportions.

Constant vigilance and immediate action when hazards are identified will prevent fire outbreaks and save lives. The potential consequences of vibrating pipes, leaking glands and joints, patches of oil, oily waste, dirty tank tops, inattention during oil transfer and bunkering or to oil pressure gauge piping and electrical equipment, and overloaded temporary wiring or plugs are evident to all knowledgeable engineer officers, yet fires do occur from these causes.

Deck officers are well aware of the dangers of spontaneous combustion and regularly check cargo holds for outbreaks but it still occurs in rags and cotton waste which have been used for white spirit, paint or varnish left in paint lockers and storerooms, often with serious consequences. Portable lamps and clusters lowered or transported by the cable, in poor condition, unprotected or wet with oil or water are also sources of ignition although the hazards are understood.

The dangers from smoking in bed and the careless disposal of cigarettes and matches have been impressed upon all seafarers yet these actions remain major causes of shipboard fires. Smoking in bed should be a disciplinary matter and smoking in holds and on deck when cargo hatches are open should be prohibited. However, areas for smokers should be set aside and suitable containers for cigarette ends provided, as discarded cigarette ends thrown overboard may return on board due to air currents around the vessel. Thoughtless actions or indifference to obvious hazards have cost many lives.

References

1. J. Cowley, '*Machinery spaces, extinguishing media and fires*', International Symposium on Fire Safety of Ships, Hellenic Institute of Marine Technology, May 1989.
2   Unitor Ship Service a.s. fire extinguisher service manual.
3. Chapter II-2 of SOLAS 1974/78 and subsequent amendments.
4. IMO Resolution A602(15). *Revised Guidelines for Marine Portable Fire Extinguishers*.
5. I.R.Noble, '*Structural fire protection of cargo ships*', Conference on Ship Fires in the 1980s, IMarE, 1985.
6. D.G Heard, '*Fire protection in modern ships*', IMAS 88, IMarE, 1988
7. J.Cowley, '*A marine administration's approach to polymers*', Polymers in a Marine Environment Conference, IMarE, 1988.

Chapter 12
Propellers and Shafting

D G Redpath

INTRODUCTION

The importance of line shafting, tailshaft, propeller and thrust shaft cannot be over-emphasised. Failure of any one of them will render the ship inoperable with possible disastrous consequences. Single line shafting is used on the majority of ships, but not in passenger ships and on short voyage ro-ro services, where twin screws are employed.

Propellers, because they are outside the ship, are often neglected and are usually only inspected when the ship is in drydock. More frequent examination can be undertaken when a ship is alongside and the shafting is being rotated with the turning gear. Damage to the propeller blading can lead to vibrations being set up in the line shafting causing overheating of the shafting bearings, main thrust, etc.

The selection of shafting and propeller materials is usually within manufacturers' specifications, and complies with the various classification society requirements as well as the statutory requirements of governments.

After initial inspection during the construction of a ship, the line shafting, tailshaft and propeller have to be examined during their service life. The time period for examination is laid down by the classification societies.

INTERMEDIATE SHAFTING

These shafts are made by forging carbon or carbon-manganese steel where minimum tensile strength is within the range of 400–600 N/mm². Alloy steels can also be used depending upon the mechanical properties of the material and their chemical composition. If they are to be used their maximum tensile strength should not exceed 800 N/mm². The forgings used should be subjected to ultrasonic examination.

The diameter of an intermediate shaft is worked out by an empirical formula relating the power developed by the prime mover, various constants and the minimum tensile strength of the material to be used. Reference for this calculation can be made to any of the classification societies, bearing in mind that it usually gives the minimum diameter required.

Intermediate shafts are used to transmit the power from the main engine to the tailshaft, and as such must be supported on bearings. These bearings are also referred to as plummer blocks, tunnel bearings or line shaft bearings. The shafting may be supported on one or two bearings depending upon the design. The bearings are required to hold the shaft and support the shaft load as well as maintaining a satisfactory alignment.

Plummer blocks are individual bearings which usually have their own oil supply contained within the bearing. There are arrangements in which they can be supplied from an external source with their own oil supply and cooler system. Individual bearings, however, have a cooler contained within the plummer block, with cooling supplied from one of the sea water cooling systems.

Plummer block bearings are required to operate over the full range of speeds from 0 rev/min to the rated rev/min in both the ahead and astern directions. The bearings are expected to last the life of the ship, so the actual dimensions are much more substantial than the basic design.

Plummer block bearings

There are two types of bearing used in the intermediate shafting. The first type, most familiar to engineers, is that of the steel shaft rotating in a white metal bearing which is oil lubricated. This type of arrangement is used in high powered installations. The second type, similar to bearings used in pumps etc., is a roller surface bearing. These bearings are split because of the difficulty in fitting them.

The aim of the first type of bearing is to provide a good hydrodynamic oil film for lubrication whilst the shaft is rotating, so avoiding metal-to-metal contact. The ability to produce the hydrodynamic oil film is governed by the peripheral speed of the shaft, the thickness or viscosity of the oil and the load on the shaft. The load is carried by the oil wedge. The casing which holds the bearing can either be cast or fabricated steel, and is split on the horizontal joint, allowing easy access for maintenance. Because the load is downward there may only be a white metal bearing in the bottom half of the casing, although complete bearings are also fitted (Fig 1).

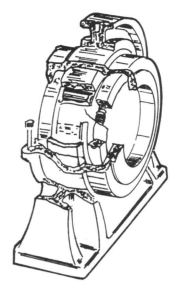

Figure 3 Split roller bearing.

theory will support a greater load. Conversely a smaller bearing area is required for the same load. Once again a complete bearing can be provided depending on its application (Fig 2).

Split roller bearings which are similar to the white metal type can be used, and because rolling friction is slightly less than sliding friction there is generally less power loss. This can make a significant saving in energy during the lifetime of a ship. Generally speaking, however, this type of bearing is used more in small and medium speed tonnage, usually when higher speed shafting is used. A typical split type bearing is illustrated in Fig 3.

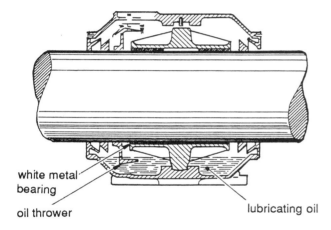

white metal bearing

oil thrower

lubricating oil

Figure 1 Plummer block.

Another type of bearing that works on the sliding surface principal has a bottom half bearing which is divided into three sections. These bearings have a pivoting pad mechanism which allows the bearing to tilt when the hydrodynamic wedge forms, and in

Intermediate shafting couplings

The coupling arrangement can either have a flange forged integral with the shaft or loose, depending on requirements.

Flanges that are forged integral with the shaft have their thickness, determined by classification society rules, at least equal to the diameter of the flange coupling bolts measured at the coupling face. By using this ruling the possibility of using tapered or stepped bolts can be accommodated. The flange thickness should not be less than 0.2 times the diameter of the shaft.

The forging of the flange with the shaft must be provided with a fillet radius which is machined in and must not be less than 0.08 times the diameter of the shaft. These fillets must have a smooth finish.

Loose couplings are usually fitted to the last line of intermediate shafting connecting it to the tailshaft. This method of coupling permits the removal of the

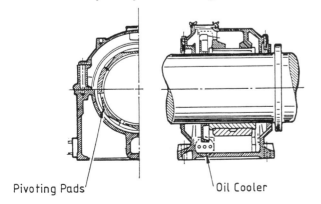

Pivoting Pads

Oil Cooler

Figure 2 Michell plummer block.

tailshaft out through the stern bearing. It is common practice to fit them in twin screw vessels. There are two types of loose coupling in common use in current practice:

a) muff coupling;

b) keyed and flanged couplings.

Muff coupling

This type of coupling does not have any flanges and is hydraulically connected and released. The sleeves that make up the coupling have to be accurately machined to a smooth finish and are made in various sizes up to 900 mm. There is an inner sleeve and an outer sleeve. The inner sleeve is bored parallel to the shaft, being a sliding fit over the shaft. On its outer diameter is a slight taper, 1:80, forming a cone. The outer sleeve is bored with a similar taper and is parallel on its outer diameter. The outer sleeve is also much thicker than the inner sleeve, so providing the elastic friction grip, thereby allowing the torque to be transmitted. A nut and oil sealing arrangement is fitted at the smaller diameter end of the inner sleeve and screwed to it (Fig 4).

To fit the coupling to the shafts hydraulic oil is injected at high pressure between the two sleeves forming a load bearing film. As the pressure increases in the annular space between the oil seal and the outer sleeve an axial force is created which pushes the outer sleeve up the taper and expands it. The inner sleeve is compressed due to the pressure and so grips the shafts to be connected, creating the coupling. After removing the hydraulic pressure the 'friction' grip is maintained.

To remove the coupling the reverse procedure takes place. Hydraulic oil is once again pressurised into the annular space between the conical faces so relieving pressure from the seal end. The axial component of the force acting on the taper drives the outer sleeve off the taper thereby allowing the inner sleeve to relax its friction grip, returning it to a sliding fit. The complete operation is only successful if the compressive load on the inner sleeve is kept within the material's elastic limit.

Keyed and flanged couplings

This type of coupling is also used, having up to three keyways cut into the taper. A securing nut is used which is recessed into the coupling as shown in Fig 5. The securing nut itself is locked in place with a locking device. This type of coupling is used in medium and high speed installations.

Coupling bolt holes

The bolt holes are usually drilled to an appropriate size in the workshops. The final dimension is reamed out when the coupling flanges are brought together.

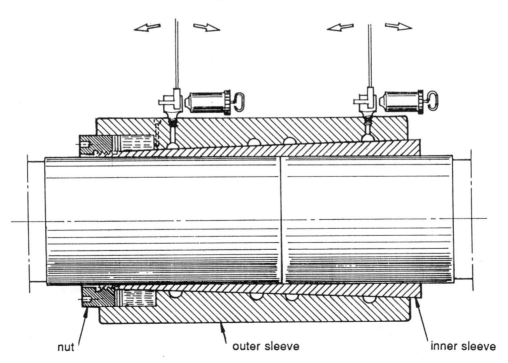

nut   outer sleeve   inner sleeve

Figure 4   Muff coupling.

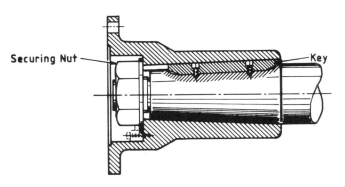

Figure 5 Keyed and flanged coupling.

The final size is designed to give an interference fit between bolt and hole.

Coupling bolts

There are various types of coupling bolts, the diameter of which must comply with classification requirements. The material used should have a tensile strength at least equal to that of the shaft material.

Parallel non-standard bolts

This type of bolt has a parallel shank as shown in Fig 6 and is in common use in current practice. The surface finish is to a high standard, giving a good fit in the hole.

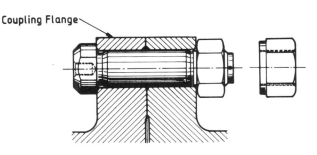

Figure 6 Parallel non standard coupling bolts.

Stepped bolts

These are rarely used. They limit the interference distance over which it is necessary to drive the bolt home when fitting. The cost of machining such a bolt, and the fact that there are no such machining difficulties with parallel bolts, limits their use.

Special type bolts

These are used in high powered installations and offer the following design features.

Each bolt has an accurately bored hole over its full length. The bolt head has an arrangement to take an hydraulic attachment. On fitting the bolt, a high tensile steel rod is inserted into the bolt and, using the hydraulic attachment, pressure is exerted, stretching

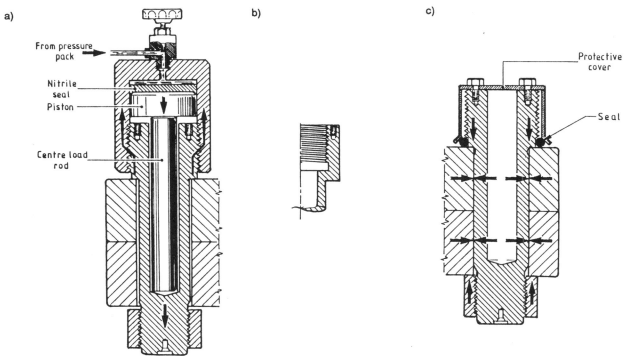

Figure 7 Special type of coupling bolt: a) insertion; b) alternative design of bolt head with internal thd. connection; c) final assembly.

the bolt within its elastic limit. This reduces the diameter of the bolt by 0.5 µm per mm of bolt diameter.

The bolt is inserted into the hole in the stretched condition. On releasing the pressure the bolt returns to its original diameter, so exerting radial grip. The nut is fitted before releasing the hydraulic pressure, thereby transferring the compressive force to the coupling assembly.

Figure 7 shows a special type of coupling bolt.

Examination of intermediate shafting

Line shafting is examined once every 5 years for classification purposes, and unless something has gone wrong this is the only time the shafting is looked at. When examined for the classification survey it is usual to open up the main bearings, but it is not necessary to remove coupling bolts if everything has been operating satisfactorily. As well as examination of the bearing, the holding down arrangement should also be looked at. Sometimes the holding down bolts may have slackened back.

Operational problems

After initial alignment, when the ship is new and has undergone sea trials, no problems are expected to occur with the line shafting. However, there have been many instances, under differing operational conditions, when the line shafting bearings have overheated. The solution is to reduce the loading until the cause has been investigated and the fault rectified. One possible cause might simply be an alteration in the trim of the ship, which changes the bending moment of the ship. Overheating can also occur due to a lack of lubricating oil in the bearing, allowing metal-to-metal contact with possible wiping of the white metal. It can be argued that a lack of oil should not occur, but it is probably the most common cause of overheating of bearings.

The lubricating oil cooler inserted in the bearing is another potential cause of overheating. Corrosion of the cooler tubes permits sea water to mix with the lubricating oil thus destroying its properties, and can eventually lead to corrosion of the steel shaft. To overcome this problem the holed tubes should be plugged or the cooler replaced and the oil replenished. It may also be necessary to re-polish the shaft journal.

It has been suggested that the storing of fuel oil, lubricating oil etc., in double bottom tanks has an effect on plummer blocks attached to the tank top but it has been generally accepted that the heat is dissipated into the engine room space. There have been instances where realignment has had to be undertaken.

The structure of the ship inside the double bottom tanks has been strengthened in way of the plummer blocks in order to support the line shafting. The double bottom tanks can hold sea water ballast or fresh water. Generally speaking, they are not coated for protection against corrosion, so over a period of time the plummer block support structure can corrode.

TAILSHAFTS

Tailshafts in merchant ships are neglected because they are out of sight, and there is no way of telling what is happening unless a visual inspection is undertaken.

Tailshafts with continuous liners

In older ships the method of lubricating the stern bearing was simply by using sea water. The tailshaft had a bronze liner shrunk on to the forged steel shaft. The thickness of the liner, following classification society rules, was approximately 25 mm for a 600 mm shaft. An extra allowance was added to allow for machining at a future date. The bush in which the shaft ran was made from staves of lignum vitae or, more recently, of resin bonded asbestos or other fibres. As powers increased, the stern bearing loading increased, resulting in greater wear rates which became excessive, requiring re-wooding of the bush at much shorter intervals. In lower powered ships, re-wooding would only be required at, possibly, alternate tailshaft surveys (8 years). With higher powered tankers this could be reduced to every drydocking (2 years). In some instances the vessel might need to be specially drydocked at annual intervals to deal with excessive vibration in the stern bearing.

At the drydocking of a vessel the tailshaft wear down reading is recorded. For a tailshaft with a continuous liner (TCSL) the reading should be less than 6 mm. If the reading approaches this figure, the tailshaft should be withdrawn for the bush to be re-wooded.

A typical tailshaft of the continuous liner type is shown in Fig 8. Although this type of stern bearing has been superseded in most merchant ships by oil lubricated bearings a number of smaller ships may still have them fitted. The bronze liner must be continuous over the length of the shaft from inside the ship to the end of the taper, to protect the forged steel shaft from corrosion from sea water lubrication. Sea water could also attack the shaft externally where the liner finishes, but this can be prevented by fitting a sealing ring at the end of the liner, which is com-

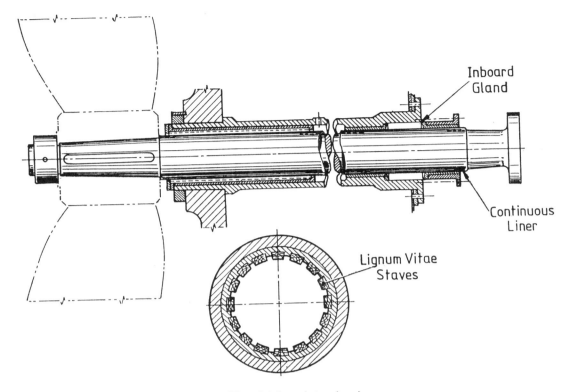

Figure 8 Water lubricated stern bearing.

pressed when the propeller is fitted. With this type of stern bearing there is no external seal, but an internal one; a stuffing box with soft packing. The packing is in contact with the shaft liner so it hardens in service. This, together with topping up the stuffing box with additional rounds of packing, leads to grooving of the bronze liner in way of the stuffing box. The bronze liner can be returned to good condition by machining (an allowance having been added to take care of this situation). Care must be taken not to reduce the thickness of the bronze liner below the required limit, particularly if the liner has a history of previous machining.

If the minimum thickness has been reached, it is possible to effect a repair acceptable to classification societies. The bronze liner can be machined down to an approved thickness in way of grooving. Then a split sleeve is welded on the horizontal and circumferential joints fitted closely around the original liner, the sleeve being machined to the overall diameter required. It should be noted that this repair should be undertaken with the approval of the relevant classification society and that the correct material must be used for the sleeve and the electrodes for welding.

There may be circumstances when the complete bronze liner requires renewal, and where this is the case the opportunity should be taken to examine the steel shaft under the liner. There have been cases where sea water has penetrated between the liner and shaft, causing unseen corrosion. Before renewing the bronze liner it is necessary to machine away the corrosion until an acceptable surface is produced. A recalculation may be necessary for maximum power transmission. It will be appreciated that all these operations take time and it would be more prudent to fit a spare tailshaft to reduce time in drydock.

When this type of tailshaft is being examined for survey great attention is given to the condition of the shaft at the top and on the cone. This area is subjected to an approved crack detection method such as magnetic particle, or ultrasonic examination. Depending on the condition, it might become necessary to skim a few millimetres off the end of the bronze liner before magnetic crack detection, depending on the condition.

A tailshaft with a continuous bronze liner, being of an older type, would have a keyway cut in the taper. The machining out of this keyway is a potential source of cracking and careful attention should be given to the keyway during survey. The top end of the keyway should be blended into the contours of the cone producing a spoonbill shape and reducing stress concentrations.

The nature of water lubrication leads to the ingress of foreign matter such as coarse sand, in particular to vessels trading in coastal waters. In this hostile environment there tends to be a rapid wear down of the stern bush which requires re-wooding at more regular intervals. Screw shafts have been known to fail under the resulting high bending stresses coupled with cyclic loading.

In smaller vessels such as work boats twin screws may be used, the shafting being angled from the main engine. The tailshaft in this instance may be made of stainless steel or may be a steel shaft with stainless steel liner shrunk on in way of the stern tube bearing and 'A' bracket. The length of shaft between the bearings is protected by a coating such as glass fibre. This protective coating is a source of possible corrosion attack on the carbon steel shaft with the ingress of sea water. If a corrosion pit occurs on the surface of the shaft it provides a stress concentration which, combined with the cyclic stresses in the shaft, will eventually lead to failure of the shaft.

Magnetic particle crack detection consists of applying a magna flux solution to the steel shaft in the area to be examined and creating a magnetic field in the shaft using a permanent magnet or an electromagnetic yolk. If there is a crack within the magnetic field the iron filings in the magna flux trace the crack. Sub-surface cracks are also highlighted in this way. The procedure continues until the whole area has been covered. A dye penetrant check can quickly be made around the cone; but this only indicates surface cracks, and is not an approved method. If an approved method is not used, the time between the survey of tailshafts can be reduced by one year, perhaps causing difficulties for future drydocking schedules.

The coupling end of this type of tailshaft should also receive close examination, because the sea water that supplies the bearing lubrication leaks into the ship at the inboard gland. The sea water pours over the unprotected coupling, which is steel, giving rise to corrosion. The stress at this end of the shaft is mainly torsional and the combination can lead to corrosion fatigue. If there is misalignment as well, bending stress is set up which adds to the problem. Some ship operators give protection to the shaft between the liner and the coupling by coating the shaft.

Tailshafts lubricated by oil

Oil lubricated stern bearings are by far the most common type fitted to modern ships. With this type it is not necessary for the steel shaft to have a bronze liner fitted. In most instances, the shaft runs in a white metal bearing, and is protected from metal-to-metal contact by oil lubrication which is supplied from a

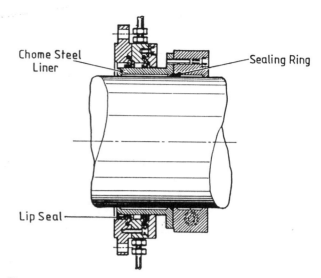

Figure 9 Inboard gland.

header tank in the engine room. Because of this arrangement it is necessary to prevent the loss of oil into the engine room or the sea. Because the shaft is rotating, a mechanical type seal is required, as illustrated in Fig 9.

The outer seal has a chrome steel bush which is bolted onto the boss of the propeller and has a clearance over the diameter of the tailshaft. Ingress of sea water is prevented by fitting a rubber sealing ring between the propeller boss and the chrome bush. The stationary part of the seal consists of a carrier arrangement which contains the sealing rings. The carrier is bolted on to the stern frame. There are two outer sealing rings made of oil and water resistant rubber which are shaped to prevent the sea water penetrating the lubricating oil space. The inner sealing ring is fitted in the opposite fashion and prevents the oil in the stern tube leaking into the sea. The sealing rings are all held on the rotating chrome sleeve by a garter spring.

The inner seal is of similar construction to the outer seal. Only two sealing rings are used, this time running on a special quality cast iron or chrome sleeve and so preventing leakage of oil into the engine room. The sleeve is bolted to a collar which is fitted round the tailshaft, with a rubber sealing ring between the collar and sleeve.

The forward seal incorporates an oil circulator as a standard fitting. Oil from a 4 litre tank is circulated continuously through the annular chamber. This ensures effective cooling, as well as permanent lubrication with clean oil. The oil circulation system not only boosts operating reliability but also increases the service life of the sealing rings and the liners.

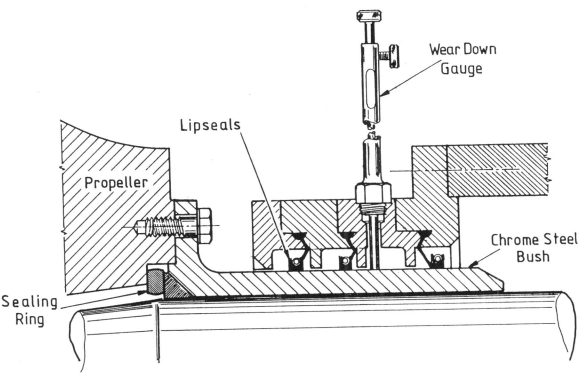

Figure 10 Outer seal.

The aft seal incorporates a pressure control device. This system offers numerous advantages; e.g. increased service life of sealing rings and liners, as well as the ability to withstand severe operating conditions. The pressure control device also facilitates the optimum operating reliability of Viton plain sealing rings.

The ideal situation would be a complete separation of the lubricating oil and sea water. If however the operating conditions are considered, the problem of the separation of the two liquids is aggravated by the presence of a lubrication film between the sliding faces (Fig 10).

The manufacturers of the Simplex-compact type seal have produced a leak proof system to combat this situation. This is effected by specifically arranging the pressure difference on the seal so that the lubrication film is reduced on one side only—on the side of the lower liquid pressure. This is achieved in practice in the aft seal which has one chamber of sealing rings and casing, the static pressure of which is set lower than the pressure of the liquid to be sealed. This chamber is between the second and third sealing rings which face in opposite directions, and is connected to a tank effecting the low pressure level required (*PK*) below the ballast water line (*PAMIN*). This is also below the stern tube oil pressure (*PL*) giving:

$$PAMIN > PK << PL$$

A pressure differential of 0.3 bar is considered satisfactory. With this system any leakage from either sea water or lubricating oil is taken up in the annular space between sealing rings two and three, thereby increasing the level in the settling tank. An alarm signal is arranged to monitor any increase in settling tank level. A leakage of water into the system can then be dealt with by draining off. The system guarantees a continuous supply of good oil to sealing rings two and three. The system is shown in figs 11 and 12.

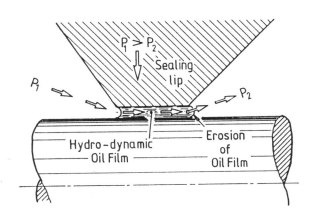

Figure 11 Pressure difference on the seal.

1. Conventional system

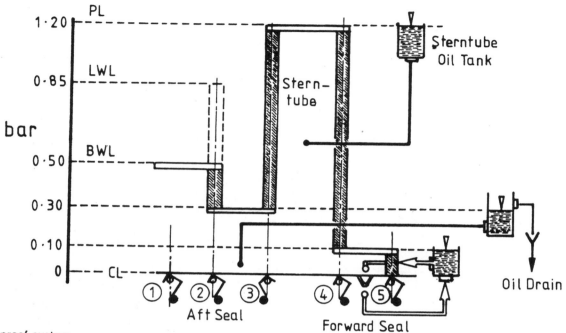

2. Leakproof system

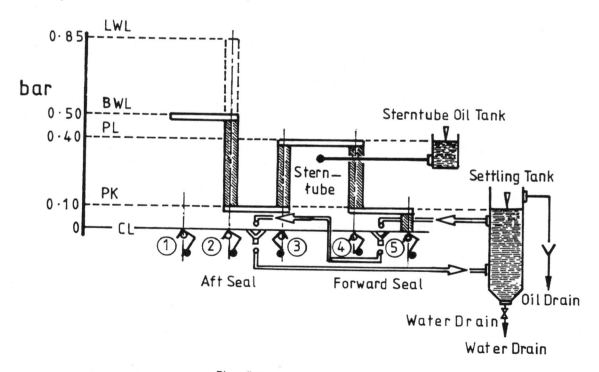

PL   oil pressure in sterntube
LWL   water pressure on load draught
BWL   water pressure on ballast draught
CL   centre of shafting
PK   pressure in circulator chambers

Figure 12   Comparison of differential pressures on sealing rings.

Survey of tailshafts with oil glands

The survey of this type of tailshaft is basically similar to that of continuous liner tailshafts and takes place at 5-yearly intervals, depending on classification society rules. Initially, when the vessel enters drydock, the tailshaft wear down reading is taken. When the vessel is new an initial reading is taken and recorded. The instrument used, usually a poker-type gauge, should be kept on board by the Chief Engineer. It is difficult to generalise, but a figure of 0.9 mm has been recorded for a 600 mm tailshaft. Because the tailshaft has to be withdrawn for survey a more accurate picture can be achieved by visual examination and by taking micrometer readings externally on the tailshaft, and internally on the stern bearing. If the bearing has been performing satisfactorily the condition of the bearing and tailshaft should be as new. A crack detection method should be included in the examination to permit the maximum time between surveys.

The condition of the inner and outer seals should also be examined and the opportunity taken to renew the rubber lip seals. There have been occasions when, after the seals have been reassembled, they were found to leak even though there was no report of leakage previously. There is a tendency for overheating of the lip faces causing cracking, hence the leakage of oil.

When a vessel has an intermediate drydock, even though the recorded wear down is satisfactory, many companies prefer to renew the outer sealing rings.

Another classification survey point is that most modern ships have to survey the sternshaft system every 5 years but that the leading classification societies, certainly Lloyd's Register, will consider an extension of this time subject to approval by their 'committees' on an individual ship basis. Various criteria must be put before the committee including analysis results from three sequential oil system samples which in effect means that samples are now taken from stern tubes approximately every 4 months. An extension is very cost-effective for the owner.

Possible defects

Because the lip seals run on the liners there is a tendency to groove the outer diameter of the liners. There may be no reported leakage of the gland initially but if grooving is found an allowance is made to accommodate skimming and polishing of the outer diameter of the liner. The reduction in diameter should be within the manufacturer's recommendation, e.g. Simplex-compact recommend a maximum skim of 4.8 mm on an original outside diameter of 1000 mm. The springs must be shortened by 3 mm per 1 mm reduction in diameter (Fig 13).

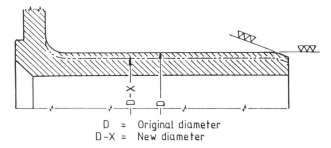

D = Original diameter
D–X = New diameter

Figure 13 Skimming of chrome liner.

Another method of avoiding grooving of the liner is by fitting a distance piece between the stern frame and the seal carrier. This has the effect of moving the lip seals on to a good part of the liner so that the skimming of the liner is avoided, so increasing its service life. A typical arrangement is shown in Fig 14. Once again the manufacturers should be consulted about the dimensions of the distance piece.

When examination of the white metal bearing takes place it is possible to find cracking on the surface, and even pieces of the white metal lying loose. Depending on the extent of the damage various courses of action can be taken. If the damage is extensive the stern bearing will have to be completely re-metalled, the whole bearing being removed ashore for this process. If however, small pieces of white metal have come adrift they can be removed and the remaining sharp edges removed by scraping and blending down to the cast iron backing material.

There have been instances when a vessel on its maiden voyage has reported leakage of the outer seal, with the situation becoming so bad that it has had to be dealt with afloat. It is possible to tip the ship, great care being taken to ensure that the bending moment of the vessel is within design specifications, with the whole operation taking place in still water. With this operation the rubber sealing rings cannot

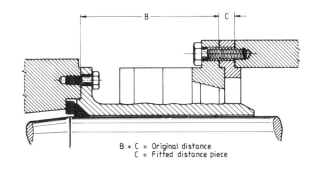

B + C = Original distance
C = Fitted distance piece

Figure 14 Fitting of distance piece.

be fitted as a whole but are joined with a compound supplied by the seal makers, who usually have a team skilled in such bonding operations.

The threads on the aft end of the tailshaft are another area where damage can occur if care is not taken when removing the securing nut. The nut can seize on the threads and its removal, effected by cutting the nut off with an oxyacetylene torch, can damage the threads. Care should be taken in chasing up the tailshaft threads when fitting a new nut to the tailshaft.

On completion of the survey and reassembly of the tailshaft and its seals the stern tube should be refilled with the recommended lubricating oil and circulated by the system provided to ensure that there is oil in the stern tube.

A small vessel that drydocked on a slipway had the unfortunate experience of the tailshaft welding itself to the stern bush when the lubricating oil was not replenished, necessitating the manufacture of a new tailshaft, stern bush etc., at great cost.

Special materials

With low loading, water lubricated lignum vitae or plastic bearings were used in merchant ships. With the increase in ship size and the corresponding higher powers required, stern bearing loading increased rapidly. This led to the development of oil lubricated white metal bearings, which are, on the whole, satisfactory, provided the outer seal remains intact and prevents the ingress of sea water. Tailshaft diameters have increased to such an extent that they have produced greater bearing loads and misalignment problems.

It is obvious that white metal in stern bearings is being stretched to and beyond its load carrying capacity under these conditions. High peripheral speeds on large shafts often create overheating at the rubber seal faces. With deep draught ships the pressure from the head of sea water leads to the possibility of water entering the lubricating oil and contaminating it.

From these observations, a material has been developed to satisfy these demanding conditions. The material, developed by Railko, employs a high grade asbestos yarn with synthetic strengthening filaments and an anti-scuffing thermosetting resin.

Because of the importance of the stern tube bearing, tests were carried out on a VLCC and the following observations were noted.

1. Thickness of the oil film at the end of the bearing was 0.4 to 0.6 mm at normal speed. This reduced to zero when:

a) the shaft rotation speed was lower than 20 rev/min;

b) the rudder was hard over;

c) going astern.

2. The oil thickness changed with a certain vibration mode—when the short wave of the blade frequency was superimposed on the long wave with a frequency $\frac{1}{3}$ to $\frac{1}{6}$ of the shaft revolutions.

3. In rough seas the shaft was found to collide with the bearing metal.

Recorded failures have shown on larger ships a 6% failure rate where stern shafts were in excess of 600 mm. These were considered to be due to high local loading at the aft end of the bearing.

With slow steaming at speeds of less than 25 rev/min the stern bearing is operating under boundary lubrication conditions at the aft end of the bearing. This, together with impulses from the propeller and hull vibrations cause the shaft to break through the oil film, thus making contact with the white metal. In an attempt to overcome this problem the bearing was slope bored, but this was not completely successful because of variations in the shaft-to-hull alignment under various loading conditions, i.e. from fully loaded to ballast conditions.

Being a relatively soft and weak alloy possessing poor resistance to impact loads, white metal suffers severe degradation of strength at high temperatures. High wear rates can be expected under high loading and boundary lubrication conditions.

If the outer seal fails causing an ingress of sea water the lubricating properties of the oil diminish. Although this is unlikely to cause seizure it is possible that the oil will be replaced completely with sea water and the bearing will suffer from wear down.

The material produced by Railko has superior qualities to white metal in terms of:

a) resistance;

b) fatigue resistance to shock loads;

c) load carrying capacity under boundary lubricated conditions;

d) great wear life when lubricated by sea water or emulsions of oil and water.

Stern bearings can be produced with diameters of up to 1500 mm.

Tailshaft examination whilst afloat

There are various arrangements from different manufacturers which allow examination of the

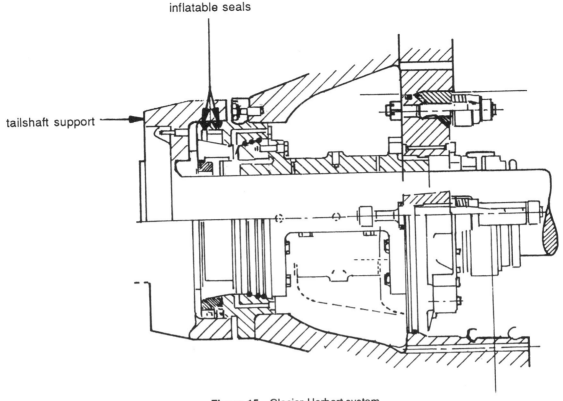

Figure 15 Glacier-Herbert system.

tailshaft while the vessel is afloat. One such arrangement is known as the 'Glacier-Herbert system' (Fig 15).

With this design it is necessary to support the tailshaft. This is achieved by having a permanent fixture of the forward end of the propeller boss which rests on the stern frame during withdrawal. Associated with this support are inflatable seals that are used to prevent the ingress of sea water during the operation.

When the seals are inflated their tightness can be checked by draining the water to inside the vessel by two pipes which are fitted to the top and bottom of the enclosed cavity. The cavity is clear of water when the lower pipe stops discharging water into the machinery space. As there are two sets of inflatable seals, the same procedure is adopted for the space between the seals. Both seals must be proved to be effective before withdrawal can commence.

If these seals are found to be leaking a diver must be employed to fit an external neoprene bandage and the above procedure adopted to prove that the seal is tight. The stern tube bearing oil is then drained off and the inboard seal assembly disconnected and slid along the shaft.

The stern bearing can then be withdrawn with the assistance of horizontally mounted hydraulic jacks

that are coupled together and apply pressure between the diaphragm and the two half flanges located behind the diaphragm housing. A supporting jack is also placed under the shaft inboard near the assembly. The hydraulic nuts are then removed and load is applied to the shaft jack, lifting the shaft clear of the bearing.

Load is then applied to the horizontal jacks, disengaging the spherical seat, and moving the assembly forward. At this stage, the bearing is left hanging on the shaft, the bearing chocks having been removed. The vertical jack can then be lowered, allowing the shaft to settle, supported fully on the external carrier. The stern bearing can then be drawn into the vessel ready for dismantling.

The reverse procedure is adopted for reassembling; the sealing rings being replaced after complete examination.

As the propeller and inflatable seals require examination for the classification survey, this is usually accomplished in dry dock.

MAIN THRUST

The main thrust is the means of transmitting the propeller thrust to the hull, thereby moving the ship.

The thrust shaft can be found at the aft end of most engines as a separate unit, or incorporated within the main engine bedplate in modern diesel engines. The separate thrust shaft is aligned between the main engine and the intermediate line shafting and thus can be subjected to misalignment problems. Because of its function, the complete thrust block must be anchored securely to the ship's structure by fitting end chocks at the forward and aft ends, ensuring that it cannot be moved in any direction.

A thrust shaft which is incorporated into the engine bedplate has a number of advantages. Firstly, the thrust shaft bearing housing can be line bored at the same time as the engine main bearing housings to within a high degree of accuracy, no separate alignment being necessary. The transmission of the thrust to the hull of the ship is accommodated by the main bedplate itself, the bedplate being securely anchored to the engine room tank top. With this type of arrangement the lubricating oil can be supplied via the main engine oil supply at a controlled temperature.

A thrust shaft which is separate from the main engine can have its own lubricating oil sump and must have a means of cooling the lubricating oil, because of the heat generated in the thrust. This is done by inserting a cooler in the oil sump which has a water supply from an auxiliary or main circulating pump. This type of thrust may also have a forced lubrication oil supply taken off the main engine oil system.

The thrust shaft is made of forged steel with two journals either side of the thrust collar structuring, only one of which is used. The ends of the shaft have solid forged flanges which are coupled to the main engine and intermediate shafting. The thrust pads themselves are steel backed with white metal facing. The back of the pad is stepped which allows it to pivot or tilt about the pivot point. The lubricating oil is fed to the space between the pads in order to lubricate the bearings.

Principle of operation

The thrust system is sometimes called Michell thrust, after the manufacturer. The principle of operation of the pivoting pad is based on the formation of a taper oil film between the pad and the moving collar (Fig 16). The inclination of the pad is not fixed, but is supported on a pivot about which it is free to tilt, thereby automatically adjusting itself to produce the pressure required to balance the thrust load. The tilting allows for self-compensation of the load, speed and oil viscosity.

The position of the pivot is usually offset beyond the centre of the circumferential centre of the thrust

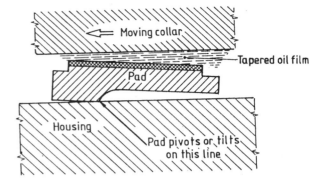

Figure 16   Principle of operation of pivoting pad.

pad at a position of 0.6. Such offset pivot pads can withstand heavy axial loads even if the rotation of the collar reverses. Alternatively, centre pivoted pads can be used.

Thrust shoes are located in retaining rings in the form of an inverted horseshoe and are situated either side of the collar. The shoes are identical, one for ahead running and the other for astern. Attached to the back of each are adjustable liners that can be made up to give the axial clearance required.

The centroid of the thrust load on each shoe lies within the area covered by the liner, which abuts to the casing bottom. The whole thrust load is transmitted through the lower half of the casing. This relieves the top half casing and joint bolts of any load.

The front of each retaining ring faces the collar and has a recess machined concentric with the shaft. The thrust pads, six for ahead and six for astern, slide around this recess between the horseshoe and the collar.

The white metal bearing faces have a slight spherical crown which prevents the pads from sticking to the collar when oiled. This crowning also enhances the anti-wear and lubrication properties of the bearing.

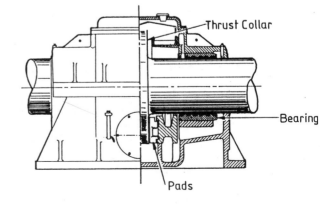

Figure 17   Main thrust.

Two stop pads are secured to the casing top for both the forward and aft sides. They:

a) prevent rotation of the thrust shoes and pads;

b) act as oil catchers and distributors;

c) form supports for the oil scraper.

The thrust block is enclosed with a cover that can be removed for inspection purposes (Fig 17).

Thrust block designs also exist where the pads extend over the full circumference of the collar. The oil is again delivered by a scraper of similar design to the back of the retaining ring from where it is guided to the inner diameter of the thrust pads.

Power loss

Because there is no metal-to-metal contact, the power loss is only the internal friction in the oil film, which is caused by the shearing of adjacent layers of oil within the film and varies according to speed, load and viscosity of the lubricant. The friction loss generates heat.

Survey of thrust blocks

The survey of thrust blocks takes place under the continuous survey of machinery at 5-yearly intervals. The top cover should be removed, exposing the thrust shaft. The journals of the thrust shaft are exposed and an ahead and astern pad are usually removed for examination. The condition of the thrust shaft should be as new, except for a few scratches; the surface of the journals and collar highly polished. If the block is self-contained, a sample of the lubricating oil can be extracted for laboratory tests. It is good practice to remove the oil cooler for hydraulic testing and visual examination. At all times during dismantling and reassembly, great care should be taken to prevent dirt from getting into the system. The inspection should therefore take as little time as possible. The surveyor will pay attention to the thrust collar itself, and in particular to the radius between the shaft and collar.

Problems associated with thrust blocks

If the system is clean, with good alignment, and the clearance is correct, there should be no problems with thrust blocks. However, if the lubricating oil has been contaminated with dirt it may score the thrust collar, giving it the appearance of a gramophone record. As these scoring marks become worse, through metal-to-metal contact with the white metal, the oil pressure wedge tends to break down, driving the thrust collar against the pads.

The scoring marks can be removed by machining and polishing the thrust collar *in situ*. Various companies specialise in this procedure. A generous allowance is left on the collar thickness, up to about 25% above the design thickness. Care must be taken to maintain the correct radius with the shaft.

Contamination of the lubricating oil can also occur from damage to the lubricating oil cooler, the cooling water breaking down the properties of the oil. The only remedy for this problem is to repair the cooler.

Incorrect adjustment of the thrust clearance has two extremes. If the clearance is too great, the ability to form the oil wedge is diminished. The wedge forms and then breaks down, giving parallel flow between the surfaces. The pressure increases and decreases, and is incapable of supporting the thrust. If the clearance is too small, the forward edge comes into contact with the collar as the pads tilt, and wipes the white metal on the forward edge.

PROPELLERS

Propellers can be divided into the three main categories fixed pitch, controllable pitch and directional pitch.

Fixed pitch propellers are most likely to be found on deep sea merchant vessels. The name suggests that the pitch is constant over the radius of the blade but this is not so. The pitch varies from the root to the tip of the blade, the effective pitch being a mean value found by calculation or experiment.

Materials used in this type of propeller vary from copper, nickel, aluminium alloys, to cast iron and aluminium. The alloy used by Stone Manganese Marine Ltd is nikalium, a typical composition being:

copper	80.2%
aluminium	9.3%
nickel	4.3%
iron	5.0%
manganese	1.2%

This alloy has typical mechanical properties as follows:

Tensile properties

0.2% proof stress	27.4 kg/mm²
tensile strength	70 kg/mm²
elongation	27%

Propellers as large as 100 tonnes can be cast in nikalium, the blades having a thickness of 0.5 m at the root. It has to be appreciated that some sections cool at slower rates than others, which can set up internal stresses and significantly lower the proof stress compared with separately cast test bars. The most important property affecting the life of the propeller is corrosion fatigue resistance, and with nikalium this is not badly affected by slow cooling, retaining approximately three-quarters of the strength of small castings, even in the heaviest sections.

Corrosion resistance

The sea water corrosion rate of nikalium is negligible. Under certain conditions, however, copper based alloys suffer from wastage. This is an impingement attack which occurs in regions of high velocity water flow and leads to dissolution of the metal. Nikalium is considered to be three times more resistant to this type of attack than manganese bronze.

Cavitation erosion

This is caused by excessive wake inequalities due to the hull form at the stern of the vessel. If these inequalities cannot be reduced to acceptable limits, the resulting cavitation will lead to erosion of the blade surfaces. Nikalium has a high resistance to this type of attack.

Efficiency of a propeller

The function of the propeller is to absorb the power delivered by the main engine at the revolutions ensuring optimum engine running conditions. The propeller itself must be efficient to produce maximum thrust, and so maximum ship speed. The efficiency of the propeller is given by the thrust power divided by the delivered power at specific revolutions.

Slip

Think of the straightforward concept of a screw going into a block of wood. After one complete revolution of a screwdriver, the screw would advance a

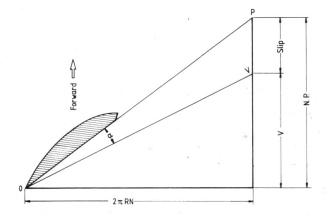

Figure 18   Representation of slip.

distance equal to the pitch. However, a propeller works in a different medium, i.e. water, and, due to its fluidity, advances a distance somewhat less than its pitch. The difference between these distances is called the slip. This is represented in Fig 18.

In Fig 18 it can be seen that if the velocity is at right angles to the direction of advance, it is plotted as $2\pi RN$. If the ship speed V is plotted in the direction of advance, the resultant water flow will be along the line $0V$. The attitude of the blade is defined by the pitch and revolutions and thus for a given propeller the angle of incidence is defined by the slip as shown.

Slip is expressed as a percentage of the pitch (P), and if a propeller rotates at N rev/min and the forward speed is V,

$$\text{slip} = \frac{NP - V\dfrac{6080}{60}}{NP} \times 100$$

$$= 1 - \frac{101.3V}{NP} \times 100\%.$$

Real and apparent slip

Apparent slip is usually calculated by the ship's engineers and is obtained by using the measured ship's speed obtained by observations in association with the propeller revolutions. In general, the speed of the propeller disc is less than the ship's speed. The difference is due to the frictional effect of the ship's hull slowing down the water passing the ship, and is called the 'wake' speed. The mean speed of the propeller relative to the surrounding water is called the speed of advance V_a.

The relationship between ship speed V_s and the speed of advance is $V_a = V_s (1 - W_t)$ where W_t is the wake fraction. 'Real slip' is calculated using this speed of advance, V_a, and is thus always greater than the apparent slip. This explains how engineers have often calculated a negative slip. This is 'apparent slip'; the related 'real slip' is always positive.

Propeller surface roughness

During normal service, roughness of the blade surface occurs and can be attributed to the following.

a) Marine growth

Marine growth of the animal or vegetable variety forms on propeller blade surfaces when the propeller is stationary. The attachment of barnacles results in a loss of propeller efficiency, an increase in absorbed power and a lower rev/min. When the vessel returns to service the action of the water may remove some of the barnacles, but the surface does not return to normal until the propeller is properly cleaned.

b) Impingement attack

Impingement attack usually occurs at the leading edges and outer parts of the propeller blades where circumferential velocities are highest. The effect on the blades is a large area of surface roughness of shallow depth.

c) Corrosion attack—
chemical and electro-chemical

Corrosion attack can be minimised by the use of cathodic protection systems.

d) Cavitation erosion

Cavitation erosion is usually concentrated on small blade areas and can be very deep, and in some cases leads to complete wastage of the outer parts of the blade.

e) Bad maintenance

Grinding of the blade surfaces by inexperienced operators using grinding discs that are too coarse can accelerate surface roughness.

Roughness measurement

There are two main methods of roughness measurement: peak to valley average (PVA) and centre line average (Ra). There is no direct relationship between the two measurements.

The International Standards Organisation has standards for the surface finish of propellers, and recommends that ships' propellers be manufactured to Class 1 tolerances, giving a surface finish of better that 3 μm Ra. Surface finish to below 1 μm Ra can be achieved, but the cost of producing this finish is not considered to be economical as the superfine finish can be quickly reduced in service.

Method of measurement or assessment of surface roughness

A portable instrument can be used which gives direct readings of mm Ra.

A simple measure of surface condition is provided by using a comparator gauge, which provides six samples ranging from Ra = 1 μm to Ra = 30 μm.

Survey of propellers

The survey of propellers is usually associated with the survey of tailshafts at their due date. However, propellers are also surveyed as part of the drydock survey at approximately 2-yearly intervals. The propeller is examined *in situ* and any recommendations should be carried out.

Maintenance and repairs

On examination, if the blade surfaces are found to be smooth, with no sign of roughness or distortion of the blades due to fouling in service, they are best left alone. If there is roughness due to corrosion around the blade tips this can be ground out and polished to return the blade to its original condition.

For pitting of up to 1 mm in depth, the grinding and polishing operation is also successful. If time is of the essence the roughness can be temporarily removed by use of synthetic resin fillers. Small tears, cracks and local edge deformation should receive attention as quickly as possible. Deformed leading edges create conditions of disturbed flow or turbulence over the blade surface which causes an increase in general wastage or severe cavitation damage. Minor repairs and polishing can be undertaken with the propeller in place but more serious damage requires removal of the propeller.

Repairs

In general, repairs fall into three categories.

a) Straightening of distorted blade

This operation requires considerable experience to return the deformed blade to its original pitch and track. Straightening can be achieved by the use of weights and levers, the damaged area being heated slowly and uniformly to the correct temperature. Cooling should also be slow to avoid the creation of internal stresses.

b) Welding

If welding is required, an inert gas shielded metal arc process is preferred. A skilled operator is required and if flux coated electrodes are used they should be preheated to 120°C for approximately 1 h.

All slag should be removed between consecutive weld runs. No preheating of the area to be welded is necessary because of the possible introduction of cracking. If an area has been repaired before, the original repair should be removed before attempting a new repair.

While the above process is suitable for nikalium, if the propeller is made from other alloys the manufacturers should be consulted regarding the type of electrode to be used and any post-weld stress relieving process which may be required.

c) Burning on

Missing portions of blades can be replaced and small cracks repaired by cutting them out and fusing in new metal. Care should be taken in selecting the material to be used and the electrodes, as incorrect selection can lead to eating away of the weld metal, and the replaced part of the blade falling off.

The above repairs can be carried out on the outer parts of the blade but should not be considered inside 0.45 of the radius of the propeller.

It must be stressed that all repairs are carried out with the approval of the vessel's classification society and by approved operators. Manufacturers of propellers have representatives throughout the world who have been trained to undertake propeller repairs.

Attachment of a propeller to the tailshaft

In older ships (of the 1950s and 1960s), the traditional method of attaching the propeller to the tailshaft was by taper and key. A taper of 1 in 15 or, more commonly, 1 in 12 was used, the propeller being driven up hard using wedges and spanners on the propeller nut. It can be appreciated that the mating surfaces of the tailshaft and propeller were of utmost importance. Scraping of the propeller boss taper demanded good workmanship to give the required fit. The fit was tested by blueing the tailshaft, pushing on the propeller, and then examining the marking on the propeller boss taper. A contact of 70–80% was considered necessary, particularly at the top end of the taper, to give the necessary interference fit after final push up. A poor fit resulted in the key itself being subjected to extremes of torque and therefore the key suffering damage. The thrust from the propeller assisted in the push up and sometimes led to difficulties when the propeller had to be removed.

The introduction of higher powers, and hence the high torque on the shaft, can cause high stress concentrations on the taper, in particular at the keyway. These stress concentrations are present if the key is taking any appreciable load and can lead to shaft failure. To this end removal of the key and keyway is desirable. Various methods are available.

Keyless fittings
There are several methods of fitting keyless propellers.

a) Flange mounting
This method is generally standard practice for controllable pitch propellers but can also be found on a number of fixed pitch propellers. With flange mounted propellers a muff coupling is required inboard to facilitate withdrawal of the tailshaft out through the stern. The flange attachment requires fitted bolts to transmit the torque to the propeller without risk of movement. This enables the propeller boss to be hollow which can be achieved in the casting process.

b) Pilgrim fitting
This method was introduced in 1968 and has proved successful on large ships transmitting large powers. A cast-iron sleeve is set into the bronze boss of the propeller and the whole assembly is pushed on to the drive shaft, to the required degree of interference fit, using a Pilgrim nut, the axial travel being monitored by use of a clock gauge.

On earlier propellers, the cast-iron sleeve was force fitted into the propeller with the required degree of interference. On current propellers the sleeve

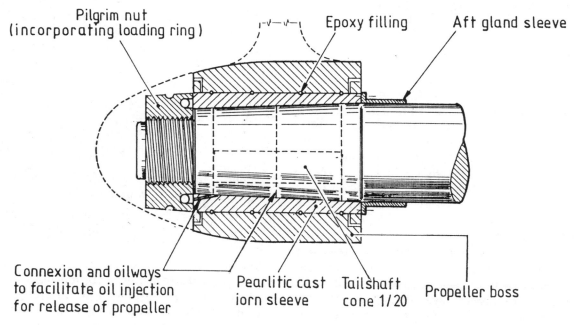

Figure 19   Pilgrim fitting.

a)

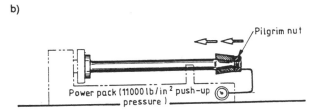

b)

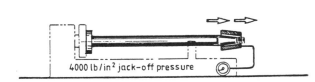

c)

d)

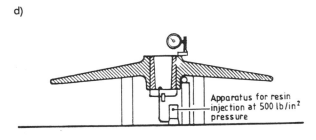

e)

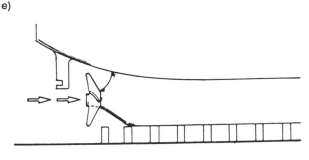

Figure 20 Pilgrim fitting—method of fitting: operations a), b) and c) at tailshaft manufacturer's works; operation d) at foundry or shaft manufacturer's works; operation e) at shipyard: a) bedding contract; b) sleeve push-up shaft cone; c) sleeve jacked off by oil injection; d) sleeve secured in boss; e) push-up on board.

is set into the boss by injecting Araldite under pressure into the interface. A typical example is shown in Fig 19.

The following advantages are claimed for this method of fitting.

1. A controlled degree of interference fit without stress raisers in the key and keyway.

2. A reduction in the allowance required for temperature, as the coefficient of expansion for cast-iron is similar to that of the shaft, which reduces the amount of interference required for the same torque transmission. This also reduces the high stresses due to thermal contraction when fitting at sub-zero temperatures.

3. An increase in the coefficient of friction available for torque transmission is obtained, compared with oil injection method. The actual coefficient can be monitored by means of a graph of push-up travel against push-up load.

4. Using the graph results in lower interference stresses at proof stress of nikalium, compared with 60–70% of proof stress that might be required with the oil injection system. This method of fitting is shown in Fig 20.

c. Oil injection fitting

This is a major method of keyless fitting which does not employ the cast-iron sleeve but relies on the coefficient of friction between the propeller boss and the steel shaft. A typical value of coefficient of friction is 0.12 but depends on classification society rules. The fitting of this type of propeller is shown in Figs 20 and 21.

Oil is injected into the annular spaces around the propeller boss thereby expanding the boss. At the same time, the hydraulic nut is used to push the

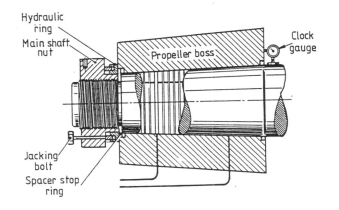

Figure 21 Propeller boss.

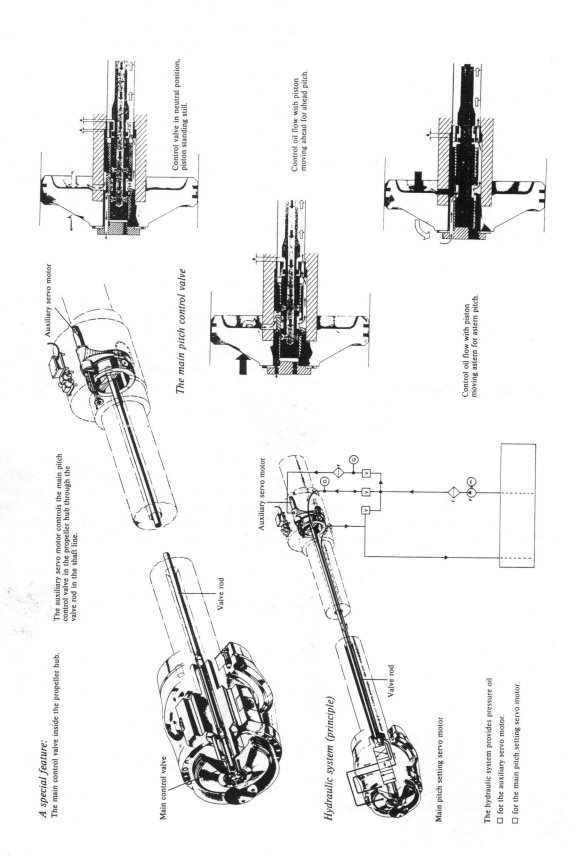

Control valve in neutral position, piston standing still.

Control oil flow with piston moving ahead for ahead pitch.

The main pitch control valve

Control oil flow with piston moving astern for astern pitch.

A special feature:
The main control valve inside the propeller hub.

Auxiliary servo motor

The auxiliary servo motor controls the main pitch control valve in the propeller hub through the valve rod in the shaft line.

Valve rod

Main control valve

Hydraulic system (principle)

Auxiliary servo motor

Valve rod

Main pitch setting servo motor

The hydraulic system provides pressure oil
☐ for the auxiliary servo motor.
☐ for the main pitch setting servo motor.

Figure 22 Working principle of the controllable pitch propeller.

propeller up the shaft taper. It should be noted that the load on the hydraulic nut before oil is injected is recorded and should be approximately 10% of the final load. The most important aspect of the fitting is to monitor the axial movement of the boss up the shaft taper using clock gauges which ensures the correct degree of interference fit. If the oil pressure is out of line with that expected it indicates that some part of the boss is not expanding properly, and either oil is escaping too freely or there is a blockage in the hydraulic system.

Highly skewed propellers

The need to reduce fuel costs has meant that more efficient propellers are used. Propellers with large diameters, reduced blade areas and operating at lower speeds, together with increased skew and blade tip areas help to meet these requirements. It is claimed that the best advantages of skewed propellers are obtained where the skew angle is between 35 and 40 deg.

Controllable pitch propellers

This type of propeller is usually associated with medium speed diesel engines and reduces speed through a uni-directional gear box to the output shafting, rotating at constant speed. There are other arrangements which use reversing gear boxes, and can reverse the output shafting.

The propeller is attached to the tailshaft by means of a flange. The boss is hollowed out to accommodate the operating mechanism. The operating mechanism is a crosshead which can be operated hydraulically or mechanically, pushing the crosshead forward or aft. Set into the crosshead is a sliding shoe with a hole into which fits the crankpin. The crankpin ring is bolted onto the propeller blade. The crankpin being offset thus, when the crosshead is moved, the blade is rotated. Each blade is set into the boss and is connected to the crosshead as described above. For the system to operate, the tailshaft has to be hollow to allow room for the valve rod and pressure oil for the hub. The pressure oil flows to the propeller hub within the valve rod. The return oil flows through the hollow shaft outside the valve rod back to the oil distribution box (OD box).

The hydraulic system provides pressure oil for the auxiliary servomotor and for the main pitch setting servomotor. With the control on zero pitch the valve is in the neutral position. The hydraulic oil is supplied up the centre of the valve rod and returns to the supply tank around the outside of the control valve rod. In the neutral position, the high pressure hydraulic oil exerts equal pressure on both sides of the main piston. When the auxiliary servomotor receives a signal to move the propeller blade to the required pitch, the control rod is moved in the appropriate direction. The control valve then permits the high pressure hydraulic oil to pressurise one side of the main piston, pushing it in the appropriate direction. The pressure on the other side of the piston is relieved and returns to the supply tank, the required degree of pitch being put on the blades. When astern pitch is required, the valve control rod moves from the neutral position in the opposite direction, thereby pressurising the opposite side of the main piston and putting astern pitch on the blade. The working principle is illustrated in Fig 22. A complete system is shown in Fig 23.

Directional pitch propellers

These units are usually found on smaller vessels such as tugs or inter-island ferries where the vessel requires a great deal of manoeuvrability. The units give both power and thrust, and a rudder is therefore not required.

Although individual units can be fitted singly, it is usual to fit two giving greater manoeuvrability. The blades of the unit protrude under the vessel and in most cases are protected by a guard, but obviously the blades are in danger of damage through contact.

An advantage of this type of unit is that the prime mover driving the hydraulic pumps can be placed in a position remote from the unit itself and coupled to it by hydraulic piping. A typical setup is shown in Fig 24.

INITIAL ALIGNMENT AND BORING OUT

On older ships the stern frame was set up and the vessel's framing and plating built up to form the hull of the ship. The stern tube was set in place and the lignum vitae bearing bored out. The tailshaft was entered into the stern bush and the line shafting and main engine aligned from the tailshaft.

Today, with modern technology, the vessel is constructed in modular form, the modules being constructed under controlled conditions, and connected together in a building dock. With this type of construction the engine space is usually connected before the section containing the stern tube is lifted into place. Whereas the procedure varies from shipyard to shipyard, a typical alignment procedure for VLCCs is described below.

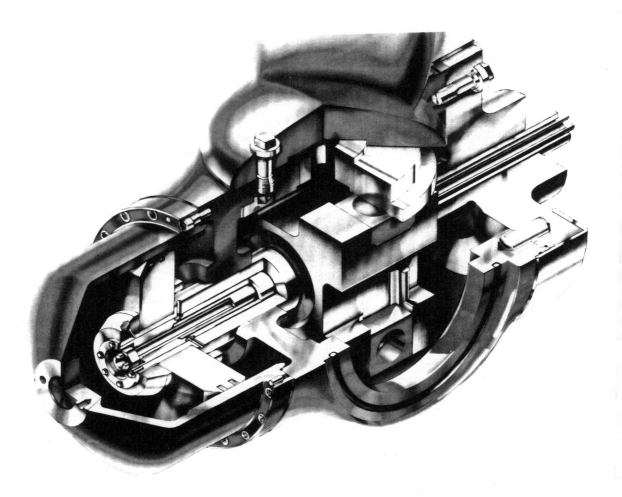

Figure 23   Controllable pitch propeller.

The stern frame casting, together with the rough machined stern tube, are connected with pre-formed plating to form what would become the lower aft peak section of the ship. A steel hoop is welded to the tube internally and externally giving a watertight seal. The complete lower aft peak section is lowered into the building dock and rigged so that it can be moved forward or aft and from port to starboard. The rough machining of the stern tube in the workshop represents an angle of 1:61, which is the shaft alignment requirement.

Vertical alignment

Situated in the building dock are two brass plates with punch marks at their centres, these being in direct line with the vessel's centre line. An optical instrument is placed over the aft mark and adjusted until the centre of the tripod is on the punch mark. The instrument is then used to site the forward brass plate at its punch mark, so giving a reference line and ensuring that the instrument is set up on the vessel's centre line. The horizontal vernier should read zero.

The outer boss should have three vertical centre punch marks on the upper and lower faces, and a flat plate fitted across the stern tube boss with a small hole bored at the centre of the bore. A punch mark is also made on the uppermost part of the section on the centre line.

All of these marks can be sited by the optical instrument in the vertical plane, the section being adjusted until they are in line. If the correct dimensions have been adhered to, the lower aft peak section should lie in position in the vertical plane and match up to the plating already in place.

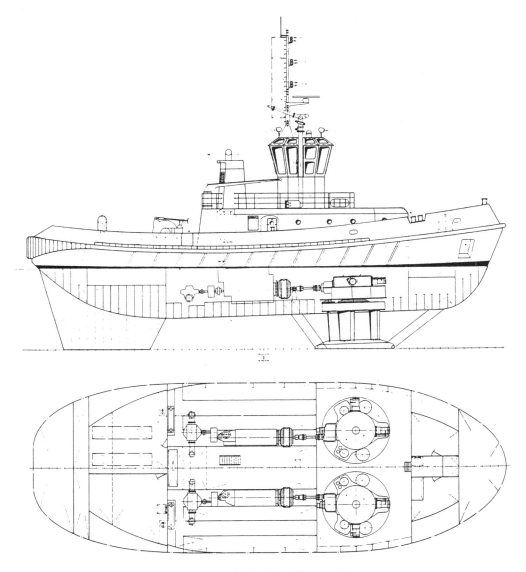

Figure 24 Voith Schneider propulsion.

Horizontal alignment

If tolerances are correct, only the height of the centre line needs to be adjusted to give the rise of 1:61. A reference mark is made on the pump room bulkhead on the centre line of the ship, to give an inclination from the centre of the stern tube outer boss of 1:61. This gives the true alignment at any intermediate point. This is necessary as an intermediate reference will be required if machinery is being fitted in the engine room. The optical instrument is set up at the intermediate point and can be offset in the horizontal plane and locked to swivel at the incline of 1:61. The centre line at the outer stern tube boss can then be sited, the complete section being adjusted until the centre point is in alignment with the incline. At the

forward stern tube boss a calculation can be made to give the height required for complete stern section alignment, the section being tilted about the outer boss until this height is attained. When this is reached the complete section is correct, both vertically and horizontally, and is ready for welding. After the lower aft peak section has been welded the alignment is checked, and through the stern tube any small adjustment can be undertaken when boring out the stern tube prior to fitting the white metal bush. This is shown diagrammatically in Fig 25.

Main line shafting alignment

The alignment of intermediate shafting, and in some

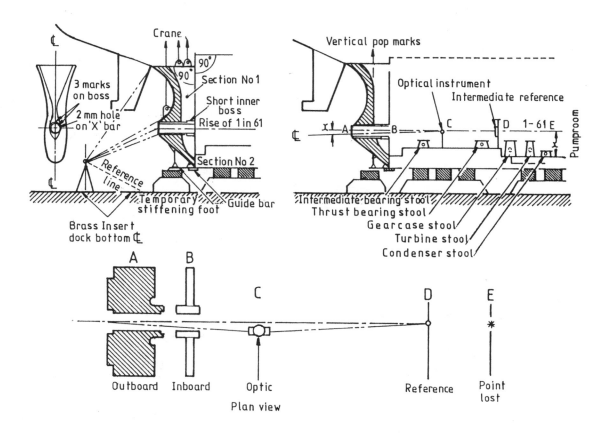

Figure 25   Vertical and horizontal alignment of tailshaft.

instances thrust shaft to the main engine, and tailshaft, is a very precarious business. It is essential that the alignment is correct. Otherwise there will be problems with overheating of bearings. The conditions under which the initial alignment takes place can be quite different to those of actual operation. The initial alignment might take place in a western European shipyard whereas the vessel will operate in the warmer climate of the Gulf area. Also, during the different loading conditions of the vessel the initial alignment may be found to be wanting.

There have been many instances where vessels on their maiden voyage have had problems with alignment, requiring a complete realignment programme. In some cases damage has occurred to line shaft, thrust, gearing and main engine bearings of diesel engines. It is important therefore for a procedure to be followed to ensure that the best accuracy possible is obtained in the initial alignment. One such procedure is known as the gaps and sags method.

Gaps and sags method

The basic principle of this method is that all the loadings of the tailshaft and line shafting are known,

together with their bearing supports. From this information the bending of the various shafts can be calculated and illustrated diagrammatically. It is considered necessary that the accuracy in machining the shaft flanges is good, the faces being at 90 deg to the body of the shaft. The calculations give the shape of the shafting and the gaps between the flanges that are required for true alignment. All these calculations are undertaken with the shafting uncoupled and in a cold condition. A general arrangement is illustrated in Fig 26 for a geared turbine installation.

Method for diesel engine installation

The following method is currently used by Harland & Wolff Limited, Belfast. With this method the main diesel engine is in place and adjusted to give the required slope with acceptable deflection readings of the main engine crankshaft. The main thrust is incorporated inside the engine bedplate. The installation has two intermediate line shafts supported on single bearings. With the engine in place, the aft thrust coupling is broken and the aftermost bearing is low-

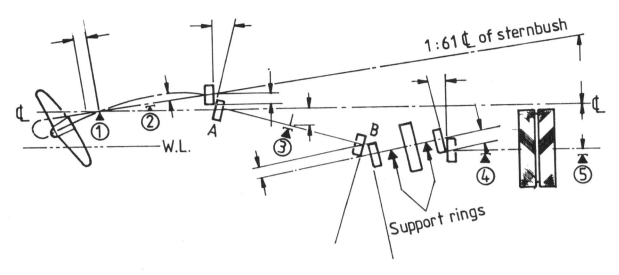

Figure 26 Gaps and sags method.

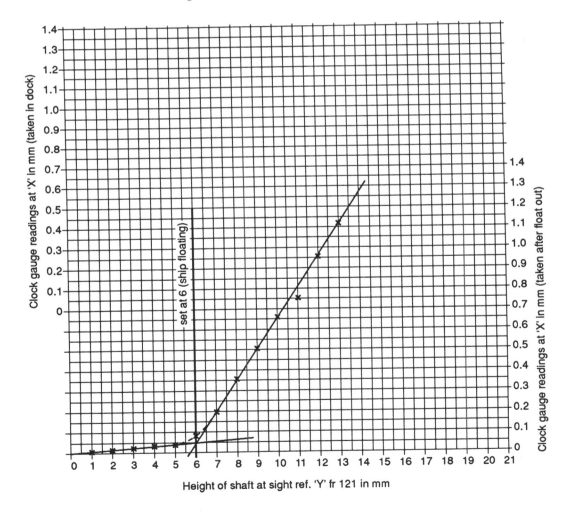

Figure 27 Intermediate shaft alignment graphs.

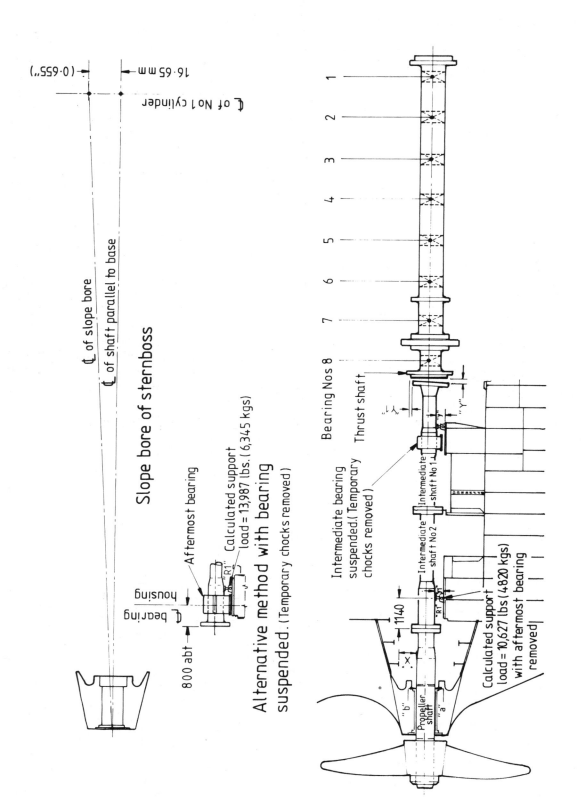

16.65 mm (0.655")

℄ of No1 cylinder

℄ of slope bore

℄ of shaft parallel to base

Slope bore of sternboss

℄ bearing housing

Aftermost bearing

"R1"

Calculated support
load = 13,987 lbs. (6,345 kgs)

800 abt

Alternative method with bearing
suspended. (Temporary chocks removed)

1
2
3
4
5
6
7
Bearing Nos 8

Thrust shaft

"Y"

"Y"

Intermediate bearing
suspended. (Temporary
chocks removed)

Intermediate
shaft No 1

Intermediate
shaft No2

1140

"R1"

"X"

Calculated support
load = 10,627 lbs (4820 kgs)
with aftermost bearing
removed|

"b"

Propeller
shaft

"a"

Figure 28   Diesel engine installation.

ered clear of the shaft. A graduated hydraulic jack is placed at the position R1 and the calculated support load sustained by the hydraulic jack. The shaft at y is raised by increments of 0.5 mm and the dimensions at X recorded.

The same procedure is repeated when lowering the shaft by the same increments at Y and both graphs are plotted. The position of the shaft at Y relative to the line of sight when the shaft just touches the stern bush at a is ascertained from the graphs (Fig 27).

When the position of the shafting is such that it is just touching at a, the intermediate bearing can be finally chocked. References are taken from poker gauges of final dimensions Y and Y1, also at positions a and b.

The graduated hydraulic jack can be removed from the aftermost bearing position, the bearing being fitted with temporary chocks to give final dimension at Y1. At this point the line shafting and tailshaft should be in the correct alignment. The position of the main engine can then be adjusted to give the dimensions Y and Y1 at the aftermost thrust coupling when the crankshaft deflections are satisfactory. The intermediate shafting, No 1 shaft, can then be coupled to the thrust coupling. The final chocking of the aftermost line shafting bearing is left as late as possible, to give the final dimension Y1. The complete procedure is illustrated in Fig 28.

CONCLUSIONS

Whilst this chapter aims to deal with line shafting, thrust, stern sealing, tailshafts, bearings and propellers they are by no means the only arrangements found in machinery spaces. Line shafting can have power take off, and in some older installations, pumps were also driven from the line shafting.

The thrust can also be incorporated into the gear box of medium speed diesel engines and in lower powered units within the diesel engine itself.

The regulations regarding survey of machinery vary from classification society to classification society but are always superseded by the statutory requirements of the Government under whose flag the vessel is registered.

There are many manufacturers of equipment in the marine field and their advice should always be sought regarding any problems with their product. Most manufacturers have experienced such occurrences and have expert staff to deal with them.

For engine room staff the best solution is to familiarise themselves with the machinery on board their own vessel and to know the limits under which it can operate. The seagoing marine engineer should, when the opportunity arises, have a look at the line shafting and tailshaft bearings and seals to have a thorough knowledge of their condition should problems occur in the future.

Index